Pontiac Firebird Automotive Repair Manual

by Scott Mauck and John H Haynes

Member of the Guild of Motoring Writers

Models covered:

Pontiac Firebird, Trans Am, Formula, Esprit
All V8 models with manual or automatic transmissions
1970 through 1981

(79018-6S10)

J H Haynes & Co. Ltd.
Haynes North America, Inc.
www.haynes.com

Acknowledgements

We are grateful for the help and cooperation of Tomco Industries, 1435 Woodsen Road, St. Louis, Missouri 63132 for their assistance with technical information and illustrations. Wiring diagrams originated exclusively for Haynes North America, Inc by George Edward Brodd. Certain illustrations originated by Valley Forge Technical Information Services.

A book in the Haynes Automotive Repair Manual Series

ISBN-13: 978-0-85696-882-2
ISBN-10: 0-85696-882-X

Contents

Pontiac Firebird Trans Am

About this manual

Its purpose

The purpose of this manual is to help you get the best value from your vehicle. It can do so in several ways. It can help you decide what work must be done, even if you choose to have it done by a dealer service department or a repair shop; it provides information and procedures for routine maintenance and servicing; and it offers diagnostic and repair procedures to follow when trouble occurs.

We hope you use the manual to tackle the work yourself. For many simpler jobs, doing it yourself may be quicker than arranging an appointment to get the vehicle into a shop and making the trips to leave it and pick it up. More importantly, a lot of money can be saved by avoiding the expense the shop must pass on to you to cover its labor and overhead costs. An added benefit is the sense of satisfaction and accomplishment that you feel after doing the job yourself.

Using the manual

The manual is divided into Chapters. Each Chapter is divided into numbered Sections, which are headed in bold type between horizontal lines. Each Section consists of consecutively numbered paragraphs.

At the beginning of each numbered Section you will be referred to any illustrations which apply to the procedures in that Section. The reference numbers used in illustration captions pinpoint the pertinent Section and the Step within that Section. That is, illustration 3.2 means the illustration refers to Section 3 and Step (or paragraph) 2 within that Section.

Procedures, once described in the text, are not normally repeated. When it's necessary to refer to another Chapter, the reference will be given as Chapter and Section number. Cross references given without use of the word "Chapter" apply to Sections and/or paragraphs in the same Chapter. For example, "see Section 8" means in the same Chapter.

References to the left or right side of the vehicle assume you are sitting in the driver's seat, facing forward.

Even though we have prepared this manual with extreme care, neither the publisher nor the author can accept responsibility for any errors in, or omissions from, the information given.

NOTE

A **Note** provides information necessary to properly complete a procedure or information which will make the procedure easier to understand.

CAUTION

A **Caution** provides a special procedure or special steps which must be taken while completing the procedure where the Caution is found. Not heeding a Caution can result in damage to the assembly being worked on.

WARNING

A **Warning** provides a special procedure or special steps which must be taken while completing the procedure where the Warning is found. Not heeding a Warning can result in personal injury.

Introduction to the Firebird

The 11-year model range, which this manual covers, gives an indication of the success that this American sports car has enjoyed.

During this eleven year reign, the Firebirds remained basically the same, undergoing only slight body and engine changes. Due to this, the majority of the repair procedures included in this manual will be applicable to all models 1970 through 1981. Where differences appear, they will be duly noted in the text to prevent confusion.

General dimensions

Dimensions

1970
Overall length .... 188.0 in
Overall width... 74.4 in
Height .... 50.1 in
Wheelbase.. 108.0 in

1971 and 1972
As 1970 models except:
Height .... 50.5 in

1973
As 1970 models except:
Overall length .... 193.0 in

1974
As 1970 models except:
Overall length .... 196.0 in

1975 and 1976
As 1970 models except:
Overall length .... 196.0 in
Overall width... 73.0 in

1977
As 1970 models except:
Overall length .... 197.0 in
Overall width... 73.0 in

1978
As 1970 models except:
Overall length .... 197.0 in
Overall width... 74.0 in

1979 through 1981
As 1970 models except:
Overall length .... 199.0 in
Overall width... 73.0 in

Vehicle identification numbers

Modifications are a continuing and unpublicized process in vehicle manufacture. Spare parts manuals and lists are compiled on a numerical basis, the individual vehicle numbers being essential to identify correctly the component required.

Vehicle identification number (VIN)

This very important identification number can be found on a plate attached to the left top of the dashboard and can be easily seen while looking through the windshield from the outside of the car **(see illustrations)**. The VIN also appears on the Vehicle Certificates of Title and Registration. It gives such valuable information as where and when the vehicle was manufactured, the model year of manufacture and the body style.

The Vehicle Identification Number (VIN) is visible on the driver's side cowling inside the windshield

	1	2	3	4	5	6
	MANUFACTURER IDENTITY	SERIES	BODY STYLE	MODEL YEAR	ASSEMBLY PLANT	UNIT NUMBER
	2	F	22387	1	N	100025

Typical VIN used on 1970 and 1971 models

1   Manufacturer's identity number assigned to all Pontiac built vehicles
2   Series designation
3   Model identification
4   Last number of model year (1971)
5   Norwood
6   Unit numbering will start at 000001 or 100001, depending on the vehicle

1	2	3	4	5	6	7
MANUFACTURER IDENTITY	SERIES CODE LETTER	BODY STYLE	ENGINE MODEL	MODEL YEAR	ASSEMBLY PLANT	UNIT NUMBER
2	F	47	R	4	L	100025

Typical VIN used on 1972 thru 1980 models

1	Manufacturer's identity number assigned to all Pontiac built vehicles	3	Body style	6	Van Nuys
2	Series	4	Engine code	7	Unit numbering will start at 000001 or 100001, depending on the vehicle
		5	Last number of the model year (1974)		

Note: On 1981 models, the engine code letter designation is the 8th character and the model year letter designation is the 10th character.

Typical body number plate (early models)

A	Model year
B	Time build code
C	Division
D	Series
E	Body style
F	Assembly plant
G	Unit number
H	Trim combinations
I	Seat option
J	Lower body color
K	Upper body color of fabric top
L	Accent color
M	Paint type

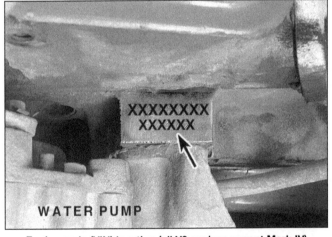
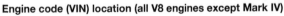

Engine code (VIN) location (all V8 engines except Mark IV)

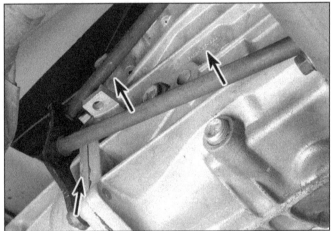

Typical 4-speed manual transmission number locations (arrows)

Since 1972, the VIN also gives the type of engine installed in the car. Since the Pontiac plant uses engines from Buick, Oldsmobile and Chevrolet, besides Pontiac engines, knowing the exact engine manufacturer is imperative when purchasing replacement parts. To identify which type of engine your Firebird has by using the VIN, refer to Engine Identification in Chapter 2.

Body identification plate

This metal plate is located on the upper surface of the shroud. Like the VIN it contains valuable information about the manufacture of the car, as well as information about the way in which the vehicle is equipped (see illustration). This plate is especially useful for matching the color and type of paint for repair work.

Engine identification number

Due to the various manufacturer's who have supplied engines for the Firebird models, the engine numbers may appear in a variety of locations. If the car is 1972 – 1981, the easiest way to determine what type of engine is installed in the vehicle is by using the VIN (see illustration) which is readily accessible for viewing (see Chapter 2). Many of the Fire-

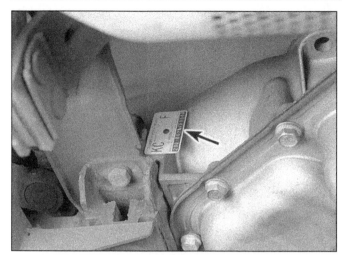

Location of the automatic transmission identification number (arrow)

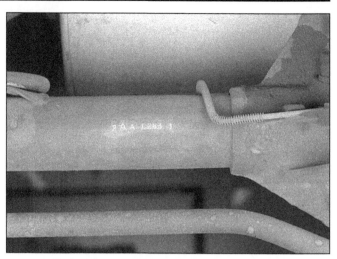

Typical rear axle identification number location

bird engines will have the identification number stamped on a pad, at the front right hand side of the engine block. It may be necessary to move the metal fuel line which is often routed directly over the stamped number code. Some later model engines may have the engine number at the front of the front side valve cover. The engine number code could be stamped into the valve cover or onto a label called a "scanner label". Lastly, certain engines will have a label which is attached to the oil filler tube.

Manual transmission number

3-Speed Saginaw - lower right-hand side of the case, adjacent to the cover **(see illustration)**.

4-speed Borg Warner - rear vertical surface of the extension housing.

4-speed Muncie - rear right-hand side of the case flange.

4-speed Saginaw - lower right-hand side of case adjacent to the cover.

Automatic transmission number

Powerglide - right rear surface of the oil pan.

Type 350 - right-hand vertical surface of the oil pan.

Type 400 - on blue tag right-hand side of the transmission **(see illustration)**.

Rear axle number

On right or left axle tube adjacent to the carrier **(see illustration)**.

Generator

On top drive end frame.

Starter

Stamped on outer case, toward the rear.

Tune-up decal:

Located in varying positions inside the engine compartment (see Chapter 1 for example).

Buying parts

Replacement parts are available from many sources, which generally fall into one of two categories - authorized dealer parts departments and independent retail auto parts stores. Our advice concerning these parts is as follows:

Retail auto parts stores: Good auto parts stores will stock frequently needed components which wear out relatively fast, such as clutch components, exhaust systems, brake parts, tune-up parts, etc. These stores often supply new or reconditioned parts on an exchange basis, which can save a considerable amount of money. Discount auto parts stores are often very good places to buy materials and parts needed for general vehicle maintenance such as oil, grease, filters, spark plugs, belts, touch-up paint, bulbs, etc. They also usually sell tools and general accessories, have convenient hours, charge lower prices and can often be found not far from home.

Authorized dealer parts department: This is the best source for parts which are unique to the vehicle and not generally available elsewhere (such as major engine parts, transmission parts, trim pieces, etc.).

Warranty information: If the vehicle is still covered under warranty, be sure that any replacement parts purchased - regardless of the source - do not invalidate the warranty!

To be sure of obtaining the correct parts, have engine and chassis numbers available and, if possible, take the old parts along for positive identification.

Maintenance techniques, tools and working facilities

Maintenance techniques

There are a number of techniques involved in maintenance and repair that will be referred to throughout this manual. Application of these techniques will enable the home mechanic to be more efficient, better organized and capable of performing the various tasks properly, which will ensure that the repair job is thorough and complete.

Fasteners

Fasteners are nuts, bolts, studs and screws used to hold two or more parts together. There are a few things to keep in mind when working with fasteners. Almost all of them use a locking device of some type, either a lockwasher, locknut, locking tab or thread adhesive. All threaded fasteners should be clean and straight, with undamaged threads and undamaged corners on the hex head where the wrench fits. Develop the habit of replacing all damaged nuts and bolts with new ones. Special locknuts with nylon or fiber inserts can only be used once. If they are removed, they lose their locking ability and must be replaced with new ones.

Rusted nuts and bolts should be treated with a penetrating fluid to ease removal and prevent breakage. Some mechanics use turpentine in a spout-type oil can, which works quite well. After applying the rust penetrant, let it work for a few minutes before trying to loosen the nut or bolt. Badly rusted fasteners may have to be chiseled or sawed off or removed with a special nut breaker, available at tool stores.

If a bolt or stud breaks off in an assembly, it can be drilled and removed with a special tool commonly available for this purpose. Most automotive machine shops can perform this task, as well as other repair procedures, such as the repair of threaded holes that have been stripped out.

Flat washers and lockwashers, when removed from an assembly, should always be replaced exactly as removed. Replace any damaged washers with new ones. Never use a lockwasher on any soft metal surface (such as aluminum), thin sheet metal or plastic.

Fastener sizes

For a number of reasons, automobile manufacturers are making wider and wider use of metric fasteners. Therefore, it is important to be able to tell the difference between standard (sometimes called U.S. or SAE) and metric hardware, since they cannot be interchanged.

All bolts, whether standard or metric, are sized according to diameter, thread pitch and length. For example, a standard 1/2 - 13 x 1 bolt is 1/2 inch in diameter, has 13 threads per inch and is 1 inch long. An M12 - 1.75 x 25 metric bolt is 12 mm in diameter, has a thread pitch of 1.75 mm (the distance between threads) and is 25 mm long. The two bolts are nearly identical, and easily confused, but they are not interchangeable.

In addition to the differences in diameter, thread pitch and length, metric and standard bolts can also be distinguished by examining the bolt heads. To begin with, the distance across the flats on a standard bolt head is measured in inches, while the same dimension on a metric bolt is sized in millimeters (the same is true for nuts). As a result, a standard wrench should not be used on a metric bolt and a metric wrench should not be used on a standard bolt. Also, most standard bolts have slashes radiating out from the center of the head to denote the grade or strength of the bolt, which is an indication of the amount of torque that can be applied to it. The greater the number of slashes, the greater the strength of the bolt. Grades 0 through 5 are commonly used on automobiles. Metric bolts have a property class (grade) number, rather than a slash, molded into their heads to indicate bolt strength. In this case, the higher the number, the stronger the bolt. Property class numbers 8.8, 9.8 and 10.9 are commonly used on automobiles.

Strength markings can also be used to distinguish standard hex nuts from metric hex nuts. Many standard nuts have dots stamped into one side, while metric nuts are marked with a number. The greater the number of dots, or the higher the number, the greater the strength of the nut.

Metric studs are also marked on their ends according to property class (grade). Larger studs are numbered (the same as metric bolts), while smaller studs carry a geometric code to denote grade.

It should be noted that many fasteners, especially Grades 0 through 2, have no distinguishing marks on them. When such is the case, the only way to determine whether it is standard or metric is to measure the thread pitch or compare it to a known fastener of the same size.

Standard fasteners are often referred to as SAE, as opposed to metric. However, it should be noted that SAE technically refers to a non-metric fine thread fastener only. Coarse thread non-metric fasteners are referred to as USS sizes.

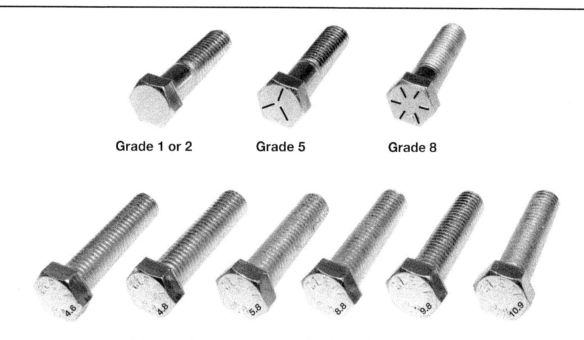

Grade 1 or 2   Grade 5   Grade 8

Bolt strength marking (standard/SAE/USS; bottom - metric)

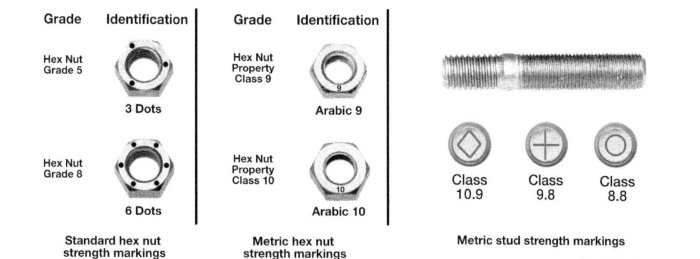

Grade	Identification
Hex Nut Grade 5	3 Dots
Hex Nut Grade 8	6 Dots

Standard hex nut strength markings

Grade	Identification
Hex Nut Property Class 9	Arabic 9
Hex Nut Property Class 10	Arabic 10

Metric hex nut strength markings

Class 10.9   Class 9.8   Class 8.8

Metric stud strength markings

Since fasteners of the same size (both standard and metric) may have different strength ratings, be sure to reinstall any bolts, studs or nuts removed from your vehicle in their original locations. Also, when replacing a fastener with a new one, make sure that the new one has a strength rating equal to or greater than the original.

Tightening sequences and procedures

Most threaded fasteners should be tightened to a specific torque value (torque is the twisting force applied to a threaded com-ponent such as a nut or bolt). Overtightening the fastener can weaken it and cause it to break, while undertightening can cause it to eventually come loose. Bolts, screws and studs, depending on the material they are made of and their thread diameters, have specific torque values, many of which are noted in the Specifications at the beginning of each Chapter. Be sure to follow the torque recommendations closely. For fasteners not assigned a specific torque, a general torque value chart is presented here as a guide. These torque values are for dry (unlubricated) fasteners threaded into steel or cast iron (not aluminum). As was previously mentioned, the size and grade of a fastener determine the amount of torque that can safely be applied to it. The figures listed here are approximate for Grade 2 and Grade 3 fasteners. Higher grades can tolerate higher torque values.

Fasteners laid out in a pattern, such as cylinder head bolts, oil pan bolts, differential cover bolts, etc., must be loosened or tight-ened in sequence to avoid warping the com-ponent. This sequence will normally be shown in the appropriate Chapter. If a specific pat-tern is not given, the following procedures can be used to prevent warping.

	Ft-lbs	Nm
Metric thread sizes		
M-6	6 to 9	9 to 12
M-8	14 to 21	19 to 28
M-10	28 to 40	38 to 54
M-12	50 to 71	68 to 96
M-14	80 to 140	109 to 154
Pipe thread sizes		
1/8	5 to 8	7 to 10
1/4	12 to 18	17 to 24
3/8	22 to 33	30 to 44
1/2	25 to 35	34 to 47
U.S. thread sizes		
1/4 - 20	6 to 9	9 to 12
5/16 - 18	12 to 18	17 to 24
5/16 - 24	14 to 20	19 to 27
3/8 - 16	22 to 32	30 to 43
3/8 - 24	27 to 38	37 to 51
7/16 - 14	40 to 55	55 to 74
7/16 - 20	40 to 60	55 to 81
1/2 - 13	55 to 80	75 to 108

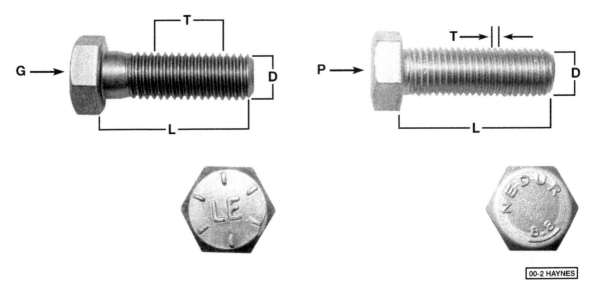

00-2 HAYNES

Standard (SAE and USS) bolt dimensions/grade marks

- G   Grade marks (bolt strength)
- L   Length (in inches)
- T   Thread pitch (number of threads per inch)
- D   Nominal diameter (in inches)

Metric bolt dimensions/grade marks

- P   Property class (bolt strength)
- L   Length (in millimeters)
- T   Thread pitch (distance between threads in millimeters)
- D   Diameter

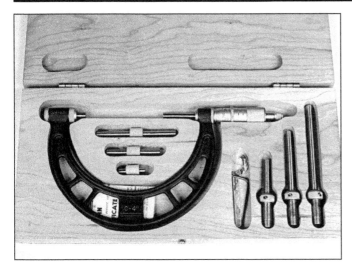

Micrometer set

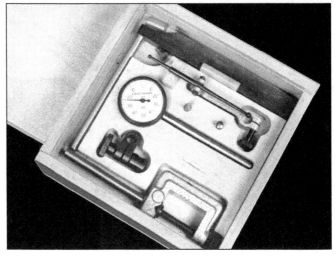

Dial indicator set

Initially, the bolts or nuts should be assembled finger-tight only. Next, they should be tightened one full turn each, in a criss-cross or diagonal pattern. After each one has been tightened one full turn, return to the first one and tighten them all one-half turn, following the same pattern. Finally, tighten each of them one-quarter turn at a time until each fastener has been tightened to the proper torque. To loosen and remove the fasteners, the procedure would be reversed.

Component disassembly

Component disassembly should be done with care and purpose to help ensure that the parts go back together properly. Always keep track of the sequence in which parts are removed. Make note of special characteristics or marks on parts that can be installed more than one way, such as a grooved thrust washer on a shaft. It is a good idea to lay the disassembled parts out on a clean surface in the order that they were removed. It may also be helpful to make sketches or take instant photos of components before removal.

When removing fasteners from a component, keep track of their locations. Sometimes threading a bolt back in a part, or putting the washers and nut back on a stud, can prevent mix-ups later. If nuts and bolts cannot be returned to their original locations, they should be kept in a compartmented box or a series of small boxes. A cupcake or muffin tin is ideal for this purpose, since each cavity can hold the bolts and nuts from a particular area (i.e. oil pan bolts, valve cover bolts, engine mount bolts, etc.) A pan of this type is especially helpful when working on assemblies with very small parts, such as the carburetor, alternator, valve train or interior dash and trim pieces. The cavities can be marked with paint or tape to identify the contents.

Whenever wiring looms, harnesses or connectors are separated, it is a good idea to identify the two halves with numbered pieces of masking tape so they can be easily reconnected.

Gasket sealing surfaces

Throughout any vehicle, gaskets are used to seal the mating surfaces between two parts and keep lubricants, fluids, vacuum or pressure contained in an assembly.

Many times these gaskets are coated with a liquid or paste-type gasket sealing compound before assembly. Age, heat and pressure can sometimes cause the two parts to stick together so tightly that they are very difficult to separate. Often, the assembly can be loosened by striking it with a soft-face hammer near the mating surfaces. A regular hammer can be used if a block of wood is placed between the hammer and the part. Do not hammer on cast parts or parts that could be easily damaged. With any particularly stubborn part, always recheck to make sure that every fastener has been removed.

Avoid using a screwdriver or bar to pry apart an assembly, as they can easily mar the gasket sealing surfaces of the parts, which must remain smooth. If prying is absolutely necessary, use an old broom handle, but keep in mind that extra clean up will be necessary if the wood splinters.

After the parts are separated, the old gasket must be carefully scraped off and the gasket surfaces cleaned. Stubborn gasket material can be soaked with rust penetrant or treated with a special chemical to soften it so it can be easily scraped off. A scraper can be fashioned from a piece of copper tubing by flattening and sharpening one end. Copper is recommended because it is usually softer than the surfaces to be scraped, which reduces the chance of gouging the part. Some gaskets can be removed with a wire brush, but regardless of the method used, the mating surfaces must be left clean and smooth. If for some reason the gasket surface is gouged, then a gasket sealer thick enough to fill scratches will have to be used during reassembly of the components. For most applications, a non-drying (or semi-drying) gasket sealer should be used.

Hose removal tips

Warning: *If the vehicle is equipped with air conditioning, do not disconnect any of the A/C hoses without first having the system depressurized by a dealer service department or a service station.*

Hose removal precautions closely parallel gasket removal precautions. Avoid scratching or gouging the surface that the hose mates against or the connection may leak. This is especially true for radiator hoses. Because of various chemical reactions, the rubber in hoses can bond itself to the metal spigot that the hose fits over. To remove a hose, first loosen the hose clamps that secure it to the spigot. Then, with slip-joint pliers, grab the hose at the clamp and rotate it around the spigot. Work it back and forth until it is completely free, then pull it off. Silicone or other lubricants will ease removal if they can be applied between the hose and the outside of the spigot. Apply the same lubricant to the inside of the hose and the outside of the spigot to simplify installation.

As a last resort (and if the hose is to be replaced with a new one anyway), the rubber can be slit with a knife and the hose peeled from the spigot. If this must be done, be careful that the metal connection is not damaged.

If a hose clamp is broken or damaged, do not reuse it. Wire-type clamps usually weaken with age, so it is a good idea to replace them with screw-type clamps whenever a hose is removed.

Tools

A selection of good tools is a basic requirement for anyone who plans to maintain and repair his or her own vehicle. For the owner who has few tools, the initial investment might seem high, but when compared to the spiraling costs of professional auto maintenance and repair, it is a wise one.

To help the owner decide which tools are needed to perform the tasks detailed in this manual, the following tool lists are offered: *Maintenance and minor repair,*

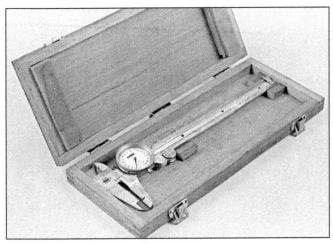

Dial caliper

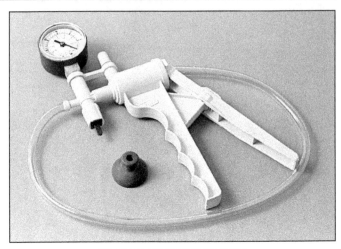

Hand-operated vacuum pump

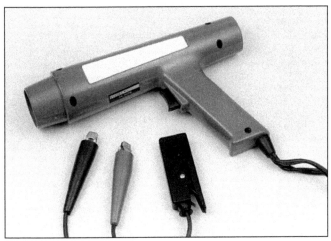

Timing light

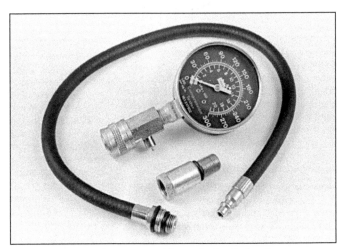

Compression gauge with spark plug hole adapter

Damper/steering wheel puller

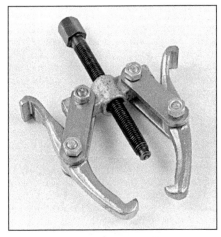

General purpose puller

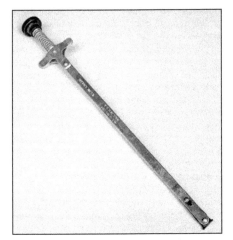

Hydraulic lifter removal tool

Repair/overhaul and *Special*.

The newcomer to practical mechanics should start off with the *maintenance and minor repair* tool kit, which is adequate for the simpler jobs performed on a vehicle. Then, as confidence and experience grow, the owner can tackle more difficult tasks, buying additional tools as they are needed.

Eventually the basic kit will be expanded into the *repair and overhaul* tool set. Over a period of time, the experienced do-it-yourselfer will assemble a tool set complete enough for most repair and overhaul procedures and will add tools from the special category when it is felt that the expense is justified by the frequency of use.

Maintenance and minor repair tool kit

The tools in this list should be considered the minimum required for performance of routine maintenance, servicing and minor repair work. We recommend the purchase of combination wrenches (box-end and open-

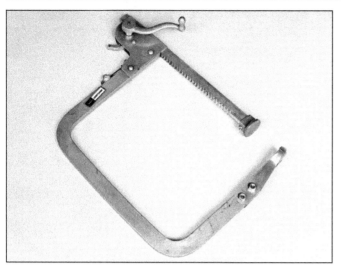

Valve spring compressor

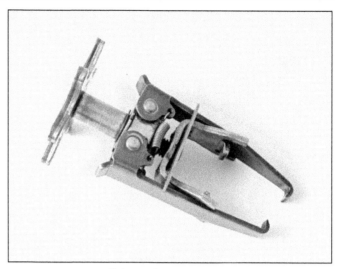

Valve spring compressor

Ridge reamer

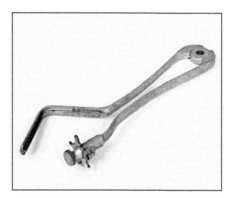

Piston ring groove cleaning tool

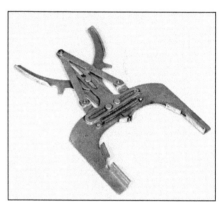

Ring removal/installation tool

end combined in one wrench). While more expensive than open end wrenches, they offer the advantages of both types of wrench.

> *Combination wrench set (1/4-inch to 1 inch or 6 mm to 19 mm)*
> *Adjustable wrench, 8 inch*
> *Spark plug wrench with rubber insert*
> *Spark plug gap adjusting tool*
> *Feeler gauge set*

Ring compressor

> *Brake bleeder wrench*
> *Standard screwdriver (5/16-inch x 6 inch)*
> *Phillips screwdriver (No. 2 x 6 inch)*
> *Combination pliers - 6 inch*
> *Hacksaw and assortment of blades*
> *Tire pressure gauge*
> *Grease gun*
> *Oil can*
> *Fine emery cloth*
> *Wire brush*
> *Battery post and cable cleaning tool*
> *Oil filter wrench*
> *Funnel (medium size)*
> *Safety goggles*
> *Jackstands (2)*
> *Drain pan*

Note: *If basic tune-ups are going to be part of routine maintenance, it will be necessary to purchase a good quality stroboscopic timing light and combination tachometer/dwell meter. Although they are included in the list of special tools, it is mentioned here because they are absolutely necessary for tuning most vehicles properly.*

Repair and overhaul tool set

These tools are essential for anyone who plans to perform major repairs and are in addition to those in the maintenance and

minor repair tool kit. Included is a comprehensive set of sockets which, though expensive, are invaluable because of their versatility, especially when various extensions and drives are available. We recommend the 1/2-inch drive over the 3/8-inch drive. Although the larger drive is bulky and more expensive, it has the capacity of accepting a very wide range of large sockets. Ideally, however, the mechanic should have a 3/8-inch drive set and a 1/2-inch drive set.

> *Socket set(s)*
> *Reversible ratchet*
> *Extension - 10 inch*
> *Universal joint*
> *Torque wrench (same size drive as sockets)*
> *Ball peen hammer 8 ounce*
> *Soft-face hammer (plastic/rubber)*
> *Standard screwdriver (1/4-inch x 6 inch)*
> *Standard screwdriver (stubby - 5/16-inch)*
> *Phillips screwdriver (No. 3 x 8 inch)*
> *Phillips screwdriver (stubby - No. 2)*
> *Pliers - vise grip*
> *Pliers - lineman's*
> *Pliers - needle nose*
> *Pliers - snap-ring (internal and external)*
> *Cold chisel - 1/2-inch*

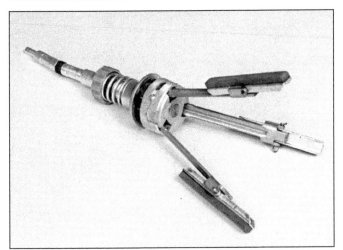

Cylinder hone

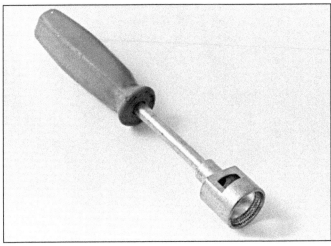

Brake hold-down spring tool

Scribe
Scraper (made from flattened copper tubing)
Centerpunch
Pin punches (1/16, 1/8, 3/16-inch)
Steel rule/straightedge - 12 inch
Allen wrench set (1/8 to 3/8-inch or 4 mm to 10 mm)
A selection of files
Wire brush (large)
Jackstands (second set)
Jack (scissor or hydraulic type)

Note: *Another tool which is often useful is an electric drill with a chuck capacity of 3/8-inch and a set of good quality drill bits.*

Special tools

The tools in this list include those which are not used regularly, are expensive to buy, or which need to be used in accordance with their manufacturer's instructions. Unless these tools will be used frequently, it is not very economical to purchase many of them. A consideration would be to split the cost and use between yourself and a friend or friends. In addition, most of these tools can be obtained from a tool rental shop on a temporary basis.

This list primarily contains only those tools and instruments widely available to the public, and not those special tools produced by the vehicle manufacturer for distribution to dealer service departments. Occasionally, references to the manufacturer's special tools are included in the text of this manual. Generally, an alternative method of doing the job without the special tool is offered. However, sometimes there is no alternative to their use. Where this is the case, and the tool cannot be purchased or borrowed, the work should be turned over to the dealer service department or an automotive repair shop.

Valve spring compressor
Piston ring groove cleaning tool
Piston ring compressor
Piston ring installation tool
Cylinder compression gauge
Cylinder ridge reamer
Cylinder surfacing hone
Cylinder bore gauge
Micrometers and/or dial calipers
Hydraulic lifter removal tool
Balljoint separator
Universal-type puller
Impact screwdriver
Dial indicator set

Stroboscopic timing light (inductive pick-up)
Hand operated vacuum/pressure pump
Tachometer/dwell meter
Universal electrical multimeter
Cable hoist
Brake spring removal and installation tools
Floor jack

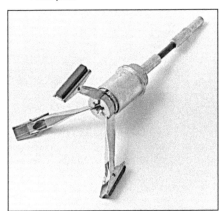

Brake cylinder hone

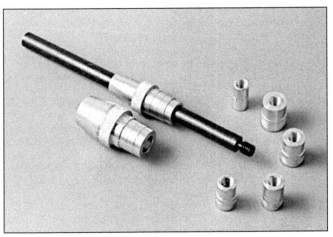

Clutch plate alignment tool

Tap and die set

Buying tools

For the do-it-yourselfer who is just starting to get involved in vehicle maintenance and repair, there are a number of options available when purchasing tools. If maintenance and minor repair is the extent of the work to be done, the purchase of individual tools is satisfactory. If, on the other hand, extensive work is planned, it would be a good idea to purchase a modest tool set from one of the large retail chain stores. A set can usually be bought at a substantial savings over the individual tool prices, and they often come with a tool box. As additional tools are needed, add-on sets, individual tools and a larger tool box can be purchased to expand the tool selection. Building a tool set gradually allows the cost of the tools to be spread over a longer period of time and gives the mechanic the freedom to choose only those tools that will actually be used.

Tool stores will often be the only source of some of the special tools that are needed, but regardless of where tools are bought, try to avoid cheap ones, especially when buying screwdrivers and sockets, because they won't last very long. The expense involved in replacing cheap tools will eventually be greater than the initial cost of quality tools.

Care and maintenance of tools

Good tools are expensive, so it makes sense to treat them with respect. Keep them clean and in usable condition and store them properly when not in use. Always wipe off any dirt, grease or metal chips before putting them away. Never leave tools lying around in the work area. Upon completion of a job, always check closely under the hood for tools that may have been left there so they won't get lost during a test drive.

Some tools, such as screwdrivers, pliers, wrenches and sockets, can be hung on a panel mounted on the garage or workshop wall, while others should be kept in a tool box or tray. Measuring instruments, gauges, meters, etc. must be carefully stored where they cannot be damaged by weather or impact from other tools.

When tools are used with care and stored properly, they will last a very long time. Even with the best of care, though, tools will wear out if used frequently. When a tool is damaged or worn out, replace it. Subsequent jobs will be safer and more enjoyable if you do.

How to repair damaged threads

Sometimes, the internal threads of a nut or bolt hole can become stripped, usually from overtightening. Stripping threads is an all-too-common occurrence, especially when working with aluminum parts, because aluminum is so soft that it easily strips out.

Usually, external or internal threads are only partially stripped. After they've been cleaned up with a tap or die, they'll still work. Sometimes, however, threads are badly damaged. When this happens, you've got three choices:

1) Drill and tap the hole to the next suitable oversize and install a larger diameter bolt, screw or stud.
2) Drill and tap the hole to accept a threaded plug, then drill and tap the plug to the original screw size. You can also buy a plug already threaded to the original size. Then you simply drill a hole to the specified size, then run the threaded plug into the hole with a bolt and jam nut. Once the plug is fully seated, remove the jam nut and bolt.
3) The third method uses a patented thread repair kit like Heli-Coil or Slimsert. These easy-to-use kits are designed to repair damaged threads in straight-through holes and blind holes. Both are available as kits which can handle a variety of sizes and thread patterns. Drill the hole, then tap it with the special included tap. Install the Heli-Coil and the hole is back to its original diameter and thread pitch.

Regardless of which method you use, be sure to proceed calmly and carefully. A little impatience or carelessness during one of these relatively simple procedures can ruin your whole day's work and cost you a bundle if you wreck an expensive part.

Working facilities

Not to be overlooked when discussing tools is the workshop. If anything more than routine maintenance is to be carried out, some sort of suitable work area is essential.

It is understood, and appreciated, that many home mechanics do not have a good workshop or garage available, and end up removing an engine or doing major repairs outside. It is recommended, however, that the overhaul or repair be completed under the cover of a roof.

A clean, flat workbench or table of comfortable working height is an absolute necessity. The workbench should be equipped with a vise that has a jaw opening of at least four inches.

As mentioned previously, some clean, dry storage space is also required for tools, as well as the lubricants, fluids, cleaning solvents, etc. which soon become necessary.

Sometimes waste oil and fluids, drained from the engine or cooling system during normal maintenance or repairs, present a disposal problem. To avoid pouring them on the ground or into a sewage system, pour the used fluids into large containers, seal them with caps and take them to an authorized disposal site or recycling center. Plastic jugs, such as old antifreeze containers, are ideal for this purpose.

Always keep a supply of old newspapers and clean rags available. Old towels are excellent for mopping up spills. Many mechanics use rolls of paper towels for most work because they are readily available and disposable. To help keep the area under the vehicle clean, a large cardboard box can be cut open and flattened to protect the garage or shop floor.

Whenever working over a painted surface, such as when leaning over a fender to service something under the hood, always cover it with an old blanket or bedspread to protect the finish. Vinyl covered pads, made especially for this purpose, are available at auto parts stores.

Booster battery (jump) starting

Observe the following precautions when using a booster battery to start a vehicle:

a) *Before connecting the booster battery, make sure the ignition switch is in the Off position.*
b) *Turn off the lights, heater and other electrical loads.*
c) *Your eyes should be shielded. Safety goggles are a good idea.*
d) *Make sure the booster battery is the same voltage as the dead one in the vehicle.*
e) *The two vehicles MUST NOT TOUCH each other.*
f) *Make sure the transmission is in Neutral (manual transaxle) or Park (automatic transaxle).*
g) *If the booster battery is not a maintenance-free type, remove the vent caps and lay a cloth over the vent holes.*

Connect the red jumper cable to the positive (+) terminals of each battery.

Connect one end of the black cable to the negative (-) terminal of the booster battery. The other end of this cable should be connected to a good ground on the engine block **(see illustration)**. Make sure the cable will not come into contact with the fan, drivebelts or other moving parts of the engine.

Start the engine using the booster battery, then, with the engine running at idle speed, disconnect the jumper cables in the reverse order of connection.

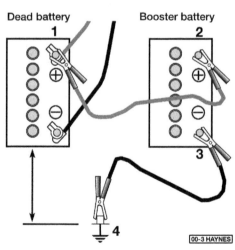

Make the booster battery cable connections in the numerical order shown (note that the negative cable of the booster battery is NOT attached to the negative terminal of the dead battery)

Jacking and towing

Jacking

The jack supplied with the car should be used only for changing a wheel due to a roadside flat or for raising the car enough to allow jack stands to support the weight. Under no circumstances should repair work be done under the car while it is supported by this jack, nor should the engine be started or run while this jack is being used.

All Firebirds have come equipped with a ratchet type bumper jack designed to lift one corner of the car from either the front or rear bumper. All types are used in basically the same fashion, the difference being that earlier models have a load rest bracket and a notch in the bumper as opposed to the hook which fits into a slot in the bumper for later types.

The car should be on level ground with the transmission in 'Park' (automatic) or 'Reverse' (manual transmissions). The parking brake should be firmly set. Blocking the front and rear of the wheel on the same side as the one being changed will further prevent the car from rolling.

With the lever on the jack in the Up' position, locate the load rest bracket or hook (depending on model) to the bumper. Before the load is taken up, remove the hubcap using the flat end of the lug wrench and slightly loosen each of the lug nuts on the wheel to be changed. Using the lug wrench as a handle, raise the car enough to remove the wheel.

Before installing the spare, remove any built-up corrosion or dirt from the drum or hub and the rear side of the spare.

Place the spare into position and slightly tighten the lug nuts, with the cone-shaped end of the nuts towards the wheel. The wheel must be seated on the hub. Change the jack lever to the 'Down' position and slowly lower the car. Once it is completely on the ground tighten all lug nuts in a diagonal fashion until tight. The hubcap can be installed now or later by placing it into position and using the heel of your hand or a rubber mallet to fully seat it.

Towing

The vehicle can be towed on all four wheels providing that speeds do not exceed 35 mph and the distance is not over 50 miles. Towing equipment specifically designed for this purpose should be used and should be attached to the main structural members of the car and not the bumper or brackets.

Safety is a major consideration when towing, and all applicable state and local laws should be obeyed. A safety chain system must be used for all towing.

While towing, the parking brake should be fully released and the transmission should be in 'Neutral'. The steering must be unlocked (ignition switch in the 'off' position). Remember that power steering and power brakes will not work with the engine off.

Automotive chemicals and lubricants

A number of automotive chemicals and lubricants are available for use during vehicle maintenance and repair. They include a wide variety of products ranging from cleaning solvents and degreasers to lubricants and protective sprays for rubber, plastic and vinyl.

Cleaners

Carburetor cleaner and choke cleaner is a strong solvent for gum, varnish and carbon. Most carburetor cleaners leave a dry-type lubricant film which will not harden or gum up. Because of this film it is not recommended for use on electrical components.

Brake system cleaner is used to remove grease and brake fluid from the brake system, where clean surfaces are absolutely necessary. It leaves no residue and often eliminates brake squeal caused by contaminants.

Electrical cleaner removes oxidation, corrosion and carbon deposits from electrical contacts, restoring full current flow. It can also be used to clean spark plugs, carburetor jets, voltage regulators and other parts where an oil-free surface is desired.

Demoisturants remove water and moisture from electrical components such as alternators, voltage regulators, electrical connectors and fuse blocks. They are non-conductive, non-corrosive and non-flammable.

Degreasers are heavy-duty solvents used to remove grease from the outside of the engine and from chassis components. They can be sprayed or brushed on and, depending on the type, are rinsed off either with water or solvent.

Lubricants

Motor oil is the lubricant formulated for use in engines. It normally contains a wide variety of additives to prevent corrosion and reduce foaming and wear. Motor oil comes in various weights (viscosity ratings) from 0 to 50. The recommended weight of the oil depends on the season, temperature and the demands on the engine. Light oil is used in cold climates and under light load conditions. Heavy oil is used in hot climates and where high loads are encountered. Multi-viscosity oils are designed to have characteristics of both light and heavy oils and are available in a number of weights from 5W-20 to 20W-50.

Gear oil is designed to be used in differentials, manual transmissions and other areas where high-temperature lubrication is required.

Chassis and wheel bearing grease is a heavy grease used where increased loads and friction are encountered, such as for wheel bearings, balljoints, tie-rod ends and universal joints.

High-temperature wheel bearing grease is designed to withstand the extreme temperatures encountered by wheel bearings in disc brake equipped vehicles. It usually contains molybdenum disulfide (moly), which is a dry-type lubricant.

White grease is a heavy grease for metal-to-metal applications where water is a problem. White grease stays soft under both low and high temperatures (usually from -100 to +190-degrees F), and will not wash off or dilute in the presence of water.

Assembly lube is a special extreme pressure lubricant, usually containing moly, used to lubricate high-load parts (such as main and rod bearings and cam lobes) for initial start-up of a new engine. The assembly lube lubricates the parts without being squeezed out or washed away until the engine oiling system begins to function.

Silicone lubricants are used to protect rubber, plastic, vinyl and nylon parts.

Graphite lubricants are used where oils cannot be used due to contamination problems, such as in locks. The dry graphite will lubricate metal parts while remaining uncontaminated by dirt, water, oil or acids. It is electrically conductive and will not foul electrical contacts in locks such as the ignition switch.

Moly penetrants loosen and lubricate frozen, rusted and corroded fasteners and prevent future rusting or freezing.

Heat-sink grease is a special electrically non-conductive grease that is used for mounting electronic ignition modules where it is essential that heat is transferred away from the module.

Sealants

RTV sealant is one of the most widely used gasket compounds. Made from silicone, RTV is air curing, it seals, bonds, waterproofs, fills surface irregularities, remains flexible, doesn't shrink, is relatively easy to remove, and is used as a supplementary sealer with almost all low and medium temperature gaskets.

Anaerobic sealant is much like RTV in that it can be used either to seal gaskets or to form gaskets by itself. It remains flexible, is solvent resistant and fills surface imperfections. The difference between an anaerobic sealant and an RTV-type sealant is in the curing. RTV cures when exposed to air, while an anaerobic sealant cures only in the absence of air. This means that an anaerobic sealant cures only after the assembly of parts, sealing them together.

Thread and pipe sealant is used for sealing hydraulic and pneumatic fittings and vacuum lines. It is usually made from a Teflon compound, and comes in a spray, a paint-on liquid and as a wrap-around tape.

Chemicals

Anti-seize compound prevents seizing, galling, cold welding, rust and corrosion in fasteners. High-temperature anti-seize, usually made with copper and graphite lubricants, is used for exhaust system and exhaust manifold bolts.

Anaerobic locking compounds are used to keep fasteners from vibrating or working loose and cure only after installation, in the absence of air. Medium strength locking compound is used for small nuts, bolts and screws that may be removed later. High-strength locking compound is for large nuts, bolts and studs which aren't removed on a regular basis.

Oil additives range from viscosity index improvers to chemical treatments that claim to reduce internal engine friction. It should be noted that most oil manufacturers caution against using additives with their oils.

Gas additives perform several functions, depending on their chemical makeup. They usually contain solvents that help dissolve gum and varnish that build up on carburetor, fuel injection and intake parts. They also serve to break down carbon deposits that form on the inside surfaces of the combustion chambers. Some additives contain upper cylinder lubricants for valves and piston rings, and others contain chemicals to remove condensation from the gas tank.

Miscellaneous

Brake fluid is specially formulated hydraulic fluid that can withstand the heat and pressure encountered in brake systems. Care must be taken so this fluid does not come in contact with painted surfaces or plastics. An opened container should always be resealed to prevent contamination by water or dirt.

Weatherstrip adhesive is used to bond weatherstripping around doors, windows and trunk lids. It is sometimes used to attach trim pieces.

Undercoating is a petroleum-based, tar-like substance that is designed to protect metal surfaces on the underside of the vehicle from corrosion. It also acts as a sound-deadening agent by insulating the bottom of the vehicle.

Waxes and polishes are used to help protect painted and plated surfaces from the weather. Different types of paint may require the use of different types of wax and polish. Some polishes utilize a chemical or abrasive cleaner to help remove the top layer of oxidized (dull) paint on older vehicles. In recent years many non-wax polishes that contain a wide variety of chemicals such as polymers and silicones have been introduced. These non-wax polishes are usually easier to apply and last longer than conventional waxes and polishes.

Conversion factors

Length (distance)

Inches (in)	X	25.4	= Millimeters (mm)	X 0.0394	= Inches (in)
Feet (ft)	X	0.305	= Meters (m)	X 3.281	= Feet (ft)
Miles	X	1.609	= Kilometers (km)	X 0.621	= Miles

Volume (capacity)

Cubic inches (cu in; in^3)	X	16.387	= Cubic centimeters (cc; cm^3)	X 0.061	= Cubic inches (cu in; in^3)
Imperial pints (Imp pt)	X	0.568	= Liters (l)	X 1.76	= Imperial pints (Imp pt)
Imperial quarts (Imp qt)	X	1.137	= Liters (l)	X 0.88	= Imperial quarts (Imp qt)
Imperial quarts (Imp qt)	X	1.201	= US quarts (US qt)	X 0.833	= Imperial quarts (Imp qt)
US quarts (US qt)	X	0.946	= Liters (l)	X 1.057	= US quarts (US qt)
Imperial gallons (Imp gal)	X	4.546	= Liters (l)	X 0.22	= Imperial gallons (Imp gal)
Imperial gallons (Imp gal)	X	1.201	= US gallons (US gal)	X 0.833	= Imperial gallons (Imp gal)
US gallons (US gal)	X	3.785	= Liters (l)	X 0.264	= US gallons (US gal)

Mass (weight)

Ounces (oz)	X	28.35	= Grams (g)	X 0.035	= Ounces (oz)
Pounds (lb)	X	0.454	= Kilograms (kg)	X 2.205	= Pounds (lb)

Force

Ounces-force (ozf; oz)	X	0.278	= Newtons (N)	X 3.6	= Ounces-force (ozf; oz)
Pounds-force (lbf; lb)	X	4.448	= Newtons (N)	X 0.225	= Pounds-force (lbf; lb)
Newtons (N)	X	0.1	= Kilograms-force (kgf; kg)	X 9.81	= Newtons (N)

Pressure

Pounds-force per square inch (psi; lbf/in^2; lb/in^2)	X	0.070	= Kilograms-force per square centimeter (kgf/cm^2; kg/cm^2)	X 14.223	= Pounds-force per square inch (psi; lbf/in^2; lb/in^2)
Pounds-force per square inch (psi; lbf/in^2; lb/in^2)	X	0.068	= Atmospheres (atm)	X 14.696	= Pounds-force per square inch (psi; lbf/in^2; lb/in^2)
Pounds-force per square inch (psi; lbf/in^2; lb/in^2)	X	0.069	= Bars	X 14.5	= Pounds-force per square inch (psi; lbf/in^2; lb/in^2)
Pounds-force per square inch (psi; lbf/in^2; lb/in^2)	X	6.895	= Kilopascals (kPa)	X 0.145	= Pounds-force per square inch (psi; lbf/in^2; lb/in^2)
Kilopascals (kPa)	X	0.01	= Kilograms-force per square centimeter (kgf/cm^2; kg/cm^2)	X 98.1	= Kilopascals (kPa)

Torque (moment of force)

Pounds-force inches (lbf in; lb in)	X	1.152	= Kilograms-force centimeter (kgf cm; kg cm)	X 0.868	= Pounds-force inches (lbf in; lb in)
Pounds-force inches (lbf in; lb in)	X	0.113	= Newton meters (Nm)	X 8.85	= Pounds-force inches (lbf in; lb in)
Pounds-force inches (lbf in; lb in)	X	0.083	= Pounds-force feet (lbf ft; lb ft)	X 12	= Pounds-force inches (lbf in; lb in)
Pounds-force feet (lbf ft; lb ft)	X	0.138	= Kilograms-force meters (kgf m; kg m)	X 7.233	= Pounds-force feet (lbf ft; lb ft)
Pounds-force feet (lbf ft; lb ft)	X	1.356	= Newton meters (Nm)	X 0.738	= Pounds-force feet (lbf ft; lb ft)
Newton meters (Nm)	X	0.102	= Kilograms-force meters (kgf m; kg m)	X 9.804	= Newton meters (Nm)

Vacuum

Inches mercury (in. Hg)	X	3.377	= Kilopascals (kPa)	X 0.2961	= Inches mercury
Inches mercury (in. Hg)	X	25.4	= Millimeters mercury (mm Hg)	X 0.0394	= Inches mercury

Power

Horsepower (hp)	X	745.7	= Watts (W)	X 0.0013	= Horsepower (hp)

Velocity (speed)

Miles per hour (miles/hr; mph)	X	1.609	= Kilometers per hour (km/hr; kph)	X 0.621	= Miles per hour (miles/hr; mph)

Fuel consumption*

Miles per gallon, Imperial (mpg)	X	0.354	= Kilometers per liter (km/l)	X 2.825	= Miles per gallon, Imperial (mpg)
Miles per gallon, US (mpg)	X	0.425	= Kilometers per liter (km/l)	X 2.352	= Miles per gallon, US (mpg)

Temperature

Degrees Fahrenheit = (°C x 1.8) + 32   Degrees Celsius (Degrees Centigrade; °C) = (°F - 32) x 0.56

*It is common practice to convert from miles per gallon (mpg) to liters/100 kilometers (l/100km), where mpg (Imperial) x l/100 km = 282 and mpg (US) x l/100 km = 235

Safety first!

Regardless of how enthusiastic you may be about getting on with the job at hand, take the time to ensure that your safety is not jeopardized. A moment's lack of attention can result in an accident, as can failure to observe certain simple safety precautions. The possibility of an accident will always exist, and the following points should not be considered a comprehensive list of all dangers. Rather, they are intended to make you aware of the risks and to encourage a safety conscious approach to all work you carry out on your vehicle.

Essential DOs and DON'Ts

DON'T rely on a jack when working under the vehicle. Always use approved jackstands to support the weight of the vehicle and place them under the recommended lift or support points.

DON'T attempt to loosen extremely tight fasteners (i.e. wheel lug nuts) while the vehicle is on a jack - it may fall.

DON'T start the engine without first making sure that the transmission is in Neutral (or Park where applicable) and the parking brake is set.

DON'T remove the radiator cap from a hot cooling system - let it cool or cover it with a cloth and release the pressure gradually.

DON'T attempt to drain the engine oil until you are sure it has cooled to the point that it will not burn you.

DON'T touch any part of the engine or exhaust system until it has cooled sufficiently to avoid burns.

DON'T siphon toxic liquids such as gasoline, antifreeze and brake fluid by mouth, or allow them to remain on your skin.

DON'T inhale brake lining dust - it is potentially hazardous (see *Asbestos* below).

DON'T allow spilled oil or grease to remain on the floor - wipe it up before someone slips on it.

DON'T use loose fitting wrenches or other tools which may slip and cause injury.

DON'T push on wrenches when loosening or tightening nuts or bolts. Always try to pull the wrench toward you. If the situation calls for pushing the wrench away, push with an open hand to avoid scraped knuckles if the wrench should slip.

DON'T attempt to lift a heavy component alone - get someone to help you.

DON'T rush or take unsafe shortcuts to finish a job.

DON'T allow children or animals in or around the vehicle while you are working on it.

DO wear eye protection when using power tools such as a drill, sander, bench grinder, etc. and when working under a vehicle.

DO keep loose clothing and long hair well out of the way of moving parts.

DO make sure that any hoist used has a safe working load rating adequate for the job.

DO get someone to check on you periodically when working alone on a vehicle.

DO carry out work in a logical sequence and make sure that everything is correctly assembled and tightened.

DO keep chemicals and fluids tightly capped and out of the reach of children and pets.

DO remember that your vehicle's safety affects that of yourself and others. If in doubt on any point, get professional advice.

Asbestos

Certain friction, insulating, sealing, and other products - such as brake linings, brake bands, clutch linings, torque converters, gaskets, etc. - may contain asbestos. Extreme care must be taken to avoid inhalation of dust from such products, since it is hazardous to health. If in doubt, assume that they do contain asbestos.

Fire

Remember at all times that gasoline is highly flammable. Never smoke or have any kind of open flame around when working on a vehicle. But the risk does not end there. A spark caused by an electrical short circuit, by two metal surfaces contacting each other, or even by static electricity built up in your body under certain conditions, can ignite gasoline vapors, which in a confined space are highly explosive. Do not, under any circumstances, use gasoline for cleaning parts. Use an approved safety solvent.

Always disconnect the battery ground (-) cable at the battery before working on any part of the fuel system or electrical system. Never risk spilling fuel on a hot engine or exhaust component. It is strongly recommended that a fire extinguisher suitable for use on fuel and electrical fires be kept handy in the garage or workshop at all times. Never try to extinguish a fuel or electrical fire with water.

Fumes

Certain fumes are highly toxic and can quickly cause unconsciousness and even death if inhaled to any extent. Gasoline vapor falls into this category, as do the vapors from some cleaning solvents. Any draining or pouring of such volatile fluids should be done in a well ventilated area.

When using cleaning fluids and solvents, read the instructions on the container carefully. Never use materials from unmarked containers.

Never run the engine in an enclosed space, such as a garage. Exhaust fumes contain carbon monoxide, which is extremely poisonous. If you need to run the engine, always do so in the open air, or at least have the rear of the vehicle outside the work area.

If you are fortunate enough to have the use of an inspection pit, never drain or pour gasoline and never run the engine while the vehicle is over the pit. The fumes, being heavier than air, will concentrate in the pit with possibly lethal results.

The battery

Never create a spark or allow a bare light bulb near a battery. They normally give off a certain amount of hydrogen gas, which is highly explosive.

Always disconnect the battery ground (-) cable at the battery before working on the fuel or electrical systems.

If possible, loosen the filler caps or cover when charging the battery from an external source (this does not apply to sealed or maintenance-free batteries). Do not charge at an excessive rate or the battery may burst.

Take care when adding water to a non maintenance-free battery and when carrying a battery. The electrolyte, even when diluted, is very corrosive and should not be allowed to contact clothing or skin.

Always wear eye protection when cleaning the battery to prevent the caustic deposits from entering your eyes.

Household current

When using an electric power tool, inspection light, etc., which operates on household current, always make sure that the tool is correctly connected to its plug and that, where necessary, it is properly grounded. Do not use such items in damp conditions and, again, do not create a spark or apply excessive heat in the vicinity of fuel or fuel vapor.

Secondary ignition system voltage

A severe electric shock can result from touching certain parts of the ignition system (such as the spark plug wires) when the engine is running or being cranked, particularly if components are damp or the insulation is defective. In the case of an electronic ignition system, the secondary system voltage is much higher and could prove fatal.

Troubleshooting

Contents

Engine

1 Engine will not rotate when attempting to start

1   Battery terminal connections loose or corroded. Check the cable terminals at the battery: tighten or clean corrosion as necessary.
2   Battery discharged or faulty. If the cable connectors are clean and tight on the battery posts, turn the key to the "On" position and switch on the headlights and/or windshield wipers. If these fail to function, the battery is discharged.
3   Automatic transmission not fully engaged in "Park" or manual transmission clutch not fully depressed.
4   Broken, loose or disconnected wiring in the starting circuit. Inspect all wiring and connectors at the battery, starter solenoid (at lower right side of engine) and ignition switch (on steering column).
5   Starter motor pinion jammed on flywheel ring gear. If manual transmission, place gearshift in gear and rock the car to manually turn the engine. Remove starter (Chapter 5) and inspect pinion and flywheel (Chapter 2) at earliest convenience.
6   Starter solenoid faulty (Chapter 5).
7   Starter motor faulty (Chapter 5).
8   Ignition switch faulty (Chapter 10).

2 Engine rotates but will not start

1   Fuel tank empty.
2   Battery discharged (engine rotates slowly). Check the operation of electrical components as described in previous Section (see Chapter 1).
3   Battery terminal connections loose or corroded. See previous Section.
4   Carburetor flooded and/or fuel level in carburetor incorrect. This will usually be accompanied by a strong fuel odor from under the hood. Wait a few minutes, depress the accelerator pedal all the way to the floor and attempt to start the engine.
5   Choke control inoperative (Chapters 1 and 4).
6   Fuel not reaching carburetor. With ignition switch in "Off" position, open hood, remove the top plate of air cleaner assembly and observe the top of the carburetor (manually move choke plate back if necessary). Have an assistant depress accelerator pedal fully and check that fuel spurts into carburetor. If not, check fuel filter (Chapters 1 and 4), fuel lines and fuel pump (Chapter 4).
7   Excessive moisture on, or damage to, ignition components (Chapter 1).
8   Worn, faulty or incorrectly adjusted spark plugs (Chapter 1).
9   Broken, loose or disconnected wiring in the starting circuit (see previous Section).
10 Distributor loose, thus changing ignition timing. Turn the distributor body as neces-

sary to start the engine, then set ignition timing as soon as possible (Chapter 1).
11 Ignition condenser faulty (Chapter 5).
12 Broken, loose or disconnected wires at the ignition coil, or faulty coil (Chapter 5).

3 Starter motor operates without rotating engine

1   Starter pinion sticking. Remove the starter (Chapter 5) and inspect.
2   Starter pinion or engine flywheel teeth worn or broken. Remove the inspection cover at the rear of the engine and inspect.

4 Engine hard to start when cold

1   Battery discharged or low. Check as described in Section 1.
2   Choke control inoperative or out of adjustment (Chapters 1 and 4).
3   Carburetor flooded (see Section 2).
4   Fuel supply not reaching the carburetor (see Section 2).
5   Carburetor worn and in need of overhauling (Chapter 4).

5 Engine hard to start when hot

1   Choke sticking in the closed position (Chapter 1).
2   Carburetor flooded (see Section 2).
3   Air filter in need of replacement (Chapter 1).
4   Fuel not reaching the carburetor (see Section 2).
5   Thermac air cleaner faulty (Chapter 1).
6   EFE (heat riser) sticking in the closed position (Chapter 1).

6 Starter motor noisy or excessively rough in engagement

1   Pinion or flywheel gear teeth worn or broken. Remove the inspection cover at the rear of the engine and inspect.
2   Starter motor retaining bolts loose or missing.

7 Engine starts but stops immediately

1   Loose or faulty electrical connections at distributor, coil or alternator.
2   Insufficient fuel reaching the carburetor. Disconnect the fuel line at the carburetor and remove the filter (Chapter 1). Place a container under the disconnected fuel line. If equipped with HEI system (1975 and later), disconnect wiring connector marked "BAT" from distributor cap. If conventional system (1970 - 1974), disconnect the coil wire from

the center of the distributor cap. These steps will prevent the engine from starting. Have an assistant crank the engine several revolutions by turning the ignition key. Observe the flow of fuel from the line. If little or none at all, check for blockage in the lines and/or replace the fuel pump (Chapter 4).
3   Vacuum leak at the gasket surfaces or the intake manifold and/or carburetor. Check that all mounting bolts (nuts) are tightened to specifications and all vacuum hoses connected to the carburetor and manifold are positioned properly and are in good condition.

8 Engine "lopes" while idling or idles erratically

1   Vacuum leakage. Check mounting bolts (nuts) at the carburetor and intake manifold for tightness. Check that all vacuum hoses are connected and are in good condition. Use a doctor's stethoscope or a length of fuel line hose held against your ear to listen for vacuum leaks while the engine is running. A hissing sound will be heard. A soapy water solution will also detect leaks. Check the carburetor and intake manifold gasket surfaces.
2   Leaking EGR valve or plugged PCV valve (see Chapter 6).
3   Air cleaner clogged and in need of replacement (Chapter 1).
4   Fuel pump not delivering sufficient fuel to the carburetor (see Section 7).
5   Carburetor out of adjustment (Chapter 4).
6   Leaking head gasket. If this is suspected, take the car to a repair shop or GM dealer where this can be pressure checked without the need to remove the heads.
7   Timing chain or gears worn and in need of replacement (Chapter 2).
8   Camshaft lobes worn, necessitating the removal of the camshaft for inspection (Chapter 2).

9 Engine misses at idle speed

1   Spark plugs faulty or not gapped properly (Chapter 1).
2   Faulty spark plug wires (Chapter 1).
3   Faulty or incorrectly set contact breaker points (1970 - 1974 models only). Also check for excessive moisture on distributor components and/or damage (Chapter 1).
4   Carburetor choke not operating properly (Chapter 1).
5   Sticking or faulty emissions systems (see Troubleshooting in Chapter 6).
6   Clogged fuel filter and/or foreign matter in fuel. Remove the fuel filter (Chapter 1) and inspect.
7   Vacuum leaks at carburetor, intake manifold or at hose connections. Check as described in Section 8.
8   Incorrect idle speed (Chapter 1) or idle mixture (Chapter 4).

9   Incorrect ignition timing (Chapter 1).
10 Uneven or low cylinder compression. Remove plugs and use compression tester as per manufacturer's instructions.

10 Engine misses throughout driving speed range

1   Carburetor fuel filter clogged and/or impurities in the fuel system (Chapter 1). Also check fuel output at the carburetor (see Section 7).
2   Faulty or incorrectly gapped spark plugs (Chapter 1).
3   Incorrectly set ignition timing (Chapter 1).
4   Contact points faulty or incorrectly set (1970 - 1974 models only). At the same time check for a cracked distributor cap, disconnected distributor wires, or damage to the distributor components (Chapter 1).
5   Leaking spark plug wires (Chapter 1).
6   Emissions system components faulty (see Troubleshooting section, Chapter 6).
7   Low or uneven cylinder compression pressures. Remove spark plugs and test compression with gauge.
8   Weak or faulty ignition coil or condenser (1970 - 1974 models, see Chapter 5).
9   Weak or faulty HEI ignition system (1975 and later models, see Chapter 5).
10 Vacuum leaks at carburetor, intake manifold or vacuum hoses (see Section 8).

11 Engine stalls

1   Carburetor idle speed incorrectly set (Chapter 1).
2   Carburetor fuel filter clogged and/or water and impurities in the fuel system (Chapter 1).
3   Choke improperly adjusted or sticking (Chapter 1).
4   Distributor components damp, points out of adjustment or damage to distributor cap, rotor, etc. (Chapter 1).
5   Emission system components faulty (Troubleshooting section, Chapter 6.
6   Faulty or incorrectly gapped spark plugs. (Chapter 1). Also check spark plug wires (Chapter 1).
7   Vacuum leak at the carburetor, intake manifold or vacuum hoses. Check as described in Section 8.
8   Valve lash incorrectly set (Chapter 2).

12 Engine lacks power

1   Incorrect ignition timing (Chapter 1).
2   Excessive play in distributor shaft. At the same time check for worn or maladjusted contact points, faulty distributor cap, wires, etc. (Chapter 1).
3   Faulty or incorrectly gapped spark plugs (Chapter 1).

4   Carburetor not adjusted properly or excessively worn (Chapter 4).
5   Weak coil or condenser (Chapter 5).
6   Faulty HEI system coil (Chapter 5).
7   Brakes binding (Chapters 1 and 9).
8   Automatic transmission fluid level incorrect, causing slippage (Chapter 1).
9   Manual transmission clutch slipping (Chapter 1).
10 Fuel filter clogged and/or impurities in the fuel system (Chapter 1).
11 Emission control systems not functioning properly (see Troubleshooting, Chapter 6).
12 Use of sub-standard fuel. Fill tank with proper octane fuel.
13 Low or uneven cylinder compression pressures. Test with compression tester, which will also detect leaking valves and/or blown head gasket.

13 Engine backfires

1   Emissions systems not functioning properly (see Troubleshooting, Chapter 6).
2   Ignition timing incorrect (Section 1).
3   Carburetor in need of adjustment or worn excessively (Chapter 4).
4   Vacuum leak at carburetor, intake manifold or vacuum hoses. Check as described in Section 8.
5   Valve lash incorrectly set, and/or valves sticking (Chapter 2).

14 Pinging or knocking engine sounds on hard acceleration or uphill

1   Incorrect grade of fuel. Fill tank with fuel of the proper octane rating.
2   Ignition timing incorrect (Chapter 1).
3   Carburetor in need of adjustment (Chapter 4).
4   Improper spark plugs. Check plug type with that specified on tune-up decal located inside engine compartment. Also check plugs and wires for damage (Chapter 1).
5   Worn or damaged distributor components (Chapter 1).
6   Faulty emission systems (see Troubleshooting, Chapter 6).
7   Vacuum leak. (Check as described in Section 8).

15 Engine "diesels" (continues to run) after switching off

1   Idle speed too fast (Chapter 1).
2   Electrical solenoid at side of carburetor not functioning properly (not all models, see Chapter 1).
3   Ignition timing incorrectly adjusted (Chapter 1).
4   Thermac air cleaner valve not operating properly (see Troubleshooting, Chapter 6).

5   Excessive engine operating temperatures. Probable causes of this are: malfunctioning thermostat, clogged radiator, faulty water pump. (See Chapter 3).

Engine electric

16 Battery will not hold a charge

1   Alternator drive belt defective or not adjusted properly (Chapter 1).
2   Electrolyte level too low or too weak (Chapter 1).
3   Battery terminals loose or corroded (Chapter 1).
4   Alternator not charging properly (Chapter 5).
5   Loose, broken or faulty wiring in the charging circuit (Chapter 5).
6   Short in vehicle circuitry causing a continual drain on battery.
7   Battery defective internally.

17 Ignition light fails to go out

1   Fault in alternator or charging circuit (Chapter 5).
2   Alternator drive belt defective or not properly adjusted (Chapter 1).

18 Ignition light fails to come on when key is turned

1   Ignition light bulb faulty (Chapter 10).
2   Alternator faulty (Chapter 5).
3   Fault in the printed circuit, dash wiring or bulb holder (Chapter 10).

Engine fuel system

19 Excessive fuel consumption

1   Dirty or choked air filter element (Chapter 1).
2   Incorrectly set ignition timing (Chapter 1).
3   Choke sticking or improperly adjusted (Chapter 1).
4   TCS emission system not functioning properly (not all cars, see Chapter 6).
5   Carburetor idle speed and/or mixture not adjusted properly (Chapters 1 and 4).
6   Carburetor internal parts excessively worn or damaged (Chapter 4).
7   Low tire pressure or incorrect tire size (Chapter 1).

20 Fuel leakage and/or fuel odor

1   Leak in a fuel feed or vent line (Chapter 6).

2   Tank overfilled. Fill only to automatic shut-off.
3   ECS emission system filter in need of replacement (Chapter 6).
4   Vapor leaks from ECS system lines (Chapter 6).
5   Carburetor internal parts excessively worn or out of adjustment (Chapter 4).

Engine cooling system

21 Overheating

1   Insufficient coolant in system (Chapter 1).
2   Fan belt defective or not adjusted properly (Chapter 1).
3   Radiator core blocked or radiator grille dirty and restricted (Chapter 3)-
4   Thermostat faulty (Chapter 3).
5   Freewheeling clutch fan not functioning properly. Check for oil leakage at the rear of the cooling fan, indicating the need for replacement (Chapter 3).
6   Radiator cap not maintaining proper pressure. Have cap pressure tested by gas station or repair shop.
7   Ignition timing incorrect (Chapter 1).

22 Overcooling

1   Thermostat faulty (Chapter 3).
2   Inaccurate temperature gauge (Chapter 10).

23 External water leakage

1   Deteriorated or damaged hoses. Loose clamps at hose connections (Chapter 1).
2   Water pump seals defective. If this is the case, water will drip from the "weep" hole in the water pump body (Chapter 3).
3   Leakage from radiator core or header tank. This will require the radiator to be professionally repaired (see Chapter 3 for removal procedures) .
4   Engine drain plugs or water jacket freeze plugs leaking (see Chapters 2 and 3).

24 Internal water leakage

Note: *Internal coolant leaks can usually be detected by examining the oil. Check the dipstick and inside of valve cover for water deposits and an oil consistency like that of a milkshake.*
1   Faulty cylinder head gasket. Have the system pressure-tested professionally or remove the cylinder heads (Chapter 2) and inspect.
2   Cracked cylinder bore or cylinder head. Dismantle engine and inspect (Chapter 2).

25 Water loss

1   Overfilling system (Chapter 1).
2   Coolant boiling away due to overheating (see causes in Section 15).
3   Internal or external leakage (see Sections 22 and 23).
4   Faulty radiator cap. Have the cap pressure tested.

26 Poor coolant circulation

1   Inoperative water pump. A quick test is to pinch the top radiator hose closed with your hand while the engine is idling, then let loose. You should feel a surge of water if the pump is working properly (Chapter 3).
2   Restriction in cooling system. Drain, flush and refill the system (Chapter 1). If it appears necessary, remove the radiator (Chapter 3) and have it reverse-flushed or professionally cleaned.
3   Fan drive belt defective or not adjusted properly (Chapter 1).
4   Thermostat sticking (Chapter 3).

Clutch

27 Fails to release (pedal pressed to the floor - shift lever does not move freely in and out of reverse)

1   Improper linkage adjustment (Chapter 8).
2   Clutch fork off ball stud. Look under the car, on the left side of transmission.
3   Clutch disc warped, bent or excessively damaged (Chapter 8).

28 Clutch slips (engine speed increases with no increase in road speed)

1   Linkage in need of adjustment (Chapter 8).
2   Clutch disc oil soaked or facing worn. Remove disc (Chapter 8) and inspect.
3   Clutch disc not seated in. It may take 30 or 40 normal starts for a new disc to seat.

29 Grabbing (chattering) on take-up

1   Oil on clutch disc facings. Remove disc (Chapter 8) and inspect. Correct any leakage source.
2   Worn or loose engine or transmission mounts. These units may move slightly when clutch is released. Inspect mounts and bolts.
3   Worn splines on clutch gear. Remove clutch components (Chapter 8) and inspect.
4   Warped pressure plate or flywheel. Remove clutch components and inspect.

30 Squeal or rumble with clutch fully engaged (pedal released)

1   Improper adjustment; no lash (Chapter 8).
2   Release bearing binding on transmission bearing retainer. Remove clutch components (Chapter 8) and check bearing. Remove any burrs or nicks, clean and relubricate before reinstallation.
3   Weak linkage return spring. Replace the spring.

31 Squeal or rumble with clutch fully disengaged (pedal depressed)

1   Worn, faulty or broken release bearing (Chapter 8).
2   Worn or broken pressure plate springs (or diaphragm fingers) (Chapter 8).

32 Clutch pedal stays on floor when disengaged

1   Bind in linkage or release bearing. Inspect linkage or remove clutch components as necessary.
2   Linkage springs being over-traveled. Adjust linkage for proper lash. Make sure proper pedal stop (bumper) is installed.

Manual transmission
Note: *All the following Section references contained within Chapter 7.*

33 Noisy in neutral with engine running

1   Input shaft bearing worn (Sections 11 - 14).
2   Damaged main drive gear bearing (Sections 11 - 14).
3   Worn countergear bearings (Sections 11 - 14).
4   Worn or damaged countergear anti-lash plate (Sections 11 - 14).

34 Noisy in all gears

1   Any of the above causes, and/or:
2   Insufficient lubricant (see checking procedures in Chapter 1).

35 Noisy in one particular gear

1   Worn, damaged or chipped gear teeth for that particular gear (Sections 11 - 14).
2   Worn or damaged synchronizer for that particular gear (Sections 11 - 14).

36 Slips out of high gear

1   Transmission loose on clutch housing (Section 3).
2   Shift rods interfering with engine mounts or clutch lever (Section 2).
3   Shift rods not working freely (Section 2).
4   Damaged mainshaft pilot bearing (Section 10).
5   Dirt between transmission case and clutch housing, or misalignment of transmission (Section 10).
6   Worn or improperly adjusted linkage (Section 2).

37 Difficulty in engaging gears

1   Clutch not releasing fully (see clutch adjustment, Chapter 8).
2   Loose, damaged or maladjusted shift linkage. Make a thorough inspection, replacing parts as necessary. Adjust as described in Section 2.

38 Fluid leakage

1   Excessive amount of lubricant in transmission (see Chapter 1 for correct checking procedures. Drain lubricant as required).
2   Side cover loose or gasket damaged (Sections 7 - 9).
3   Rear oil seal or speedometer oil seal in need of replacement (Section 6).

Automatic transmission

Note: *Due to the complexity of the automatic transmission, it is difficult for the home mechanic to properly diagnose and service this component. For problems other than the following, the vehicle should be taken to a reputable mechanic.*

39 Fluid leakage

1   Automatic transmission fluid is a deep red color, and fluid leaks should not be confused with engine oil which can easily be blown by air flow to the transmission.
2   To pinpoint a leak, first remove all built-up dirt and grime from around the transmission. Degreasing agents and/or steam cleaning will achieve this. With the underside clean, drive the car at low speeds so the air flow will not blow the leak far from its source. Raise the car and determine where the leak is coming from. Common areas of leakage are:

a) *Fluid pan: tighten mounting bolts and/ or replace pan gasket as necessary (see Chapter 1).*

b) *Rear extension: tighten bolts and/or replace oil seal as necessary (Chapter 8).*
c) *Filler pipe: replace the rubber oil seal where pipe enters transmission case.*
d) *Transmission oil lines: tighten connectors where lines enter transmission case and/or replace lines.*
e) *Vent pipe: transmission over-filled and/ or water in fluid (see checking procedures, Chapter 1).*
f) *Speedometer connector: replace the O-ring where speedometer cable enters transmission case.*

40 General shift mechanism problems

Sections 4 and 5 in Chapter 7 deal with checking and adjusting the shift linkage on automatic transmissions. Common problems which may be attributed to maladjusted linkage are:

a) *Engine starting in gears other than "P" (Park) or "N" (Neutral).*
b) *Indicator on quadrant pointing to a gear other than the one actually being used.*
c) *Vehicle will not hold firm when in "P" (Park) position. Refer to Sections 4 or 5 in Chapter 7 to adjust the manual linkage.*

41 Transmission will not downshift with accelerator pedal pressed to the floor

Sections 6 and 7 in Chapter 7 deal with adjusting the downshift cable or downshift switch to enable the transmission to downshift properly.

42 Engine will start in gears other than "P" (Park) or "N" (Neutral)

Sections 8 and 9 in Chapter 7 deal with adjusting the neutral start switches used with automatic transmissions.

43 Transmission slips, shifts rough, is noisy or has no drive in forward or reverse gears

1   There are many probable causes for the above problems, but the home mechanic should concern himself. only with one possibility; fluid level.
2   Before taking the vehicle to a specialist, check the level of the fluid and condition of the fluid as described in Chapter 1. Correct fluid level as necessary or change the fluid and filter if needed. If problem persists, have a professional diagnose the probable cause.

Drive shaft

44 Leakage of fluid at front of drive shaft

1   Defective transmission rear oil seal. See Chapter 7 for replacing procedures. While this is done, check the splined yoke for burrs or a rough condition which may be damaging the seal. If found, these can be dressed with crocus cloth or a fine dressing stone.

45 Knock or clunk when transmission is under initial load (just after transmission is put into gear)

1   Loose or disconnected rear suspension components. Check all mounting bolts and bushings (Chapter 1).
2   Loose drive shaft bolts. Inspect all bolts and nuts and tighten to torque specifications (Chapter 8).
3   Worn or damaged universal joint bearings. Test for wear (Chapter 8).

46 Metallic grating sound consistent with road speed

Pronounced wear in the universal joint bearings. Test for wear (Chapter 8).

47 Vibration

Note: *Before it can be assumed that the drive shaft is at fault, make sure the tires are perfectly balanced and perform the following test.*
1   Install a tachometer inside the car to monitor engine speed as the car is driven. Drive the car and note the engine speed at which the vibration (roughness) is most pronounced. Now shift the transmission to a different gear and bring the engine speed to the same point.
2   If the vibration occurs at the same engine speed (rpm) regardless of which gear the transmission is in, the drive shaft is NOT at fault since the drive shaft speed varies.
3   If the vibration decreases or is eliminated when the transmission is in a different gear at the same engine speed, refer to the following probable causes.
4   Bent or dented drive shaft. Inspect and replace as necessary (Chapter 8).
5   Undercoating or built-up dirt, etc. on the drive shaft. Clean the shaft thoroughly and test.
6   Worn universal joint bearings. Remove and inspect (Chapter 8).
7   Drive shaft and/or companion flange out of balance. Check for missing weights on the shaft. Remove drive shaft (Chapter 8) and reinstall 180° from original position. Retest.

Have drive shaft professionally balanced if problem persists.

Rear axle

48 Noise - same when in drive as when vehicle is coasting

1   Road noise. No corrective procedures available.
2   Tire noise. Inspect tires and tire pressures (Chapter 1).
3   Front wheel bearings loose, worn or damaged (Chapter I).

49 Vibration

1   See probable causes under "Drive shaft". Proceed under the guidelines listed for the drive shaft. If the problem persists, check the rear wheel bearings by raising the rear of the car and spinning the wheels by hand. Listen for evidence of rough (noisy) bearings. Remove and inspect (Chapter 8).

50 Oil leakage

1   Pinion oil seal damaged (Chapter 8).
2   Axle shaft oil seals damaged (Chapter 8).
3   Differential inspection cover leaking. Tighten mounting bolts or replace the gasket as required (Chapter 1).

Brakes

Note: *Before assuming a brake problem exists, check: that the tires are in good condition and are inflated properly (see Chapter 1); the front end alignment is correct; and that the vehicle is not loaded with weight in an unequal manner.*

51 Vehicle pulls to one side under braking

1   Defective, damaged or oil contaminated disc pad on one side. Inspect as described in Chapter 1. Refer to Chapter 9 if replacement is required.
2   Excessive wear of brake pad material or disc on one side. Inspect and correct as necessary.
3   Loose or disconnected front suspension components. Inspect and tighten all bolts to specifications (Chapter 1).
4   Defective caliper assembly. Remove caliper and inspect for stuck piston or damage (Chapter 9).

52 Noise (high pitched squeak without brake applied)

1   Front brake pads worn out. This noise comes from the wear sensor rubbing against the disc. Replace pads with new ones immediately (Chapter 9).

53 Excessive brake pad travel

1   Partial brake system failure. Inspect entire system (Chapter 1) and correct as required.
2   Insufficient fluid in master cylinder. Check (Chapter 1) and add fluid and bleed system if necessary.
3   Rear brakes not adjusting properly. Make a series of starts and stops while the vehicle is in "R" (Reverse). If this does not correct the situation remove drums and inspect self-adjusters (Chapter 1).

54 Brake pedal appears spongy when depressed

1   Air in hydraulic lines. Bleed the brake system (Chapter 9).
2   Faulty flexible hoses. Inspect all system hoses and lines. Replace parts as necessary.
3   Master cylinder mountings insecure. Inspect master cylinder bolts (nuts) and torque-tighten to specifications.
4   Master cylinder faulty (Chapter 9).

55 Excessive effort required to stop vehicle

1   Power brake servo not operating properly (Chapter 9).
2   Excessively worn linings or pads. Inspect and replace if necessary (Chapter 1).
3   One or more caliper pistons (front wheels) or wheel cylinders (rear wheels) seized or sticking. Inspect and rebuild as required (Chapter 9).
4   Brake linings or pads contaminated with oil or grease. Inspect and replace as required (Chapter 1).
5   New pads or linings fitted and not yet "bedded in". It will take a while for the new material to seat against the drum (or rotor).

56 Pedal travels to floor with little resistance

1   Little or no fluid in the master cylinder reservoir caused by: leaking wheel cylinder(s); leaking caliper piston(s); loose, damaged or disconnected brake lines. Inspect entire system and correct as necessary.

57 Brake pedal pulsates during brake application

1   Wheel bearings not adjusted properly or in need of replacement (Chapter 1).
2   Caliper not sliding properly due to improper installation or obstructions. Remove and inspect (Chapter 9).
3   Rotor not within specifications. Remove the rotor (Chapter 9) and check for excessive lateral run-out and parallelism. Have the rotor professionally machined or replace it with a new one.

Suspension and steering

58 Car pulls to one side

1   Tire pressures uneven (Chapter 1).
2   Defective tire (Chapter 1).
3   Excessive wear in suspension or steering components (Chapter 1).
4   Front end in need of alignment. Take car to a qualified specialist.
5   Front brakes dragging. Inspect braking system as described in Chapter 1.

59 Shimmy, shake or vibration

1   Tire or wheel out of balance or out of round. Have professionally balanced.
2   Loose, worn or out of adjustment wheel bearings (Chapter 1).
3   Shock absorbers and/or suspension components worn or damaged (Chapter 11).

60 Excessive pitching and/or rolling around corners or during braking

1   Defective shock absorbers. Replace as a set (Chapter 11).
2   Broken or weak coil springs and/or suspension components. Inspect as described in Chapter 11.

61 Excessively stiff steering

1   Lack of lubricant in steering box (manual) or power steering fluid reservoir (Chapter 1).
2   Incorrect tire pressures (Chapter 1).
3   Lack of lubrication at steering joints (Chapter 1).
4   Front end out of alignment.
5   See also Section 63 "Lack of power assistance".

62 Excessive play in steering

1   Loose wheel bearings (Chapter 1).
2   Excessive wear in suspension or steering components (Chapter 1).

3   Steering gear out of adjustment (Chapter 11).

63   Lack of power assistance

1   Steering pump drive belt faulty or not adjusted properly (Chapter 1).
2   Fluid level low (Chapter 1).
3   Hoses or pipes restricting the flow. Inspect and replace parts as necessary.
4   Air in power steering system. Bleed system (Chapter 11).

64   Excessive tire wear (not specific to one area)

1   Incorrect tire pressures (Chapter 1).

2   Tires out of balance. Have professionally balanced.
3   Wheels damaged. Inspect and replace as necessary.
4   Suspension or steering components excessively worn (Chapter 1).

65   Excessive tire wear on outside edge

1   Inflation pressures not correct (Chapter 1).
2   Excessive speed on turns.
3   Front end alignment incorrect (excessive toe-in). Have professionally aligned.
4   Suspension arm bent or twisted.

66   Excessive tire wear on inside edge

1   Inflation pressures incorrect (Chapter 1).
2   Front end alignment incorrect (toe-out). Have professionally aligned.
3   Loose or damaged steering components (Chapter 1).

67   Tire tread worn in one place

1   Tires out of balance. Balance tires professionally.
2   Damaged or buckled wheel. Inspect and replace if necessary.
3   Defective tire.

Notes

Chapter 1
Tune-up and routine maintenance

Contents

Specifications

Note 1: *Additional specifications and torque settings can be found in each individual Chapter.*

Note 2: *1970 and 1971 models have a three-letter engine designation stamped onto the front side of the block while later models have the engine identification code stamped as the fifth digit of the Vehicle Identification Number in the left corner of the instrument panel.*

General
Displacement
  V8 engines

4.3 liter (VIN S)	265 cubic inches
4.9 liter (VIN Y, W and T)	301 cubic inches
5.0 liter (VIN U, G and H)	305 cubic inches
5.7 liter (VIN M, N, E, P, H, J, L and R)	350 cubic inches
6.4 liter (VIN R, P, N, S, T and Z)	400 cubic inches
7.4 liter (VIN X, W and Y)	455 cubic inches

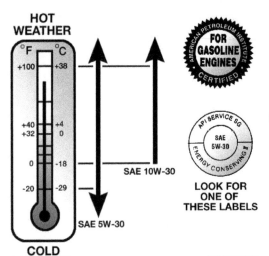

Engine oil viscosity chart - for best fuel economy and cold starting, select the lowest SAE viscosity grade for the expected temperature range

LOOK FOR ONE OF THESE LABELS

1-a3 HAYNES

Recommended lubricants and fluids

Note: *Listed here are manufacturer recommendations at the time this manual was written. Manufacturers occasionally upgrade their fluid and lubricant specifications, so check with your local auto parts store for current recommendations.*

Engine oil
Type	API approved multigrade and fuel efficient engine oil
Viscosity	See accompanying chart
Automatic transmission fluid type	DEXRON II ATF
Manual transmission fluid type	SAE 80W or 80W-90 GL-5 lubricant

Differential lubricant type
Standard differential	SAE 80W or 80W-90 GL-5 gear lubricant
Limited slip differential	Add 4 fluid ounces of GM limited slip additive to the specified lubricant
Brake fluid type	DOT 3 brake fluid
Power steering fluid	GM power steering fluid or equivalent
Steering gear fluid type	GM power steering fluid or equivalent
Chassis grease	SAE NLGI no. 2 chassis grease

Capacities

Cooling system

	Quarts
1970	
350 CID	19.6
400 CID	18.0
455 CID	17.2
1971 and 1972	
350 CID	19.5
400 CID	18.6
455 CID	18.0
1973	
350 CID	22.3
400 CID	22.3
455 CID	20.8
1974 and 1975	
350 CID	22.0
400 CID	22.0
455 CID	19.3
1976	
350 CID	21.2
400 CID	21.2
455 CID	23.3
1977	
301 CID (std.cooling)	19.1
301 CID (H.D. cooling)	20.1
305 CID	17.2
350 CID (VIN code R)	15.6
350 CID (VIN code P)	20.3
400 CID	20.4
403 CID	16.8

1978	
305 CID	17.2
350 CID	17.2
400 CID	19.7
403 CID	17.4
1979	
301 CID	19.9
305 CID	17.2
350 CID	17.2
400 CID	19.7
403 CID	17.4
1980 and 1981	
265 CID	20.4
301 CID	20.4
350 CID	16.4

*With A/C add 1 quart
**With A/C add 2 quarts

Engine oil
All V-8 engines	5 quarts*

*With oil filter change

Fuel tank (approx.):
	US gallons
1970	19.0
With evaporative control system	18.0
1971	17.0
1972 - 1973	18.0
1974 - 1978	21.0
1979 - 1981	20.8

Manual transmission:
1970 - 1980 (all)	3.0 pints *

* Approx. to fill after draining

Automatic transmission:
	US quarts
Powerglide	
Routine change	3
Fill from dry	9.0
Turbo Hydramatic 350	
Routine change	3.0
Fill from dry	10.0
Turbo Hydramatic 400	
Routine change	3.5
Fill from dry	11.0

Ignition system
Distributor type	
1970 through 1974	Mechanical breaker point type
1975 through 1981	Breakerless, electronic (designated HEI)
Distributor direction of rotation	See diagram below
Breaker point gap	0.019 in
Firing order	1-8-4-3-6-5-7-2

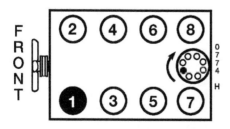

Chevrolet-built engines

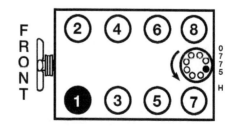

**Pontiac and
Oldsmobile-built engines**

Cylinder location and distributor rotation

The blackened terminal shown on the distributor cap indicates the Number One spark plug wire position

Spark plugs

Year and engine	Spark plug	Electrode gap
1970		
350	AC R46S	0.035 in
400 (265 HP)	AC R46S	0.035 in
400 (330 HP)	AC R45S	0.035 in
402 (345 HP)	AC R44S	0.035 in
402 (370 HP)	AC R44S	0.035 in
1971		
350	AC R46S	0.035 in
400 (265 HP)	AC R46S	0.035 in
400 (300 HP)	AC R46S	0.035 in
455 (280 HP)	AC R46S	0.035 in
455 (325 HP)	AC R46S	0.035 in
455 (335 HP)	AC R46S	0.035 in
1972		
350	AC R46TS	0.040 in
400 (175 HP)	AC R46TS	0.040 in
400 (250 HP)	AC R45TS	0.040 in
455	AC R45TS	0.040 in
1973		
350 (150 HP)	AC R46TS	0.040 in
350 (175 HP)	AC R46TS	0.040 in
400 (170 HP)	AC R45TS	0.040 in
400 (230 HP)	AC R45TS	0.040 in
455 (250 HP)	AC R45TS	0.040 in
455 (310 HP)	AC R44TS	0.040 in
1974		
350	AC R46TS	0.040 in
400 (175, 190 HP)	AC R46TS	0.040 in
400 (225 HP)	AC R45TS	0.040 in
455 (250 HP)	AC R46TS	0.040 in
455 (290 HP)	AC R45TS	0.040 in
1975		
350	AC R46TSX	0.060 in
400	AC R45TSX	0.060 in
455	AC R45TSX	0.060 in
1976		
350	AC R46TSX	0.060 in
400	AC R45TSX	0.060 in
455	AC R45TSX	0.060 in
1977		
301	AC R46TSX	0.060 in
305	AC R45TS	0.045 in
350 (Pontiac)	AC R45TSX	0.060 in
350 (Chevy)	AC R45TS	0.045 in
350 (Olds)	AC R46SZ	0.060 in
400	AC R45TSX	0.060 in
403	AC R46SZ	0.060 in
1978		
305	AC R45TS	0.045 in
350	AC R45TS	0.045 in
400	AC R45TSX	0.060 in
403	AC R46SZ	0.060 in
1979		
301 (140 HP)	AC R46TSX	0.060 in
301 (150 HP)	AC R45TSX	0.060 in
305	AC R45TS	0.045 in
350	AC R45TS	0.045 in
400	AC R45TSX	0.060 in
403	AC R46SZ	0.060 in
1980		
301 non-turbocharged	AC R45TSX	0.060 in
301 turbocharged	AC R45TSX	0.060 in
305	AC R45TS	0.045 in

Year and engine	Spark plug	Electrode gap
1981		
265	AC R45TSX	0.060 in
301 non-turbocharged	AC R45TSX	0.060 in
301 turbocharged	AC R45TSX	0.060 in
305	AC R45TS	0.045 in

Ignition timing

1970

350
- Manual transmission .... 9 degrees BTDC @ 800 rpm
- Automatic transmission .... 9 degrees BTDC @ 650 rpm

400 (265 HP)
- Manual transmission .... 9 degrees BTDC @ 800 rpm
- Automatic transmission .... 9 degrees BTDC @ 650 rpm

400 (330 HP)
- Manual transmission .... 9 degrees BTDC @ 950 rpm
- Automatic transmission .... 9 degrees BTDC @ 650 rpm

400 (345 HP)
- Manual transmission .... 9 degrees BTDC @ 950 rpm
- Automatic transmission .... 9 degrees BTDC @ 650 rpm

400 (370 HP)
- Manual transmission .... 15 degrees BTDC @ 1000 rpm
- Automatic transmission .... 15 degrees BTDC @ 750 rpm

1971

350
- Manual transmission .... 12 degrees BTDC @ 800 rpm
- Automatic transmission .... 12 degrees BTDC @ 600 rpm

400 (265 HP)
- Automatic transmission .... 8 degrees BTDC @ 600 rpm

400 (300 HP)
- Manual transmission .... 12 degrees BTDC @ 1000 rpm
- Automatic transmission .... 12 degrees BTDC @ 700 rpm

455 (325 HP)
- Automatic transmission .... 12 degrees BTDC @ 650 rpm

455 (335 HP)
- Manual transmission .... 12 degrees BTDC @ 1000 rpm
- Automatic transmission .... 12 degrees BTDC @ 700 rpm

1972

350
- Manual transmission .... 8 degrees BTDC @ 800 rpm
- Automatic transmission .... 10 degrees BTDC @ 625 rpm

400 (175 HP)
- Automatic transmission .... 10 degrees BTDC @ 625 rpm

400 (250 HP)
- Manual transmission .... 8 degrees BTDC @ 1000 rpm
- Automatic transmission .... 10 degrees BTDC @ 700 rpm

455
- Manual transmission .... 8 degrees BTDC @ 1000 rpm
- Automatic transmission .... 10 degrees BTDC @ 700 rpm

1973

350
- Manual transmission .... 10 degrees BTDC @ 900 rpm
- Automatic transmission .... 12 degrees BTDC @ 650 rpm

400 (170 HP)
- Manual transmission .... 10 degrees BTDC @ 1100 rpm
- Automatic transmission .... 12 degrees BTDC @ 650 rpm

400 (230 HP)
- Manual transmission .... 10 degrees BTDC @ 1000 rpm
- Automatic transmission .... 12 degrees BTDC @ 650 rpm

455 (250 HP)
- Manual transmission .... 10 degrees BTDC @ 1000 rpm
- Automatic transmission .... 12 degrees BTDC @ 650 rpm

455 (310 HP)
- Manual transmission .... 10 degrees BTDC @ 1000 rpm
- Automatic transmission .... 12 degrees BTDC @ 750 rpm

Ignition timing (continued)

1974
350
    Manual transmission... 10 degrees BTDC @ 900 rpm
    Automatic transmission .... 12 degrees BTDC @ 650 rpm
400 (170, 190 HP)
    Manual transmission... 10 degrees BTDC @ 900 rpm
    Automatic transmission .... 12 degrees BTDC @ 650 rpm
400 (225 HP)
    Manual transmission... 10 degrees BTDC @ 1000 rpm
    Automatic transmission .... 12 degrees BTDC @ 650 rpm
455 (250 HP)
    Manual transmission... 10 degrees BTDC @ 1000 rpm
    Automatic transmission .... 12 degrees BTDC @ 650 rpm
455 (290 HP)
    Manual transmission... 10 degrees BTDC @ 1000 rpm
    Automatic transmission .... 12 degrees BTDC @ 750 rpm

1975
350
    Manual transmission... 12 degrees BTDC @ 775 rpm
    Automatic transmission .... 16 degrees BTDC @ 600 rpm
400
    Manual transmission... 12 degrees BTDC @ 775 rpm
    Automatic transmission .... 16 degrees BTDC @ 650 rpm
455
    California models... 10 degrees BTDC @ 675 rpm
    Except California models.. 16 degrees BTDC @ 675 rpm

1976
350 (155 HP)
    Automatic transmission .... 16 degrees BTDC @ 550 rpm
350 (175 HP)
    Manual and automatic transmissions......................... 16 degrees BTDC @ 600 rpm
400 (185 HP)
    Manual transmission... 12 degrees BTDC @ 775 rpm
    Automatic transmission .... 16 degrees BTDC @ 575 rpm
455
    Manual transmission... 12 degrees BTDC @ 775 rpm
    Automatic transmission .... 16 degrees BTDC @ 550 rpm

1977
301 (185 HP)
    Manual transmission... 16 degrees BTDC @ 800 rpm
    Automatic transmission .... 12 degrees BTDC @ 550 rpm
350 (Pontiac)
    Automatic transmission .... 16 degrees BTDC @ 575 rpm
350 (Olds)
    Automatic transmissions .... 20 degrees BTDC @ 575 rpm
400
    Manual transmission... 18 degrees BTDC @ 775 rpm
    Automatic transmission .... 16 degrees BTDC @ 575 rpm
403
    Automatic transmission .... 20 degrees BTDC @ 600 rpm

1978
305 .... 4 degrees BTDC @ 500 rpm
350
    Manual transmission... 6 degrees BTDC @ 700 rpm
    Automatic transmission .... 8 degrees BTDC @ 500 rpm
400 (180 HP)
    Automatic transmission .... 16 degrees BTDC @ 650 rpm
400 (220 HP) .... 18 degrees BTDC @ 775 rpm
403 .... 20 degrees BTDC @ 700 rpm

1979
301 (140 HP)
    Automatic transmission .... 12 degrees BTDC @ 650 rpm
301 (150 HP)
    Manual transmission... 14 degrees BTDC @ 750 rpm
    Automatic transmission .... 12 degrees BTDC @ 650 rpm

305
    Automatic transmission .... 4 degrees BTDC @ 500 rpm
350
    Automatic transmission .... 8 degrees BTDC @ 600 rpm
400
    Manual transmission... 18 degrees BTDC @ 775 rpm
403
    Automatic transmission .... 18 degrees BTDC @ 550 rpm

1980
265
    Automatic transmission .... 10 degrees BTDC @ 700 rpm
301 non-turbocharged
    Automatic transmission .... 12 degrees BTDC @ 500 rpm
301 turbocharged
    Automatic transmission .... 8 degrees BTDC @ 600 rpm
305
    Automatic transmission .... 4 degrees BTDC @ 550 rpm

1981
265
    Automatic transmission .... 12 degrees BTDC @ 600 rpm
301 non-turbocharged
    Automatic transmission .... 12 degrees BTDC @ 600 rpm
301 turbocharged
    Automatic transmission .... 6 degrees BTDC @ 700 rpm
305
    Manual transmission... 6 degrees BTDC @ 800 rpm
    Automatic transmission .... 15 degrees BTDC @ 1100 rpm

Torque specifications   lb-ft
Oil pan drain plug 20
Spark plugs 15
Carburetor mounting nuts 12
Fuel inlet nut (fuel filter) 18
Manual transmission fill plug:
    All except Muncie 4-speed 18
    Muncie 4-speed 30
Automatic transmission pan bolts.. 12
Rear axle filler/inspection plug 22
Rear axle cover bolts.. 27
Brake caliper mounting bolts 35
Wheel nuts:
    1970 models 65
    1971 - 1975... 70
    1976 - 1981... 80

Pontiac Firebird
Routine maintenance intervals

Every 250 miles or weekly - whichever comes first

Check the engine oil level (Section 2).
Check the engine coolant level (Section 2).
Check the windshield washer fluid level (Section 2).
Check the battery water level (if equipped with removable vent caps) (Section 2).
Check the tires and tire pressures (Section 3).
Check the automatic transmission fluid level (Section 2).
Check the power steering fluid level (Section 2).

Every 3,750 miles or 6 months - whichever comes first

Change engine oil and filter (Section 4).
Lubricate the chassis components (Section 5).
Check the cooling system (Section 6).
Check the exhaust system (Section 7).
Check the suspension and steering components (Section 8).
Check and adjust (if necessary) the engine drive belts (Section 9).
Check the fuel system components (Section 10).
Check the brake master cylinder fluid level (Section 2).
Check the manual transmission fluid level (Section 2).
Check the rear axle fluid level (Section 2).
Replace the PCV valve (Section 11).
Replace the air filter and PCV filter (Section 12).

Every 7,500 miles or 12 months - whichever comes first

Check the clutch pedal free-play (manual transmission only (Section 13).
Rotate the tires (Section 14).
Check the Thermo Controlled air cleaner for proper operation (Section 15).

Check and adjust (if necessary) the engine idle speed (Section 16).
Check the EFE system (Section 17).
Replace the fuel filter (Section 18).
Check and adjust (if necessary) the engine ignition timing (Section 19).
Check the operation of the choke (Section 20).
Check the operation of the EGR valve (Section 21).
Change rear axle fluid (if car is used to pull a trailer) (Section 22).

Every 15,000 miles or 12 months - whichever comes first

Replace the spark plugs (Section 23).
Check and repack the front wheel bearings (perform this procedure whenever brakes are relined, regardless of maintenance interval) (Section 24).
Change the automatic transmission fluid and filter (if mainly driven under following conditions: heavy city traffic in hot-climate regions; in hill or mountain areas: frequent trailer pulling (Section 25).
Check the braking system (Section 26).
Check the mounting torque of the carburetor (Section 27).
Check the spark plug wires (Section 28).
Drain, flush and refill the cooling system (Section 29?).
Replace the contact points, adjust dwell angle and check the distributor (1970 - 1974 models only) (Section 30).

Every 30,000 miles or 24 months - whichever comes first

Change the rear axle fluid (if car is used to pull a trailer, change at 7500 miles) (Section 2).
Change the automatic transmission fluid and filter (if driven under abnormal conditions, see 15 000 miles servicing) (Section 25).
Check the ECS emissions system and replace the charcoal canister filter (Section 31).

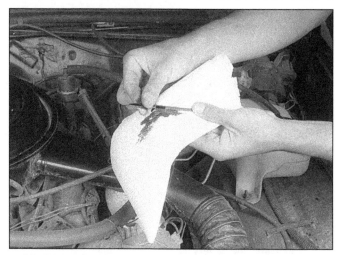

2.4 Checking the oil level at the bottom of the dipstick

2.7 Wiping the oil on the dipstick to check for contamination

1   Introduction

This Chapter was designed to help the home mechanic maintain his (or her) car for peak performance, economy, safety and longevity.

On the following pages you will find a maintenance schedule along with sections which deal specifically with each item on the schedule. Included are visual checks, adjustments and item replacements.

Servicing your car using the time/mileage maintenance schedule and the sequenced sections will give you a planned program of maintenance. Keep in mind that it is a full plan, and maintaining only a few items at the specified intervals will not give you the same results.

You will find as you service your car that many of the procedures can, and should, be grouped together, due to the nature of the job at hand. Examples of this are as follows:

If the car is fully raised for a chassis lubrication, for example, this is the ideal time for the following checks: manual transmission fluid, rear axle fluid, exhaust system, suspension, steering and the fuel system.

If the tires and wheels are removed. as during a routine tire rotation, go ahead and check the brakes and wheel bearings at the same time.

If you must borrow or rent a torque wrench, you will do best to service the spark plugs, repack (or replace) the wheel bearings and check the carburetor mounting torque all in the same day to save time and money.

The first step of this or any maintenance plan is to prepare yourself before the actual work begins. Read through the appropriate sections for all work that is to be performed before you begin. Gather together all necessary parts and tools. If it appears you could have a problem during a particular job, don't hesitate to ask advice from your local parts man or dealer service department.

2   Fluid levels check

1   There are a number of components on a vehicle which rely on the use of fluids to perform their job. Through the normal operation of the car, these fluids are used up and must be replenished before damage occurs. See the Recommended Lubricants Section for the specific fluid to be used when adding is required. When checking fluid levels it is important that the car is on a level surface.

Engine oil

Refer to illustrations 2.4 and 2.7

2   The engine oil level is checked with a dipstick which is located at the side of the engine block. This dipstick travels through a tube and into the oil pan to the bottom of the engine.

3   The oil level should be checked preferably before the car has been driven, or about 15 minutes after the engine has been shut off. If the oil is checked immediately after driving the car, some of the oil will remain in the upper engine components, thus giving an inaccurate reading on the dipstick.

4   Pull the dipstick from its tube and wipe all the oil from the end with a clean rag. insert the clean dipstick all the way back into the oil pan and pull it out again. Observe the oil at the end of the dipstick **(see illustration)**. At its highest point, the level should be between the 'Add' and 'Full' marks.

5   It takes approximately 1 quart of oil to raise the level from the 'Add' mark to the 'Full' mark on the dipstick. Do not allow the level to drop below the 'Add' mark as this may cause engine damage due to oil starvation. On the other hand, do not overfill the engine by adding oil above the 'Full' mark as this may result in oil-fouled spark plugs, oil leaks or oil seal failures.

6   Oil is added to the engine after removing a twist-off cap located either on the rocker arm cover or through a raised tube near the front of the engine. The cap should be duly marked 'Engine oil' or similar wording. An oil can spout or funnel will reduce spills as the oil is poured in.

7   Checking the oil level can also be a step towards preventative maintenance. If you find the oil level dropping abnormally, this is an indication of oil leakage or internal engine wear which should be corrected. If there are water droplets in the oil, or it is milky looking, this also indicates component failure and the engine should be checked immediately. The condition of the oil can also be checked along with the level. With the dipstick removed from the engine, take your thumb and index finger and wipe the oil up the dipstick, looking for small dirt particles or engine filings which will cling to the dipstick **(see illustration)**. This is an indication that the oil should be drained and fresh oil added (Section 4).

Engine coolant

Warning 1: *Do not allow antifreeze to come in contact with your skin or painted surfaces of the vehicle. Flush contaminated areas immediately with plenty of water. Don't store new coolant or leave old coolant lying around where it's accessible to children or pets – they're attracted by its sweet smell. Ingestion of even a small amount of coolant can be fatal! Wipe up garage floor and drip pan spills immediately. Keep antifreeze containers covered and repair cooling system leaks as soon as they're noticed.*

Warning 2: *DO NOT remove the radiator cap or the coolant recovery cap while the cooling system is hot as escaping steam could cause serious injury.*

8   Most vehicles are equipped with a pressurized coolant recovery system which makes coolant level checks very easy. A clear or white coolant reservoir attached to the inner fender panel is connected by a hose to the radiator cap. As the engine heats up during operation, coolant is forced from the radi-

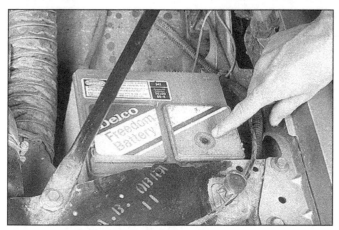

2.17 Many GM maintenance-free batteries have an 'eye' which indicates the battery condition by changing color

2.18 Removing the vent caps to check the water level in maintenance-type batteries

ator, through the connecting tube and into the reservoir. As the engine cools, this coolant is automatically drawn back into the radiator to keep the correct level.

9   The coolant level should be checked when the engine is cold. Merely observe the level of fluid in the reservoir, which should be at or near the 'Full cold' mark on the side of the reservoir. If the system is completely cooled, also check the level in the radiator by removing the cap. Some systems also have a 'Full hot' mark to check the level when the engine is hot.

10   If your particular vehicle is not equipped with a coolant recovery system, the level should be checked by removing the radiator cap. However, the cap should not under any circumstances be removed while the system is hot, as escaping steam could cause serious injury. Wait until the engine has completely cooled, then wrap a thick cloth around the cap and turn it to its first stop. if any steam escapes from the cap, allow the engine to cool further. Then remove the cap and check the level in the radiator. It should be about 2 to 3 inches below the bottom of the filler neck.

11   If only a small amount of coolant is required to bring the system up to the proper level, regular water can be used. However, to maintain the proper antifreeze/water mixture in the system, both should be mixed together to replenish a low level. High-quality antifreeze offering protection to -20° should be mixed with water in the proportion specified on the container. Do not allow antifreeze to come in contact with your skin or painted surfaces of the car. Flush contacted areas immediately with plenty of water.

12   On systems with a coolant recovery tank, coolant should be added to the reservoir after removing the cap at the top of the reservoir. Coolant should be added directly into the radiator on systems without a coolant recovery tank.

13   As the coolant level is checked, observe the condition of the coolant. It should be relatively clear. If the fluid is brown or a rust color, this is an indication that the system should be drained, flushed and refilled (Section 29).

14   If the cooling system requires repeated additions to keep the proper level, have the pressure radiator cap checked for proper sealing ability. Also check for leaks in the system (cracked hoses, loose hose connections, leaking gaskets, etc.).

Windshield washer

15   The fluid for the windshield washer system is located in a plastic reservoir. The level inside the reservoir should be maintained at the 'Full' mark.

16   General Motors 'Optikleen' washer solvent or its equivalent should be added through the plastic cap whenever replenishing is required. Do not use plain water alone in this system, especially in cold climates where the water could freeze.

Battery

Refer to illustrations 2.17 and 2.18
Warning: *Certain precautions must be followed when checking and servicing the battery. Hydrogen gas, which is highly flammable, is always present in the battery cells, so keep lighted tobacco and all other open flames and sparks away from the battery. The electrolyte inside the battery is actually dilute sulfuric acid, which will cause injury if splashed on your skin or in your eyes. It will also ruin clothes and painted surfaces. When removing the battery cables, always detach the negative cable first and hook it up last!*

17   Vehicles equipped with 'Freedom' or maintenance-free batteries require no maintenance as the battery case is sealed and has no removal caps for adding water **(see illustration)**. Nearly all replacement batteries are of this type.

18   If a maintenance-type battery is installed, the caps on the top of the battery should be removed periodically to check for a low water level **(see illustration)**. This check will be more critical during the warm summer months.

19   Remove each of the caps and add distilled water to bring the level of each cell to the split ring in the filler opening.

20   At the same time the battery water level

is checked, the overall condition of the battery and its related components should be inspected. If corrosion is found on the cable ends or battery terminals, remove the cables and clean away all corrosion using a baking soda/water solution or a wire brush cleaning tool designed for this purpose. See Chapter 5 for complete battery care and servicing.

Brake master cylinder

Refer to illustrations 2.22, 2.24a and 2.24b
Warning: *Brake fluid can harm your eyes and damage painted surfaces, so use extreme caution when handling or pouring it. Do not use brake fluid that has been standing open or is more than one year old. Brake fluid absorbs moisture from the air, which can cause a dangerous loss of braking effectiveness.*

21   The brake master cylinder is located on the left side of the engine compartment firewall and has a cap which must be removed to check the fluid level.

22   Before removing the cap, use a rag to clean all dirt, grease, etc. from around the cap area **(see illustration)**. If any foreign matter enters the master cylinder with the

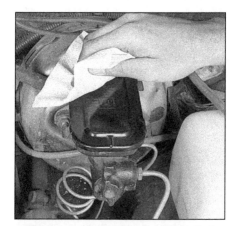

2.22 Before removing the master cylinder cap, use a clean cloth to remove dirt, grease, etc.

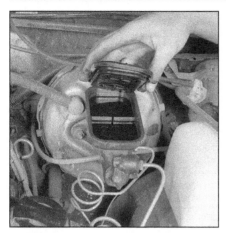

2.24a Removing the master cylinder cap to check the brake fluid level

2.24b Some master cylinder reservoirs are equipped with fluid level sights (arrows)

2.37 Checking the automatic transmission fluid level with the dipstick

cap removed, blockage in the brake system lines can occur. Also make sure all painted surfaces around the master' cylinder are covered, as brake fluid will ruin paintwork.

23   Release the clip(s) securing the cap to the top of the master cylinder. In most cases, a screwdriver can be used to pry the wire clip(s) free.

24   Carefully lift the cap off the cylinder and observe the fluid level **(see illustrations)** It should be approximately 1/4-inch below the top edge of each reservoir.

25   If additional fluid is necessary to bring the level up to the proper height, carefully pour the specified brake fluid into the master cylinder. Be careful not to spill the fluid on painted surfaces. Be sure the specified fluid is used, as mixing different types of brake fluid can cause damage to the system. See Recommended Lubricants or your owner's manual.

26   At this time the fluid and master cylinder can be inspected for contamination. Normally, the braking system will not need periodic draining and refilling, but if rust deposits, dirt particles or water droplets are seen in the fluid, the system should be dismantled, drained and refilled with fresh fluid.

27   Reinstall the master cylinder cap and secure it with the clip(s). Make sure the lid is properly seated to prevent fluid leakage and/or system pressure loss.

28   The brake fluid in the master cylinder will drop slightly as the brake shoes or pads at each wheel wear down during normal operation. If the master cylinder requires repeated replenishing to keep it at the proper level, this is an indication of leakage in the brake system which should be corrected immediately. Check all brake lines and their connections, along with the wheel cylinders and booster (see Chapter 9 for more information).

29   If upon checking the master cylinder fluid level you discover one or both reservoirs empty or nearly empty, the braking system should be bled(Chapter 9). When the fluid level gets low, air can enter the system and should be removed by bleeding the brakes.

Manual transmission

30   Manual shift transmissions do not have a dipstick. The fluid level is checked by removing a plug in the side of the transmission case. Locate this plug and use a rag to clean the plug and the area around it.

31   With the vehicle components cold, remove the plug. If fluid immediately starts leaking out, thread the plug back into the transmission because the fluid level is all right. If there is no fluid leakage, completely remove the plug and place your little finger inside the hole. The fluid level should be just at the bottom of the plug hole.

32   If the transmission needs more fluid, use a syringe to squeeze the appropriate lubricant into the plug hole to bring the fluid up to the proper level.

33   Thread the plug back into the transmission and tighten it securely. Drive the car and check for leaks around the plug.

Automatic transmission

Refer to illustrations 2.37 and 2.41

34   The fluid inside the transmission must be at normal operating temperature to get an accurate reading on the dipstick. This is done by driving the car for several miles, making frequent starts and stops to allow the transmission to shift through all gears.

35   Park the car on a level surface, place the selector lever in 'Park' and leave the engine running at an idle.

36   Remove the transmission dipstick

(located on the right side, near the rear of the engine) and wipe all the fluid from the end of the dipstick with a clean rag.

37   Push the dipstick back into the transmission until the cap seats firmly on the dipstick tube. Now remove the dipstick again and observe the fluid on the end **(see illustration)**. The highest point of fluid should be between the 'Full' mark and 4 inch below the 'Full' mark.

38   If the fluid level is at or below the 'Add' mark on the dipstick, add sufficient fluid to raise the level to the 'Full' mark. One pint of fluid will raise the level from 'Add' to 'Full'. Fluid should be added directly into the dipstick guide tube, using a funnel to prevent spills.

39   It is important that the transmission not be overfilled. Under no circumstances should the fluid level be above the 'Full' mark on the dipstick, as this could cause internal damage to the transmission. The best way to prevent overfilling is to add fluid a little at a time, driving the car and checking the level between additions.

40   Use only transmission fluid specified by GM. This information can be found in the Recommended Lubricants Section.

41   The condition of the fluid should also be checked along with the level **(see illustration)**. If the fluid at the end of the dipstick is a dark reddish-brown color, or if the fluid has a 'burnt' smell, the transmission fluid should be changed with fresh. If you are in doubt about the condition of the fluid, purchase some new fluid and compare the two for color and smell.

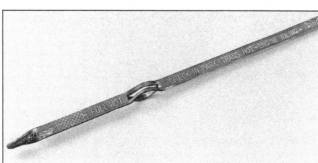

2.41 A clue to the fluid quality can be obtained by inspecting the fluid on the dipstick

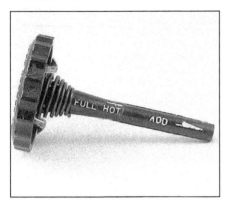

2.49 Checking of the power steering fluid level is done with the engine at normal operating temperature

Rear axle

42   Like the manual transmission, the rear axle has an inspection and fill plug which must be removed to check the fluid level.
43   Remove the plug which is located either in the removable cover plate or on the side of the differential carrier. Use your little finger to reach inside the rear axle housing to feel the level of the fluid. It should be at the bottom of the plug hole.
44   If this is not the case, add the proper lubricant into the rear axle carrier through the plug hole. A syringe or a small funnel can be used for this.
45   Make certain the correct lubricant is used, as regular and Positraction rear axles require different lubricants. You can ascertain which type of axle you have by reading the stamped number on the axle tube (See Vehicle Identification Numbers at the front of this manual).
46   Tighten the plug securely and check for leaks after the first few miles of driving.

Power steering

Refer to illustration 2.49
47   Unlike manual steering, the power steering system relies on fluid which may, over a period of time, require replenishing.
48   The reservoir for the power steering pump will be located near the front of the engine, and can be mounted on either the left or right side.
49   The power steering fluid level should be checked only after the car has been driven, with the fluid at operating temperature **(see illustration)**. The front wheels should be pointed straight ahead.
50   With the engine shut off, use a rag to clean the reservoir cap and the areas around the cap. This will help to prevent foreign material from falling into the reservoir when the cap is removed.
51   Twist off the reservoir cap which has a built-in dipstick attached to it. Pull off the cap and clean the fluid at the bottom of the dipstick with a clean rag. Now reinstall the dipstick/cap assembly to get a fluid level reading. Remove the dipstick/cap and observe the fluid level. It should be at the 'Full hot' mark on the dipstick.
52   If additional fluid is required, pour the specified lubricant directly into the reservoir using a funnel to prevent spills.
53   If the reservoir requires frequent fluid additions, all power steering hoses, hose connections, the power steering pump and the steering box should be carefully checked for leaks.

3   Tire and tire pressure checks

Refer to illustrations 3.3, 3.6, 3.8a and 3.8b
1   Periodically inspecting the tires can not only prevent you from being stranded with a flat tire, but can also give you clues as to possible problems with the steering and suspension systems before major damage occurs.
2   Proper tire inflation adds miles to the lifespan of the tires, allows the car to achieve maximum miles per gallon figures, and helps the overall riding comfort of the car.
3   When inspecting the tire, first check the wear on the tread **(see illustration)**. Irregularities in the tread pattern (cupping, flat spots,

UNDERINFLATION

CUPPING

Cupping may be caused by:
• Underinflation and/or mechanical irreguarities such as out-of-balance condition of wheel and/or tire, and bent or damaged wheel.
• Loose or worn steering tie-rod or steering idler arm.
• Loose, damaged or worn front suspension parts.

OVERINFLATION

INCORRECT TOE-IN OR EXTREME CAMBER

FEATHERING DUE TO MISALIGNMENT

3.3 This chart will help you to determine the condition of the tires, the probable cause of the abnormal wear and the corrective action necessary

3.6 To extend the life of your tires, check the air pressure at least once a week with an accurate gauge (don't forget the spare!)

3.8a If a tire loses air on a steady basis, check the valve core first to make sure it's snug (special inexpensive wrenches are commonly available at auto parts stores)

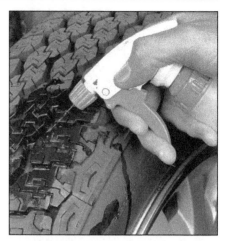

3.8b If the valve core is tight, raise the corner of the vehicle with the low tire and spray a soapy water solution onto the tread as the tire is turned slowly - slow leaks will cause small bubbles to appear

more wear on one side than the other) are indications of front end alignment and/or balance problems. If any of these conditions are found you would do best to take the car to a competent repair shop which can correct the problem.

4 Also check the tread area for cuts or punctures. Many times a nail or tack will imbed itself into the tire tread and yet the tire will hold its air pressure for a short time. In most cases, a repair shop or gas station can repair the punctured tire.

5 It is also important to check the side-walls of the tire, both inside and outside. Check for the rubber being deteriorated, cut or punctured. Also inspect the inboard side of the tire for signs of brake fluid leakage, indicating a thorough brake inspection is needed immediately (Section 26).

6 Incorrect tire pressure cannot be determined merely by looking at the tire **(see illustration)**. This is especially true for radial tires. A tire pressure gauge must be used. If you do not already have a reliable gauge, it is a good idea to purchase one and keep it in the glove box. Built-in pressure gauges at gas stations are often unreliable. If you are in doubt as to the accuracy of your gauge, many repair shops have 'master' pressure gauges which you can use for comparison purposes.

7 Always check tire inflation when the tires are cold. Cold, in this case, means the car has not been driven more than one mile after sitting for three hours or more. It is normal for the pressure to increase 4 to 8 pounds or more when the tires are hot.

8 Unscrew the valve cap protruding from the wheel or hubcap and firmly press the gauge onto the valve stem **(see illustrations)**. Observe the reading on the gauge and check this figure against the recommended tire pressure listed on the tire placard. This tire placard is usually found attached to the rear portion of the driver's door.

9 Check all tires and add air as necessary to bring all tires up to the recommended pressure levels. Do not forget the spare tire.

Be sure to reinstall the valve caps which will keep dirt and moisture out of the valve stem mechanism.

4 Engine oil and filter change

Refer to illustrations 4.9a, 4.9b, 4.11, 4.12, 4.14, 4.18, 4.19 and 4.20

1 Frequent oil changes may be the best form of preventative maintenance available for the home mechanic. When engine oil ages, it gets diluted and contaminated which ultimately leads to premature parts wear.

2 Although some sources recommend oil filter changes every other oil change, we feel that the minimal cost of an oil filter and the relative ease with which it is installed dictates that a new filter be used whenever the oil is changed.

3 The tools necessary for a normal oil and filter change are: a wrench to fit the drain plug at the bottom of the oil pan: an oil filter wrench to remove the old filter: a container with at least a six-quart capacity to drain the old oil into: and a funnel to help pour fresh oil into the engine.

4 In addition, you should have plenty of clean rags and newspapers handy to mop up any spills. Access to the underside of the car is greatly improved if the car can be lifted on a hoist, driven onto ramps or supported by jack stands. Do not work under a car which is supported only by a bumper, hydraulic or scissors-type jack.

5 If this is your first oil change on the car, it is a good idea to crawl underneath and familiarize yourself with the locations of the oil drain plug and the oil filter. Since the engine and exhaust components will be warm during the actual work, it is best to figure out any potential problems before the car and its accessories are hot.

6 Allow the car to warm up to normal operating temperature. If the new oil or any tools are needed, use this warm-up time to

4.9a Some engines have the oil drain plug on the side of the oil pan

gather everything necessary for the job. The correct type of oil to buy for your application can be found in *Recommended lubricants and fluids*.

7 With the engine oil warm (warm engine oil will drain better and more built-up sludge will be removed with the oil), raise the vehicle for access beneath. Make sure the car is firmly supported. If jack stands are used they should be placed towards the front of the frame rails which run the length of the car.

8 Move all necessary tools, rags and newspaper under the car. Position the drain pan under the drain plug. Keep in mind that the oil will initially flow from the pan with some force, so place the pan accordingly.

9 Being careful not to touch any of the hot exhaust pipe components, use the wrench to remove the drain plug near the bottom of the oil pan **(see illustrations)**. Depending on how hot the oil has become, you may want to wear gloves while unscrewing the plug the final few turns.

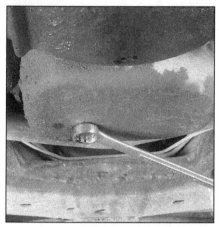

4.9b Removing an oil drain plug which is located on the bottom of the oil pan

4.11 Before reinstalling, thoroughly clean the oil drain plug

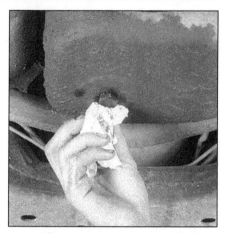

4.12 Once tightened securely, clean the area around the drain plug. This will help to readily identify any leakage

4.14 Using an oil filter wrench to loosen the filter, the canister is less likely to collapse if grasped near the bottom

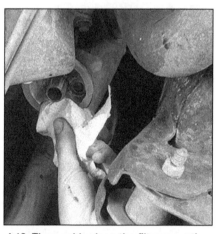

4.18 Thoroughly clean the filter mounting pedestal and check that the old rubber gasket is not stuck to the filter mount

4.19 A thin coat of clean engine oil on the new filter gasket will ensure a good seal

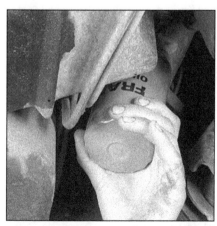

4.20 Tighten the new filter as instructed by the manufacturer. Most are tightened hand-tight, 1/4 turn after the filter contacts the pedestal

10   Allow the old oil to drain into the pan. It may be necessary to move the pan further under the engine as the oil flow reduces to a trickle.

11   After all the oil has drained, clean the

drain plug thoroughly with a clean rag **(see illustration)**. Small metal filings may cling to this plug which could immediately contaminate your new oil.

12   Clean the area around the drain plug opening and reinstall the drain plug **(see illustration)**. Tighten the plug securely with your wrench. If a torque wrench is available, the torque setting is 20 ft-lb.

13   Move the drain pan in position under the oil filter.

14   Now use the filter wrench to loosen the oil filter **(see illustration)**. Chain or metal band-type filter wrenches may distort the filter canister, but don't worry too much about this as the filter will be discarded anyway.

15   Sometimes the oil filter is on so tight it cannot be loosened, or it is positioned in an area which is inaccessible with a filter wrench. As a last resort, you can punch a metal bar or long screwdriver directly through the bottom of the canister and use this as a T-bar to turn the filter. If this must be done, be prepared for oil to spurt out of the canister as it is punctured.

16   Completely unscrew the old filter. Be careful, it is full of oil. Empty the old oil inside

the filter into the drain pan.

17   Compare the old filter with the new one to make sure they are of the same type.

18   Use a clean rag to remove all oil, dirt and sludge from the area where the oil filter mounts to the engine **(see illustration)**. Check the old filter to make sure the rubber gasket is not stuck to the engine mounting surface. If this gasket is stuck to the engine (use a flashlight if necessary), remove it.

19   Open one of the containers of new oil and fill the new filter with fresh oil. Also smear a light coat of this fresh oil onto the rubber gasket of the new oil filter **(see illustration)**.

20   Screw the new filter to the engine following the tightening directions printed on the filter canister or packing box **(see illustration)**. Most filter manufacturers recommend against using a filter wrench due to possible overtightening or damage to the canister.

21   Remove all tools, rags, etc. from under the car, being careful not to spill the oil in the drain pan. Lower the car off its support devices.

22   Move to the engine compartment and locate the oil filler cap on the engine. In most cases there will be a screw-off cap on the

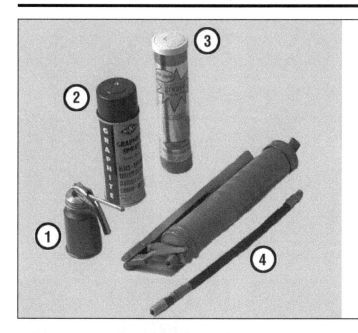

5.1 Tools and materials necessary for chassis lubrication

1 *Engine oil* - *Light engine oil in a can like this can be used for door and hood hinges*
2 *Graphite spray* - *Used to lubricate lock cylinders*
3 *Grease* - *Grease, in a variety of types and weights, is available for use in a grease gun. Check the specifications for your requirements*
4 *Grease gun* - *A common grease gun, shown here with a detachable hose and nozzle, is needed for chassis lubrication. After use, clean it thoroughly!*

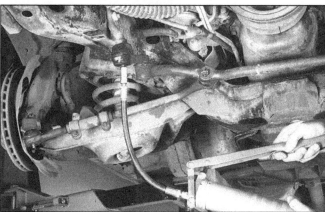

5.6a Pumping grease into one of the steering system grease fittings

5.6b The balljoints (upper balljoint shown) should not be over-greased

rocker arm cover (at the side of the engine) or a cap at the end of a fill tube at the front of the engine. In any case, the cap will most likely be labeled 'Engine Oil' or something similar.

23   Place the funnel into the oil filler opening. A shop rag wrapped around the base of the funnel will help catch spills.

24   Pour about 3 qts. of fresh oil into the engine. Wait a few minutes to allow the oil to drain to the pan, then check the level on the oil dipstick (see Section 2 if necessary). If the oil level is at or near the lower 'Add' mark, start the engine and allow the new oil to circulate.

25   Run the engine for only about a minute and then shut it off. Immediately look under the car and check for leaks at the oil pan drain plug and around the oil filter. If either is leaking, tighten with a bit more force.

26   With the new oil circulated and the filter now completely full, recheck the level on the dipstick and add enough oil to bring the level to the 'Full' mark on the dipstick.

27   During the first few trips after an oil

change, make a point to check for leaks and also the oil level.

28   The old oil drained from the engine cannot be reused in its present state and should be disposed of. Check with your local auto parts store, disposal facility or environmental agency to see if they will accept the oil for recycling. After the oil has cooled, it can be drained into a suitable container (capped plastic jugs, topped bottles, milk cartons, etc.) for transport to one of these disposal sites. Do *not* dump dirty oil onto the ground, down a drain or into the sewer.

5   Chassis lubrication

Refer to illustrations 5.1, 5.6a and 5.6b

1   A grease gun and a cartridge filled with the proper grease (see Recommended Lubricants) are usually the only equipment necessary to lubricate the chassis components **(see illustration)**. Occasionally on later model vehicles, plugs will be installed rather than

grease fittings, in which case grease fittings will have to be purchased and installed.

2   Look under the car to find these components and ascertain if grease fittings or solid plugs are installed. if there are plugs, remove them with the correct wrench and buy grease fittings which will thread into the component. A GM dealer or auto parts store will be able to find replacement fittings. Straight, as well as angled, fittings are available for easy greasing.

3   For easier access under the car, raise the vehicle with a jack and place jack stands under the frame. Make sure the car is firmly supported by the stands.

4   Before you do any greasing, force a little of the grease out the nozzle to remove any dirt from the end of the gun. Wipe the nozzle clean with a rag.

5   With the grease gun, plenty of clean rags and the location diagram, go under the car to begin lubricating the components.

6   Wipe the grease fitting nipple clean and push the nozzle firmly over the fitting nipple. Squeeze the trigger on the grease gun to

6.3 Inspecting the radiator pressure cap

6.4a Checking the upper radiator hose for cracks by squeezing it

force grease into the component **(see illustrations)**. **Note:** *The balljoints (one upper and one lower for each wheel) should be lubricated until the rubber reservoir is firm to the touch. Do not pump too much grease into these fittings as this could rupture the reservoir. For all other suspension and steering fittings, continue pumping grease into the nipple until grease seeps out of the joint between the two components. If the grease seeps out around the grease gun nozzle, the nipple is clogged or the nozzle is not fully seated around the fitting nipple. Re-secure the gun nozzle to the fitting and try again. If necessary, replace the fitting.*

7   Wipe the excess grease from the components and the grease fitting. Follow these procedures for the remaining fittings.

8   Check the universal joints on the driveshaft: some have fittings, some are factory sealed. About two pumps is all that is required for grease type universal joints. While you are under the car, clean and lubricate the parking brake cable along with its cable guides and levers. This can be done by smearing some of the chassis grease onto the cable and its related parts with your fingers. Place a few drops of light engine oil on the transmission shifting linkage rods and swivels.

9   Lower the car to the ground for the remaining body lubrication process.

10   Open the hood and smear a little chassis grease on the hood latch mechanism. If the hood has an inside release, have an assistant pull the release knob from inside the car as you lubricate the cable at the latch.

11   Lubricate all the hinges (door, hood, trunk) with a few drops of light engine oil to keep them in proper working order.

12   Finally, the key lock cylinders can be lubricated with spray-on graphite which is available at auto parts stores.

---

6   Cooling system check

Refer to illustrations 6.3, 6.4a and 6.4b

1   Many major engine failures can be attributed to a faulty cooling system. If equipped

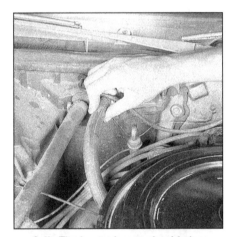

6.4b The heater hoses should also be inspected

with an automatic transmission, the cooling system also plays an integral role in transmission longevity.

2   The cooling system should be checked with the engine cold. Do this before the car is driven for the day or after it has been shut off for one or two hours.

3   Remove the radiator cap and thoroughly clean the cap (inside and out) with clean water **(see illustration)**. Also clean the filler neck on the radiator. All traces of corrosion should be removed.

4   Carefully check the upper and lower radiator hoses along with the smaller diameter heater hoses. Inspect their entire length, replacing any hose which is cracked, swollen or shows signs of deterioration. Cracks may become more apparent if the hose is squeezed **(see illustrations)**.

5   Also check that all hose connections are tight. A leak in the cooling system will usually show up as white or rust colored deposits on the areas adjoining the leak.

6   Use compressed air or a soft brush to remove bugs, leaves, etc. from the front of the radiator or air conditioning condenser. Be careful not to damage the delicate cooling fins, or cut yourself on the sharp fins.

7   Finally, have the cap and system tested

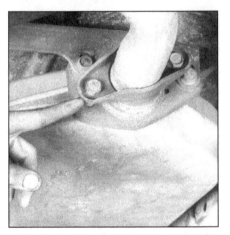

7.2 All exhaust system flanges and their connections should be inspected for signs of leakage

for proper pressure. If you do not have a pressure tester, most gas stations and repair shops will do this for a minimal charge.

---

7   Exhaust system check

Refer to illustrations 7.2 and 7.5

1   With the exhaust system cold (at least three hours after being driven), check the complete exhaust system from its starting point at the engine to the end of the tailpipe. This is best done on a hoist where full access is available.

2   Check the pipes and their connections for signs of leakage and/or corrosion indicating a potential failure. Check that all brackets and hangers are in good condition and are tight **(see illustration)**.

3   At the same time, inspect the underside of the body for holes, corrosion, open seams, etc. which may allow exhaust gases to enter the trunk or passenger compartment. Seal all body openings with silicone or body putty.

4   Rattles and other driving noises can often be traced to the exhaust system, especially the mounts and hangers. Try to move

7.5 Black, sooty deposits at the end of the exhaust pipe may be an indication that the carburetor needs adjustment or the engine is in need of a tune-up

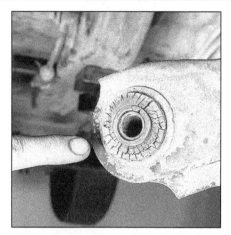

8.6 Rubber bushings in the steering and suspension systems will deteriorate and crack after a time, indicating replacement is necessary

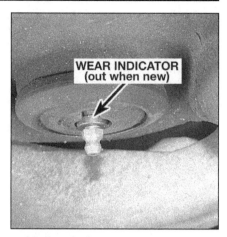

8.7 Wear indicators are built into the lower balljoints to aid in their inspection

the pipes, muffler and catalytic converter (if equipped). If the components can come into contact with the body or driveline parts, secure the exhaust system with new mountings.

5   This is also an ideal time to check the running condition of the engine by inspecting the very end of the tailpipe. The exhaust deposits here are an indication of engine tune. if the pipe is black and sooty **(see illustration)**, or bright white deposits are found here, the engine is in need of a tune-up including a thorough carburetor inspection and adjustment.

8   Suspension and steering check

Refer to illustration 8.6 and 8.7
1   Whenever the front of the car is raised for service it is a good idea to visually check the suspension and steering components for wear.
2   Indications of a fault in these systems are: excessive play in the steering wheel before the front wheels react: excessive sway around corners or body movement over rough roads; binding at some point as the steering wheel is turned.
3   Before the car is raised for inspection, test the shock absorbers by pushing downward to rock the car at each corner. If you push the car down and it does not come back to a level position within one or two bounces, the shocks are worn and need to be replaced. As this is done, check for squeaks and strange noises from the suspension components. Information on shock absorber and suspension components can be found in Chapter 11.
4   Now raise the front end of the car and support firmly by jack stands placed under the frame rails. Because of the work to be done, make sure the car cannot fall from the stands.
5   Grab the top and bottom of the front tire with your hands and rock the tire/wheel on its

spindle. If there is movement of more than 0.005 in, the wheel bearings should be serviced (see Section 24).
6   Crawl under the car and check for loose bolts, broken or disconnected parts and deteriorated rubber bushings **(see illustration)** on all suspension and steering components. Look for grease or fluid leaking from around the steering box. Check the power steering hoses and their connections for leaks.
7   Check the balljoints for wear **(see illustration)**.
8   Have an assistant turn the steering wheel from side to side and check the steering components for free movement, chafing or binding. If the steering does not react with the movement of the steering wheel, try to determine where the slack is located.

9   Engine drive belt check and adjustment

Refer to illustrations 9.1, 9.4, 9.6 and 9.7
1   The drive belts, or V-belts as they are sometimes called, at the front of the engine play an important role in the overall operation of the car and its components. Due to their function and material make-up, the belts are prone to failure after a period of time and should be inspected and adjusted periodically to prevent major engine damage **(see illustration)**.
2   The number of belts used on a particular car depends on the accessories installed. Drive belts are used to turn: the generator (alternator); A.I.R. smog pump; power steering pump; water pump; fan; and air conditioning compressor. Depending on the pulley arrangement, a single belt may be used for more than one of these ancillary components.
3   With the engine off, open the hood and locate the various belts at the front of the engine. Using your fingers (and a flashlight if

necessary), move along the belts checking for cracks or separation. Also check for fraying and for glazing which gives the belt a shiny appearance. Both sides of the belts should be inspected, which means you will have to twist the belt to check the underside.

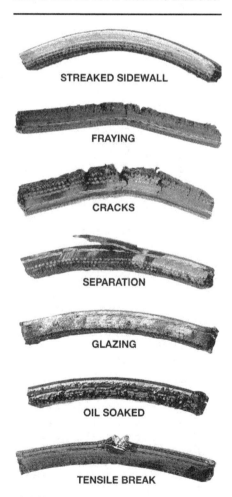

STREAKED SIDEWALL

FRAYING

CRACKS

SEPARATION

GLAZING

OIL SOAKED

TENSILE BREAK

9.1 Here are some of the more common problems associated with drivebelts (check the drivebelts very carefully to prevent untimely breakdown)

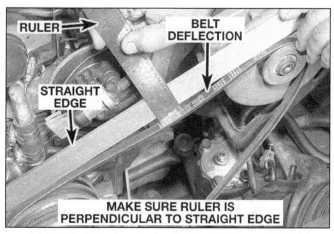

9.4 Drivebelt tension can be checked with a straightedge and a ruler

9.6 Nearly all belt-driven components have a pivot bolt {top} and a strap or adjusting bolt (near bottom of alternator shown)

4   The tension of each belt is checked by pushing on the belt at a distance halfway between the pulleys. Push firmly with your thumb and see how much the belt moves downward (deflects) **(see illustration)**. A rule of thumb, so to speak, is that if the distance (pulley center to pulley center) is between 7 inches and 11 inches the belt should deflect 1/4-inch. If the belt is longer and travels between pulleys spaced 12 inches to 16 inches apart, the belt should deflect 1/2-in.

5   If it is found necessary to adjust the belt tension, either to make the belt tighter or looser, this is done by moving the belt-driven accessory on its bracket.

6   For each component there will be an adjustment or strap bolt and a pivot bolt. Both bolts must be loosened slightly to enable you to move the component **(see illustration)**.

7   After the two bolts have been loosened, move the component away from the engine (to tighten the belt) or toward the engine (to loosen the belt) **(see illustration)**. Hold the accessory in this position and check the belt tension. If it is correct, tighten the two bolts until snug, then recheck the tension. If it is all right, fully tighten the two bolts.

8   It will often be necessary to use some sort of pry bar to move the accessory while the belt is adjusted. If this must be done to gain the proper leverage, be very careful not to damage the component being moved, or the part being pried against.

10   Fuel system check

Warning: *Gasoline is extremely flammable, so take extra precautions when you work on any part of the fuel system. Don't smoke or allow open flames or bare light bulbs near the work area, and don't work in a garage where a natural gas-type appliance (such as a water heater or clothes dryer) with a pilot light is present. Since gasoline is carcinogenic, wear latex gloves when there's a possibility of being exposed to fuel, and, if you spill any fuel on your skin, rinse it off immediately with* soap and water. *Mop up any spills immediately and do not store fuel-soaked rags where they could ignite. The fuel system is under constant pressure, so, if any fuel lines are to be disconnected, the fuel pressure in the system must be relieved first (see Chapter 4 for more information). When you perform any kind of work on the fuel system, wear safety glasses and have a Class B type fire extinguisher on hand.*

1   There are certain precautions to take when inspecting or servicing the fuel system components. Work in a well ventilated area and do not allow open flames (cigarettes, appliance pilot lights, etc.) to get near the work area. Mop up spills immediately and do not store fuel-soaked rags where they could ignite.

2   The fuel system is under some amount of pressure, so if any fuel lines are disconnected for servicing, be prepared to catch the fuel as it spurts out. Plug all disconnected fuel lines immediately after disconnection to prevent the tank from emptying itself.

3   The fuel system is most easily checked with the car raised on a hoist where the components under the car are readily visible and accessible.

4   If the smell of gasoline is noticed while driving, or after the car has sat in the sun, the system should be thoroughly inspected immediately.

5   Remove the gas filler cap and check for damage, corrosion and a proper sealing imprint on the gasket. Replace the cap with a new one if necessary,

6   With the car raised, inspect the gas tank and filler neck for punctures, cracks or any damage. The connection between the filler neck and the tank is especially critical. Sometimes a rubber filler neck will leak due to loose clamps or deteriorated rubber; problems a home mechanic can usually rectify.

7   Do not under any circumstances try to repair a fuel tank yourself (except rubber components) unless you have considerable experience. A welding torch or any open flame can easily cause the fuel vapors to explode if the proper precautions are not taken.

9.7 Adjusting the belt tension by gently prying on the component as the adjustment bolt is tightened

8   Carefully check all rubber hoses and metal lines leading away from the fuel tank. Check for loose connections, deteriorated hose, crimped lines or damage of any kind. Follow these lines up to the front of the car, carefully inspecting them all the way. Repair or replace damaged sections as necessary.

9   If a fuel odor is still evident after the inspection, refer to Section 31 on the evaporative emissions system and Section 16 for carburetor. adjustment.

11   Positive Crankcase Ventilation (PCV) valve replacement

Refer to illustrations 11.3, 11.4 and 11.5

1   The PCV valve can usually be found pushed into one of the rocker arm covers at the side of the engine. There will be a hose connected to the valve which runs to either the carburetor or the intake manifold.

2   When purchasing a replacement PCV valve, make sure it is for your particular vehicle, model year and engine size.

3   Pull the valve (with the hose attached) from its rubber grommet in the rocker arm

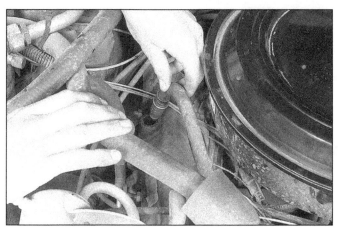

11.3 Pulling the PCV valve and hose from the rocker arm cover

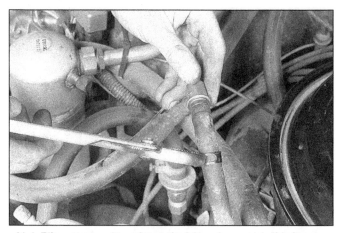

11.4 Pliers are used to release the hose clamp and slide it away from the valve

cover **(see illustration)**.

4   Using pliers or a screwdriver, depending on the type of clamp, loosen the clamp at the end of the hose and move the clamp upwards on the PCV hose **(see illustration)**.

5   Now pull the PCV valve from the end of the hose, noting its installed position and direction **(see illustration)**.

6   Compare the old valve with the new one to make sure they are the same.

7   Push the new valve into the end of the hose until it is fully seated.

8   Move the hose clamp down the hose and tighten the clamp securely around the end of the hose.

9   Inspect the rubber grommet in the cover for damage and replace it with a new one if faulty.

10   Push the PCV valve and hose securely into the rocker arm cover.

11   More information on the PCV system can be found in Chapter 6.

12 Air filter and PCV filter replacement

Refer to illustrations 12.2, 12.4, 12.5, 12.6 and 12.12

1   At the specified intervals, the air filter

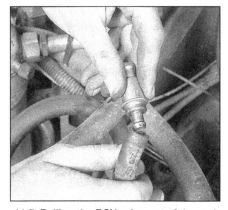

11.5 Pulling the PCV valve out of the end of the hose. Note its direction as this is done

and PCV filter should be replaced with new ones. A thorough program of preventative maintenance would call for the two filters to be inspected periodically between changes.

2   The air filter is located inside the air cleaner housing on the top of the engine. To remove the filter, unscrew the wing nut at the top of the air cleaner and lift off the top plate **(see illustration)**. If there are vacuum hoses connected to this plate, note their positions and disconnect them.

12.2a If equipped, loosen the hood scoop clamp (arrow) and separate the scoop from the air cleaner

3   While the top plate is off, be careful not to drop anything down into the carburetor.

4   Lift the air filter out of the housing **(see illustration)**.

5   To check the filter, hold it up to strong sunlight, or place a flashlight or droplight on the inside of the ring-shaped filter **(see illustration)**. If you can see light coming through the paper element, the filter is all right. Check all the way around the filter.

12.2b Removing the wing nut at the top of the air cleaner assembly

12.4 With the top plate set aside, the air filter can be lifted out of the housing

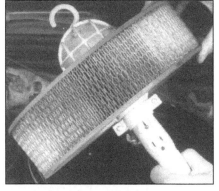

12.5 If light can be easily seen through the filter element. the filter can be reused. If in doubt, replace the filter with a new one

12.6 Before installing the filter, thoroughly clean the interior of the housing

12.12 The PCV filter on most vehicles is located inside the air cleaner housing

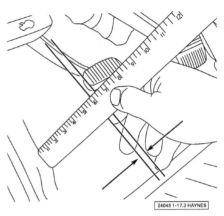

13.3 Clutch pedal free play is the distance the pedal moves before resistance is felt

6   Wipe the inside of the air cleaner clean with a rag **(see illustration)**.

7   Place the old filter (if in good condition) or the new filter (if specified interval has elapsed) back into the air cleaner housing.

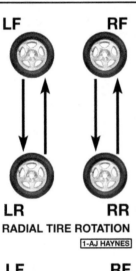

RADIAL TIRE ROTATION

1-AJ HAYNES

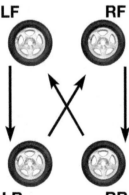

BIAS BELTED TIRE ROTATION

1-AJ HAYNES

14.2 Tire rotation schematics for radial and bias ply tires

Make sure it seats properly in the bottom of the housing.

8   Connect any disconnected vacuum hoses to the top plate and reinstall the top plate with the wing nut.

9   On nearly all cars the PCV filter is also located inside the air cleaner housing. Remove the top plate as described previously and locate the filter on the side of the housing.

10   Loosen the hose clamp at the end of the PCV hose leading to the filter. Disconnect the hose from the filter.

11   Remove the metal locking clip which secures the filter holder to the air cleaner housing. Pliers can be used for this.

12   Remove the filter and plastic holder from the inside of the air cleaner **(see illustration)**.

13   Compare the new filter with the old one to make sure they are the same.

14   Place the new filter assembly into position and install the metal locking clip on the outside of the air cleaner.

15   Connect the PCV hose and tighten the clamp around the end of the hose.

16   Reinstall the air cleaner top plate and any vacuum hoses which were disconnected.

17   A few engines will not have the PCV filter at the air cleaner, but rather the filter will be in the PCV hose at some point. To locate the filter, find the hose leading into the side of the air cleaner housing and follow this hose to the filter.

18   Replacing 'in-line' PCV filters is usually a simple matter of disconnecting the hose from the filter and then pushing a replacement filter into the hose.

19   For more information on these filters and the systems they are a part of, see Chapter 4 and Chapter 6.

13   Clutch pedal free play check and adjustment

Refer to illustration 13.3.

Check

1   On manual transmission models, it is

important to have the clutch free play at the proper point. Free play is the distance between the clutch pedal when it is all the way up and the point at which the clutch starts to disengage.

2   Slowly depress the clutch pedal until you can feel resistance. Do this a number of times until you can pinpoint exactly where the resistance is felt.

3   Now measure the distance the pedal travels before the resistance is felt **(see illustration)**.

4   If the distance is not as specified, the clutch pedal free play should be adjusted.

Adjustment

5   Disconnect the clutch fork return spring.

6   Hold the clutch pedal against the stop and loosen the jam nut so the clutch fork pushrod can be turned out of the swivel and back against the clutch fork. The release bearing must contact the pressure plate fingers lightly.

7   Turn the clutch fork pushrod three and a half turns.

8   Tighten the jam nut, taking care not to change the pushrod length, and reconnect the return spring.

9   Recheck the free play.

14   Tire rotation

Refer to illustration 14.2

1   The tires should be rotated at the specified intervals and whenever uneven wear is noticed. Since the car will be raised and the tires removed anyway, this is a good time to check the brakes (Section 26) and/or repack the wheel bearings (Section 24). Read over these sections if this is to be done at the same time.

2   The location for each tire in the rotation sequence depends on the type of tire used on your car. Tire type can be determined by reading the raised printing on the sidewall of the tire **(see illustration)**.

3   See the information in *Jacking and Tow-*

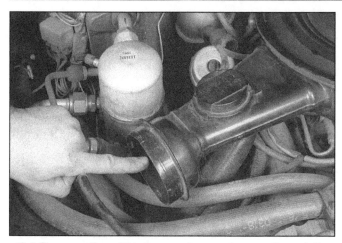

15.4 The operation of the damper door can be seen through the end of the air cleaner snorkel tube

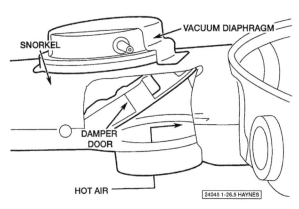

15.5 When the engine is cold, the damper door closes off the snorkel passage, allowing air warmed by the exhaust to enter the carburetor

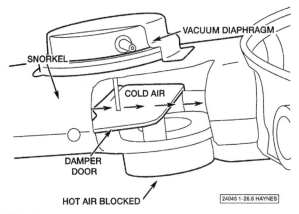

15.6 As the engine warms up, the damper door moves down to close off the heat stove passage and open the snorkel passage so outside air can enter the carburetor

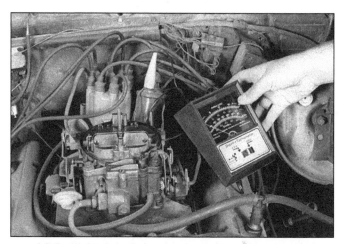

16.2 A reliable hand-held tachometer is necessary for idle speed adjustment

ing at the front of this manual for the proper procedures to follow in raising the car and changing a tire; however, if the brakes are to be checked do not apply the parking brake as stated. Make sure the tires are blocked to prevent the car from rolling.

4   Preferably, the entire car should be raised at the same time. This can be done on a hoist or by jacking up each corner of the car and then lowering the car onto jack stands placed under the frame rails. Always use four jack stands and make sure the car is firmly supported all around.

5   After rotation, check and adjust the tire pressures as necessary and be sure to check wheel nut tightness.

15   Thermo controlled air cleaner check

Refer to illustrations 15.4, 15.5 and 15.6

1   All models are equipped with a thermo-statically controlled air cleaner which draws air to the carburetor from different locations depending upon engine temperature.

2   This is a simple visual check; however, if access is tight, a small mirror may have to be used.

3   Open the hood and find the vacuum flapper door on the air cleaner assembly. It will be located inside the long 'snorkel' of the metal air cleaner. Check that the flexible air hose(s) are securely attached and are not damaged.

4   If there is a flexible air duct attached to the end of the snorkel, leading to an area behind the grille, disconnect it at the snorkel. This will enable you to look through the end of the snorkel and see the flapper door inside **(see illustration)**.

5   The testing should preferably be done when the engine and outside air are cold. Start the engine and look through the snorkel at the flapper door which should move to a closed position. With the door closed, air cannot enter through the end of the snorkel, but rather air enters the air cleaner through the flexible duct attached to the exhaust manifold **(see illustration)**.

6   As the engine warms up to operating temperature, the door should open to allow air through the snorkel end. Depending on

ambient temperature, this may take 10 to 15 minutes. To speed up this check you can reconnect the snorkel air duct, drive the car and then check that the door is fully open **(see illustration)**.

7   If the thermo controlled air cleaner is not operating properly, see Chapter 6 for more information.

16   Engine idle speed adjustment

Refer to illustrations 16.2, 16.3 and 16.4

1   Engine idle speed is the speed at which the engine operates when no accelerator pedal pressure is applied. This speed is critical to the performance of the engine itself, as well as many engine sub-systems.

2   A hand-held tachometer must be used when adjusting idle speed to get an accurate reading **(see illustration)**. The exact hook-up for these meters varies with the manufacturer, so follow the particular directions included.

3   Since GM used many different carburetors for their vehicles in the time period covered by this book, and each has its own

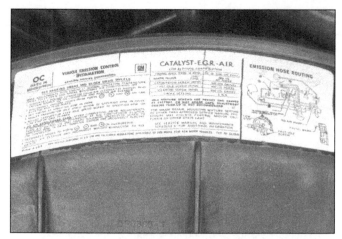

16.3 A typical tune-up decal giving valuable information specific to your engine

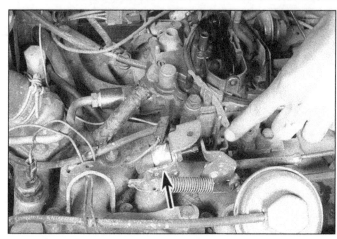

16.4 The carburetor idle speed screw located on the left side of the carburetor. Arrow points to electrically-operated idle solenoid

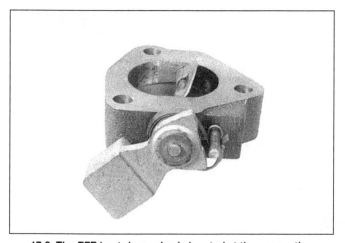

17.2 The EFE heat riser valve is located at the connection between the exhaust manifold and the exhaust pipe

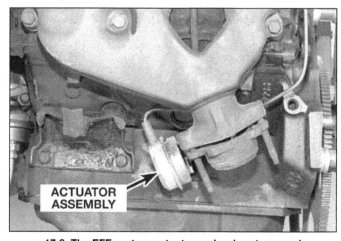

17.6 The EFE system actuator and rod system used on later models

peculiarities when setting idle speed, it would be impractical to cover all types in this Section. Chapter 4 contains information on each individual carburetor used. The carburetor used on your particular engine can be found in the Specifications Section of Chapter 4. However, all vehicles covered in this manual should have a tune-up decal in the engine compartment, usually placed near the top of the radiator **(see illustration)**. The printed instructions for setting idle speed can be found on this decal, and should be followed since they are for your particular engine.

4   Basically, for most applications, the idle speed is set by turning an adjustment screw located at the side of the carburetor **(see illustration)**. This screw changes the linkage, in essence, depressing or letting up on your accelerator pedal. This screw may be on the linkage itself or may be part of the idle stop solenoid. Refer to the tune-up decal or Chapter 4.

5   Once you have found the idle screw, experiment with different length screwdrivers until the adjustments can be easily made, without coming into contact with hot or moving engine components.

6   Follow the instructions on the tune-up

decal or in Chapter 4, which will probably include disconnecting certain vacuum or electrical connections. To plug a vacuum hose after disconnecting it, insert a properly-sized metal rod into the opening, or thoroughly wrap the open end with tape to prevent any vacuum loss through the hose.

7   If the air cleaner is removed, the vacuum hose to the snorkel should be plugged.

8   Make sure the parking brake is firmly set and the wheels blocked to prevent the car from rolling. This is especially true if the transmission is to be in 'Drive'. An assistant inside the car pushing on the brake pedal is the safest method.

9   For all applications, the engine must be completely warmed-up to operating temperature, which will automatically render the choke fast idle inoperative.

17   EFE system (heat riser) check

Refer to illustrations 17.2 and 17.6

1   The heat riser (used until around 1975) and the Early Fuel Evaporation (EFE) system both perform the same job, but function in a

slightly different manner.

2   The heat riser is a valve located inside the right side exhaust pipe, near the junction between exhaust manifold and pipe **(see illustration)**. It can be identified by an external weight and spring.

3   With the engine and exhaust pipe cold, try moving the weight by hand. It should move freely.

4   Again with the engine cold, start the engine and observe the heat riser. Upon starting, the weight should move to the closed position. As the engine warms to normal operating temperature, the weight should move the valve to the open position, allowing a free flow of exhaust through the tailpipe. Since it could take several minutes for the system to heat up, you could mark the 'cold' weight position, drive the car, and then recheck the weight.

5   The EFE system also blocks off exhaust flow when the engine is cold. However, this system uses more precise temperature sensors and vacuum to open and close the exhaust pipe valve.

6   Locate the EFE actuator which is bolted to a bracket on the right side of the engine **(see illustration)**. It will have an actuating rod

18.1 The fuel filter is located inside the fuel inlet

18.3 Whenever the air cleaner is removed, make sure the positions of all vacuum hoses are noted for easy reassembly

18.6 Two wrenches are required to loosen the fuel inlet connectors

18.8a Withdrawing the fuel inlet fitting and filter assembly

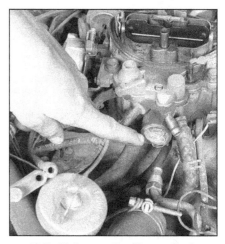
18.8b Make sure the filter spring is properly positioned

attached to it which will lead down to the valve inside the pipe. In some cases the entire mechanism, including actuator. will be located at the exhaust pipe-to-manifold junction.

7 With the engine cold, have an assistant start the engine as you observe the actuating rod. It should immediately move to close off the valve. Continue observing the rod, which should slowly open the valve as the engine warms. This process may take some time, so you might want to mark the position of the rod when the valve is closed, drive the car to reach normal operating temperature, then open the hood and check that the rod has moved to the open position.

8 Further information and testing procedures can be found in Chapter 6.

18 Fuel filter replacement

Refer to illustrations 18.1, 18.3, 18.6, 18.8a, 18.8b and 18.11
Warning: *Gasoline is extremely flammable, so take extra precautions when you work on any part of the fuel system. See the* **Warning**

in Chapter 4.
1 On all GM cars, the fuel filter is located inside the fuel inlet to the carburetor **(see illustration)**. It is made of pleated paper (later models) or bronze (early models). Neither type can be cleaned and reused.
2 This job should be done with the engine cold (after sitting at least three hours). The necessary tools are open end wrenches to fit the fuel line nuts. Flare nut wrenches which wrap around the nut should be used if available. In addition you will need to gather together the replacement filter (make sure it is for your specific vehicle and engine), and clean rags.
3 Remove the air cleaner assembly. If vacuum hoses must be disconnected, make sure you note their positions and/or tag them to help during the reassembly process **(see illustration)**.
4 Now follow the fuel hose from the fuel pump to the point where it enters the carburetor. The fuel pump is located low on the engine, at the right front. In most cases the fuel line will be metal all the way from the pump to the carburetor.
5 Place some rags under the fuel inlet fit-

tings to catch any fuel as the fittings are disconnected.
6 With the proper size wrench, hold the nut immediately next to the carburetor body. Now loosen the nut-fitting and the end of the metal fuel line **(see illustration)**. A flare nut wrench on this fitting will help prevent slipping and possible damage. However, an open-end wrench should do the job. Make sure the larger nut next to the carburetor is held firmly while the fuel line is disconnected.
7 With the fuel line disconnected, move it slightly for better access to the inlet filter nut. Do not crimp the fuel line.
8 Now unscrew the fuel inlet filter nut which was previously held steady. As this fitting is drawn away from the carburetor body, be careful not to lose the thin washer-type gasket or the spring located behind the fuel filter. Also, pay close attention to how the filter was installed **(see illustrations)**.
9 Compare the old filter with the new one to make sure they are of the same length and design.
10 Reinstall the spring into the carburetor body, after inspecting it for damage or defects.

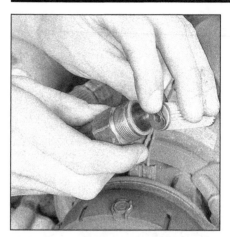

18.11 Most paper element fuel filters have a rubber gasket which should be installed away from the carburetor

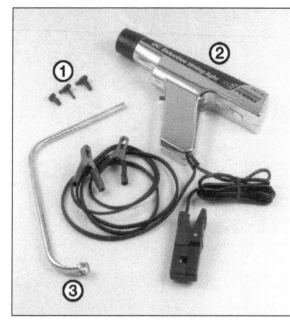

19.5 Tools needed to check and adjust the ignition timing

1 **Vacuum plugs** - Vacuum hoses will, in most cases, have to be disconnected and plugged. Molded plugs in various shapes and sizes are available for this
2 **Inductive pick-up timing light** - Flashes a bright concentrated beam of light when the number one spark plug fires. Connect the leads according to the instructions supplied with the light
3 **Distributor wrench** - On some models, the hold-down bolt for the distributor is difficult to reach and turn with a conventional wrench or socket. A special wrench like this must be used

11 Place the new filter into position behind the spring. If a bronze, cone-shaped filter is used, the smaller end of the cone points away from the carburetor. The later model paper filters will have a rubber gasket and check valve at one end which should point away from the carburetor **(see illustration)**.
12 Install a new washer-type gasket on the fuel inlet filter nut (a gasket is usually supplied with the new filter) and tighten the nut into the carburetor. Make sure it is not cross-threaded. Tighten securely, and if a torque wrench is available, tighten the nut to 18 ft-lbs. Do not over-tighten, as this area can strip easily, causing fuel leaks.
13 Hold the fuel inlet nut securely with a wrench while the fuel line is connected. Again, be careful not to cross-thread the connector. Tighten securely.
14 Plug the vacuum hose which leads to the air cleaner snorkel motor so the engine can be run.
15 Start the engine and check carefully for leaks. If the fuel line connector leaks, disconnect it using the above procedures and check for stripped or damaged threads. If the fuel line connector has stripped threads, remove the entire line and have a repair shop install a new fitting. If the threads look all right, purchase some thread sealing tape and tightly wrap the connector threads with the tape. Now reinstall and tighten securely. Inlet repair kits are available at most auto parts stores to overcome leaking at the fuel inlet filter nut.
16 Reinstall the air cleaner assembly, connecting all hoses to their original positions.

---

19   Ignition timing - adjustment

Refer to illustrations 19.5, 19.6 and 19.10
1 All vehicles are equipped with a tune-up decal inside the engine compartment. This decal gives important ignition timing settings and procedures to be followed specific to that vehicle. If information on the tune-up decal supersedes the information given in

this Section, the decal should be followed.
2 At the specified intervals, whenever the contact points have been replaced, the distributor removed or a change made in the fuel type, the ignition timing must be checked and adjusted if necessary.
3 Before attempting to check the timing, make sure the contact point dwell angle is correct (Section 30 1970-1974 models only), and the idle speed is as specified (Section 16).
4 Disconnect the vacuum hose from the distributor and plug the now-open end of the hose with a rubber plug, rod or bolt of the proper size. Make sure the idle speed remains correct; adjust as necessary.
5 Connect a timing light in accordance with the manufacturer's instructions. Generally, the light will be connected to power and ground sources and to the number 1 spark plug in some fashion **(see illustration)**. The number 1 spark plug is the first one on the right as you are facing the engine from the front.
6 Locate the numbered timing tag on the front cover of the engine **(see illustration)**. It is just behind the lower crankshaft pulley. Clean it off with solvent if necessary to read the printing and small grooves.
7 Locate the notched groove across the crankshaft pulley. It may be necessary to have an assistant temporarily turn the ignition off and on in short bursts without starting the engine to bring this groove into a position where it can easily be cleaned and marked. Stay clear of all moving engine components if the engine is turned over in this manner.
8 Use white soap-stone, chalk or paint to mark the groove on the crankshaft pulley. Also put a mark on the timing tab in accordance with the number of degrees called for in the Specifications (Chapter 5) or on the tune-up decal inside the engine compartment. Each peak or notch on the timing tab represents 2°. The word 'Before' or the letter 'A'

19.6 A typical timing tag attached to the engine front cover - as shown here, the timing is set to 4 degrees advanced

indicates advance and the letter 'O' indicates Top Dead Center (TDC). Thus if your vehicle specifications call for 8° BTDC (Before Top Dead Center), you will make a mark on the timing tab 4 notches 'before' the 'O'.
9 Check that the wiring for the timing light is clear of all moving engine components, then start the engine.
10 Point the flashing timing light at the timing marks, again being careful not to come in contact with moving parts **(see illustration)**. The marks you made should appear stationary. If the marks are in alignment, the timing is correct. If the marks are not aligned, turn off the engine.
11 Loosen the locknut at the base of the distributor. On GM cars this task is made much easier with a special curved distributor wrench. Loosen the locknut only slightly, just enough to turn the distributor. (See Chapter 5 for further details, if necessary).

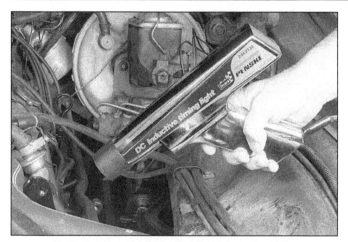

19.10 Pointing the timing light at the marks at the front of the engine

20.3 The choke plate can be seen once the air cleaner top plate has been removed

12   Now restart the engine and turn the distributor until the timing marks coincide.

13   Shut off the engine and tighten the distributor locknut, being careful not to move the distributor.

14   Start the engine and recheck the timing to make sure the marks are still in alignment.

15   Disconnect the timing light, unplug the distributor vacuum hose and connect the hose to the distributor.

16   Drive the car and listen for 'pinging' noises. These will be most noticeable when the engine is hot and under load (climbing a hill, accelerating from a stop). If you hear engine pinging, the ignition timing is too far advanced (Before Top Dead Center). Reconnect the timing light and turn the distributor to move the mark 1 degree or 2 degrees in the retard direction. Road test the car again for proper operation.

17   To keep 'pinging' at a minimum, yet still allow you to operate the car at the specified timing setting, it is advisable to use gasoline of the same octane at all times. Switching fuel brands and octane levels can decrease performance and economy, and possibly damage the engine.

20   Carburetor choke check

Refer to illustration 20.3

1   The choke only operates when the engine is cold, and thus this check can only be performed before the car has been started for the day.

2   Open the hood and remove the top plate of the air cleaner assembly. It is held in place by a wing-nut at the center. If any vacuum hoses must be disconnected, make sure you tag the hoses for reinstallation to their original positions. Place the top plate and wing nut aside, out of the way of moving engine components.

3   Look at the top of the carburetor at the center of the air cleaner housing. You will notice a flat plate at the carburetor opening **(see illustration).**

4   Have an assistant press the accelerator pedal to the floor. The plate should close fully. Start the engine while you observe the plate at the carburetor. Do not position your face directly over the carburetor, as the engine could backfire, causing serious burns. When the engine starts, the choke plate should open slightly.

5   Allow the engine to continue running at an idle speed. As the engine warms up to operating temperature, the plate should slowly open, allowing more cold air to enter through the top of the carburetor.

6   After a few minutes, the choke plate should be fully open to the vertical position.

7   You will notice that the engine speed corresponds with the plate opening. With the plate fully closed, the engine should run at a fast idle speed. As the plate opens, the engine speed will decrease.

8   If during the above checks a fault is detected, refer to Chapter 4 for specific information on adjusting and servicing the choke components.

21   Exhaust Gas Recirculation (EGR) valve check

Refer to illustration 21.2

1   On GM vehicles the EGR valve is located on the intake manifold, adjacent to the carburetor. The majority of the time, when a fault develops in this emissions system it is due to a stuck or corroded EGR valve.

2   With the engine cold to prevent burns, reach under the EGR valve and manually push on the diaphragm **(see illustration)**. Using moderate pressure, you should be able to press the diaphragm up and down within the housing.

3   If the diaphragm does not move or moves only with much effort, replace the EGR valve with a new one. If you are in doubt about the quality of the valve, go to your local parts store and compare the free movement of your EGR valve with a new valve.

4   Further testing of the EGR system and

21.2 The EGR valve is a disc-shaped device mounted to the intake manifold, adjacent to the carburetor. Most are open underneath to check the diaphragm

component replacement procedures can be found in Chapter 6.

22   Rear axle fluid change

1   To change the fluid in the rear axle it is necessary to remove the cover plate on the differential housing. Because of this, purchase a new gasket at the same time the gear lubricant is bought.

2   Move a drain pan (at least 5 pint capacity), rags, newspapers and your wrenches under the rear of the car. With the drain pan under the differential cover, loosen each of the inspection plate bolts.

3   Remove the bolts on the lower half of the plate, but use the upper bolts to keep the cover loosely attached to the differential. Allow the fluid to drain into the drain pan, then completely remove the cover.

4   Using a lint-free rag, clean the inside of the cover and the accessible areas of the differential housing. As this is done, check for chipped gears or metal filings in the fluid indi-

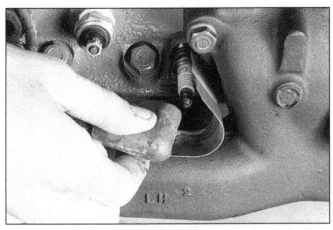

23.7 Removing a spark plug wire by grabbing at the boot rather than the wire itself

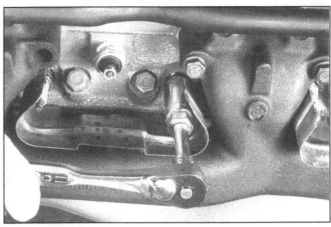

23.9a Using an insulated spark plug socket to remove a spark plug

cating the differential should be thoroughly inspected and repaired (see Chapter 8 for more information).

5   Thoroughly clean the gasket mating surface on the cover and the differential housing. Use a gasket scraper or putty knife to remove all traces of the old gasket.

6   Smear a thin film of gasket sealant on the cover flange and then press a new gasket into position on the cover. Make sure the bolt holes align properly.

7   Place the cover on the differential housing and install the securing bolts. Tighten the bolts a little at a time, working across the cover in a diagonal fashion until all bolts are tight. If a torque wrench is available, the bolt torque is 25 to 30 ft-lbs.

8   Remove the inspection plug on the side of the differential housing (or inspection cover) and fill the housing with the proper lubricant until the level is at the bottom of the plug hole.

9   Securely install the plug.

---

23   Spark plug replacement

Refer to illustrations 23.7, 23.9a, 23.9b and 23.10

1   The spark plugs are located on each side of the engine on a V8 and may or may not be easily accessible for removal. If the car is equipped with air conditioning or power steering some of the plugs may be tricky to service in which case special extension or swivel tools will be necessary. Make a survey under the hood to ascertain if special tools will be needed.

2   In most cases the tools necessary for a spark plug replacement job are: a plug wrench or spark plug socket which fits onto a ratchet wrench (this special socket will be insulated inside to protect the porcelain insulator) and a feeler gauge to check and adjust the spark plug gap. if the car is equipped with HEI ignition (1975-1980) a special spark plug wire removal tool is available for separating the wire boot from the spark plug.

3   The best policy to follow when replacing

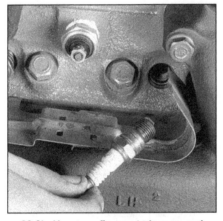

23.9b Use your fingers to loosen and tighten the spark plugs as much as possible to help prevent stripping the threads

the spark plugs is to purchase the new spark plugs beforehand adjust them to the proper gap and then replace each plug one at a time. When buying the new spark plugs it is important that the correct plug is purchased for your specific engine. This information can be found in the Specifications Section of Chapter 5 but should be checked against the information found on the tune-up decal located under the hood of your car or in the factory owners manual. If differences exist between these sources purchase the spark plug type specified on the tune-up decal as this information was printed for your specific engine.

4   With the new spark plugs at hand allow the engine to thoroughly cool before attempting the removal. During this cooling time each of the new spark plugs can be inspected for defects and the gap can be checked.

5   The gap is checked by inserting the proper thickness gauge between the electrodes at the tip of the plug. The gap between these electrodes should be the same as that given in the Specifications or on the tune-up decal. The wire should just touch each of the electrodes. if the gap is incorrect use the notched adjuster on the feeler gauge body to

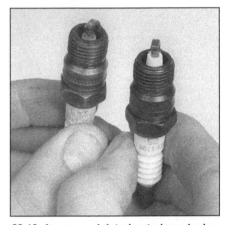

23.10 A worn and deteriorated spark plug on the left and a new one on the right

bend the curved side electrode slightly until the proper gap is achieved. Also at this time check for cracks in the spark plug body indicating the spark plug should be replaced with a new one. If the side electrode is not exactly over the center one use the notched adjuster to align the two.

6   Cover the fenders of the car to prevent damage to exterior paint.

7   With the engine cool, remove the spark plug wire from one spark plug. Do this by grabbing the boot at the end of the wire not the wire itself. Sometimes it is necessary to use a twisting motion while the boot and plug wire is pulled free **(see illustration)**. Using a plug wire removal tool is the easiest and safest method.

8   If compressed air is available use this to blow any dirt or foreign material away from the spark plug area.

9   Now place the spark plug wrench or socket over the plug and remove it from the engine by turning in a counterclockwise motion **(see illustrations)**.

10   Compare the spark plugs to get an indication of the overall running condition of the engine **(see illustration)**. Also refer to the chart on the inside back cover of this manual.

11   Insert one of the new plugs into the engine, tightening it as much as possible by

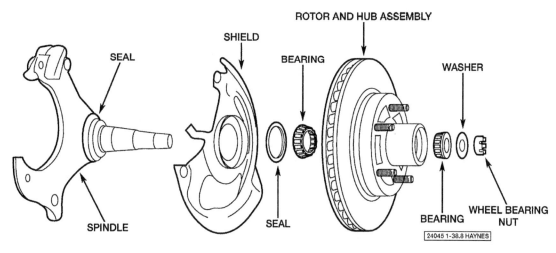

24.8 Front wheel bearing components

24.9 The outer wheel bearing and washer removed from the hub

24.11 A screwdriver is used to pry out the grease seal for the inner bearing

24.12 Removing the inner wheel bearing

hand. The spark plug should screw easily into the engine. If it doesn't, change the angle of the spark plug slightly, as chances are the threads are not matched (cross-threaded).

12 Firmly tighten the spark plug with the wrench or socket. It is best to use a torque wrench for this to ensure the plug is seated correctly. The correct torque figure is shown in Specifications.

13 Before pushing the spark plug wire onto the end of the plug, inspect it following the procedures outlined in Section 28.

14 Install the plug wire to the new spark plug, again using a twisting motion on the boot until it is firmly seated on the spark plug. Make sure wire is routed away from the hot exhaust manifold.

15 Follow the above procedures for the remaining spark plugs, replacing each one at a time to prevent mixing up the spark plug wires.

24 Wheel bearing check and repack

Refer to illustrations 24.8, 24.9, 24.11, 24.12, 24.20 and 24.21

1 In most cases, the front wheel bearings

will not need servicing until the brake pads are changed. However, these bearings should be checked whenever the front wheels are raised for any reason.

2 With the vehicle securely supported on jack stands, spin the wheel and check for noise, rolling resistance or free play. Now grab the top of the tire with one hand and the bottom of the tire with the other. Move the tire in and out on the spindle. If it moves more than 0.005 in, the bearings should be checked, then repacked with grease or replaced if necessary.

3 To remove the bearings for replacing or repacking, begin by removing the hub cap and wheel.

4 Using an Allen wrench of the proper size, remove the two bolts which secure the disc brake caliper to its support (see Chapter 9).

5 Carefully slide the caliper off the disc. Use wire to hang the caliper assembly out of the way. Be careful not to kink or damage the brake hose.

6 Pry the hub grease cap off the hub using a screwdriver. This cap is located at the center of the hub.

7 Use needle-nose pliers to straighten the bent ends of the cotter pin and then pull the cotter pin out of the locking nut. Discard the cotter pin, as a new one should be used on reassembly.

8 Remove the spindle nut and its washer from the end of the spindle **(see illustration)**.

9 Pull the hub assembly outward slightly and then push it back into its original position. This should force the outer bearing off the spindle enough so that it can be removed with your fingers **(see illustration)**. Remove the outer bearing, noting how it is installed on the end of the spindle.

10 Now the hub assembly can be pulled off the spindle.

11 On the rear side of the hub, use a screwdriver to pry out the inner bearing lip seal **(see illustration)**. As this is done, note the direction in which the seal is installed.

12 The inner bearing can now be removed from the hub, again noting how it is installed **(see illustration)**.

13 Use clean parts solvent to remove all traces of the old grease from the bearings, hub and spindle. A small brush may prove useful however, make sure no bristles from

the brush embed themselves inside the bearing rollers. Allow the parts to air dry.

14   Carefully inspect the bearings for cracks, heat discoloration, bent rollers, etc. Check the bearing races inside the hub for cracks, scoring or uneven surfaces. If the bearing races are in need of replacement, this job is best left to a repair shop which can press the new races into position.

15   Use an approved high temperature front wheel bearing grease to pack the bearings. Work the grease fully into the bearings, forcing the grease between the rollers, cone and cage.

16   Apply a thin coat of grease to the spindle at the outer bearing seat, inner bearing seat, shoulder and seal seat.

17   Put a small quantity of grease inboard of each bearing race inside the hub. Using your finger, form a dam at these points to provide extra grease availability and to keep thinned grease from flowing out of the bearing.

18   Place the grease-packed inner bearing into the rear of the hub and put a little more grease outboard of the bearing.

19   Place a new seal over the inner bearing and tap the seal with a flat plate and a hammer until it is flush with the hub.

20   Carefully place the hub assembly onto the spindle and push the grease-packed outer bearing into position **(see illustration)**.

21   Install the washer and spindle nut. Tighten the nut only slightly (12 ft-lbs of torque) **(see illustration)**.

22   In a forward direction, spin the hub to seat the bearings and remove any grease or burrs which could cause excessive bearing play later.

23   Put a little grease outboard of the outer bearing to provide extra grease availability.

24   Now check that the spindle nut is still tight (12 ft-lbs).

25   Loosen the spindle nut until it is just loose, no more.

26   Using your hand (not a wrench of any kind), tighten the nut until it is snug. Install a new cotter pin through the hole in the spindle and spindle nut. If the nut slits do not line up, loosen the nut slightly until they do. From the hand-tight position the nut should not be loosened any more than one-half flat to install the cotter pin.

27   Bend the ends of the new cotter pin until they are flat against the nut. Cut off any extra length which could interfere with the dust cap.

28   Install the dust cap, tapping it into place with a rubber mallet.

29   Slide the caliper and pads over the rotor. Tighten the caliper mounting bolts to 35 ft-lbs. Chapter 9 will give full details on the disc brake caliper assembly.

30   Install the tire/wheel assembly to the hub and tighten the mounting nuts.

31   Grab the top and bottom of the tire and check the bearings in the same manner as described at the beginning of this Section.

32   Lower the vehicle to the ground and fully tighten the wheel nuts. Install the hub cap, using a rubber mallet to fully seat it.

24.20 Installing a grease-packed wheel bearing inside the hub

25   Automatic transmission fluid change

Refer to illustrations 25.8, 25.11, 25.12, 25.14 and 25.16

1   At the specified time intervals, the transmission fluid should be changed and the filter replaced with a new one. Since there is no drain plug, the transmission oil pan must be removed from the bottom of the transmission to drain the fluid.

2   Before any draining, purchase the specified transmission fluid (see *Recommended Lubricants* and a new filter. The necessary gaskets should be included with the filter; if not, purchase an oil pan gasket and a strainer-to-valve body gasket.

3   Other tools necessary for this job include: jack stands to support the vehicle in a raised position; wrench to remove the oil pan bolts; standard screwdriver; drain pan capable of holding at least 8 pints; newspapers and clean rags.

4   The fluid should be drained immediately after the car has been driven. This will remove any built-up sediment better than if

24.21 The adjusting nut should be tightened only initially with a wrench falling into the engine cylinder as the spark plug is replaced.

the fluid were cold. Because of this, it may be wise to wear protective gloves (fluid temperature can exceed 350° in a hot transmission).

5   After the car has been driven to warm up the fluid, raise the vehicle and place it on jack stands for access underneath. Make sure it is firmly supported by the four stands placed on the frame rails.

6   Move the necessary equipment under the car, being careful not to touch any of the hot exhaust components.

7   Place the drain pan under the transmission oil pan and remove the oil pan bolts along the rear and sides of the pan. Loosen, but do not remove, the bolts at the front of the pan.

8   Carefully pry the pan downward at the rear, allowing the hot fluid to drain into the drain pan **(see illustration)**. If necessary, use a screwdriver to break the gasket seal at the rear of the pan; however, do not damage the pan or transmission in the process.

9   Support the pan and remove the remaining bolts at the front of the pan. Lower

25.8 Dropping the rear end of the transmission oil pan to drain the fluid

25.11 Removing the old filter from the inside of the transmission

25.12 The inside of the fluid pan should be inspected for contamination and metal filings

the pan and drain the remaining fluid into the drain receptacle. As this is done, check the fluid for metal filings which may be an indication of internal failure.

10 Now visible on the bottom of the transmission is the filter/strainer held in place by two screws.

11 Remove the two screws, the filter and its gasket **(see illustration)**.

12 Thoroughly clean the transmission oil pan with solvent. Inspect for metal filings or foreign matter **(see illustration)**. Dry with compressed air if available. It is important that all remaining gasket material be removed from the oil pan mounting flange. Use a gasket scraper or putty knife for this.

13 Clean the filter mounting surface on the valve body. Again, this surface should be smooth and free of any leftover gasket material.

14 Place the new filter into position, with a new gasket between it and the transmission valve body. Install the two mounting screws and tighten securely **(see illustration)**.

15 Apply a bead of gasket sealant around the oil pan mounting surface, with the sealant to the inside of the bolt holes. Press the new gasket into place on the pan, making sure all bolt holes line up.

16 Lift the pan up to the bottom of the transmission and install the mounting bolts **(see illustration)**. Tighten the bolts in a diagonal fashion, working around the pan. Using a torque wrench, tighten the bolts to about 12 ft-lbs.

17 Lower the car off its jack stands.

18 Open the hood and remove the transmission fluid dipstick from its guide tube.

19 Since fluid capacities vary between the various transmission types, it is best to add a little fluid at a time, continually checking the level with the dipstick. Allow the fluid time to drain into the pan. Add fluid until the level just registers on the end of the dipstick. In most cases, a good starting point will be 4 to 5 pints added to the transmission through the filler tube (use a funnel to prevent spills).

20 With the selector lever in 'Park', apply the parking brake and start the engine without depressing the accelerator pedal

(if possible). Do not race the engine at a high speed; run at slow idle only.

21 Depress the brake pedal and shift the transmission through each gear. Place the selector back into 'Park' and check the level on the dipstick (with the engine still idling). Look under the car for leaks around the transmission oil pan mating surface.

22 Add more fluid through the dipstick tube until the level on the dipstick is 1/4 inch below the 'Add' mark on the dipstick. Do not allow the fluid level to go above this point, as the transmission would then be overfull, necessitating the removal of the pan to drain the excess fluid.

23 Push the dipstick firmly back into its tube and drive the car to reach normal operating temperature (15 miles of highway driving or its equivalent in the city). Park the car on a level surface and check the fluid level on the dipstick with the engine idling and the transmission in 'Park'. The level should now be at the 'Full Hot' mark on the dipstick. If not, add more fluid as necessary to bring the level up to this point. Again, do not overfill.

25.14 Tightening a new filter into position

25.16 The fluid pan with a new gasket in place being lifted into position

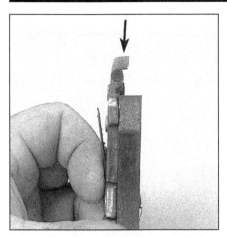

26.5 The disc brake pads have built in wear indicators that contact the rotor and emit a squealing sound when the pads have worn to their limit

26.6 Disc brake calipers have an inspection cutout to observe the disc pads

26.13a Drawing a brake drum off the wheel studs and center axle hub

26.13b Using a hammer and chisel to remove the lanced knock-out plug on the face of the drum

26.13c With the knock-out plug removed, use a small screwdriver or hook to lift the lever, then turn the sprocket with another screwdriver

26 Brakes check

Refer to illustrations 26.5, 26.6, 26.13a, 26.13b, 26.13c, 26.15, 26.16, 26.17 and 26.19

1   The brakes should be inspected every time the wheels are removed or whenever a fault is suspected. Indications of a potential braking system fault are: the car pulls to one side when brake pedal is depressed: noises coming from the brakes when they are applied; excessive brake pedal travel: pulsating pedal; and leakage of fluid, usually seen on the inside of the tire or wheel.

Disc brakes

2   Disc brakes can be visually checked without the need to remove any parts except the wheels.

3   Raise the vehicle and place securely on jack stands. Remove the front wheels (See *Jacking and Towing* at the front of this manual if necessary).

4   Now visible is the disc brake caliper which contains the pads. There is an outer brake pad and an inner pad. Both should be inspected.

5   Most later model vehicles come equipped with a 'wear sensor' attached to the inner pad **(see illustration)**. This is a small, bent piece of metal which is visible from the inboard side of the brake caliper. When the pads wear to a danger limit, the metal sensor rubs against the disc and makes a screeching sound.

6   Inspect the pad thickness by looking at each end of the caliper and through the cutout inspection hole in the caliper body **(see illustration)**. If the wear sensor clip is very close to the rotor, or the lining material is 1/32 in or less in thickness, the pads should be replaced. Keep in mind that the lining material is riveted or bonded to a metal backing shoe and the metal portion is not included in the measuring.

7   Since it will be difficult, if not impossible, to measure the exact thickness of the remaining lining material, if you are in doubt as to the pad quality, remove the pads for further inspection or replacement. See Chapter 9 for disc brake pad replacement.

8   Before installing the wheels, check for any leakage around the brake hose connections leading to the caliper or damage (cracking, splitting, etc.) to the brake hose. Replace the hose or fittings as necessary, referring to Chapter 9.

9   Also check the condition of the disc for scoring, gouging or burnt spots. If these conditions exist, the hub/rotor assembly should be removed for servicing (Chapter 9).

Drum brakes (rear)

10   Raise the vehicle and support firmly on jack stands. Block the front tires to prevent the car from rolling; however, do not apply the parking brake as this will lock the drums into place.

11   Remove the wheels, referring to *Jacking and Towing* at the front of this manual if necessary.

12   Mark the hub so it can be reinstalled in the same place. Use a scribe, chalk, etc. on drum and center hub and backing plate.

13   Pull the brake drum off the axle and brake assembly **(see illustration)**. If this proves difficult, make sure the parking brake

26.15 Inspecting the lining thickness of the forward brake shoe

26.16 Check that all springs are in good condition

26.17 Leakage often occurs from the wheel cylinder located at the top of the brake shoes

26.19 The inside surface of the brake drum should be carefully inspected for cracks, scoring, 'hot-spots' etc. lining material is riveted or bonded to a metal backing shoe and the metal portion is not included in this measuring.

is released, then squirt some penetrating oil around the center hub area. Allow the oil to soak in and try again to pull the drum off. Then, if the drum cannot be pulled off, the brake shoes will have to be adjusted inward. This is done by first removing the lanced cutout in the drum or backing plate with a hammer and chisel (see illustration). With this lanced area punched in, rotate the drum until the opening lines up with the adjuster wheel. Pull the lever off the sprocket and then use a small screwdriver to turn the sprocket wheel which will move the linings away from the drums (see illustration).

14 With the drum removed, carefully brush away any accumulations of dirt and dust. Do not blow this out with compressed air or in any similar fashion. Make an effort not to inhale this dust as it contains asbestos and is harmful to your health.

15 Observe the thickness of the lining material on both the front and rear brake shoes (see illustration). If the material has worn away to within 1/32 in of the recessed rivets or metal backing, the shoes should be replaced. If the linings look worn, but you are

unable to determine their exact thickness, compare them with a new set at the auto parts store. The shoes should also be replaced if they are cracked, glazed (shiny surface), or wet with brake fluid.

16 Check that all the brake assembly springs are connected and in good condition (see illustration).

17 Check the brake components for any signs of fluid leakage. With your finger, carefully pry back the rubber cups on the wheel cylinder located at the top of the brake shoes (see illustration). Any leakage is an indication that the wheel cylinders should be overhauled immediately (Chapter 9). Also check fluid hoses and connections for signs of leakage.

18 Wipe the inside of the drum with a clean rag, and denatured alcohol. Again, be careful not to breathe the dangerous asbestos dust.

19 Check the inside of the drum for cracks, scores, deep scratches or, hard spots which will appear as small discolorations (see illustration). If these imperfections cannot be removed with fine emery cloth, the drum must be taken to a machine shop equipped

to turn the drums.

20 If after the inspection process all parts are in good working condition, reinstall the brake drum (using a metal plug if the lanced knock-out was removed). Install the wheel and lower the car to the ground.

Parking brake

21 The easiest way to check the operation of the parking brake is to park the car on a steep hill, with the parking brake set and the transmission in Neutral . If the parking brake cannot prevent the car from rolling, it is in need of adjustment (see Chapter 9).

27 Carburetor mounting torque

1 The carburetor is attached to the top of the intake manifold by two or four nuts. These fasteners can sometimes work loose through normal engine operation and cause a vacuum leak.

2 To properly tighten the carburetor mounting nuts, a torque wrench is necessary.

28.4 Inspecting the inside of a spark plug boot

29.7 Engine drain plugs are located on each side of the engine block

If you do not own one, they can usually be rented on a daily basis.

3   Remove the air cleaner assembly, tagging each hose to be disconnected with a piece of numbered tape to make reassembly easier.

4   Locate the mounting nuts at the base of the carburetor. Decide what special tools or adapters will be necessary, if any, to tighten the nuts with a properly sized socket and the torque wrench.

5   Tighten the nuts to a torque of about 12 ft-lbs. Do not overtighten the nuts, as this may cause the threads to strip.

6   If you suspect a vacuum leak exists at the bottom of the carburetor, get a length of spare hose about the diameter of fuel hose. Start the engine and place one end of the hose next to your ear as you probe around the base of the carburetor with the other end. You will be able to hear a hissing sound if a leak exists. A soapy water solution brushed around the suspect area can also be used to pinpoint pressure leaks.

7   If, after the nuts are properly tightened, a vacuum leak still exists, the carburetor must be removed and a new gasket used. See Chapter 4 for more information.

8   After tightening nuts, reinstall the air cleaner, connecting all hoses to their original positions.

28 Spark plug wires check

Refer to illustration 28.4

1   The spark plug wires should be checked at the recommended intervals or whenever new spark plugs are installed.

2   The wires should be inspected one at a time to prevent mixing up the order which is essential for proper engine operation.

3   Disconnect the plug wire from the spark plug. A removal tool can be used for this, or you can grab the rubber boot, twist slightly and then pull the wire free. Do not pull on the wire itself, only on the rubber boot.

4   Inspect inside the boot for corrosion

which will look like a white, crusty powder **(see illustration)**. Later models use a conductive white grease which should not be mistaken for corrosion.

5   Now push the wire and boot back onto the end of the spark plug. It should be a tight fit on the plug end. If not, remove the wire and use a pair of pliers to carefully crimp the metal connector inside the wire boot until the fit is secure.

6   Now using a clean rag, clean the wire its entire length. Remove all built-up dirt and grease. As this is done, inspect for burns, cracks or any other form of damage. Bend the wires in several places to ensure the conductive inside wire has not hardened.

7   Disconnect the wire at the distributor (again, pulling and twisting only on the rubber boot). Check for corrosion and a tight fit in the same manner as the spark plug end. If equipped with HEI ignition (1975 and later), the distributor boots are connected to a circular retaining ring. Release the locking tabs, turn the ring upside-down and check all wire boots at the same time.

8   Reinstall the wire boot (or retaining ring) onto the top of the distributor.

9   Check the remaining spark plug wires in the same way, making sure they are securely fastened at the distributor and spark plug.

10   A visual check of the spark plug wires can also be made. In a darkened garage (make sure there is ventilation), start the engine and observe each plug wire. Be careful not to come into contact with any moving engine parts. If there is a break or fault in the wire, you will be able to see arcing or a small spark at the damaged area.

11   If it is decided the spark plug wires are in need of replacement, purchase a new set for your specific engine model. Wire sets can be purchased which are pre-cut to the proper size and with the rubber boots already installed. HEI ignition systems (1975-1980) use a different type of plug wire from conventional systems. Remove and replace each wire individually to prevent mix-ups in the firing sequence.

29 Cooling system servicing (draining, flushing and refilling)

Warning 1: *Do not allow antifreeze to come in contact with your skin or painted surfaces of the vehicle. Flush contaminated areas immediately with plenty of water. Don't store new coolant or leave old coolant lying around where it's accessible to children or pets – they're attracted by its sweet smell. Ingestion of even a small amount of coolant can be fatal! Wipe up garage floor and drip pan spills immediately. Keep antifreeze containers covered and repair cooling system leaks as soon as they're noticed.*
Warning 2: *DO NOT remove the radiator cap or the coolant recovery cap while the cooling system is hot as escaping steam could cause serious injury.*
Refer to illustrations 29.7 and 29.14

1   Periodically, the cooling system should be drained, flushed and refilled. This is to replenish the antifreeze mixture and prevent rust and corrosion which can impair the performance of the cooling system and ultimately cause engine damage.

2   At the same time the cooling system is serviced, all hoses and the fill cap should be inspected and replaced if faulty (see Section 6).

3   As antifreeze is a poisonous solution, take care not to spill any of the cooling mixture on the vehicle's paint or your own skin. If this happens, rinse immediately with plenty of clear water. Also, it is advisable to consult your local authorities about the dumping of antifreeze before draining the cooling system. In many areas reclamation centers have been set up to collect automobile oil and drained antifreeze/water mixtures rather than allowing these liquids to be added to the sewage and water facilities.

4   With the engine cold, remove the radiator pressure fill cap.

5   Move a large container under the radiator to catch the water/antifreeze mixture as it is drained.

29.14 Using a funnel to add coolant to the reservoir

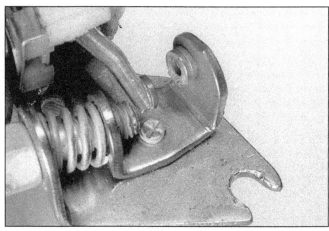

30.1 A set of used contact points showing the deterioration which comes after a time

6   Drain the radiator. Most models are equipped with a drain plug at the bottom of the radiator which can be opened using a wrench to hold the fitting while the petcock is turned to the open position. If this drain has excessive corrosion and cannot be turned easily, or the radiator is not equipped with a drain, disconnect the lower radiator hose to allow the coolant to drain. Be careful that none of the solution is splashed on your skin or in your eyes.

7   If accessible, remove the two engine drain plugs **(see illustration)**. There is one plug on each side of the engine, about halfway back and on the lower edge near the oil pan rail. These will allow the coolant to drain from the engine itself.

8   On systems with an expansion reservoir, disconnect the overflow pipe and remove the reservoir. Flush it out with clean water.

9   Place a cold water hose (a common garden hose is fine) in the radiator filler neck at the top of the radiator and flush the system until the water runs clean at all drain points.

10   In severe cases of contamination or clogging of the radiator, remove it (see Chapter 3) and reverse flush it. This involves simply inserting the cold pressure hose in the bottom radiator outlet to allow the clear water to run against the normal flow, draining through the top. A radiator repair shop should be consulted if further cleaning or repair is necessary.

11   Where the coolant is regularly drained and the system refilled with the correct antifreeze/inhibitor mixture there should be no need to employ chemical cleaners or descalers.

12   To refill the system, reconnect the radiator hoses and install the drain plugs securely in the engine. Special thread sealing tape (available at auto parts stores) should be used on the drain plugs going into the engine block. Install the expansion reservoir and the overflow hose where applicable.

13   On vehicles without an expansion reservoir, refill the system through the radiator filler cap until the water level is about three inches below the filler neck.

14   On vehicles with an expansion reservoir,
fill the radiator to the base of the filler neck and then add more coolant to the expansion reservoir so that it reaches the 'FULL COLD' mark **(see illustration)**.

15   Run the engine until normal operating temperature is reached and with the engine idling, add coolant up to the correct level (see Section 2), then fit the radiator cap so that the arrows are in alignment with the overflow pipe. Install the reservoir cap.

16   Always refill the system with a mixture of high quality antifreeze and water in the proportion called for on the antifreeze container or in your owner's manual. Chapter 3 also contains information on antifreeze mixtures.

17   Keep a close watch on the coolant level and the various cooling hoses during the first few miles of driving. Tighten the hose clamps and/or add more coolant mixture as necessary.

---

30   Point replacement, dwell angle adjustment and distributor check (1970-1974 models only)

Refer to illustrations 30.1, 30.4, 30.6a, 30.6b, 30.8, 30.9, 30.11, 30.18, 30.19, 30.21, 30.23 and 30.31

1   Although the contact points can be
cleaned and dressed with a fine-cut contact file, it may be a false economy for the home mechanic to attempt this **(see illustration)**. Due to the inaccessibility of the distributor components, it is more practical to merely replace the contact points during tune-ups.

2   The contact point set and condenser are replaced as one complete assembly. Point alignment and spring tension are factory set and require no further adjustment.

3   Whenever distributor servicing is required, as in contact point replacement, it is a good idea to use magnetized tools to prevent screws or nuts from falling down into the distributor body, requiring distributor disassembly to retrieve.

Contact point replacement

4   Remove the distributor cap by placing a screwdriver on the slotted head of the latch. Press down on the latch and give a 1/4 turn to release the curved section at the bottom of the latch **(see illustration)**.

5   With both latches disengaged from the distributor body, place the cap (with the spark plug wires still attached) out of the way. Use a length of wire or tape if necessary.

6   Remove the rotor, which is now visible at the top of the distributor shaft. In most cases the rotor is held in place with two screws. On some models, the rotor is merely

30.4 Removing the distributor cap from the top of the distributor

pushed onto the shaft and can simply be
lifted away. Place the rotor in a safe place
where it cannot be damaged **(see illustrations)**.

7   If equipped with a radio frequency interference shield (RFI), remove the attaching
screws and the two-piece shield to gain
access to the contact points.

8   Loosen the two screws which secure
the contact point set assembly to the breaker
plate **(see illustration)**. Do not completely
remove these screws, as most point sets
have slots at these locations. Slide the point
set off the breaker plate.

9   Disconnect the primary and condenser
wire leads at the point set **(see illustration)**.
These wires may be attached with a small nut
(which should be loosened, but not removed)
a small standard screw, or by a quick-disconnect terminal which requires the tangs to
be pressed together to unlock.

10   The contact breaker point assembly can
now be removed completely from the engine
compartment.

11   The condenser can now be removed
from the breaker plate. Loosen the mounting strap screw and slide the condenser out
of the bracket, or completely remove the

30.6a The rotor is attached to the
distributor shaft

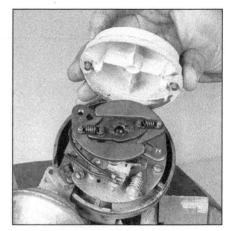

30.6b Removing the rotor which is
attached with two screws

condenser and strap depending on the
exact attachment **(see illustration)**.

12   Before installing the new points and
condenser, clean all lubricant, dirt, etc. from
the breaker plate and the rotating cam surface of the distributor shaft.

13   Fully lubricate the center cam with the
grease supplied with the new points.

14   Check the cam lubricator wick mounted
on the breaker plate. The wick can be rotated
to provide lubrication if it is still in good condition, but if in doubt replace the wick with a
new one to provide adequate lubrication to
the cam surface. It is removed by squeezing
the base of the retainer together with long-
nosed pliers and then lifting the unit out of

30.8 Loosening the two screws which secure the contact point
assembly to the mounting plate

30.9 Disconnecting the primary wires from the points

30.11 The condenser is also attached to the breaker plate and is
held by a single screw

30.18 Before adjusting the point gap, the rubbing block must be
resting on one of the center cam high points (which will
open the points)

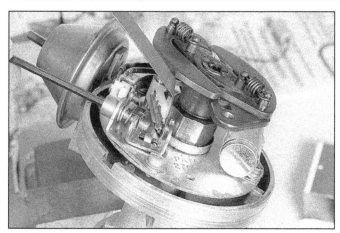

30.19 With the points separated, insert a feeler gauge of the proper thickness and turn the adjusting socket with an Allen wrench

30.21 The rotor contacts should be inspected for damage or excessive burning

the breaker plate. it is important that the cam lubricator wick be adjusted so the end of the wick just touches the cam lobes.

15 Place the new condenser into position and tighten its retaining screw.

16 Slide the new contact point set onto the breaker plate and tighten the two attaching screws.

17 Connect the primary and condenser electrical leads to the new point assembly. Make sure the leads are positioned the same as they were on removal.

18 Although the final gap between the contact points will be adjusted later (dwell angle), it is best to get an initial gap to start the engine. With the points in position and tightened to the breaker plate, see that the points rubbing block is resting on one of the high points of the center cam **(see illustration)**. To move the center cam, have an assistant just click the ignition key in short bursts. If equipped with a manual transmission, place the shifter in gear and rock the car back and forth.

19 With the rubbing block on a cam high point (points fully open), place a blade-type feeler gauge between the contacts. The gap

should be 0.019 in. If not correct, use an Allen wrench to turn the points set socket which will open and close the gap **(see illustration)**.

20 Install the RFI shield, if applicable.

21 Before installing the rotor, inspect it for cracks or damage. Carefully check the condition of the metal contact at the top of the rotor for excessive burning or pitting **(see illustration)**. If in doubt as to its quality, replace it with a new one.

22 Install the rotor. Both types are keyed to go onto the shaft only one way. Rotors having attaching screws will have raised pegs on the bottom. Make sure the rotor is firmly seated.

23 Before installing the distributor cap, inspect it for cracks or damage. Closely examine the contacts on the inside of the cap for excessive corrosion or damage **(see illustration)**. Slight scoring is normal. If in doubt as to the quality of the cap, replace it with a new one as described in Chapter 5.

24 Install the distributor cap, locking the two latches under the distributor body.

25 Start the engine and check the dwell angle and the ignition timing (Section 19).

Point dwell angle adjustment

26 Whenever new contact points are installed or original points are cleaned, the dwell angle should be checked and adjusted to proper specifications.

27 Setting the dwell angle on GM cars is actually very easy; however, a dwell meter must be used for precise adjustment. Combination tach/dwell meters are common tune-up instruments which can be purchased at a reasonable cost. An approximate setting can be achieved without a meter.

28 Connect the dwell meter following the manufacturer's instructions.

29 Start the engine and allow to run at idle until it has reached normal operating temperature. The engine must be fully warmed to achieve an accurate reading. Turn off the engine.

30 Raise the metal 'window' on the outside of the distributor cap. Prop it in the up position, using tape if necessary.

31 Just inside this window is the adjustment screw for the contact points. Insert an Allen wrench of the proper size into the adjustment screw socket **(see illustration)**.

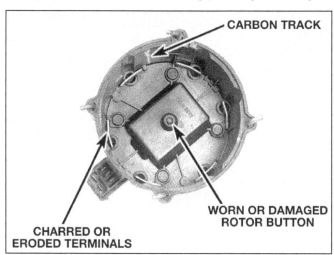

CARBON TRACK

CHARRED OR ERODED TERMINALS

WORN OR DAMAGED ROTOR BUTTON

30.23 Inspecting the inside of the distributor cap

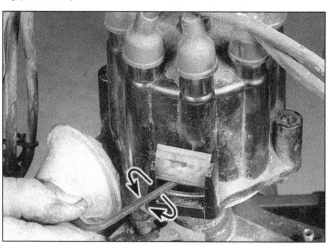

30.31 With the 'window' open, an Allen wrench can be inserted into the adjustment socket for adjusting the point dwell

31.4 The charcoal canister is located near the front of the engine compartment and can be identified by the hoses attached to the top

31.5 Removing the filter from the bottom of the charcoal canister

32   Start the engine and turn the adjusting screw as required to obtain the specified dwell reading on the meter. Dwell angle specifications are given at the beginning of Chapter 5 as well as on the tune-up decal located inside your engine compartment. If there is a discrepancy between the sources, assume the tune-up decal is correct. Remove your hand from the Allen wrench and recheck the reading.
33   Remove the Allen wrench and close the window fully. Turn off the engine and disconnect the dwell meter.
34   If you simply cannot buy, borrow or rent a dwell meter, you can get an approximate dwell setting without using a meter by the following method.
35   Start the engine and allow to idle until it has reached normal operating temperature.
36   Raise the metal window on the side of the distributor cap and insert the proper size Allen wrench into the point adjustment screw socket.
37   Turn the Allen wrench clockwise until the engine begins to misfire. Then turn the screw one half turn counter-clockwise.
38   Remove the Allen wrench and fully close the window. As soon as possible have the dwell angle checked and/or adjusted with a dwell meter. This will ensure optimum performance.

31   Evaporative Control System (ECS) filter replacement

Refer to illustrations 31.4, 31.5 and 31.6

1   The function of the ECS emissions system is to draw fuel vapors from the tank and carburetor, store them in a charcoal canister, and then burn these fumes during normal engine operation.
2   The filter at the bottom of the charcoal canister should be replaced at the specified intervals. If, however, a fuel odor is detected, the canister, filter and system hoses should immediately be inspected for fault.
3   To replace the filter, locate the canister at the front of the engine compartment. It will have between 3 and 6 hoses running out the top of it.
4   Remove the two bolts which secure the bottom of the canister to the body sheet metal **(see illustration)**.
5   Turn the canister upside-down and pull the old filter from the bottom of the canister **(see illustration)**. If you cannot turn the canister enough for this due to the short length of the hoses, the hoses must be duly marked with pieces of tape and then disconnected from the top.
6   Push the new filter into the bottom of

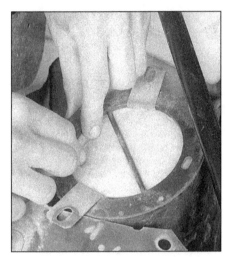

31.6 Make sure the new filter is fully seated all the way around the bottom of the canister

the canister, making sure it is seated all the way around **(see illustration)**.
7   Place the canister back into position and tighten the two mounting bolts. Connect the various hoses if disconnected.
8   The ECS system is explained in more detail in Chapter 6.

Chapter 2 Part A
V8 engines

Contents

Specifications

Note: *Engines installed in these vehicles are from several GM divisions. To determine which engine type is in your vehicle, refer to* Vehicle Identification Numbers *at the front of this manual.*

Engine - general

Type	V8 water cooled overhead valve
Firing order	1 - 8 - 4 - 3 - 6 - 5 - 7 - 2

Engine designations and performance

Model Year	Displacement (cubic inches)	Carburetor	Rated horsepower	VIN code	Manufacturer
1970					
	350	2 BC	255 HP		Pontiac
	400	2 BC	265 HP		Pontiac
	400	4 BC	330 HP		Pontiac
	*400	4 BC	345 HP		Pontiac
	*Ram Air				
1971					
	350	2 BC	250 HP		Pontiac
	400	2 BC	265 HP		Pontiac
	400	4 BC	300 HP		Pontiac
	455	4 BC	325 HP		Pontiac
	*455	4 BC	335 HP		Pontiac
	*H.O.				

Engine designations and performance

Model Year	Displacement (cubic inches)	Carburetor	Rated horsepower	VIN code	Manufacturer
1972					
	350	2 BC	160 HP	M	Pontiac
	350	2 BC	175 HP	N	Pontiac
	400	2 BC	175 HP	R	Pontiac
	400	4 BC	200 HP	S	Pontiac
	400	4 BC	250 HP	T	Pontiac
	*455	4 BC	300 HP	X	Pontiac
	*H.O.				
1973					
	350	2 BC	150 HP	M	Pontiac
	350	2 BC	175 HP	N	Pontiac
	400	2 BC	170 HP	R	Pontiac
	400	4 BC	200 HP	S	Pontiac
	400	4 BC	230 HP	T	Pontiac
	455	4 BC	215 HP	W	Pontiac
	455	4 BC	250 HP	Y	Pontiac
	*455	4 BC	310 HP	X	Pontiac
	*Super Duty				
1974					
	350	2 BC	155 HP	M	Pontiac
	350	2 BC	170 HP	N	Pontiac
	400	2 BC	175 HP	R	Pontiac
	400	4 BC	190 HP	P	Pontiac
	400	4 BC	225 HP	T	Pontiac
	455	4 BC	250 HP	Y	Pontiac
	*455	4 BC	290 HP	X	Pontiac
	*Super Duty				
1975					
	350	2 BC	155 HP	M	Pontiac
	350	4 BC	175 HP	E	Pontiac
	400	4 BC	185 HP	S	Pontiac
1976					
	350	2 BC	160 HP	M	Pontiac
	350	4 BC	165 HP	P	Pontiac
	400	4 BC	185 HP	Z	Pontiac
	455	4 BC	200 HP	W	Pontiac
1977					
	301	2 BC	135 HP	Y	Pontiac
	305	2 BC	145 HP	U	Chevrolet
	350	4 BC	170 HP	P	Pontiac
	350	4 BC	170 HP	R	Oldsmobile
	400	4 BC	180 HP	Z	Pontiac
	400	4 BC	200 HP	Z	Pontiac
	403	4 BC	185 HP	K	Oldsmobile
1978					
	305	2 BC	145 HP	U	Chevrolet
	350	4 BC	170 HP	L	Chevrolet
	400	4 BC	180 HP	Z	Pontiac
	400	4 BC	220 HP	Z	Pontiac
	403	4 BC	185 HP	K	Oldsmobile
1979					
	301	2 BC	140 HP	Y	Pontiac
	301	4 BC	155 HP	W	Pontiac
	305	2 BC	140 HP	G	Chevrolet
	350	4 BC	150 HP	L	Chevrolet
	400	4 BC	220 HP	Z	Pontiac
	403	4 BC	185 HP	K	Oldsmobile

Model Year	Displacement (cubic inches)	Carburetor	Rated horsepower	VIN code	Manufacturer
1980					
	265	2 BC	120 HP	S	Pontiac
	301	4 BC	150 HP	W	Pontiac
	301	4 BC	150 HP	T	Pontiac
	305	4 BC	150 HP	H	Chevrolet
1981					
	265	2 BC	120 HP	S	Pontiac
	301	4 BC	150 HP	W	Pontiac
	301	4 BC	150 HP	T	Pontiac
	305	4 BC	150 HP	H	Chevrolet

Chevrolet-built V8 engines

General

Displacement
  5.0 liter (VIN G, H and U) .... 305 cubic inches
  5.7 liter (VIN L) .... 350 cubic inches
Bore and stroke
  305 .... 3.736 x 3.48 in
  350 .... 4.000 x 3.48 in
Firing order 1-8-4-3-6-5-7-2

Camshaft

Bearing journal diameter.. 1.8682 to 1.8692 in
Lobe lift
  Intake lobe
    305 V8
      VIN G
        1979.. 0.2484 in
        1980 and later.. 0.2690 in
      VIN H .... 0.2484 in
      VIN U .... 0.2485 in
    350 V8
      VIN L .... 0.2600 in
  Exhaust lobe
    305 V8
      VIN G
        1979.. 0.2667 in
        1980 and later.. 0.2760 in
      VIN H .... 0.2667 in
      VIN U .... 0.2733 in
    350 V8
      VIN L .... 0.2733 in

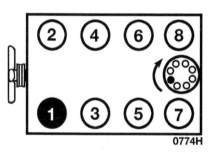

0774H

Cylinder location and distributor rotation diagram - Chevrolet-built V8 engines

The blackened terminal shown on the distributor cap indicates the Number One spark plug wire position

Torque specifications

Ft-lbs (unless otherwise noted)

Valve cover .... 45 in-lbs
Intake manifold bolts 30
Exhaust manifold bolts
  1978 20
  1979 and later
    Front port bolts 28
    Middle and rear port bolts 20
Cylinder head bolts... 65
Timing cover bolts .... 80 in-lbs
Camshaft sprocket bolts 20
Torsional (vibration) damper bolt.. 60
Oil pan bolts .... 100 in-lbs
Oil pump bolt 65
Rear oil seal housing bolts.. 135 in-lbs

Oldsmobile-built V8 engines

General
Displacement
  5.7 liter (VIN R)... 350 cubic inches
  6.6 liter (VIN K)... 403 cubic inches
Bore and stroke
  350 .... 4.057 x 3.385 in
  403 .... 4.351 x 3.385 in
Firing order 1-8-4-3-6-5-7-2

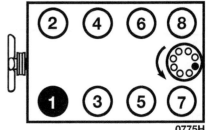

Cylinder location and distributor rotation diagram - Oldsmobile-built V8 engines

The blackened terminal shown on the distributor cap indicates the Number One spark plug wire position

Camshaft
Journal diameter
  No. 1 .... 2.0357 to 2.0365 inches
  No. 2 .... 2.0157 to 2.0165 inches
  No. 3 .... 1.9957 to 1.9965 inches
  No. 4 .... 1.9757 to 1.9765 inches
  No. 5 .... 1.9557 to 1.9565 inches
Endplay.. 0.011 to 0.077 inch
Lobe lift.. Compare the lift readings for each intake and each exhaust valve. Replace the camshaft if readings vary more than 0.003 inch (compare intake valves to intake valves and exhaust valves to exhaust valves).

Torque specifications   **Ft-lbs** (unless otherwise indicated)
Intake manifold bolts*.. 40
Exhaust manifold-to-cylinder head 25
Cylinder head bolts... 130*
Driveplate (automatic trans)... 60
Flywheel (manual trans) 90
Vibration damper-to-crankshaft .... 200 to 240
Oil pan bolts .... 120 in-lbs
Oil pan nuts 17
Oil pump cover screws.. 96 in-lbs
Valve cover .... 84 in-lbs
Rocker arm pivot bolt 25
Timing chain cover 35

* Lightly oil threads

Pontiac-built V8 engines

General
Displacement
  4.3 liter (VIN S).. 265 cubic inches
  4.9 liter (VIN Y and W) .... 301 cubic inches
  5.7 liter (VIN M, N, E and P)... 350 cubic inches
  6.6 liter (VIN R, S, T, P and Z).. 400 cubic inches
  7.5 liter (VIN X, U, W and Y) .... 455 cubic inches
Bore and stroke
  265 .... 3.75 x 3.00 in
  301 .... 4.00 x 3.00 in
  350 .... 3.88 x 3.75 in
  400 .... 4.12 x 3.75 in
  455 .... 4.15 x 4.21 in
Firing order 1-8-4-3-6-5-7-2

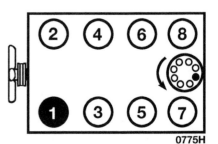

Cylinder location and distributor rotation diagram - Pontiac-built V8 engines

The blackened terminal shown on the distributor cap indicates the Number One spark plug wire position

Camshaft
Journal diameter (all) .... 1.900 inches
Lobe lift .... Compare the lift readings for each intake and each exhaust valve. Replace the camshaft if readings vary more than 0.003 inch (compare intake valves to intake valves and exhaust valves to exhaust valves).

Torque specifications   **Ft-lbs** (unless otherwise indicated)
Intake manifold bolts
  1976 and earlier.. 40
  1977 and later 35
Exhaust manifold-to-cylinder head
  1976 and earlier.. 30
  1977 and later 40

Ft-lbs (unless otherwise indicated)

Camshaft sprocket bolt	40
Cylinder head bolts	
1977 265, 301 cu in	85
1977 350 and 400 cu in	100
All others	95
Flywheel/driveplate	95
Vibration damper-to-crankshaft	160
Oil pan	144 in-lbs
Valve cover	72 in-lbs
Rocker arm nuts	20
Timing chain cover	30

1   General information

Note: *Engines installed in these vehicles are from several GM divisions. To determine which engine type is in your vehicle, refer to Vehicle Identification Numbers at the front of this manual.*

This Part of Chapter 2 is devoted to in-vehicle repair procedures for the engine. All information concerning engine removal and installation and engine block and cylinder head overhaul can be found in Part B of this Chapter.

Since the repair procedures included in this Part are based on the assumption that the engine is still installed in the vehicle, if they are being used during a complete engine overhaul (with the engine already out of the vehicle and on a stand) many of the steps included here will not apply.

The specifications included in this Part of Chapter 2 apply only to the procedures found here. The specifications necessary for rebuilding the block and cylinder heads are included in Part B.

2   Repair operations possible with the engine in the vehicle

Many major repair operations can be accomplished without removing the engine from the vehicle.

Clean the engine compartment and the exterior of the engine with some type of pressure washer before any work is done. A clean engine will make the job easier and will help keep dirt out of the internal areas of the engine.

Depending on the components involved, it may be a good idea to remove the hood to improve access to the engine as repairs are performed (refer to Chapter 11 if necessary).

If oil or coolant leaks develop, indicating a need for gasket or seal replacement, the repairs can generally be made with the engine in the vehicle. The oil pan gasket, the cylinder head gaskets, intake and exhaust manifold gaskets, timing cover gaskets and the crankshaft oil seals are accessible with the engine in place.

Exterior engine components, such as the water pump, the starter motor, the alter-nator, the distributor and the fuel system components, as well as the intake and exhaust manifolds, can be removed for repair with the engine in place.

Since the cylinder heads can be removed without pulling the engine, valve component servicing can also be accomplished with the engine in the vehicle.

Replacement of, repairs to, or inspection of the timing chain and sprockets, camshaft and the oil pump are all possible with the engine in place.

In extreme cases, caused by a lack of necessary equipment, repair or replacement of piston rings, pistons, connecting rods and rod bearings is possible with the engine in the vehicle. However, this practice is not recommended because of the cleaning and preparation work that must be performed on the components involved.

3   Top Dead Center (TDC) for number one piston - locating

Refer to illustrations 3.6 and 3.7

1   Top Dead Center (TDC) is the highest point in the cylinder that each piston reaches as it travels up and down when the crankshaft turns. Each piston reaches TDC on the compression stroke and again on the exhaust stroke, but TDC generally refers to piston position on the compression stroke. The timing marks on the vibration damper installed on the front of the crankshaft are referenced to the number one piston at TDC on the compression stroke.

2   Positioning the piston(s) at TDC is an essential part of many procedures such as rocker arm removal, valve adjustment, timing chain and sprocket replacement and distributor removal.

3   In order to bring any piston to TDC, the crankshaft must be turned using one of the methods outlined below. When looking at the front of the engine, normal crankshaft rotation is clockwise. **Warning:** *Before beginning this procedure, be sure to place the transmission in Neutral and unplug the wire connector at the distributor to disable the ignition system (electronic ignition) or remove the center wire from the distributor cap and ground it (conventional ignition).*

a) *The preferred method is to turn the crankshaft with a large socket and breaker bar attached to the vibration damper bolt threaded into the front of the crankshaft.*

b) *A remote starter switch, which may save some time, can also be used. Attach the switch leads to the S (switch) and B (battery) terminals on the starter motor. Once the piston is close to TDC, use a socket and breaker bar as described in the previous paragraph.*

c) *If an assistant is available to turn the ignition switch to the Start position in short bursts, you can get the piston close to TDC without a remote starter switch. Use a socket and breaker bar as described in paragraph a) to complete the procedure.*

4   Make a mark on the distributor housing directly below the number one spark plug wire terminal on the distributor cap. **Note:** *The terminal numbers may be marked on the spark plug wires near the distributor.*

5   Remove the distributor cap as described in Chapter 1.

6   Turn the crankshaft (see paragraph 3 above) until the line on the vibration damper is aligned with the zero mark on the timing plate **(see illustration)**. The timing plate and vibration damper are located low on the front of the engine, near the pulley that turns the drivebelt.

3.6 Turn the crankshaft until the line on the vibration damper is directly opposite the zero mark on the timing plate as shown here

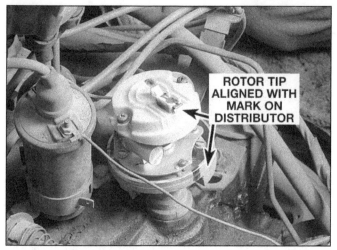

3.7 The rotor tip should point to the mark on the distributor housing

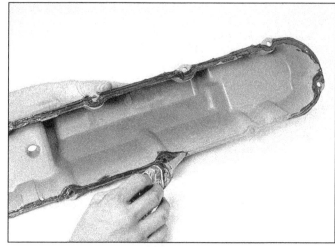

4.9 If your engine had RTV sealer, apply a bead inside of the bolt holes as shown

7   The rotor should now be pointing directly at the mark on the distributor housing **(see illustration)**. If it isn't, the piston may be at TDC on the exhaust stroke, so follow Step 8.

8   To get the piston to TDC on the compression stroke, turn the crankshaft one complete turn (360 degrees) clockwise. The rotor should now be pointing at the mark. When the rotor is pointing at the number one spark plug wire terminal in the distributor cap (which is indicated by the mark on the housing) and the ignition timing marks are aligned, the number one piston is at TDC on the compression stroke.

9   After the number one piston has been positioned at TDC on the compression stroke, TDC for any of the remaining cylinders can be located by turning the crankshaft 120 degrees at a time for V6 engines or 90 degrees for V8 engines and following the firing order (refer to the Specifications).

---

4   Valve covers - removal and installation

Refer to illustration 4.9

1   Disconnect the negative cable from the battery.

2   Remove the air cleaner assembly.

3   Label and disconnect any emissions or vacuum lines and wires which are routed over the valve cover(s).

4   Remove any braces or brackets which block access to the cover(s), noting the way they are mounted to ease reassembly.

5   Detach any remaining accessories as necessary. If removal of the air conditioning compressor is required, unbolt the unit and carefully set it aside without disconnecting the refrigerant lines. **Warning:** *The air conditioning system is under high pressure. Do not disconnect any refrigerant line or fitting without first having the system discharged by an air conditioning technician.*

5.2 On Oldsmobile engines, loosen the bolts (arrows) and remove the rocker arm pivots

6   Remove the valve cover attaching bolts, along with any spark plug wire looms and hardware.

7   Remove the valve cover. **Caution:** *Do not pry on the sealing flange. To do so may damage the surface, causing oil leaks. Tap on the sides of the cover with a rubber hammer until it pops loose.*

8   Thoroughly clean the mating surfaces, removing all traces of old gasket material. Use acetone or lacquer thinner and a clean rag to remove any traces of oil.

9   Prepare the cover for installation by applying a continuous bead of RTV sealer **(see illustration)** or a new gasket to the sealing flange. Use the same sealing method the vehicle had, otherwise new bolts of a different length may be required.

10   Install the cover(s) and bolts and tighten them securely. Do not overtighten them, as the covers may be deformed.

11   Reinstall the remaining parts in the reverse order of removal.

12   Run the engine and check for leaks.

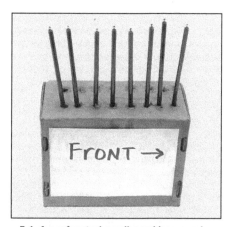

5.4 A perforated cardboard box can be used to store the pushrods to ensure that they are reinstalled in their original locations - note the label indicating the front of the engine

---

5   Rocker arms and pushrods - removal, inspection and installation

---

Removal

Refer to illustrations 5.2 and 5.4

1   Refer to Section 4 and detach the valve cover(s) from the cylinder head(s).

2   Remove each of the rocker arm nuts (Chevrolet and Pontiac engines), or bolts (Olds engines) **(see illustration)**. Place them at their correct location in a cardboard box or rack. **Note:** *On Chevrolet and Pontiac built engines, if the pushrods are the only items being removed, loosen each nut just enough to allow the rocker arms to be rotated to the side so the pushrods can be lifted out.*

3   Remove each rocker arm assembly, placing each component on the numbered box or rack.

4   Remove the pushrods and store them separately to make sure they don't get mixed up during installation **(see illustration)**.

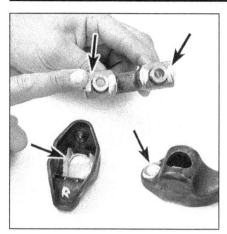

5.10 Apply moly-based lubricant to the wear points (arrows) of the rocker components before assembly - Oldsmobile rocker assembly shown

5.13 Rotate each pushrod as the rocker arm nut is tightened to determine the point at which all play is removed, then tighten each nut an additional 3/4-turn

Inspection

5   Check each rocker arm for wear, cracks and other damage, especially where the pushrods and valve stems contact the rocker arm faces.

6   Make sure the hole at the pushrod end of each rocker arm is open.

7   Check each rocker arm pivot area for wear, cracks and galling. If the rocker arms are worn or damaged, replace them with new ones and use new pivot balls as well.

8   Inspect the pushrods for cracks and excessive wear at the ends. Roll each pushrod across a piece of plate glass to see if it's bent (if it wobbles, it's bent).

Installation

Refer to illustration 5.10

9   Lubricate the lower end of each pushrod with clean engine oil or moly-base grease and install them in their original locations. Make sure each pushrod seats completely in the lifter.

10   Apply moly-base grease to the ends of the valve stems and the upper ends of the pushrods before positioning the rocker arms onto the cylinder head **(see illustration)**.

11   Set the rocker arms in place, then install the pivot balls (except engines with rocker shafts) and nuts. Apply moly-base grease to the pivot balls or shafts to prevent damage to the mating surfaces before engine oil pressure builds up. Be sure to install each nut with the flat side against the pivot ball.

Valve adjustment

Chevrolet engines

Refer to illustration 5.13

12   Refer to Section 3 and bring the number one piston to top dead center on the compression stroke.

13   Tighten the rocker arm nuts (number one cylinder only) until all play is removed at the pushrods. This can be determined by rotating each pushrod between your thumb

and index finger as the nut is tightened **(see illustration)**. At the point where a slight drag is just felt as you spin the pushrod, all lash has been removed.

14   Tighten each nut an additional 3/4-turn (270-degrees) to center the lifters. Valve adjustment for cylinder number one is now complete.

15   Turn the crankshaft 90 degrees in the normal direction of rotation until the next piston in the firing order (number eight for V8 engines) is at TDC on the compression stroke. The distributor rotor should be pointing in the direction of the next terminal on the cap (see Section 3 for additional information).

16   Repeat the procedure described in Steps 13 and 14 for the number eight cylinder valves (next cylinder in the firing order).

17   Follow the firing order sequence and adjust both valves for each cylinder before proceeding to the next cylinder. A cylinder number illustration and firing order sequence is also included - in the Specifications Section at the beginning of this Chapter.

18   Refer to Section 4 and install the valve covers. Start the engine, listen for unusual valvetrain noises and check for oil leaks at the valve cover joints.

All other engines

19   The valves on Pontiac and Oldsmobile engines cannot be adjusted. If the clearance is excessive in the valve train, check that the pivot bolt is tightened to the proper torque Specification (or the nylon retainer is seated). Then inspect for worn components.

---

6   Valve spring, retainer and seals - replacement

Refer to illustrations 6.4, 6.8, 6.9, 6.16 and 6.17

Note: *Broken valve springs and defective valve stem seals can be replaced without removing the cylinder heads. Two special*

tools and a compressed air source are normally required to perform this operation, so read through this Section carefully and rent or buy the tools before beginning the job.

1   Refer to Section 4 and remove the valve cover from the affected cylinder head. If all of the valve stem seals are being replaced, remove both valve covers.

2   Remove the spark plug from the cylinder which has the defective component. If all of the valve stem seals are being replaced, all of the spark plugs should be removed.

3   Turn the crankshaft until the piston in the affected cylinder is at top dead center on the compression stroke (refer to Section 3 for instructions). If you are replacing all of the valve stem seals, begin with cylinder number one and work on the valves for one cylinder at a time. Move from cylinder to cylinder following the firing order sequence (see specifications).

4   Thread an adapter into the spark plug hole and connect an air hose from a compressed air source to it **(see illustration)**. Most auto parts stores can supply the air hose adapter. **Note:** *Many cylinder compression gauges utilize a screw-in fitting that may work with your air hose quick-disconnect fitting.*

5   Remove the rocker arm(s) for the valve with the defective part and pull out the pushrod. If all of the valve stem seals are being replaced, all of the rocker arms and pushrods should be removed (refer to Section 5).

6   Apply compressed air to the cylinder. The valves should be held in place by the air pressure. If the valve faces or seats are in poor condition, leaks may prevent air pressure from retaining the valves - refer to the alternative procedure below.

7   If you don't have access to compressed air, an alternative method can be used. Position the piston at a point approximately 45-degrees before TDC on the compression stroke, then feed a long piece of nylon rope through the spark plug hole until it fills the

6.4 Use compressed air and an air hose adapter (arrow) to hold the valves closed when the valve springs are removed - air hose adapters are commonly available from auto parts stores

6.8 Once the spring is depressed, the keepers can be removed with a small magnet or needle-nose pliers (a magnet is preferred to prevent dropping the keepers)

6.9 Some engines also have an umbrella type seal which fits over the valve guide boss

combustion chamber. Be sure to leave the end of the rope hanging out of the engine so it can be removed easily. Use a large breaker bar and socket to rotate the crankshaft in the normal direction of rotation until slight resistance is felt.

8　Stuff shop rags into the cylinder head holes above and below the valves to prevent parts and tools from falling into the engine, then use a valve spring compressor to compress the spring/damper assembly. Remove the keepers with small needle-nose pliers or a magnet **(see illustration)**. **Note:** *A couple of different types of tools are available for compressing the valve springs with the head in place. One type, shown here, grips the lower spring coils and presses on the retainer as the knob is turned, while the other type utilizes the rocker arm stud and nut for leverage. Both types work very well, although the lever type is usually less expensive and won't work on all cylinders of engines with rocker shafts.*

9　Remove the spring retainer or rotator, oil shield and valve spring assembly, then remove the valve stem O-ring seal (the O-ring seal will most likely be hardened and will probably break when removed, so plan on installing a new one each time the original is removed). and the umbrella-type guide seal on later models engines **(see illustration)**. **Note:** *If air pressure fails to hold the valve in the closed position during this operation, the valve face and/or seat is probably damaged. If so, the cylinder head will have to be removed for additional repair operations.*

10　Wrap a rubber band or tape around the top of the valve stem so the valve won't fall into the combustion chamber, then release the air pressure. **Note:** *If a rope was used instead of air pressure, turn the crankshaft slightly in the direction opposite normal rotation.*

11　Inspect the valve stem for damage. Rotate the valve in the guide and check the end for eccentric movement, which would indicate that the valve is bent.

12　Move the valve up and down in the guide and make sure it doesn't bind. If the valve stem binds, either the valve is bent or

6.16 Make sure the O-ring seal under the retainer is seated in the groove and not twisted before installing the keepers

the guide is damaged. In either case, the head will have to be removed for repair.

13　Reapply air pressure to the cylinder to retain the valve in the closed position, then remove the tape or rubber band from the valve stem. If a rope was used instead of air pressure, rotate the crankshaft in the normal direction of rotation until slight resistance is felt.

14　Lubricate the valve stem with engine oil and install a new umbrella type guide seal (if equipped).

15　Install the spring/damper assembly and shield in position over the valve.

16　Install the valve spring retainer or rotator. Compress the valve spring assembly and carefully install the new O-ring seal in the lower groove of the valve stem. Make sure the seal isn't twisted - it must lie perfectly flat in the groove **(see illustration)**.

17　Position the keepers in the upper groove. Apply a small dab of grease to the inside of each keeper to hold it in place if necessary **(see illustration)**. Remove the pressure from the spring tool and make sure the keepers are seated.

18　Disconnect the air hose and remove the

6.17 Apply a small dab of grease to each keeper as shown here before installation - it'll hold them in place on the valve stem as the spring is released

adapter from the spark plug hole. If a rope was used in place of air pressure, pull it out of the cylinder.

19　Refer to Section 5 and install the rocker arm(s) and pushrod(s).

20　Install the spark plug(s) and hook up the wire(s).

21　Refer to Section 4 and install the valve cover(s).

22　Start and run the engine, then check for oil leaks and unusual sounds coming from the valve cover area.

7　Vibration damper - removal and installation

Refer to illustrations 7.5a, 7.5b, 7.6 and 7.7

1　Disconnect the cable from the negative terminal of the battery.

2　Remove the fan shroud and fan assembly (Chapter 3).

3　Remove the drivebelts (Chapter 1).

4　Remove the pulley retaining bolts and detach the pulleys. **Caution:** *Before removing*

7.5a The vibration damper bolt (arrow) is usually very tight, so use a six-point socket and a breaker bar to loosen it (the three other bolts hold the pulley to the vibration damper)

7.5b Have an assistant hold a large screwdriver or pry bar against the driveplate teeth

7.6 Use the recommended puller to remove the vibration damper - if a puller that applies force to the outer edge is used, the damper will be damaged!

7.7 Using a special tool to push the vibration damper onto the crankshaft

8.2 Use a screwdriver or seal removal tool to pull out the front seal, being careful not to nick the crankshaft surface

the pulleys, mark the location of each one in relation to the vibration damper in order to retain proper timing mark orientation during installation.

5   Raise the vehicle and support it securely on jackstands. Remove the lower bellhousing cover. Wedge a pry bar between the flywheel/driveplate teeth to prevent the crankshaft from turning while loosening the large vibration damper bolt **(see illustrations)**.

6   Leave the damper bolt in place (with several threads still engaged), to provide the gear puller with something to push against. Use a puller to remove the damper **(see illustration)**. **Caution:** *Don't use a puller with jaws that grip the outer edge of the damper! The puller must be the type shown in the illustration that utilizes bolts to apply force to the damper hub only.*

7   To install the damper apply a dab of grease to the seal lips, position the damper on the nose of the crankshaft, align the keyway and start it onto the crankshaft with a special installation tool **(see illustration)**. Install the bolt. Tighten the bolt to the specified torque.

8   The remaining installation steps are the reverse of the removal procedure.

8   Front crankshaft oil seal - replacement

Timing cover in place

Refer to illustrations 8.2 and 8.4

1   Remove the vibration damper as described in Section 7.

2   Carefully pry the seal out of the cover with a seal removal tool or a large screwdriver **(see illustration)**. Be careful not to distort the cover or scratch the wall of the seal bore. If the engine has accumulated a lot of miles, apply penetrating oil to the seal-to-cover joint and allow it to soak in before attempting to pull the seal out.

3   Clean the bore to remove any old seal material and corrosion. Position the new seal in the bore with the open end of the seal facing IN. A small amount of oil applied to the outer edge of the new seal will make installation easier - don't overdo it!

8.4 Use the appropriate size socket to drive the new seal squarely into the front cover

4   Drive the seal into the bore with a large socket and hammer until it's completely seated **(see illustration)**. Select a socket that's the same outside diameter as the seal

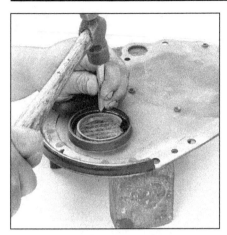

8.6a While supporting the cover near the seal bore, drive the old seal out from the inside with a hammer and punch or screwdriver - Oldsmobile timing cover shown

8.6b Chevrolet timing cover shown

8.8 Clean the bore and then apply a small amount of oil to the outer edge of the seal and drive it squarely into the opening with a large socket or a piece of pipe and a hammer - do not damage the seal in the process (Chevrolet shown)

(a section of pipe can be used if a socket isn't available).

5   Reinstall the vibration damper.

Timing cover removed

Refer to illustration 8.6a, 8.6b and 8.8

6   Use a punch or screwdriver and hammer to drive the seal out of the cover from the back side. Support the cover as close to the seal bore as possible **(see illustrations)**. Be careful not to distort the cover or scratch the wall of the seal bore. If the engine has accumulated a lot of miles, apply penetrating oil to the seal-to-cover joint on each side and allow it to soak in before attempting to drive the seal out.

7   Clean the bore to remove any old seal material and corrosion. Support the cover on blocks of wood and position the new seal in the bore with the open end of the seal facing IN. A small amount of oil applied to the outer edge of the new seal will make installation easier - don't overdo it!

8   Drive the seal into the bore with a large socket and hammer until it's completely

seated **(see illustration)**. Select a socket that's the same outside diameter as the seal (a section of pipe can be used if a socket isn't available).

9   Intake manifold - removal and installation

Refer to illustrations 9.9, 9.12, 9.14a and 9.14b

1   Place protective covers on the fenders and disconnect the cable from the negative terminal of the battery.

2   Drain the cooling system (see Chapter 1).

3   Remove the air cleaner assembly.

4   Detach all coolant hoses from the intake manifold.

5   Label and then disconnect any wiring and vacuum, emission and/or fuel lines which attach to the intake manifold.

6   Remove the EGR valve, if necessary (see Chapter 6).

7   On engines with the distributor mounted through the manifold, remove the distributor (see Chapter 5).

8   Remove the carburetor (see Chapter 4).

9   Remove the intake manifold bolts **(see illustration)** and any brackets, noting their locations, so they may be reinstalled in the same location.

10   Lift off the manifold. If it is difficult to break loose, carefully pry against a casting protrusion. **Caution:** *Do not pry against a sealing surface.* **Note:** *If your engine has a valley cover under the intake manifold, this must be removed to access the valve lifters. Unbolt the cover and lift it out.*

11   Stuff rags in the exposed ports and passages. Thoroughly clean all sealing surfaces, removing all traces of gasket material. Check the exhaust crossover passages below the carburetor for carbon blockage.

12   Position new gaskets and seals into place, using RTV sealer in the corners and to hold them in place. Use plastic gasket retainers, if provided. Follow the gasket manufacturer's instructions **(see illustration)**. On Pontiac-built engines, install a new seal ring between the intake manifold and the water pump housing.

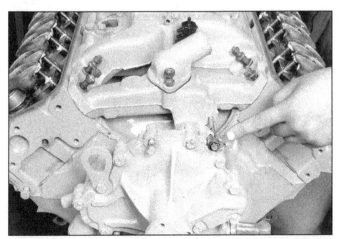

9.9 Pontiac-manufactured engines use a bolt to mate the intake manifold to the front timing cover

9.12 Make sure the intake manifold gaskets are installed right side up or all the passages and bolt holes may not line up properly

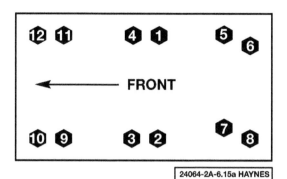

9.14a Intake manifold bolt tightening sequence for Chevrolet and Pontiac engines

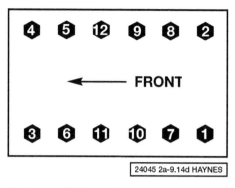

9.14b Intake manifold bolt tightening sequence for Oldsmobile engines

10.11 Some spark plug heat shields are held in place by bolts located under the exhaust manifold (Chevrolet-built engine)

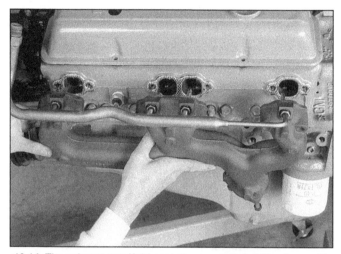

10.14 The exhaust manifold gaskets are easily held in place with sealant as the manifold is installed

13 Set the manifold into position. Be sure all the bolt holes are lined up and start all the bolts by hand before tightening any. On Pontiac built engines, tighten the timing cover-to-manifold bolt first.

14 Tighten the bolts in three stages, following the appropriate sequence (see illustrations) until the specified torque is reached.

15 The remainder of installation is the reverse of removal. Be sure to refill the cooling system and change the oil and filter (see Chapter 1), as coolant often gets into the oil during manifold removal.

16 Run the engine and check for fluid and vacuum leaks. Adjust the ignition timing, if the distributor was disturbed (see Chapter 1). Road test the vehicle, checking for proper operation of engine and accessories.

10 Exhaust manifolds - removal and installation

Refer to illustrations 10.11 and 10.14

1 Allow the engine to cool completely.
2 Place protective covers on the fenders.
3 Disconnect the cable from the negative terminal of the battery.
4 Raise the vehicle and support it securely on jackstands.
5 Spray penetrating oil on the threads of fasteners holding the hot air shrouds and the exhaust pipe(s) to the manifold(s) you wish to remove. Go on to the next steps, allowing the penetrating oil to soak in.
6 Remove the air cleaner and hot air duct.
7 Detach the hot air shroud(s) or heat stove assembly from the manifold.
8 Label and then remove spark plug and oxygen sensor wires and any hoses such as EFE or AIR, as needed.
9 Unbolt any engine accessories which block access to the manifold(s) such as the alternator, air conditioning compressor or power steering pump. Refer to the appropriate Chapters (5, 3, 10) for further information. When unbolting the air conditioning compressor, leave the refrigerant lines connected and tie the compressor aside without putting a strain on the fittings. Warning: Do not disconnect any air conditioning line or fitting unless the system pressure has been discharged by a qualified A/C specialist.
10 Remove the manifold-to-exhaust pipe fasteners. Note: On some models it may be

necessary to remove the starter (see Chapter 5), the lower bellhousing cover, and/or a front wheel for access to the manifolds.
11 Bend back any lock tabs from the manifold bolt heads and remove the bolts and any spark plug heat shields (see illustration), noting their types and locations for reassembly.
12 Remove the manifold(s) from the engine compartment.
13 Thoroughly clean and inspect the sealing surfaces, removing all traces of old gasket material. Look for cracks and damaged threads. If the gasket was leaking, take the manifold to an automotive machine shop to inspect/correct for warpage.
14 If replacing the manifold, transfer all parts to the new unit. Using new gaskets (when equipped), install the manifold (see illustration) and start the bolts by hand.
15 Working from the center outward, tighten the bolts to the specified torque. Bend the lock tabs (if equipped) against the bolt heads.
16 Reinstall the remaining components in the reverse order of removal.
17 Run the engine and check for exhaust leaks.

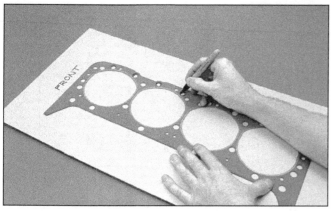

11.7 To avoid mixing up the head bolts, use a new gasket to transfer the bolt hole pattern to a piece of cardboard, then punch holes to accept the bolts

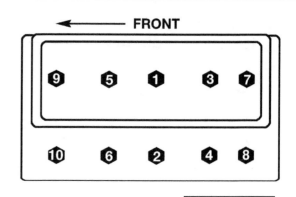

11.8a Cylinder head bolt tightening sequence for Pontiac engines

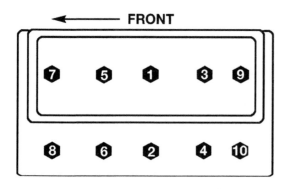

11.8b Cylinder head bolt tightening sequence for Oldsmobile engines

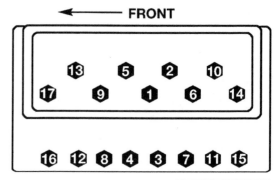

11.8c Cylinder head bolt tightening sequence for Chevrolet engines

11 Cylinder heads - removal and installation

Refer to illustrations 11.7, 11.8a, 11.8b, 11.8c and 11.14
Caution: *The engine must be completely cool when the heads are removed. Failure to allow the engine to cool off could result in head warpage.*

Removal

1   Remove the intake manifold (see Section 9).
2   Remove the valve cover(s) as described in Section 4.
3   Remove the rocker arms and pushrods (see Section 5). **Note:** *If any pushrods or head bolts cannot be removed because of interference with components such as the vacuum brake booster, lift them up as far as possible and wrap a rubber band around them to keep them from dropping during head removal. Be sure to do the same during installation.*
4   Remove the exhaust manifolds (see Section 10).
5   Unbolt the engine accessories and brackets as necessary and set them aside. See Chapter 5 for alternator removal. When removing a power steering pump (see Chapter 10), leave the hoses attached and secure the unit in an upright position. Refrigerant lines should remain attached to air conditioning compressors (see Chapter 3). **Warning:** *The air conditioning system is under high pressure. Do not loosen any hose or fitting until the refrigerant gas has been discharged by an auto air conditioning technician.*
6   Recheck to be sure nothing is still connected to the head(s) you intend to remove. Remove anything that is still attached.
7   Using a new gasket, outline the cylinders and bolt pattern on a piece of cardboard **(see illustration)**. Be sure to indicate the front of the engine for reference. Punch holes at the bolt locations.
8   Loosen the head bolts in 1/4-turn increments until they can be removed by hand. Work from bolt to bolt in a pattern that's the reverse of the tightening sequence **(see illustrations)**. Store the bolts in the cardboard holder as they are removed; this will insure that the bolts are reinstalled in their original holes.
9   Lift the head(s) off the engine. If excessive resistance is felt, do not pry between the head and block as damage to the mating surfaces may result. To dislodge the head, place a block of wood against the end of it and strike the wood with a hammer. Store the head(s) on their sides to prevent damage to the gasket surface.
10   Cylinder head disassembly and inspection procedures are covered in detail in Chapter 2B.
11   Use a gasket scraper to remove all traces of carbon and old gasket material, then clean the mating surfaces with lacquer thinner or acetone. If there's oil on the mating surfaces when the heads are installed, the gaskets may not seal properly and leaks may develop. When working on the block, cover the lifter valley with shop rags to keep out debris. Use a vacuum cleaner to remove any debris that falls into the cylinders.
12   Check the block and head mating surfaces for nicks, deep scratches and other damage. If damage is slight, it can be removed with a file. If the gasket seemed to be leaking, have the head(s) checked for cracks and warpage by an automotive machine shop. Surface damage or warpage can usually be corrected by machining. Cracks normally require replacement.

11.14 Steel gaskets must be installed with the raised bead (arrow) facing UP

12.7 A putty knife or screwdriver can be used to break the timing chain cover-to-block seal, but be careful when prying it off as damage to the cover may result - Chevrolet

12.11 Oil slinger installation - typical

Installation

13   Use a tap of the correct size to chase the threads in the head bolt holes. Mount each bolt in a vise and run a die down the threads to remove any corrosion and restore the threads. Dirt, corrosion, sealant and damaged threads will affect torque readings.

14   If an all-metal gasket is used, apply a thin, even coat of sealant such as K & W Copper Coat to both sides prior to installation. Metal gaskets must be installed with the raised bead UP **(see illustration)**. Most gaskets have "This side up" stamped into them. Composition gaskets must be installed dry - don't use sealant. Follow the gasket manufacturer's instructions, if available. Position a new gasket over the dowel pins in the block.

15   Carefully position the head on the block without denting or disturbing the gasket.

16   Be sure the head bolt holes are clean. On 301 cubic inch and all Chevrolet-built engines covered by this manual, apply non-hardening sealant such as Permatex no. 2 to the head bolt threads. Apply a light coating of engine oil to the head bolts of the other engines (Olds and Pontiac V8's).

17   Install the bolts in their original locations and tighten them finger tight. Follow the recommended sequence **(see illustration 11.8a, 11.8b and 11.8c)** and tighten the bolts in several steps to the specified torque.

18   The remaining installation steps are the reverse order of removal. Check the index for the appropriate Sections for installation of the various components.

19   Add coolant, change the oil and filter (see Chapter 1), then start the engine and check carefully for leaks.

12   Timing cover, chain and sprockets

Refer to illustrations 12.7, 12.11, 12.12a, 12.12b and 12.13

Removal

1   Disconnect the cable from the negative terminal of the battery.

2   If necessary, remove the alternator and brackets as well as the distributor (Chapter 5).

3   Drain the cooling system and disconnect the radiator hoses, heater hose (where applicable) and the small by-pass hose (except Chevrolet engine).

4   Remove the top radiator support, the fan shroud, the fan and pulley and the radiator (Chapter 3).

5   Remove the crankshaft drive pulley and the vibration damper (see Section 7).

6   If equipped with a Chevrolet or Oldsmobile engine, remove the water pump (Chapter 3). If equipped with a Pontiac engine, remove the fuel pump. Unbolt and set aside any engine accessories which are in the way without disconnecting the hoses. Refer to the appropriate Chapters for further information.

7   Remove the nuts and bolts that attach the cover to the engine, then pull the cover free **(see illustration)**. Pontiac engines have bolts attaching the oil pan to the cover (Pontiac engines also have a bolt that threads into the intake manifold). Remove the camshaft thrust spring and button, on vehicles so equipped.

8   Thoroughly clean all gasket mating surfaces (do not allow the old gasket material to fall into the oil pan), then wipe them with a cloth soaked in solvent.

9   On Oldsmobile and Pontiac engines, remove the fuel pump drive eccentric by unscrewing the bolt from the end of the camshaft.

10   On Oldsmobile and Pontiac engines, slide the fuel pump drive eccentric off the camshaft.

11   On Oldsmobile engines, slide the oil slinger off of the end of the crankshaft **(see illustration)**.

12   Turn the crankshaft until the marks on the camshaft and crankshaft sprockets are perfectly aligned **(see illustrations)**. DO NOT attempt to remove either sprocket or the chain until this is done. Also, do not turn the camshaft or the crankshaft after the sprockets are removed.

13   On Chevrolet engines, remove the bolts

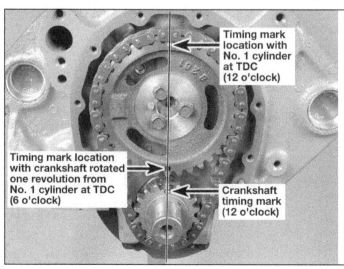

Timing mark location with No. 1 cylinder at TDC (12 o'clock)

Timing mark location with crankshaft rotated one revolution from No. 1 cylinder at TDC (6 o'clock)

Crankshaft timing mark (12 o'clock)

12.12 On Chevrolet, Oldsmobile and Pontiac-built engines, carefully note the positions of the timing marks on the camshaft sprocket and the crankshaft gear

12.13 Remove the three bolts from the end of the camshaft (arrows) - Chevrolet-built engine shown

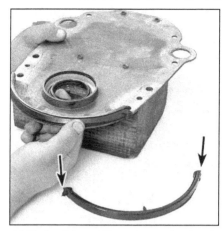

12.22 On Oldsmobile engines, trim the oil pan gasket as shown before installing the front cover

12.25 The cover must be forced down against the pan, compressing the seal, to align the bolt holes - use screwdrivers through two of the lower holes to align the cover holes until two upper bolts can be installed

that attach the sprocket to the end of the camshaft **(see illustration)**.

14 Generally speaking, the camshaft sprocket, the crankshaft sprocket and the timing chain can be slipped off the shafts together. If resistance is encountered, it may be necessary to use two screwdrivers to carefully pry the sprockets off of the shafts. If extreme resistance is encountered (which may happen with the crankshaft sprocket), a gear puller will be required. It should be noted that on Oldsmobile engines, the key that indexes the sprocket to the crankshaft must be removed before sliding or pulling the sprocket off of the shaft. On models with spring loaded timing chain dampers, hold the damper back as you slip the chain off.

15 If the crankshaft and the camshaft are not disturbed while the timing chain and sprockets are out of place, then installation can begin with Step 18. If the engine is completely dismantled, or if the crankshaft or camshaft are disturbed while the timing chain is off, then the No. 1 piston must be positioned at TDC before the timing chain and sprockets are installed.

16 Align the hole in the camshaft sprocket with the dowel pin in the end of the camshaft, then slip the sprocket onto the end of the camshaft. **Note:** *With the No. 1 piston at TDC, the timing mark on the camshaft sprocket must be pointed straight up* **(see illustration 12.12)**.

17 Slip the crankshaft sprocket onto the end of the crankshaft (make sure the key and keyway are properly aligned), then turn the crankshaft until the timing mark on the sprocket is pointed straight up (all engines).

18 Next, remove the camshaft sprocket from the camshaft and lay the chain over it. Slip the other end of the chain over the crankshaft sprocket (keep the timing marks aligned as this is done) and reinstall the camshaft sprocket. When the sprockets are properly installed, the timing marks on the sprockets will be perfectly aligned; refer to **illustration 12.12** and Step 16).

19 On Chevrolet engines, install the bolts

that attach the sprocket to the camshaft, then recheck the alignment of the timing marks. On Oldsmobile engines, install the crankshaft key after the sprocket is in place (use a brass hammer to seat the key in the keyway).

20 The rest of the installation procedure is basically the reverse of removal. On Pontiac engines, the camshaft should extend through the sprocket so that the hole in the fuel pump drive eccentric will locate on the end of the shaft. Install the eccentric and index the tangs on the eccentric with the small hole in the sprocket hub.

21 Be sure to tighten the crankshaft and camshaft sprocket retaining bolts to the specified torque (if applicable).

Installation

Oldsmobile engines

Refer to illustrations 12.22 and 12.25

22 Cut off the excess gasket material at the front of the oil pan until it is flush with the engine block **(see illustration)**.

23 Using a razor knife, trim about 1/8-inch from each end of the new front pan seal.

24 Install a new gasket to the engine block and a new front seal on the cover (see Section 8). Use RTV gasket sealant on these gaskets and also at the junction of the cover, block and oil pan.

25 Tilt the cover into place and press downward to compress the lower pan seal. Rotate the cover back and forth and guide the pan seal into the cavity using a small screwdriver **(see illustration)**.

26 Apply engine oil to the bolt threads and loosely install two of the bolts to hold the cover in place.

27 Install the dowel pins, chamfered end first, into the engine block.

28 Install the water pump with a new gasket (if removed from cover).

29 Tighten all bolts to the proper torque specifications and install all components in the reverse order of removal. Apply lubricant to the front hub seal before installing the vibration damper hub.

Chevrolet engines

30 Ensure that all gasket surfaces are clean and free of excess gasket material.

31 Use a sharp knife to trim any protruding gasket material at the front of the oil pan.

32 Apply a 1/8-inch bead of RTV gasket sealer to the joint formed at the oil pan and engine block, as well as the front lip of the oil pan.

33 Coat the cover gasket with a non-setting sealant, position it on the cover, then loosely install the cover. First install the top four bolts loosely, then install two 1/4 - 20 x 1/2 inch long screws at the lower cover holes. Apply a bead of sealer on the bottom of the cover, then install the cover, tightening the screws alternately and evenly and at the same time aligning the dowel pins.

34 Remove the two 1/4 - 20 x 1/2 inch long screws and install the remaining cover bolts. Torque all cover bolts to the proper specifications.

35 Install the water pump using new gaskets (see Chapter 3).

36 Follow the removal steps in the reverse order for the remaining components.

Pontiac engines

37 Remove the O-ring seal from the recess in the intake manifold water recirculation passage.

38 Transfer the water pump to the new cover, if used.

39 Position a new gasket over the studs against the engine block. If the oil pan gasket was damaged during removal, new front portions should be cemented in place on the oil pan flanges.

40 Install a new O-ring into the intake manifold passage.

41 Place the cover in position over the indexing studs and secure with the bolts and nuts. Install the oil pan-to-timing cover screws after the other fasteners are installed.

42 Install the remaining components in the

13.3 When checking the camshaft lobe lift, the dial indicator plunger must be positioned directly above the pushrod

13.12a Removing the camshaft thrust plate (Pontiac engine)

reverse order of disassembly, referring to the appropriate Sections in this Chapter or other Chapters.

---

13   Camshaft, bearings and lifters - removal, inspection and installation

Refer to illustrations 13.3, 13.12a, 13.12b, and 13.18

Camshaft lobe lift check

1   In order to determine the extent of cam lobe wear, the lobe lift should be checked prior to camshaft removal. Refer to Section 4 and remove the valve covers.

2   Position the number one piston at TDC on the compression stroke (see Section 3).

3   Beginning with the number one cylinder valves, mount a dial indicator on the engine and position the plunger against the top surface of the first rocker arm. The plunger should be directly above and in line with the pushrod **(see illustration)**.

4   Zero the dial indicator, then very slowly turn the crankshaft in the normal direction of rotation (clockwise) until the indicator needle stops and begins to move in the opposite direction. The point at which it stops indicates maximum cam lobe lift.

5   Record this figure for future reference, then reposition the piston at TDC on the compression stroke.

6   Move the dial indicator to the remaining number one cylinder rocker arm and repeat the check. Be sure to record the results for each valve.

7   Repeat the check for the remaining valves. Since each piston must be at TDC on the compression stroke for this procedure, work from cylinder to cylinder following the firing order sequence (refer to the Specifications).

8   After the check is complete, compare the results to the Specifications. If camshaft lobe lift is less than specified, cam lobe wear has occurred and a new camshaft should be installed.

13.12b A long bolt can be threaded into one of the camshaft bolt holes to provide a handle for removal and installation of the camshaft

Note: *On air-conditioned models, have the refrigerant discharged and remove the condenser prior to commencing the following procedure (see Chapter 3).*

Removal

9   Refer to the appropriate Sections and remove the intake manifold, the rocker arms, the pushrods and the timing chain and camshaft sprocket. The radiator, fuel pump and distributor should be removed as well (see Chapters 3, 4 and 5).

10   There are several ways to extract the lifters from the bores. A special tool designed to grip and remove lifters is manufactured by many tool companies and is widely available, but it may not be required in every case. On newer engines without a lot of varnish buildup, the lifters can often be removed with a small magnet or even with your fingers. A machinists scribe with a bent end can be used to pull the lifters out by positioning the point under the retainer ring in the top of each lifter. **Caution:** *Do not use pliers to remove the lifters unless you intend to replace them with new ones (along with the camshaft). The pliers may damage the precision machined and hardened lifters, rendering them useless.*

11   Before removing the lifters, arrange to store them in a clearly labeled box to ensure that they are reinstalled in their original locations.

Remove the lifters and store them where they will not get dirty. Do not attempt to withdraw the camshaft with the lifters in place.

12   Unbolt and remove the thrust plate, if equipped **(see illustration)**. Thread a long bolt of the proper thread into one of the camshaft sprocket bolt holes to use as a handle when removing the camshaft from the block **(see illustration)**.

13   Carefully pull the camshaft out. Support the cam near the block so the lobes do not nick or gouge the bearings as it is withdrawn.

Inspection

Camshaft and bearings

14   After the camshaft has been removed from the engine, cleaned with solvent and dried, inspect the bearing journals for uneven wear, pitting and evidence of seizure. If the journals are damaged, the bearing inserts in the block are probably damaged as well. Both the camshaft and bearings will have to be replaced.

15   Measure the bearing journals on the camshaft with a micrometer to determine if they are excessively worn or out-of-round.

16   Check the camshaft lobes for heat discoloration, score marks, chipped areas, pitting and uneven wear. If the lobes are in good condition and if the lobe lift measurements are as specified, the camshaft can be reused.

13.18 The foot of each lifter should be slightly convex - the side of another lifter can be used as a straightedge to check it; if it appears flat, it is worn and must not be reused

14.18 Tilt the oil pan down (as shown) at the rear to clear the front crossmember

14.21a Sealant is applied at the area where the front gasket meets the side gasket (Chevrolet engine shown)

Conventional lifters

17   Clean the lifters with solvent and dry them thoroughly without mixing them up.
18   Check each lifter wall, pushrod seat and foot for scuffing, score marks and uneven wear. Each lifter foot (the surface that rides on the cam lobe) must be slightly convex, although this can be difficult to determine by eye **(see illustration)**. If the base of the lifter is concave, the lifters and camshaft must be replaced. If the lifter walls are damaged or worn (which is not very likely), inspect the lifter bores in the engine block as well. If the pushrod seats are worn, check the pushrod ends.
19   If new lifters are being installed, a new camshaft must also be installed. If a new camshaft is installed, use new lifters as well. Never install used lifters unless the original camshaft is used and the lifters can be installed in their original locations.

Roller lifters

20   Check the rollers carefully for wear and damage and make sure they turn freely without excessive play. The inspection procedure for conventional lifters also applies to roller lifters.
21   Unlike conventional lifters, used roller lifters can be reinstalled with a new camshaft, and the original camshaft can be used if new lifters are installed.

Bearing replacement

22   Camshaft bearing replacement requires special tools and expertise that place it outside the scope of the home mechanic. Take the block to an automotive machine shop to ensure that the job is done correctly.

Installation

23   Lubricate the camshaft bearing journals and cam lobes with molybase grease or engine assembly lube.
24   Slide the camshaft into the engine. Support the cam near the block and be careful not to scrape or nick the bearings.
25   Lubricate and then install the thrust

plate, if equipped.
26   Refer to Section 12 and install the timing chain and sprockets.
27   Lubricate the lifters with clean engine oil and install them in the block. If the original lifters are being reinstalled, be sure to return them to their original locations. If a new camshaft is being installed, be sure to install new lifters as well (except for engines with roller lifters).
28   The remaining installation steps are the reverse of removal.
29   Before starting and running the engine, change the oil and install a new oil filter (see Chapter 1).

14 Oil pan - removal and installation

Refer to illustrations 14.18, 14.21a and 14.21b
Warning: *Do not place any part of your body below the engine when it is supported solely by a jack or hoist.*
1   Disconnect the cable from the negative terminal of the battery.
2   Remove the air cleaner assembly and set aside.
3   Remove the distributor cap to prevent breakage as the engine is raised (models with distributor at rear of engine only).
4   Unbolt the radiator shroud from the radiator support and hang the shroud over the cooling fan.
5   If necessary, remove the oil dipstick and dipstick tube.
6   Raise the car and support firmly on jack stands.
7   Drain the engine oil into a suitable container. Disconnect the AIR hose from the catalytic converter (if equipped).
8   Disconnect the exhaust crossover pipe at the exhaust manifold flanges. Lower the exhaust pipes and suspend them from the frame with wire.
9   If equipped with an automatic transmission, remove the lower bellhousing cover.
10   If equipped with a manual transmission, remove the starter (Chapter 5) and the flywheel cover.

11   Use the bolt at the center of the vibration damper to rotate the engine until the timing mark is straight down, at the 6 o'clock position. This will move the forward crankshaft throw upward, providing clearance at the front of the oil pan.
12   Remove the through bolt at each engine mount.
13   At this time the engine must be raised slightly to enable the oil pan to slide clear of the crossmember. The preferred method is to use an engine hoist or "cherry picker". Hook up the lifting chains as described in Chapter 2B, Section 6.
14   An alternative method can be used if extreme care is exercised. Use a floor jack and a block of wood placed under the oil pan. The wood block should spread the load across the oil pan, preventing damage or collapse of the oil pan metal. The oil pump pickup and screen is very close to the oil pan bottom, so any collapsing of the pan may damage the pickup or prevent the oil pump from drawing oil properly.
15   With either method, raise the engine slowly until wood blocks can be placed between the frame front crossmember and the engine block. The blocks should be approximately three inches thick. Check clearances all around the engine as it is raised. Pay particular attention to the distributor, the cooling fan and the A/C unit mounted to the firewall (if equipped).
16   Lower the engine onto the wood blocks. Make sure it is firmly supported. If a hoist is being used, keep the lifting chains secured to the engine.
17   Remove the oil pan bolts. Note the different sizes used and their locations.
18   Remove the oil pan by tilting it downwards at the rear and then working the front clear of the crossmember **(see illustration)**. It may be necessary to use a rubber mallet to break the seal.
19   Before installing, thoroughly clean the gasket sealing surfaces on the engine block and on the oil pan. All sealer and gasket material must be removed.
20   Apply a thin film of sealer to the new

side gaskets and fit them to the engine block. All bolt holes should line up properly. If equipped with retainers, mount the retainers over the gasket and secure the gasket to the oil pan.

21 Again using sealer, install the front and rear seals to the engine. Make sure the ends butt with the ends of the side gaskets **(see illustrations)**.

22 Lift the pan into position and install all the bolts loosely, then once all the bolts are installed use a criss cross pattern to tighten the oil pan bolts. There is no specific order for tightening the bolts; however, it is a good policy to tighten the end bolts first. Do not overtighten them, as the oil pan may be deformed or the gasket may tear.

23 Lower the engine onto its mounts and install the through bolts. Tighten the nuts/bolts securely.

24 Follow the removal steps in a reverse order. Fill the engine with the correct grade and quantity of oil, start the engine and check for leaks.

15 Oil pump - removal, inspection and installation

Refer to illustration 15.4

Removal

1 Remove the oil pan as described in Section 14.

2 Remove the bolts securing the oil pump assembly to the main bearing cap. Remove the oil pump with its pickup tube and screen as an assembly from the engine block. Once the pump is removed, the oil pump driveshaft can be withdrawn from the block. **Note:** *On Oldsmobile engines, do not attempt to remove the washers from the driveshaft. Note that the end with the washers fits into the pump.*

Inspection

3 In most cases it will be more practical and economical to replace a faulty oil pump with a new or rebuilt unit. If it is decided to overhaul the oil pump, check on internal parts availability before beginning.

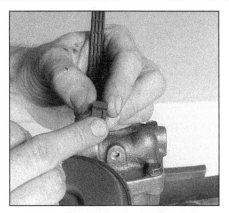

14.21b The front oil seal (Chevrolet engine) has an indentation which fits into the side gasket

4 Remove the pump cover retaining screws **(see illustration)** and the pump cover (Oldsmobile engines also have a gasket installed). Index mark the gear teeth to permit reassembly in the same position.

5 Remove the idler gear, drive gear and shaft from the body.

6 Remove the pressure regulator valve retaining pin (Pontiac engines utilize a threaded cap), the regulator valve and the related parts.

7 If necessary, the pick-up screen and pipe assembly can be extracted from the pump body. **Note:** *On Pontiac engines, the oil pickup tube/screen assembly should not be disturbed.*

8 Wash all the parts in solvent and thoroughly dry them. Inspect the body for cracks, wear or other damage. Similarly inspect the gears.

9 Check the drive gear shaft for looseness in the pump body, and the inside of the pump cover for wear that would permit oil leakage past the end of the gears.

10 Inspect the pick-up screen and pipe assembly for damage to the screen, pipe or relief grommet.

11 Apply a gasket sealant to the end of the pipe (pick-up screen and pipe assembly) and tap it into the pump body, taking care that no

damage occurs. If the original press-fit cannot be obtained, a new assembly must be used to prevent air leaks and loss of pressure.

12 Install the pressure regulator valve and related parts.

13 Install the drive gear and shaft in the pump body, followed by the idler gear, with the smooth side towards the pump cover opening. **Note:** *On Oldsmobile engines, check the gear end clearance by resting a straightedge on the pump body. Try to slip a feeler gauge between the ends of the gears and the straightedge. The clearance should be between 0.0015- and 0.0085-inch. If it is not, the pump should be replaced with a new one. Lubricate the parts with engine oil.*

14 Install the cover and torque-tighten the screws to Specifications.

15 Turn the driveshaft to ensure that the pump operates freely.

Installation

16 To install, move the pump assembly into position and align the slot on the top end of the driveshaft with the drive tang on the lower end of the distributor. The distributor drives the oil pump, so it is essential that these two components mate properly. On Pontiac and Oldsmobile engines, the driveshaft fits into the distributor drive gear.

17 Install the bolts and tighten them securely. Pontiac engines require a new gasket between the pump body and the block.

18 Make sure the oil pump screen is parallel with the oil rails. The screen must be in this position to fit into the oil pan properly.

16 Flywheel/driveplate - removal and installation

Refer to illustrations 16.3 and 16.4

1 Raise the vehicle and support it securely on jackstands, then refer to Chapter 7 and remove the transmission.

2 Remove the pressure plate assembly and clutch disc (Chapter 8) (manual transmission equipped vehicles).

3 Use paint to draw a line from the fly-

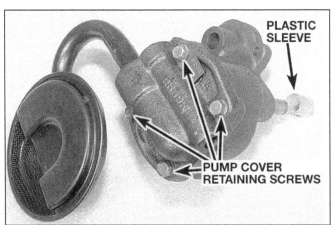

15.4 Remove the four cover bolts (arrows)

PLASTIC SLEEVE

PUMP COVER RETAINING SCREWS

16.3 To insure proper balance, mark the flywheel's relation to the crankshaft

16.4 A large screwdriver wedged in the starter ring gear teeth or one of the holes in the driveplate can be used to keep the flywheel/driveplate from turning as the mounting bolts are removed

17.5 Once the upper half of the seal has been adequately driven around the crankshaft, pull it out with a pair of pliers

wheel/driveplate to the end of the crankshaft for correct alignment during reinstallation (see illustration).

4   Remove the bolts that secure the flywheel/driveplate to the crankshaft rear flange. If difficulty is experienced in removing the bolts due to movement of the crankshaft, wedge a screwdriver to keep the flywheel/driveplate from turning (see illustration).

5   Remove the flywheel/driveplate from the crankshaft flange.

6   Clean any grease or oil from the flywheel/driveplate. On manual transmission equipped vehicles, inspect the surface of the flywheel for rivet grooves, burned areas and score marks. Light scoring can be removed with emery cloth. Check for cracked or broken teeth. Lay the flywheel on a flat surface and use a straightedge to check for warpage.

7   Clean the mating surfaces of the flywheel/driveplate and the crankshaft.

8   Position the flywheel/driveplate against the crankshaft, matching the alignment marks made during removal. Before installing the bolts, apply a non-hardening thread locking compound to the threads.

9   Wedge a screwdriver through the driveplate or into the ring gear teeth to keep the crankshaft from turning. Tighten the bolts to the specified torque in two or three steps, working in a criss-cross pattern.

10   The remainder of installation is the reverse of the removal procedure.

17   Rear main oil seal - replacement (engine in car)

Two-piece neoprene type seal

Refer to illustrations 17.5, 17.9, 17.13 and 17.14

1   Always replace both halves of the rear main oil seal as a unit. While the replacement of this seal is much easier with the engine removed from the car, the job can be done with engine in place.

2   Remove the oil pan and oil pump as described previously in this Chapter.

3   Remove the rear main bearing cap from the engine.

4   Using a screwdriver, pry the lower half of the oil seal from the bearing cap.

5   To remove the upper half of the seal, use a small hammer and a brass pin punch to roll the seal around the crankshaft journal. Tap one end of the seal with the hammer and punch (be careful not to strike the crankshaft) until the other end of the seal protrudes enough to pull the seal out with a pair of pliers (see illustration).

6   Clean all seal and foreign material from the bearing cap and block. Do not use an abrasive cleaner for this.

7   Inspect components for nicks, scratches or burrs at all sealing surfaces.

8   Coat the seal lips of the new seal with light engine oil. Do not get oil on the seal mating ends.

9   Included in the purchase of the rear main oil seal should be a small plastic installation tool. If not included, make your own by cutting an old feeler gauge blade or shim stock (see illustration).

10   Position the narrow end of this installation tool between the crankshaft and the seal seat. The idea is to protect the new seal from being damaged by the sharp edge of the seal seat.

11   Raise the new upper half of the seal into position with the seal lips facing towards the front of the engine. Push the seal onto its seat, using the installation tool as a protector against the seal contacting the sharp edge.

12   Roll the seal around the crankshaft, all the time using the tool as a "shoehorn" for protection. When both ends of the seal are flush with the engine block, remove the installation tool, being careful not to withdraw the seal as well.

13   Install the lower half of the oil seal in the bearing cap, again using the installation tool to protect the seal against the sharp edge (see illustration). Make sure the seal is firmly seated, then withdraw the installation tools.

17.9 Installation tool for neoprene rear main oil seals

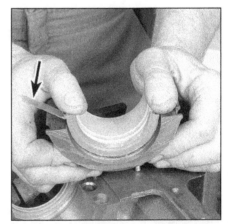

17.13 Use the protector tool (arrow) when pushing the seal into place

17.14 Sealant should be used where the rear main cap touches the engine block

14   Smear a bit of sealant on the bearing cap areas immediately adjacent to the seal ends **(see illustration)**.
15   Install the bearing cap (with seal) and torque the attaching bolts to about 10 to 12 ft-lbs only. Now tap the end of the crankshaft first rearward, then forward to line up the thrust surfaces. Retorque the bearing cap bolts to the proper Specification (See Chapter 2B for main bearing cap torque specifications).

Braided fabric (rope) type seal

Refer to illustrations 17.16a, 17.16b, 17.17 and 17.20

16   With the oil pan, oil pump and main bearing cap removed (see previous Sections), insert the special seal packing tool, available at most auto parts stores **(see illustration)** against the seal. Drive the old seal into its groove until it is packed tight at each end **(see illustration)**.
17   Measure the amount which the seal was driven upwards, then add 1/16-inch. Cut two pieces that length from the old seal taken from the bearing cap. Use the bearing cap as a guide when cutting **(see illustration)**.
18   Place a drop of sealant on each end of these seal pieces and then pack them into the upper groove to fill the gap made previously.
19   Trim the remaining material perfectly flush with the block. Be careful not to harm the bearing surface.
20   Install a new rope seal into the main bearing cap groove and push firmly all around using a hammer handle **(see illustration)** or a large diameter socket. Make sure the seal is firmly seated, then trim the ends flush with the bearing cap mating surface **(see illustration 17.17)**.
21   Install the cap and remaining components in reverse order, tightening all parts to Specifications (See Chapter 2B for main bearing cap torque specifications).

One-piece neoprene type seal

Refer to illustration 17.23

22   The one-piece rear main oil seal is

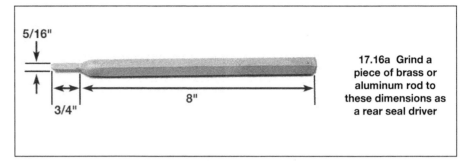

17.16a Grind a piece of brass or aluminum rod to these dimensions as a rear seal driver

5/16"
3/4"
8"

17.16b Drive each end of the seal into the groove until it feels tightly packed

installed in a bolt-on housing. Replacing this seal requires removal of the transmission, clutch assembly and flywheel (manual transmission) or the driveplate (automatic transmission). Refer to Chapter 7 for the transmission removal procedures and Section 16 of this Chapter for flywheel/driveplate removal.
23   Insert a screwdriver blade into the notches in the seal housing and pry out the old seal **(see illustration)**. Be sure to note how far it's recessed into the housing bore before removal so the new seal can be installed to the same depth. Although the

17.20 The new seal material used in the cap can be settled into the groove with a hammer handle or by taping it in with a hammer and large-diameter socket

17.17 Use the bearing cap as a holding fixture when cutting short sections of the old seal

seal can be removed this way, installation with the housing still mounted on the block requires the use of a special tool which attaches to the threaded holes in the crankshaft flange and then presses the new seal into place.
24   If the special installation tool is not available, remove the oil pan (see Section 14) and the bolts securing the housing to the block, then detach the housing and gasket. Whenever the housing is removed from the block a new seal and gasket must be installed. **Note:**

17.23 To remove the seal from the housing, insert the tip of the screwdriver into each notch and pry the seal out

The oil pan must be removed because the two rear most oil pan fasteners are studs that are part of the rear seal retainer, and the pan must come away enough to clear these studs to allow retainer removal and installation.

25 Clean the housing thoroughly, then apply a thin coat of engine oil to the lips of the new seal. Set the seal squarely into the recess in the housing, then, using two pieces of wood, one on each side of the housing, use a hammer or vise to press the seal into place.

26 Carefully slide the seal over the crankshaft and bolt the seal housing to the block. Be sure to use a new gasket, but don't use any gasket sealant.

27 The remainder of installation is the reverse of the removal procedure.

18.7 Typical engine mounting

18 Engine mounts - check and replacement

Refer to illustration 18.7

1 Engine mounts seldom require attention, but broken or deteriorated mounts should be replaced immediately or the added strain placed on the driveline components may cause damage.

Check

2 During the check, the engine must be raised slightly to remove the weight from the mounts. Disconnect the negative battery cable from the battery.

3 Raise the vehicle and support it securely on jackstands, then position the jack under the engine oil pan. Place a large block of wood between the jack head and the oil pan, then carefully raise the engine just enough to take the weight off the mounts.

4 Check the mounts to see if the rubber is cracked, hardened or separated from the metal plates. Sometimes the rubber will split right down the center. Rubber preservative may be applied to the mounts to slow deterioration.

5 Check for relative movement between the mount plates and the engine or frame (use a large screwdriver or pry bar to attempt to move the mounts). If movement is noted, lower the engine and tighten the mount fasteners.

Replacement

6 Remove the fan shroud mounting screws and place the shroud over the fan.

7 Remove the engine mount through-bolts **(see illustration)**.

8 Disconnect the shift linkage where it connects the transmission to the body (Chapter 7).

9 Raise the engine high enough to clear the clevis brackets. Do not force the engine

up too high. If it touches anything before the mounts are free, remove the part for clearance. Place a block of wood between the oil pan and crossmember as a safety precaution.

10 Unbolt the mount from the engine block and remove it from the vehicle. **Note:** *On vehicles equipped with self-locking nuts and bolts, replace them with new ones whenever they are disassembled. Prior to assembly, remove hardened residual adhesive from the engine block holes with a proper-size bottoming tap.*

11 Attach the new mount to the engine block and install the fasteners in the appropriate locations. Tighten the fasteners securely.

12 Remove the wooden block and lower the engine into place. Install the through-bolts and tighten the nuts securely.

13 Complete the installation by reinstalling all parts removed to gain access to the mounts.

Chapter 2 Part B
General engine overhaul procedures

Contents

Specifications

Chevrolet-built V8 engines

General

Displacement
- 5.0 liter (VIN G, H and U) ... 305 cubic inches
- 5.7 liter (VIN L) ... 350 cubic inches

Bore and stroke
- 305 cu in ... 3.736 x 3.48 in
- 350 cu in ... 4.000 x 3.48 in

Firing order
- V8 ... 1-8-4-3-6-5-7-2

Oil pressure (at 2400 rpm) ... 30 to 45 psi

Compression pressure
- Minimum ... 100 psi
- Allowable variation between cylinders ... 20 percent

Valves

Valve seat width
- Intake ... 1/32 to 1/16 inch
- Exhaust ... 1/16 to 3/32 inch

Valve spring installed height
- V8 engines
  - 1977 through 1979
    - Intake ... 1-23/32 inches
    - Exhaust ... 1-19/32 inches
  - 1980 and later ... 1-23/32 inches

Chevrolet-built V8 engines (continued)

Valves (continued)

Valve spring free length outer spring (all)	2.03 inches
Valve stem-to-guide clearance	
1977 through 1979 (305 cu in)	0.0010 to 0.0027 inch
1980	
305 cu in	
Intake..	0.001 to 0.0037 inch
Exhaust..	0.001 to 0.0047 inch
All others	0.0010 to 0.0027 inch

Engine block

Cylinder bore diameter	
305 cu in..	3.7350 to 3.7385 inches
350 cu in..	3.9995 to 4.0025 inches
Cylinder bore taper/out-of-round	Less than 0.0005 inch

Pistons and rings

Piston-to-bore clearance (measured at top of piston skirt)....................	0.0007 to 0.0027 inch
Piston ring end gap	
Top ring	0.010 to 0.030 inch
2nd ring	0.010 to 0.030 inch
Oil control rings	0.015 to 0.055 inch
Service limit (all)...	+0.010 inch
Piston ring side clearance	
Compression rings	0.0012 to 0.0032 inch
Oil control rings	0.002 to 0.008 inch

Crankshaft, connecting rods and main bearings

Connecting rod end play (total, both rods)...	0.008 to 0.014 inch
Crankshaft end play...	0.002 to 0.006 inch
Main bearing journal diameter	
No. 1 journal	2.4484 to 2.4493 inches
No. 2, 3 and 4 journal	2.4481 to 2.4490 inches
No. 5 journal	2.4479 to 2.4488 inches
Connecting rod journal diameter	2.0986 to 2.0998 inches
Rod and main journal taper/out-of-round limit	0.001 inch
Main bearing oil clearance	
No. 1 journal	0.001 to 0.0020 inch
No. 2, 3 and 4 journal	0.001 to 0.0025 inch
No. 5 journal	0.0017 to 0.0032 inch
Connecting rod bearing oil clearance...	0.0013 to 0.003 inch

Torque specifications*

	Ft-lbs (unless otherwise indicated)
Main bearing cap bolts	70 to 85
Connecting rod cap nut...	45
Rear oil seal housing bolts (when equipped)...	135 in-lbs

* **Note:** *Refer to Part A for additional torque specifications.*

Oldsmobile-built V8 engines

General

Displacement	
5.7 liter (VIN R)..	350 cubic inches
6.6 liter (VIN K)..	403 cubic inches
Bore and stroke	
350 cu in..	4.057 x 3.385 in
403 cu in..	4.351 x 3.385 in
Firing order	1-8-4-3-6-5-7-2
Oil pressure	30 to 45 @ 1500 rpm
Compression pressure	
Minimum..	100 psi
Allowable variation between cylinders	20%

Cylinder head

Warpage limit...	0.006 inch

Valves

Valve stem diameter	
Intake	0.3425 to 0.3432 inch
Exhaust	0.3420 to 0.3427 inch
Valve margin width (minimum)..	1/32 inch
Valve spring installed height..	1.67 inches
Valve stem-to-guide clearance	
Intake	0.0010 to 0.0027 inch
Exhaust	0.0015 to 0.0032 inch

Engine block

Cylinder bore diameter	
350 cu in..	4.057 inches
403 cu in..	4.351 inches
Cylinder bore taper/out-of-round	Less than 0.0005 inch
Piston-to-bore clearance...	0.0010 to 0.0020 inch

Pistons and rings

Piston ring end gap*	
Compression rings	0.010 to 0.020 inch
Oil ring	
350 cu in	0.015 to 0.035 inch
403 cu in	0.015 to 0.055 inch
Piston compression ring side clearance................................	0.0020 to 0.0040 inch

Crankshaft, connecting rods and main bearings

Connecting rod side clearance (total, both rods)	0.006 to 0.020 inch
Crankshaft end play..	0.0035 to 0.0135 inch
Main bearing journal diameter	
No.1 journal	2.4988 to 2.4998 inches
All other journals...	2.4985 to 2.4995 inches
Connecting rod journal diameter	2.1238 to 2.1248 inches
Main bearing oil clearance	
No. 1, 2, 3 and 4 journals	0.0005 to 0.0021 inch
No. 5 journal	0.0015 to 0.0031 inch
Connecting rod bearing oil clearance....................................	0.0005 to 0.0026 inch

Torque specifications*

	Ft-lbs
Main bearing cap bolts (rear no. 5).......................................	120
Main bearing cap bolts (no. 1 through no. 4)..........................	80
Connecting rod cap nut..	42

Note: Refer to Part A for additional torque specifications.

Pontiac-built V8 engines

General

Displacement	
4.3 liter (VIN S)...	265 cubic inches
4.9 liter (VIN Y, T and W)	301 cubic inches
5.7 liter (VIN M, N, E and P)...	350 cubic inches
6.6 liter (VIN R, S, T, P and Z)...	400 cubic inches
7.5 liter (VIN X, U, W and Y)	455 cubic inches
Bore and stroke	
265 cu in..	3.75 x 3.00 in
301 cu in..	4.00 x 3.00 in
350 cu in..	3.88 x 3.75 in
400 cu in..	4.12 x 3.75 in
455 cu in..	4.15 x 4.21 in
Firing order	1-8-4-3-6-5-7-2
Oil pressure	
All (except 265 and 301 cu in)..	55 to 60 psi @ 2600 rpm
265 and 301 cu in..	40 psi @ 2600 rpm
Compression pressure	
265 and 301 cu in..	120 to 160 psi @ 155 to 175 rpm
350 and 400 cu in (low compression engines).....................	150 to 170 psi @ 155 to 165 rpm
400 to 455 cu in (high compression engines)	185 to 210 psi @ 155 to 165 rpm
Allowable variation between cylinders	20%

Pontiac-built V8 engines

Cylinder head
Warpage limit .... 0.006 inch

Valves
Valve stem diameter
  Intake
    1977 and earlier .... 0.3416 inch
    1978 and later .... 0.3425 inch
  Exhaust
    1977 and earlier .... 0.3411 inch
    1978 and later .... 0.3425 inch
Valve margin width (minimum) .... 1/32 inch
Valve spring installed height
  1977 and earlier
    Two-barrel carb engines (except 301 cu in) .... 1-19/32 inches
    Four-barrel carb engines .... 1-9/16 inches
    301 cu in 1-21/32
  1978 and later
    265 and 301 cu in .... 1-21/32 inches
    400 cu in .... 1-35/64 inches
Valve stem-to-guide clearance
  Intake
    265 and 301 cu in .... 0.0010 to 0.0027 inch
    All others .... 0.0016 to 0.0033 inch
  Exhaust
    265 and 301 cu in (at top) .... 0.0010 to 0.0027 inch
    All others .... 0.0021 to 0.0038 inch

Engine block
Cylinder bore diameter (nominal)
  265 cu in .... 3.75 inches
  301 cu in .... 4.00 inches
  350 cu in .... 3.88 inches
  400 cu in .... 4.12 inches
  455 cu in .... 4.15 inches
Piston-to-bore clearance*
  1972 and earlier (all) .... 0.0025 to 0.0033 inch
  1973 and 1974 (350 and 400 cu in only) .... 0.0029 to 0.0037 inch
  1974 and later (455 cu in only) .... 0.0021 to 0.0029 inch
  1980 and 1981 (265 and 301 cu in only) .... 0.0017 to 0.0025 inch
  All others .... 0.0025 to 0.0033 inch
Measure pistons at top of skirt, perpendicular to pin

Pistons and rings
Piston ring end gap
  Compression rings
    1976 and earlier .... 0.010 to 0.020 inch
    1977 and later .... 0.010 to 0.025 inch
  Oil rings .... 0.010 to 0.035 inch
Piston ring side clearance (compression rings only)
  1976 and earlier .... 0.0015 to 0.0050 inch
  1977 and later .... 0.0015 to 0.0035 inch

Crankshaft, connecting rods and main bearings
Connecting rod side clearance (total, both rods)
  1977 and earlier (except 301 cu in) .... 0.012 to 0.017 inch
  1978 and later, and all 301 cu in .... 0.006 to 0.022 inch
Crankshaft end play .... 0.003 to 0.009 inch
Main bearing journal diameter
  455 cu in .... 3.2500 inches
  All others .... 3.0000 inches
Connecting rod journal diameter
  1977 and earlier .... 2.250 inches
  1978 and 1979 models .... 2.240 or 2.250 inches
  1980 and later .... 2.000 inches
Connecting rod bearing oil clearance .... 0.0005 to 0.0025 inch

Main bearing oil clearance
- 455 cu in .... 0.0005 to 0.0021 inch
- 1976 and earlier (except 455 cu in) .... 0.0002 to 0.0017 inch
- 1977 and later .... 0.0004 to 0.0020 inch

Torque specifications*   Ft-lbs

Main bearing cap bolts
- Rear (no. 5) main
  - 265 and 301 cu in 100
  - all other engines.. 120
- Caps no. 1 through no. 4
  - 265 and 301 cu in
    - with 7/16 in bolt... 70
    - with 1/2 in bolt.. 100
  - All other engines 100
- Connecting rod cap nut
  - 1976 and earlier.. 43
  - 265 and 301 cu in only 30
  - All others 40

* Note: *Refer to Part A for additional torque specifications.*

1 General information

Included in this portion of Chapter 2 are the general overhaul procedures for the cylinder heads and internal engine components.

The information ranges from advice concerning preparation for an overhaul and the purchase of replacement parts to detailed, step-by-step procedures covering removal and installation of internal engine components and the inspection of parts.

The following Sections have been written based on the assumption that the engine has been removed from the vehicle. For information concerning in-vehicle engine repair, as well as removal and installation of the external components necessary for the overhaul, see Part A of this Chapter and Section 7 of this Part.

The Specifications included in this Part are only those necessary for the inspection and overhaul procedures which follow. Refer to Part A for additional Specifications.

2 Engine overhaul - general information

Refer to illustration 2.4

It's not always easy to determine when, or if, an engine should be completely overhauled, as a number of factors must be considered.

High mileage is not necessarily an indication that an overhaul is needed, while low mileage doesn't preclude the need for an overhaul. Frequency of servicing is probably the most important consideration. An engine that's had regular and frequent oil and filter changes, as well as other required maintenance, will most likely give many thousands of miles of reliable service. Conversely, a neglected engine may require an overhaul very early in its life.

Excessive oil consumption is an indica-

tion that piston rings, valve seals and/or valve guides are in need of attention. Make sure that oil leaks aren't responsible before deciding that the rings and/or guides are bad. Perform a cylinder compression check to determine the extent of the work required (see Section 3).

Check the oil pressure with a gauge installed in place of the oil pressure sending unit **(see illustration)** and compare it to the Specifications. If it's extremely low, the bearings and/or oil pump are probably worn out.

Loss of power, rough running, knocking or metallic engine noises, excessive valve train noise and high fuel consumption rates may also point to the need for an overhaul, especially if they're all present at the same time. If a complete tune-up doesn't remedy the situation, major mechanical work is the only solution.

An engine overhaul involves restoring the internal parts to the specifications of a new engine. During an overhaul, the piston rings are replaced and the cylinder walls are reconditioned (rebored and/or honed). If a rebore is done by an automotive machine shop, new oversize pistons will also be installed. The main bearings, connecting rod bearings and camshaft bearings are generally replaced with new ones and, if necessary, the crankshaft may be reground to restore the journals. Generally, the valves are serviced as well, since they're usually in less-than-perfect condition at this point. While the engine is being overhauled, other components, such as the distributor, starter and alternator, can be rebuilt as well. The end result should be a like-new engine that will give many trouble-free miles. **Note:** *Critical cooling system components such as the hoses, drivebelts, thermostat and water pump MUST be replaced with new parts when an engine is overhauled. The radiator should be checked carefully to ensure that it isn't clogged or leaking (see Chapter 3). Also, we don't recommend overhauling the oil pump - always install a new one when an engine is rebuilt.*

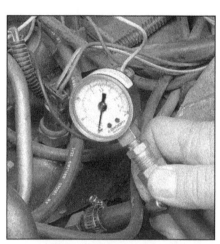

2.4 On Oldsmobile-built engines (shown) the sending unit is located at the top-front of the engine block. On Buick, and Pontiac engines, the sender is adjacent to the oil filter. On Chevrolet-built engines, the sender is located near the base of the distributor

Before beginning the engine overhaul, read through the entire procedure to familiarize yourself with the scope and requirements of the job. Overhauling an engine isn't difficult, but it is time consuming. Plan on the vehicle being tied up for a minimum of two weeks, especially if parts must be taken to an automotive machine shop for repair or reconditioning. Check on availability of parts and make sure that any necessary special tools and equipment are obtained in advance. Most work can be done with typical hand tools, although a number of precision measuring tools are required for inspecting parts to determine if they must be replaced. Often an automotive machine shop will handle the inspection of parts and offer advice concerning reconditioning and replacement. **Note:** *Always wait until the engine has been completely disassembled and all components, especially the engine block, have been*

3.5 If your engine has a coil-in-cap distributor, disconnect the wire from the BAT terminal on the distributor cap when checking the compression

3.6 A compression gauge with a threaded fitting for the plug hole is preferred over the type that requires hand pressure to maintain the seal

inspected before deciding what service and repair operations must be performed by an automotive machine shop. Since the block's condition will be the major factor to consider when determining whether to overhaul the original engine or buy a rebuilt one, never purchase parts or have machine work done on other components until the block has been thoroughly inspected. As a general rule, time is the primary cost of an overhaul, so it doesn't pay to install worn or substandard parts.

As a final note, to ensure maximum life and minimum trouble from a rebuilt engine, everything must be assembled with care in a spotlessly clean environment.

3   Cylinder compression check

Refer to illustrations 3.5 and 3.6

1   A compression check will tell you what mechanical condition the upper end (pistons, rings, valves, head gaskets) of your engine is in. Specifically, it can tell you if the compression is down due to leakage caused by worn piston rings, defective valves and seats or a blown head gasket. **Note:** *The engine must be at normal operating temperature and the battery must be fully charged for this check. Also, the choke valve must be all the way open to get an accurate compression reading (if the engine's warm, the choke should be open).*

2   Begin by cleaning the area around the spark plugs before you remove them (compressed air should be used, if available, otherwise a small brush or even a bicycle tire pump will work). The idea is to prevent dirt from getting into the cylinders as the compression check is being done.

3   Remove all of the spark plugs from the engine (see Chapter 1).

4   Block the throttle wide open.

5   On vehicles with "point-type" ignition, detach the coil wire from the center of the distributor cap and ground it on the engine block. Use a jumper wire with alligator clips on each end to ensure a good ground. On electronic ignition equipped vehicles, the ignition circuit should be disabled by unplugging the "BAT" wire going to the distributor. **(see illustration)**.

6   Install the compression gauge in the number one spark plug hole **(see illustration)**.

7   Crank the engine over at least seven compression strokes and watch the gauge. The compression should build up quickly in a healthy engine. Low compression on the first stroke, followed by gradually increasing pressure on successive strokes, indicates worn piston rings. A low compression reading on the first stroke, which doesn't build up during successive strokes, indicates leaking valves or a blown head gasket (a cracked head could also be the cause). Deposits on the undersides of the valve heads can also cause low compression. Record the highest gauge reading obtained.

8   Repeat the procedure for the remaining cylinders and compare the results to the Specifications.

9   Add some engine oil (about three squirts from a plunger-type oil can) to each cylinder, through the spark plug hole, and repeat the test.

10   If the compression increases after the oil is added, the piston rings are definitely worn. If the compression doesn't increase significantly, the leakage is occurring at the valves or head gasket. Leakage past the valves may be caused by burned valve seats and/or faces or warped, cracked or bent valves.

11   If two adjacent cylinders have equally low compression, there's a strong possibility that the head gasket between them is blown. The appearance of coolant in the combustion chambers or the crankcase would verify this condition.

12   If the compression is unusually high, the combustion chambers are probably coated with carbon deposits. If that's the case, the cylinder heads should be removed and decarbonized.

13   If compression is way down or varies greatly between cylinders, it would be a good idea to have a leak-down test performed by an automotive repair shop. This test will pinpoint exactly where the leakage is occurring and how severe it is.

4   Vacuum gauge diagnostic checks

Refer to illustration 4.5

1   A vacuum gauge provides valuable information about what is going on in the engine at a low cost. You can check for worn rings or cylinder walls, leaking head or intake manifold gaskets, vacuum leaks in the intake manifold, restricted exhaust, stuck or burned valves, weak valve springs, improper valve timing, and ignition problems. Vacuum gauge readings are easy to misinterpret, however, so they should be used in conjunction with other tests to confirm the diagnosis.

2   Both the absolute readings and the rate of needle movement are important for accurate interpretation. Most gauges measure vacuum in inches of mercury (in-Hg). The following references to vacuum assume the diagnosis is being performed at sea level. As elevation increases (or atmospheric pressure decreases), the reading will decrease. For every 1,000 foot increase in elevation above approximately 2000 feet, the gauge readings will decrease about one inch of mercury.

3   Connect the vacuum gauge directly to intake manifold vacuum, not to ported (throttle body) vacuum. Be sure no hoses are left disconnected during the test or false readings will result. **Note:** *Do not disconnect engine sensors or vacuum solenoids to connect the vacuum gauge. Disconnected engine control components can affect engine operation and produce abnormal vacuum gauge readings.*

4   Before you begin the test, warm the engine up completely. Block the wheels and set the parking brake. With the transmission in Park, start the engine and allow it to run at normal idle speed. **Warning:** *Keep your hands and the vacuum gauge clear of the fan.*

5 Read the vacuum gauge; an average, healthy engine should normally produce about 17 to 22 inches of vacuum with a fairly steady gauge needle at idle. Refer to the following vacuum gauge readings and what they indicate about the engine's condition **(see illustration)**.

6 A low steady reading usually indicates a leaking intake manifold gasket. this could be at one of the cylinder heads, between the upper and lower manifolds, or at the throttle body. Other possible causes are a leaky vacuum hose or incorrect camshaft timing.

7 If the reading is 3 to 8 inches below normal and it fluctuates at that low reading, suspect an intake manifold gasket leak at an intake port or a faulty fuel injector.

8 If the needle regularly drops about two to four inches at a steady rate, the valves are probably leaking. Perform a compression check or leakdown test to confirm this.

9 An irregular drop or downward flicker of the needle can be caused by a sticking valve or an ignition misfire. Perform a compression check or leakdown test and inspect the spark plugs to identify the faulty cylinder.

10 A rapid needle vibration of about four inches at idle combined with exhaust smoke indicates worn valve guides. Perform a leakdown test to confirm this. If the rapid vibration occurs with an increase in engine speed, check for a leaking intake manifold gasket or head gasket, weak valve springs, burned valves, or ignition misfire.

11 A slight fluctuation - one inch up and down - may mean ignition problems. Check all the usual tune-up items and, if necessary, run the engine on an ignition analyzer.

12 If there is a large fluctuation, perform a compression or leakdown test to look for a weak or dead cylinder or a blown head gasket.

13 If the needle moves slowly through a wide range, check for a clogged PCV system or intake manifold gasket leaks.

14 Check for a slow return of the gauge to a normal idle reading after revving the engine by quickly snapping the throttle open until the engine reaches about 2,500 rpm and let it shut. Normally the reading should drop to near zero, rise about 5 inches above normal idle reading, and then return to the previous idle reading. If the vacuum returns slowly and doesn't peak when the throttle is snapped shut, the rings may be worn. If there is a long delay, look for a restricted exhaust system (often the muffler or catalytic converter). One way to check this is to temporarily disconnect the exhaust ahead of the suspected part and repeat the test.

5 Engine removal - methods and precautions

If you've decided that an engine must be removed for overhaul or major repair work, several preliminary steps should be taken.

Locating a suitable place to work is extremely important. Adequate work space, along with storage space for the vehicle, will be needed. If a shop or garage isn't available, at the very least a flat, level, clean work surface made of concrete or asphalt is required.

Cleaning the engine compartment and engine before beginning the removal procedure will help keep tools clean and organized.

An engine hoist or A-frame will also be necessary. Make sure the equipment is rated in excess of the combined weight of the engine and accessories. Safety is of primary importance, considering the potential hazards involved in lifting the engine out of the vehicle.

If the engine is being removed by a novice, a helper should be available. Advice and aid from someone more experienced would also be helpful. There are many instances when one person cannot simultaneously perform all of the operations required when lifting the engine out of the vehicle.

Plan the operation ahead of time. Arrange for or obtain all of the tools and equipment you'll need prior to beginning the job. Some of the equipment necessary to perform engine removal and installation safely and with relative ease are (in addition to an engine hoist) a heavy duty floor jack, complete sets of wrenches and sockets as described in the front of this manual, wooden blocks and plenty of rags and cleaning solvent for mopping up spilled oil, coolant and gasoline. If the hoist must be rented, make sure that you arrange for it in advance and perform all of the operations possible without it beforehand. This will save you money and time.

Plan for the vehicle to be out of use for quite a while. A machine shop will be required to perform some of the work which the do-it-yourselfer can't accomplish without special equipment. These shops often have a busy schedule, so it would be a good idea to consult them before removing the engine in order to accurately estimate the amount of time required to rebuild or repair components that may need work.

Always be extremely careful when removing and installing the engine. Serious injury can result from careless actions. Plan ahead, take your time and a job of this nature, although major, can be accomplished successfully.

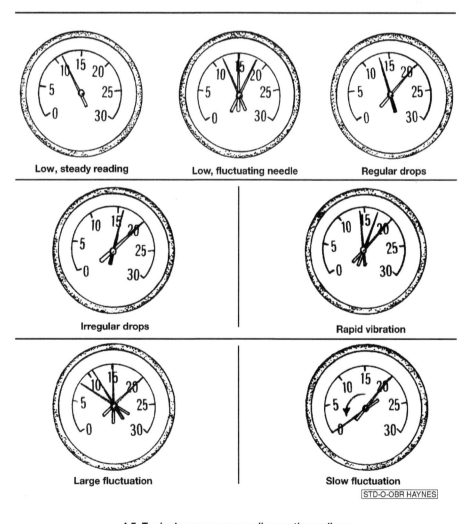

Low, steady reading · Low, fluctuating needle · Regular drops

Irregular drops · Rapid vibration

Large fluctuation · Slow fluctuation

STD-O-OBR HAYNES

4.5 Typical vacuum gauge diagnostic readings

6   Engine - removal and installation

Warning 1: *The air conditioning system is under high pressure! Have a dealer service department or service station discharge the system before disconnecting any A/C system hoses or fittings.*

Warning 2: *Gasoline is extremely flammable, so take extra precautions when you work on any part of the fuel system. Don't smoke or allow open flames or bare light bulbs near the work area, and don't work in a garage where a natural gas-type appliance (such as a water heater or a clothes dryer) with a pilot light is present. Since gasoline is carcinogenic, wear latex gloves when there's a possibility of being exposed to fuel, and, if you spill any fuel on your skin, rinse it off immediately with soap and water. Mop up any spills immediately and do not store fuel-soaked rags where they could ignite. When you perform any kind of work on the fuel system, wear safety glasses and have a Class B type fire extinguisher on hand.*

Removal

Refer to illustrations 6.5 and 6.20

1   Disconnect the cable from the negative terminal of the battery.

2   Cover the fenders and cowl and remove the hood (see Chapter 11). Special pads are available to protect the fenders, but an old bedspread or blanket will also work.

3   Remove the air cleaner assembly.

4   Drain the cooling system (see Chapter 1).

5   Label the vacuum lines, emissions system hoses, wiring connectors, and ground straps to ensure correct reinstallation, then detach them. Pieces of masking tape with numbers or letters written on them work well **(see illustration)**. If there's any possibility of confusion, make a sketch of the engine compartment and clearly label the lines, hoses and wires.

6   Label and detach all coolant hoses from the engine.

7   Remove the cooling fan, shroud and radiator (see Chapter 3).

8   Remove the drivebelts (see Chapter 1).

9   Disconnect the fuel lines running from the engine to the chassis (see Chapter 4). Plug or cap all open fittings/lines.

10   Disconnect the throttle linkage (and TV linkage/speed control cable, if equipped) from the engine (see Chapter 4).

11   On power steering equipped vehicles, unbolt the power steering pump (see Chapter 10). Leave the lines/hoses attached and make sure the pump is kept in an upright position in the engine compartment (use wire or rope to restrain it out of the way).

12   On A/C equipped vehicles, unbolt the compressor (see Chapter 3) and set it aside. Do not disconnect the hoses.

13   Drain the engine oil (see Chapter 1) and remove the filter.

14   Remove the starter motor (see Chapter 5).

15   Remove the alternator (see Chapter 5).

16   Unbolt the exhaust system from the engine (see Chapter 4).

17   If you're working on a vehicle with an automatic transmission, refer to Chapter 7 and remove the torque converter-to-driveplate fasteners.

18   Support the transmission with a jack. Position a block of wood between them to prevent damage to the transmission. Special transmission jacks with safety chains are available - use one if possible.

19   Attach an engine sling or a length of chain to the lifting brackets on the engine.

20   Roll the hoist into position and connect the sling to it **(see illustration)**. Take up the slack in the sling or chain, but don't lift the engine. **Warning:** *DO NOT place any part of your body under the engine when it's supported only by a hoist or other lifting device.*

21   Remove the transmission-to-engine block bolts.

22   Remove the engine mount-to-frame bolts.

23   Recheck to be sure nothing is still connecting the engine to the transmission or vehicle. Disconnect anything still remaining.

24   Raise the engine slightly. Carefully work it forward to separate it from the transmission. If you're working on a vehicle with an automatic transmission, be sure the torque converter stays in the transmission (clamp a pair of vise-grips to the housing to keep the converter from sliding out). If you're working

on a vehicle with a manual transmission, the input shaft must be completely disengaged from the clutch. Slowly raise the engine out of the engine compartment. Check carefully to make sure nothing is hanging up.

25   Remove the flywheel/driveplate and mount the engine on an engine stand.

Installation

26   Check the engine and transmission mounts. If they're worn or damaged, replace them.

27   If you're working on a manual transmission equipped vehicle, install the clutch and pressure plate (see Chapter 7). Now is a good time to install a new clutch.

28   Carefully lower the engine into the engine compartment - make sure the engine mounts line up.

29   If you're working on an automatic transmission equipped vehicle, guide the torque converter into the crankshaft following the procedure outlined in Chapter 7.

30   If you're working on a manual transmission equipped vehicle, apply a dab of high-temperature grease to the input shaft and guide it into the crankshaft pilot bearing until the bellhousing is flush with the engine block.

31   Install the transmission-to-engine bolts and tighten them securely. **Caution:** *DO NOT use the bolts to force the transmission and engine together!*

32   Reinstall the remaining components in the reverse order of removal.

33   Add coolant, oil, power steering and transmission fluid as needed.

34   Run the engine and check for leaks and proper operation of all accessories, then install the hood and test drive the vehicle.

35   Have the A/C system recharged and leak tested if any lines were disconnected.

7   Engine rebuilding alternatives

The do-it-yourselfer is faced with a number of options when performing an engine overhaul. The decision to replace the engine block, piston/connecting rod assemblies and crankshaft depends on a number of factors, with the number one consideration being the condition of the block. Other considerations

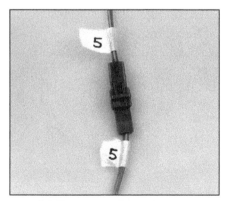

6.5   Flag each wire and hose to ease reassembly

6.20   Properly attached engine chain

are cost, access to machine shop facilities, parts availability, time required to complete the project and the extent of prior mechanical experience on the part of the do-it-yourselfer.

Some of the rebuilding alternatives include:

Individual parts - If the inspection procedures reveal that the engine block and most engine components are in reusable condition, purchasing individual parts may be the most economical alternative. The block, crankshaft and piston/connecting rod assemblies should all be inspected carefully. Even if the block shows little wear, the cylinder bores should be surface-honed.

Crankshaft kit - This rebuild package consists of a reground crankshaft and a matched set of pistons and connecting rods. The pistons will already be installed on the connecting rods. Piston rings and the necessary bearings will be included in the kit. These kits are commonly available for standard cylinder bores, as well as for engine blocks which have been bored to a regular oversize.

Short block - A short block consists of an engine block with renewed crankshaft and piston/connecting rod assemblies already installed. All new bearings are incorporated and all clearances will be correct. The existing cylinder head(s), camshaft, valve train components and external parts can be bolted to the short block with little or no machine shop work necessary.

Long block - A long block consists of a short block plus an oil pump, oil pan, cylinder heads, valve covers, camshaft and valve train components, timing sprockets, timing chain and timing cover. All components are installed with new bearings, seals and gaskets incorporated throughout. The installation of manifolds and external parts is all that is necessary.

Used engine assembly - While overhaul provides the best assurance of a like-new engine, used engines available from wrecking yards and importers are often a very simple and economical solution. Many used engines come with warranties, but always give any engine a thorough diagnostic check-out before purchase. Check compression, vacuum and also for signs of oil leakage. If possible, have the seller run the engine, ether in the vehicle or on a test stand so you can be sure it runs smoothly with no

knocking or other noises.

Give careful thought to which alternative is best for you and discuss the situation with local automotive machine shops, auto parts dealers or parts store countermen before ordering or purchasing replacement parts.

8   Engine overhaul - disassembly sequence

1   It's much easier to disassemble and work on the engine if it's mounted on a portable engine stand. A stand can often be rented quite cheaply from an equipment rental yard. Before the engine is mounted on a stand, the flywheel/driveplate should be removed from the engine.

2   If a stand isn't available, it's possible to disassemble the engine with it blocked up on the floor. Be extra careful not to tip or drop the engine when working without a stand.

3   If you're going to obtain a rebuilt engine, all external components must come off first, to be transferred to the replacement engine, just as they will if you're doing a complete engine overhaul yourself. These include:

Alternator and brackets

Emissions control components
Distributor, spark plug wires and spark plugs
Thermostat and housing cover
Water pump
Carburetor
Intake/exhaust manifolds
Oil filter
Engine mounts
Clutch and flywheel/driveplate
Engine rear plate

Note: *When removing the external components from the engine, pay close attention to details that may be helpful or important during installation. Note the installed position of gaskets, seals, spacers, pins, brackets, washers, bolts and other small items.*

4   If you're obtaining a short block, which consists of the engine block, crankshaft, pistons and connecting rods all assembled, then the cylinder heads, oil pan and oil pump will have to be removed as well. See Engine rebuilding alternatives for additional information regarding the different possibili-

ties to be considered.

5   If you're planning a complete overhaul, the engine must be disassembled and the internal components removed in the following order:

Rocker arm covers
Intake and exhaust manifolds
Rocker arms and pushrods
Valve lifters
Cylinder heads
Timing cover
Timing chain and sprockets
Camshaft
Oil pan
Oil pump
Piston/connecting rod assemblies
Crankshaft and main bearings

6   Before beginning the disassembly and overhaul procedures, make sure the following items are available. Also, refer to Engine overhaul - reassembly sequence for a list of tools and materials needed for engine reassembly.

Common hand tools
Small cardboard boxes or plastic bags for storing parts
Gasket scraper
Ridge reamer
Vibration damper puller
Micrometers
Telescoping gauges
Dial indicator set
Valve spring compressor
Cylinder surfacing hone
Piston ring groove cleaning tool
Electric drill motor
Tap and die set
Wire brushes
Oil gallery brushes
Cleaning solvent

9   Cylinder head - disassembly

Refer to illustrations 9.2, 9.3 and 9.4
Note: *New and rebuilt cylinder heads are commonly available for most engines at dealerships and auto parts stores. Due to the fact that some specialized tools are necessary for the disassembly and inspection procedures, and replacement parts may not be readily available, it may be more practical and economical for the home mechanic to purchase replacement heads rather than taking the time to disassemble, inspect and recondition the originals.*

1   Cylinder head disassembly involves removal of the intake and exhaust valves and related components. If they're still in place, remove the rocker arm nuts/bolts, ball pivots (if equipped) and rocker arms from the cylinder head studs. Label the parts or store them separately so they can be reinstalled in their original locations.

2   Before the valves are removed, arrange to label and store them, along with their related components, so they can be kept separate and reinstalled in the same valve guides they are removed from **(see illustration)**.

9.2 A small plastic bag, with an appropriate label, can be used to store the valve train components so they can be kept together and reinstalled in the correct guide

#3 Intake

9.3 Use a valve spring compressor to compress the spring, then remove the keepers from the valve stem

9.4 If the valve won't pull through the guide, deburr the edge of the stem end and the area around the top of the keeper groove with a file

10.12 Check the cylinder head gasket surface for warpage by trying to slip a feeler gauge under the straightedge (see the Specifications for the maximum warpage allowed and use a feeler gauge of that thickness)

3   Compress the springs on the first valve with a spring compressor and remove the keepers **(see illustration)**. Carefully release the valve spring compressor and remove the retainer, the spring and the spring seat (if used).

4   Pull the valve out of the head, then remove the oil seal from the guide. If the valve binds in the guide (won't pull through), push it back into the head and deburr the area around the keeper groove with a fine file or whetstone **(see illustration)**.

5   Repeat the procedure for the remaining valves. Remember to keep all the parts for each valve together so they can be reinstalled in the same locations.

6   Once the valves and related components have been removed and stored in an organized manner, the heads should be thoroughly cleaned and inspected. If a complete engine overhaul is being done, finish the engine disassembly procedures before beginning the cylinder head cleaning and inspection process.

10   Cylinder head - cleaning and inspection

1   Thorough cleaning of the cylinder head(s) and related valve train components, followed by a detailed inspection, will enable you to decide how much valve service work must be done during the engine overhaul. **Note:** *If the engine was severely overheated, the cylinder head is probably warped (see Step 12).*

Cleaning

2   Scrape all traces of old gasket material and sealing compound off the head gasket, intake manifold and exhaust manifold sealing surfaces. Be very careful not to gouge the cylinder head. Special gasket removal solvents that soften gaskets and make removal much easier are available at auto parts stores.

3   Remove all built up scale from the coolant passages.

4   Run a stiff wire brush through the various holes to remove deposits that may have formed in them.

5   Run an appropriate size tap into each of the threaded holes to remove corrosion and thread sealant that may be present. If compressed air is available, use it to clear the holes of debris produced by this operation. **Warning:** *Wear eye protection when using compressed air!*

6   Clean the rocker arm pivot stud threads, when equipped, with a wire brush.

7   Clean the cylinder head with solvent and dry it thoroughly. Compressed air will speed the drying process and ensure that all holes and recessed areas are clean. **Note:** *Decarbonizing chemicals are available and may prove very useful when cleaning cylinder heads and valve train components. They are very caustic and should be used with caution. Be sure to follow the instructions on the container.*

8   Clean the rocker arm components and pushrods with solvent and dry them thoroughly (don't mix them up during the cleaning process). Compressed air will speed the drying process and can be used to clean out the oil passages.

9   Clean all the valve springs, spring seats, keepers and retainers (or rotators) with solvent and dry them thoroughly. Do the components from one valve at a time to avoid mixing up the parts.

10   Scrape off any heavy deposits that may have formed on the valves, then use a motorized wire brush to remove deposits from the valve heads and stems. Again, make sure the valves don't get mixed up.

Inspection

Note: *Be sure to perform all of the following inspection procedures before concluding that machine shop work is required. Make a list of the items that need attention. The inspection procedures for the lifters and rocker arms, as well as the camshafts, can be found in Chapter 2A or 2B.*

Cylinder head

Refer to illustrations 10.12, 10.14a and 10.14b

11   Inspect the head very carefully for cracks, evidence of coolant leakage and other damage. If cracks are found, check with an automotive machine shop concerning repair. If repair isn't possible, a new cylinder head should be obtained.

12   Using a straightedge and feeler gauge, check the head gasket mating surface for warpage **(see illustration)**. If the warpage exceeds the specified limit, it can be resurfaced at an automotive machine shop.

13   Examine the valve seats in each of the combustion chambers. If they're pitted, cracked or burned, the head will require valve service that's beyond the scope of the home mechanic.

14   Check the valve stem-to-guide clearance with a small hole gauge and micrometer. Also check the valve stem deflection crosswise (parallel to the rocker arm) with a

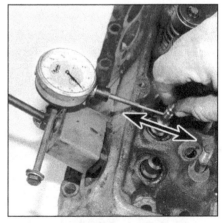

10.14a A dial indicator can be used to determine the valve stem-to-guide clearance (move the valve stem as indicated by the arrows)

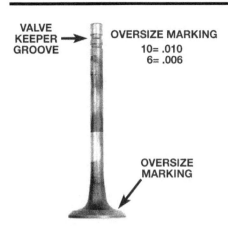

10.14b Some engines are equipped with slightly oversized valves from the factory. Valves with larger diameter stems are available to compensate for guide wear; however, a machine shop must resize the guides

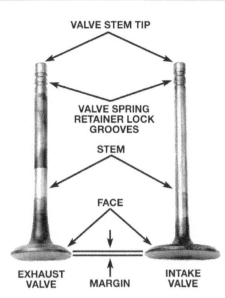

10.15 Check for valve wear at the points shown here - use a micrometer to measure the stem diameter at several points

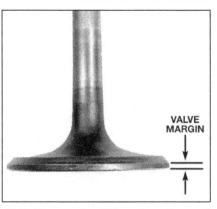

10.16 The margin width on the valve must be as specified - if the margin is smaller than specified, the valve cannot be reused

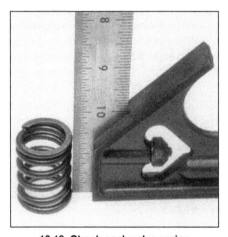

10.18 Check each valve spring for squareness

10.19 The exhaust valve rotators can be checked by turning the inner and outer sections in opposite directions - feel for smooth movement and excessive play

dial indicator attached securely to the head **(see illustration)**. The valve must be in the guide and approximately 1/16-inch off the seat. The total valve stem movement indicated by the gauge needle must be divided by two to obtain the actual clearance. After this is done, if there's still some doubt regarding the condition of the valve guides they should be checked by an automotive machine shop (the cost should be minimal). Sometimes oversize valves may be used to compensate for guide wear **(see illustration)**.

Valves

Refer to illustrations 10.15 and 10.16

15   Carefully inspect each valve face for uneven wear, deformation, cracks, pits and burned areas **(see illustration)**. Check the valve stem for scuffing and galling and the neck for cracks. Rotate the valve and check for any obvious indication that it's bent. Look for pits and excessive wear on the end of the stem. The presence of any of these conditions indicates the need for valve service by an automotive machine shop.
16   Measure the margin width on each valve **(see illustration)**. Any valve with a margin narrower than specified will have to be replaced with a new one.

Valve components

Refer to illustrations 10.18 and 10.19

17   Check each valve spring for wear (on the ends) and pits. Any springs that are shorter than specified have sagged and should not be reused. The tension of all springs should be checked with a special fixture before deciding that they're suitable for use in a rebuilt engine (take the springs to an automotive machine shop for this check).
18   Stand each spring on a flat surface and check it for squareness **(see illustration)**. If any of the springs are distorted or sagged, replace all of them with new parts.
19   Check the spring retainers (or rotators)

and keepers for obvious wear and cracks. Any questionable parts should be replaced with new ones, as extensive damage will occur if they fail during engine operation. Make sure the rotators operate smoothly with no binding or excessive play **(see illustration)**.

Rocker arm components

20   Check the rocker arm faces (the areas that contact the pushrod ends and valve stems) for pits, wear, galling, score marks and rough spots. Check the rocker arm pivot contact areas and pivot as well. Look for cracks in each rocker arm and nut or bolt.
21   Inspect the pushrod ends for scuffing and excessive wear. Roll each pushrod on a flat surface, like a piece of plate glass, to determine if it's bent.
22   Check the rocker arm studs in the cylinder heads for damaged threads and secure installation.
23   Any damaged or excessively worn parts must be replaced with new ones.
24   If the inspection process indicates that the valve components are in generally poor condition and worn beyond the limits specified, which is usually the case in an engine that's being overhauled, reassemble the valves in the cylinder head and refer to Section 11 for valve servicing recommendations.

11   Valves - servicing

1   Because of the complex nature of the job and the special tools and equipment needed, servicing of the valves, the valve seats and the valve guides, commonly known as a valve job, should be done by·a professional.

2   The home mechanic can remove and disassemble the heads, do the initial cleaning and inspection, then reassemble and deliver them to a dealer service department or an automotive machine shop for the actual service work. Doing the inspection will enable you to see what condition the heads and valvetrain components are in and will ensure that you know what work and new parts are

12.3 Positive type valve seals can be installed with a special installer or an appropriate-size deep socket - tap them down until they seat on the valve guide

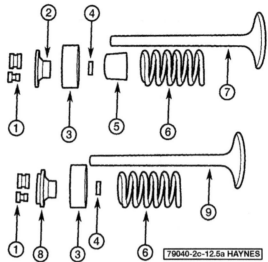

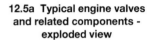

12.5a Typical engine valves and related components - exploded view

1   Keepers
2   Retainer
3   Oil shield
4   O-ring stem seal
5   Umbrella or positive type seal
6   Spring and damper
7   Intake valve
8   Retainer/rotator
9   Exhaust valve

required when dealing with an automotive machine shop.

3   The dealer service department, or automotive machine shop, will remove the valves and springs, recondition or replace the valves and valve seats, recondition the valve guides, check and replace the valve springs, spring retainers or rotators and keepers (as necessary), replace the valve seals with new ones, reassemble the valve components and make sure the installed spring height is correct. The cylinder head gasket surfaces will also be resurfaced if they're warped.

4   After the valve job has been performed by a professional, the heads will be in like-new condition. When the heads are returned, be sure to clean them again before installation on the engine to remove any metal particles and abrasive grit that may still be present from the valve service or head resurfacing operations. Use compressed air, if available, to blow out all the oil holes and coolant passages.

12   Cylinder head - reassembly

Refer to illustrations 12.3, 12.5a, 12.5b, 12.6 and 12.9

1   Regardless of whether or not the heads were sent to an automotive repair shop for valve servicing, make sure they are clean before beginning reassembly.

2   If the heads were sent out for valve servicing, the valves and related components will already be in place. Begin the reassembly procedure with Step 8.

3   Install new positive type seals on each of the intake valve guides (if originally equipped). Using a hammer and a deep socket, gently tap each seal into place until it is completely seated on the guide **(see illustration)**. Do not twist or cock the seals during installation or they will not seal properly on the valve stems. Umbrella-type seals (if originally equipped) are installed over the valves after the valves are in place (see Step 4).

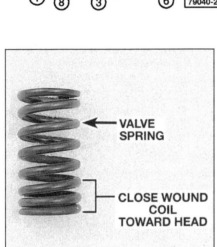

12.5b If the valve springs are wound closer at one end, install them as shown

Note: *Early model engines are typically equipped with O-ring stem seals only from the factory. Some later models engines are equipped with a positive type guide seal on the intake valve and O-ring stem seals on both the intake and exhaust valves. Other late model engines are equipped with a positive type guide seal on the intake valve, an umbrella type seal on the exhaust valve and O-ring stem seals on both the intake and exhaust valves.*

4   Beginning at one end of the head, lubricate and install the first valve. Apply moly-base grease or clean engine oil to the valve stem.

5   Drop the spring seat or shim(s) over the valve guide and set the valve springs, shield and retainer (or rotator) in place **(see illustrations)**.

6   Compress the springs with a valve spring compressor and carefully install the O-ring oil seal in the lower groove of the valve stem. Make sure the seal is not twisted - it must lie perfectly flat in the groove. Apply a

12.6 Apply a small dab of grease to each keeper as shown here before installation - it will hold them in place on the valve stem as the spring is released

small dab of grease to each keeper to hold it in place if necessary **(see illustration)** and position the keepers in the upper groove, then slowly release the spring compressor.

7   Repeat the procedure for the remaining valves. Be sure to return the components to their original locations - do not mix them up!

8   Check to see that all the keepers are seated in the retainers and installed properly.

9   Check the installed valve spring height with a ruler graduated in 1/32-inch increments or a dial caliper. If the heads were sent out for service work, the installed height should be correct (but don't automatically assume that it is). The measurement is taken from the top of each spring seat or shim(s) to the top of the oil shield (or the bottom of the retainer/rotator, the two points are the same) **(see illustration)**. If the height is greater than specified, shims can be added under the springs to correct it. **Caution:** *Do not, under any circumstances, shim the springs to the point where the installed height is less than specified.*

12.9 Be sure to check the valve spring installed height (the distance from the top of the seat/shims to the top of the oil shield)

13.1 A ridge reamer is required to remove the ridge from the top of the cylinder - do this before removing the pistons!

13.3 Check the connecting rod side clearance with a feeler gauge as shown

13.6 To prevent damage to the crankshaft journals and cylinder walls, slip sections of hose over the rod bolts before removing the pistons

10 On Chevrolet and Pontiac engines, apply moly-base grease to the rocker arm faces and the ball pivot, then install the rocker arms and pivots on the cylinder head studs. Thread the nuts on three or four turns only at this time (when the heads are installed, the nuts will be tightened following a specific procedure).

13 Pistons/connecting rod assembly - removal

Refer to illustrations 13.1, 13.3 and 13.6
Note: *Prior to removing the piston/connecting rod assemblies, remove the cylinder heads, the oil pan and the oil pump by referring to the appropriate Sections in ter 2A.*

1   Use your fingernail to feel if a ridge has formed at the upper limit of ring travel (about 1/4-inch down from the top of each cylinder). If carbon deposits or cylinder wear have produced ridges, they must be completely removed with a special tool **(see illustration)**. Follow the manufacturer's instructions provided with the tool. Failure to remove the

ridges before attempting to remove the piston/connecting rod assemblies may result in piston breakage.
2   After the cylinder ridges have been removed, turn the engine upside-down so the crankshaft is facing up.
3   Before the connecting rods are removed, check the end play with feeler gauges. Slide them between the first connecting rod and the crankshaft throw until the play is removed **(see illustration)**. The end play is equal to the thickness of the feeler gauge(s). If the end play exceeds the service limit, new connecting rods will be required. If new rods (or a new crankshaft) are installed, the end play may fall under the specified minimum (if it does, the rods will have to be machined to restore it - consult an automotive machine shop for advice if necessary). Repeat the procedure for the remaining connecting rods.
4   Check the connecting rods and caps for identification marks. If they aren't plainly marked, use a small center punch to make the appropriate number of indentations on

each rod and cap (1, 2, 3, etc., depending on the engine type and cylinder they're associated with).
5   Loosen each of the connecting rod cap nuts 1/2-turn at a time until they can be removed by hand. Remove the number one connecting rod cap and bearing insert. Don't drop the bearing insert out of the cap.
6   Slip a short length of plastic or rubber hose over each connecting rod cap bolt to protect the crankshaft journal and cylinder wall as the piston is removed **(see illustration)**.
7   Remove the bearing insert and push the connecting rod/piston assembly out through the top of the engine. Use a wooden hammer handle to push on the upper bearing surface in the connecting rod. If resistance is felt, double-check to make sure that all of the ridge was removed from the cylinder.
8   Repeat the procedure for the remaining cylinders.
9   After removal, reassemble the connecting rod caps and bearing inserts in their respective connecting rods and install the cap nuts finger tight. Leaving the old bearing inserts in place until reassembly will help prevent the connecting rod bearing surfaces from being accidentally nicked or gouged.
10   Don't separate the pistons from the connecting rods (see Section 18 for additional information).

14 Crankshaft - removal

Refer to illustrations 14.1, 14.3, 14.4a and 14.4b
Note: *The crankshaft can be removed only after the engine has been removed from the vehicle. It's assumed that the flywheel or driveplate, vibration damper, timing chain, oil pan, oil pump and piston/connecting rod assemblies have already been removed. If your engine is equipped with a one-piece rear main oil seal, the seal housing must be unbolted and separated from the block*

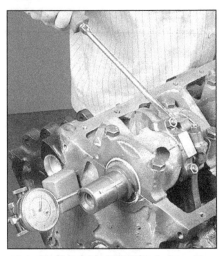

14.1 Checking crankshaft end play with a dial indicator

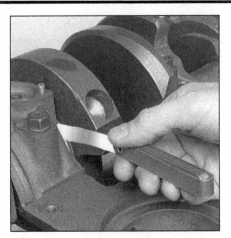

14.3 Checking crankshaft end play with a feeler gauge

14.4b The arrow on the main bearing cap indicates the front of the engine

14.4a Use a center punch or number stamping dies to mark the main bearing caps to ensure that they are reinstalled in their original locations on the block (make the punch marks near one of the bolt heads)

15.1 Use a hammer and a large punch to knock the core plugs sideways in their bores, then pull them out with pliers

before proceeding with crankshaft removal.

1   Before the crankshaft is removed, check the end play. Mount a dial indicator with the stem in line with the crankshaft and just touching one of the crank throws **(see illustration)**.

2   Push the crankshaft all the way to the rear and zero the dial indicator. Next, pry the crankshaft to the front as far as possible and check the reading on the dial indicator. The distance that it moves is the end play. If it's greater than specified, check the crankshaft thrust surfaces for wear. If no wear is evident, new main bearings should correct the end play.

3   If a dial indicator isn't available, feeler gauges can be used. Gently pry or push the crankshaft all the way to the front of the engine. Slip feeler gauges between the crankshaft and the front face of the thrust main bearing to determine the clearance **(see illustration)**.

4   Check the main bearing caps to see if they're marked to indicate their locations. They should be numbered consecutively from the front of the engine to the rear. If they aren't, mark them with number stamping dies or a center punch **(see illustration)**. Main bearing caps generally have a cast-in arrow, which points to the front of the engine **(see illustration)**. Loosen the main bearing cap bolts 1/4-turn at a time each, until they can be removed by hand. Note if any stud bolts are used and make sure they're returned to their original locations when the crankshaft is reinstalled.

5   Gently tap the caps with a soft-face hammer, then separate them from the engine block. If necessary, use the bolts as levers to remove the caps. Try not to drop the bearing inserts if they come out with the caps.

6   Carefully lift the crankshaft out of the engine. It may be a good idea to have an assistant available, since the crankshaft is quite heavy. With the bearing inserts in place in the engine block and main bearing caps, return the caps to their respective

locations on the engine block and tighten the bolts finger tight.

15 Engine block - cleaning

Refer to illustrations 15.1 and 15.10

1   Remove the core plugs from the engine block. To do this, knock one side of the plug into the block with a hammer and punch, then grasp them with large pliers and pull them back through the holes **(see illustration)**. **Caution:** *The core plugs (also known as freeze or soft plugs) may be difficult or impossible to retrieve if they're driven into the block coolant passages.*

2   Using a gasket scraper, remove all traces of gasket material from the engine block. Be very careful not to nick or gouge the gasket sealing surfaces.

3   Remove the main bearing caps and separate the bearing inserts from the caps and the engine block. Tag the bearings, indicating which cylinder they were removed from and whether they were in the cap or the block, then set them aside.

4   Remove all of the threaded oil gallery plugs from the block. The plugs are usually

very tight - they may have to be drilled out and the holes retapped. Use new plugs when the engine is reassembled.

5   If the engine is extremely dirty it should be taken to an automotive machine shop to be steam cleaned or hot tanked.

6   After the block is returned, clean all oil holes and oil galleries one more time. Brushes specifically designed for this purpose are available at most auto parts stores. Flush the passages with warm water until the water runs clear, dry the block thoroughly and wipe all machined surfaces with a light, rust preventive oil. If you have access to compressed air, use it to speed the drying process and to blow out all the oil holes and galleries. **Warning:** *Wear eye protection when using compressed air!*

7   If the block isn't extremely dirty or sludged up, you can do an adequate cleaning job with hot soapy water and a stiff brush. Take plenty of time and do a thorough job. Regardless of the cleaning method used, be sure to clean all oil holes and galleries very

15.10 A large socket on an extension can be used to drive the new core plugs into the bores

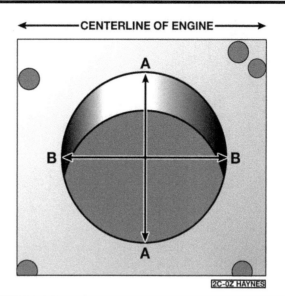

← CENTERLINE OF ENGINE →

16.4a Measure the diameter of each cylinder at a right angle to the engine centerline (A), and parallel to the engine centerline (B) - out-of-round is the difference between A and B - taper is the difference between A and B at the top of the cylinder and A and B at the bottom of the cylinder

thoroughly, dry the block completely and coat all machined surfaces with light oil.

8   The threaded holes in the block must be clean to ensure accurate torque readings during reassembly. Run the proper size tap into each of the holes to remove rust, corrosion, thread sealant or sludge and restore damaged threads. If possible, use compressed air to clear the holes of debris produced by this operation. Now is a good time to clean the threads on the head bolts and the main bearing cap bolts as well.

9   Reinstall the main bearing caps and tighten the bolts finger tight.

10   After coating the sealing surfaces of the new core plugs with Permatex no. 2 sealant, install them in the engine block (see illustration). Make sure they're driven in straight and seated properly or leakage could result. Special tools are available for this purpose, but a large socket, with an outside diameter that will just slip into the core plug, a 1/2-inch drive extension and a hammer will work just as well.

11   Apply non-hardening sealant (such as Permatex no. 2 or Teflon pipe sealant) to the new oil gallery plugs and thread them into the holes in the block. Make sure they're tightened securely.

12   If the engine isn't going to be reassembled right away, cover it with a large plastic trash bag to keep it clean.

16   Engine block - inspection

Refer to illustrations 16.4a, 16.4b and 16.4c

1   Before the block is inspected, it should be cleaned as described in Section 15.

2   Visually check the block for cracks, rust and corrosion. Look for stripped threads in the threaded holes. It's also a good idea to have the block checked for hidden cracks by an automotive machine shop that has the special equipment to do this type of work. If defects are found, have the block repaired, if possible, or replaced.

3   Check the cylinder bores for scuffing and scoring.

4   Check the cylinders for taper and out-of-round conditions as follows (see illustrations).

5   Measure the diameter of each cylinder at the top (just under the ridge area), center and bottom of the cylinder bore, parallel to the crankshaft axis.

6   Next, measure each cylinder's diameter at the same three locations across the crankshaft axis. Compare the results to the Specifications.

7   If the required precision measuring tools aren't available, the piston-to-cylinder clearances can be obtained, though not quite as accurately, using feeler gauge stock. Feeler gauge stock comes in 12-inch lengths and various thicknesses and is generally available at auto parts stores.

8   To check the clearance, select a feeler gauge and slip it into the cylinder along with the matching piston. The piston must be positioned exactly as it normally would be. The feeler gauge must be between the piston

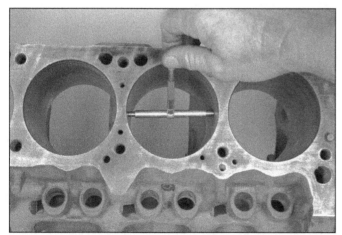

16.4b The ability to "feel" when the telescoping gauge is at the correct point will be developed over time, so work slowly and repeat the check until you are satisfied that the bore measurement is accurate

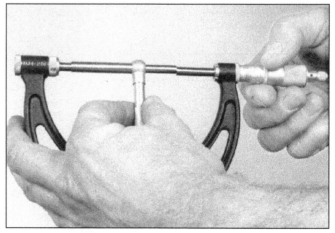

16.4c The gauge is then measured with a micrometer to determine the bore size

17.3a A "bottle brush" hone will produce better results if you have never honed cylinders before

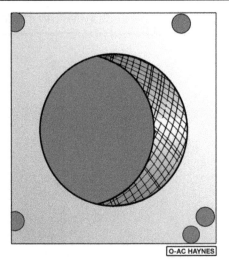

17.3b The cylinder hone should leave a smooth, crosshatch pattern with the lines intersecting at approximately a 45 to 60-degree angle

18.4a The piston ring grooves can be cleaned with a special tool, as shown here . . .

and cylinder on one of the thrust faces (90-degrees to the piston pin bore).

9   The piston should slip through the cylinder (with the feeler gauge in place) with moderate pressure.

10   If it falls through or slides through easily, the clearance is excessive and a new piston will be required. If the piston binds at the lower end of the cylinder and is loose toward the top, the cylinder is tapered. If tight spots are encountered as the piston/feeler gauge is rotated in the cylinder, the cylinder is out-of-round.

11   Repeat the procedure for the remaining pistons and cylinders.

12   If the cylinder walls are badly scuffed or scored, or if they're out-of-round or tapered beyond the limits given in the Specifications, have the engine block rebored and honed at an automotive machine shop. If a rebore is done, oversize pistons and rings will be required.

13   If the cylinders are in reasonably good condition and not worn to the outside of the limits, and if the piston-to-cylinder clearances can be maintained properly, then they don't have to be rebored. Honing is all that's necessary (see Section 17).

17   Cylinder honing

Refer to illustrations 17.3a and 17.3b

1   Prior to engine reassembly, the cylinder bores must be honed so the new piston rings will seat correctly and provide the best possible combustion chamber seal. **Note:** *If you don't have the tools or don't want to tackle the honing operation, most automotive machine shops will do it for a reasonable fee.*

2   Before honing the cylinders, install the main bearing caps and tighten the bolts to the specified torque.

3   Two types of cylinder hones are commonly available - the flex hone, or "bottle brush," type and the more traditional surfacing hone with spring-loaded stones. Both will

do the job, but for the less experienced mechanic the "bottle brush" hone will probably be easier to use. You'll also need some kerosene or honing oil, rags and an electric drill motor. Proceed as follows:

a)   *Mount the hone in the drill motor, compress the stones and slip it into the first cylinder* **(see illustration)**. *Be sure to wear safety goggles or a face shield!*

b)   *Lubricate the cylinder with plenty of honing oil, turn on the drill and move the hone up and down in the cylinder at a pace that will produce a fine crosshatch pattern on the cylinder walls. Ideally, the crosshatch lines should intersect at approximately a 60-degree angle* **(see illustration)**. *Be sure to use plenty of lubricant and don't take off any more material than is absolutely necessary to produce the desired finish.* **Note:** *Piston ring manufacturers may specify a smaller crosshatch angle than the traditional 60-degrees - read and follow any instructions included with the new rings.*

c)   *Don't withdraw the hone from the cylinder while it's running. Instead, shut off the drill and continue moving the hone up-and-down in the cylinder until it comes to a complete stop, then compress the stones and withdraw the hone. If you're using a "bottle brush" type hone, stop the drill motor, then turn the chuck in the normal direction of rotation while withdrawing the hone from the cylinder.*

d)   *Wipe the oil out of the cylinder and repeat the procedure for the remaining cylinders.*

4   After the honing job is complete, chamfer the top edges of the cylinder bores with a small file so the rings won't catch when the pistons are installed. Be very careful not to nick the cylinder walls with the end of the file.

5   The entire engine block must be washed again very thoroughly with warm, soapy water to remove all traces of the abrasive grit

produced during the honing operation. **Note:** *The bores can be considered clean when a lint-free white cloth - dampened with clean engine oil - used to wipe them out doesn't pick up any more honing residue, which will show up as gray areas on the cloth. Be sure to run a brush through all oil holes and galleries and flush them with running water.*

6   After rinsing, dry the block and apply a coat of light rust preventive oil to all machined surfaces. Wrap the block in a plastic trash bag to keep it clean and set it aside until reassembly.

18   Piston/connecting rod assembly - inspection

Refer to illustrations 18.4a, 18.4b, 18.10 and 18.11

1   Before the inspection process can be carried out, the piston/connecting rod assemblies must be cleaned and the original piston rings removed from the pistons. **Note:** *Always use new piston rings when the engine is reassembled.*

2   Using a piston ring installation tool, carefully remove the rings from the pistons. Be careful not to nick or gouge the pistons in the process.

3   Scrape all traces of carbon from the top of the piston. A hand-held wire brush or a piece of fine emery cloth can be used once the majority of the deposits have been scraped away. Do not, under any circumstances, use a wire brush mounted in a drill motor to remove deposits from the pistons. The piston material is soft and may be eroded away by the wire brush.

4   Use a piston ring groove cleaning tool to remove carbon deposits from the ring grooves. If a tool isn't available, a piece broken off the old ring will do the job. Be very careful to remove only the carbon deposits - don't remove any metal and do not nick or scratch the sides of the ring grooves **(see illustrations)**.

18.4b . . . or a section of a broken ring

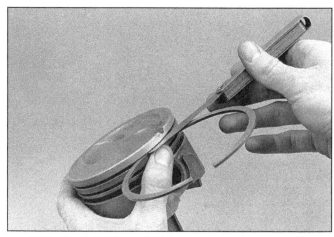

18.10 Check the ring side clearance with a feeler gauge at several points around the groove

5   Once the deposits have been removed, clean the piston/rod assemblies with solvent and dry them with compressed air (if available). Make sure the oil return holes in the back sides of the ring grooves are clear.

6   If the pistons and cylinder walls aren't damaged or worn excessively, and if the engine block is not rebored, new pistons won't be necessary. Normal piston wear appears as even vertical wear on the piston thrust surfaces and slight looseness of the top ring in its groove. New piston rings, however, should always be used when an engine is rebuilt.

7   Carefully inspect each piston for cracks around the skirt, at the pin bosses and at the ring lands.

8   Look for scoring and scuffing on the thrust faces of the skirt, holes in the piston crown and burned areas at the edge of the crown. If the skirt is scored or scuffed, the engine may have been suffering from over-heating and/or abnormal combustion, which caused excessively high operating temperatures. The cooling and lubrication systems should be checked thoroughly. A hole in the piston crown is an indication that abnormal combustion (preignition) was occurring. Burned areas at the edge of the piston crown are usually evidence of spark knock (detonation). If any of the above problems exist, the causes must be corrected or the damage will occur again. The causes may include intake air leaks, incorrect fuel/air mixture, incorrect ignition timing and EGR system malfunctions.

9   Corrosion of the piston, in the form of small pits, indicates that coolant is leaking into the combustion chamber and/or the crankcase. Again, the cause must be corrected or the problem may persist in the rebuilt engine.

10   Measure the piston ring side clearance by laying a new piston ring in each ring groove and slipping a feeler gauge in beside it **(see illustration)**. Check the clearance at three or four locations around each groove. Be sure to use the correct ring for each groove - they are different. If

the side clearance is greater than specified, new pistons will have to be used.

11   Check the piston-to-bore clearance by measuring the bore (see Section 16) and the piston diameter. Make sure the pistons and bores are correctly matched. Measure the piston across the skirt, at a 90-degree angle to and in line with the piston pin **(see illustration)**. Subtract the piston diameter from the bore diameter to obtain the clearance. If it's greater than specified, the block will have to be rebored and new pistons and rings installed.

12   Check the piston-to-rod clearance by twisting the piston and rod in opposite directions. Any noticeable play indicates excessive wear, which must be corrected. The piston/connecting rod assemblies should be taken to an automotive machine shop to have the pistons and rods resized and new pins installed.

13   If the pistons must be removed from the connecting rods for any reason, they should be taken to an automotive machine shop. While they are there have the connecting rods checked for bend and twist, since automotive machine shops have special equipment for this purpose. **Note:** *Unless new pistons and/or connecting rods must be installed, do not disassemble the pistons and connecting rods.*

14   Check the connecting rods for cracks and other damage. Temporarily remove the rod caps, lift out the old bearing inserts, wipe the rod and cap bearing surfaces clean and inspect them for nicks, gouges and scratches. After checking the rods, replace the old bearings, slip the caps into place and tighten the nuts finger tight. **Note:** *If the engine is being rebuilt because of a connecting rod knock, be sure to install new or remanufactured rods.*

19 Crankshaft - inspection

1   Clean the crankshaft with solvent and dry it with compressed air (if available). Be

18.11 Measure the piston diameter at a 90-degree angle to the piston pin and in line with it

sure to clean the oil holes with a stiff brush and flush them with solvent.

2   Check the main and connecting rod bearing journals for uneven wear, scoring, pits and cracks.

3   Rub a penny across each journal several times. If a journal picks up copper from the penny, it's too rough and must be reground.

4   Remove all burrs from the crankshaft oil holes with a stone, file or scraper.

5   Check the rest of the crankshaft for cracks and other damage. It should be magnafluxed to reveal hidden cracks - an automotive machine shop will handle the procedure.

6   Using a micrometer, measure the diameter of the main and connecting rod journals and compare the results to the Specifications. By measuring the diameter at a number of points around each journal's circumference, you'll be able to determine whether or not the journal is out-of-round. Take the measurement at each end of the journal, near the crank throws, to determine if the journal is tapered.

7   If the crankshaft journals are damaged, tapered, out-of-round or worn beyond the

limits given in the Specifications, have the crankshaft reground by an automotive machine shop. Be sure to use the correct size bearing inserts if the crankshaft is reconditioned.

8   Check the oil seal journals at each end of the crankshaft for wear and damage. If the seal has worn a groove in the journal, or if it's nicked or scratched, the new seal may leak when the engine is reassembled. In some cases, an automotive machine shop may be able to repair the journal by pressing on a thin sleeve. If repair isn't feasible, a new or different crankshaft should be installed.

9   Refer to Section 20 and examine the main and rod bearing inserts.

20   Main and connecting rod bearings - inspection

Refer to illustration 20.1

1   Even though the main and connecting rod bearings should be replaced with new ones during the engine overhaul, the old bearings should be retained for close examination, as they may reveal valuable information about the condition of the engine **(see illustration)**.

2   Bearing failure occurs because of lack of lubrication, the presence of dirt or other foreign particles, overloading the engine and corrosion. Regardless of the cause of bearing failure, it must be corrected before the engine is reassembled to prevent it from happening again.

3   When examining the bearings, remove them from the engine block, the main bearing caps, the connecting rods and the rod caps and lay them out on a clean surface in the same general position as their location in the engine. This will enable you to match any bearing problems with the corresponding crankshaft journal.

4   Dirt and other foreign particles get into the engine in a variety of ways. It may be left in the engine during assembly, or it may pass through filters or the PCV system. It may get into the oil, and from there into the bearings. Metal chips from machining operations and normal engine wear are often present. Abrasives are sometimes left in engine components after reconditioning, especially when parts are not thoroughly cleaned using the proper cleaning methods. Whatever the source, these foreign objects often end up embedded in the soft bearing material and are easily recognized. Large particles will not embed in the bearing and will score or gouge the bearing and journal. The best prevention for this cause of bearing failure is to clean all parts thoroughly and keep everything spotlessly clean during engine assembly. Frequent and regular engine oil and filter changes are also recommended.

5   Lack of lubrication (or lubrication breakdown) has a number of interrelated causes. Excessive heat (which thins the oil), overloading (which squeezes the oil from the bearing

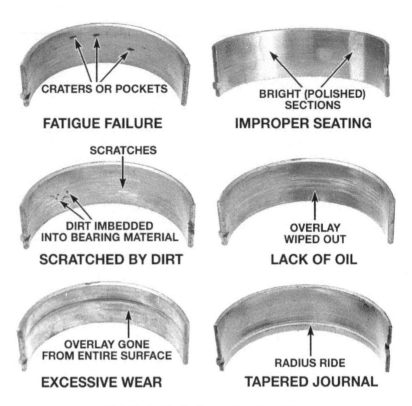

20.1 Typical indications of bearing failure

face) and oil leakage or throw off (from excessive bearing clearances, worn oil pump or high engine speeds) all contribute to lubrication breakdown. Blocked oil passages, which usually are the result of misaligned oil holes in a bearing shell, will also oil starve a bearing and destroy it. When lack of lubrication is the cause of bearing failure, the bearing material is wiped or extruded from the steel backing of the bearing. Temperatures may increase to the point where the steel backing turns blue from overheating.

6   Driving habits can have a definite effect on bearing life. Full throttle, low speed operation (lugging the engine) puts very high loads on bearings, which tends to squeeze out the oil film. These loads cause the bearings to flex, which produces fine cracks in the bearing face (fatigue failure). Eventually the bearing material will loosen in pieces and tear away from the steel backing. Short trip driving leads to corrosion of bearings because insufficient engine heat is produced to drive off the condensed water and corrosive gases. These products collect in the engine oil, forming acid and sludge. As the oil is carried to the engine bearings, the acid attacks and corrodes the bearing material.

7   Incorrect bearing installation during engine assembly will lead to bearing failure as well. Tight fitting bearings leave insufficient bearing oil clearance and will result in oil starvation. Dirt or foreign particles trapped behind a bearing insert result in high spots on the bearing which lead to failure.

21   Engine overhaul - reassembly sequence

1   Before beginning engine reassembly, make sure you have all the necessary new parts, gaskets and seals as well as the following items on hand:

Common hand tools
A 1/2-inch drive torque wrench
Piston ring installation tool
Piston ring compressor
Vibration damper installation tool
Short lengths of rubber or plastic hose to fit over connecting rod bolts
Plastigage
Feeler gauges
A fine-tooth file
New engine oil
Engine assembly lube or moly-base grease
Gasket sealant
Thread locking compound

2   In order to save time and avoid problems, engine reassembly must be done in the following general order:

New camshaft bearings (must be installed by an auto machine shop)
Piston rings
Crankshaft and main bearings
Piston/connecting rod assemblies
Oil pump - except external-mount type
Camshaft and lifters
Oil pan

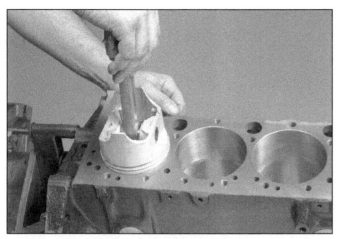

22.3 When checking piston ring end gap, the ring must be square in the cylinder bore (this is done by pushing the ring down with the top of a piston as shown)

22.4 With the ring square in the cylinder, measure the end gap with a feeler gauge

22.5 If the end gap is too small, clamp a file in a vise and file the ring ends (from the outside in only) to enlarge the gap slightly

22.9a Installing the spacer/expander in the oil control ring groove

22.9b DO NOT use a piston ring installation tool when installing the oil ring side rails

Timing chain and sprockets
Cylinder heads, pushrods and rocker
* arms*
Timing cover (and oil pump - external-
* mount type)*
Intake and exhaust manifolds
Rocker arm covers
Engine rear plate (if equipped)
Flywheel/driveplate

22 Piston rings - installation

Refer to illustrations 22.3, 22.4, 22.5, 22.9a, 22.9b and 22.12

1   Before installing the new piston rings, the ring end gaps must be checked. It's assumed that the piston ring side clearance has been checked and verified correct (see Section 18).

2   Lay out the piston/connecting rod assemblies and the new ring sets so the ring sets will be matched with the same piston and cylinder during the end gap measurement and engine assembly.

3   Insert the top (number one) ring into the first cylinder and square it up with the cylinder walls by pushing it in with the top of the piston **(see illustration)**. The ring should be near the bottom of the cylinder, at the lower limit of ring travel.

4   To measure the end gap, slip feeler gauges between the ends of the ring until a gauge equal to the gap width is found **(see illustration)**. The feeler gauge should slide between the ring ends with a slight amount of drag. Compare the measurement to the Specifications. If the gap is larger or smaller than specified, double-check to make sure you have the correct rings before proceeding.

5   If the gap is too small, it must be enlarged or the ring ends may come in contact with each other during engine operation, which can cause serious damage to the engine. The end gap can be increased by filing the ring ends very carefully with a fine file. Mount the file in a vise equipped with soft jaws, slip the ring over the file with the ends contacting the file face and slowly move the ring to remove material from the ends. When performing this operation, file only from the outside in **(see illustration)**.

6   Excess end gap isn't critical unless it's greater than 0.040-inch. Again, double-check to make sure you have the correct rings for your engine.

7   Repeat the procedure for each ring that will be installed in the first cylinder and for each ring in the remaining cylinders. Remember to keep rings, pistons and cylinders matched up.

8   Once the ring end gaps have been checked/corrected, the rings can be installed on the pistons.

9   The oil control ring (lowest one on the piston) is usually installed first. It's composed of three separate components. Slip the spacer/expander into the groove **(see illustration)**. If an anti-rotation tang is used, make sure it's inserted into the drilled hole in the ring groove. Next, install the lower side rail. Don't use a piston ring installation tool on the oil ring side rails, as they may be damaged. Instead, place one end of the side rail into the groove between the spacer/expander and the ring land, hold it firmly in place and slide a finger around the piston while pushing the rail into the groove **(see illustration)**. Next, install

22.12 Installing the compression rings with a ring expander - the mark (arrow) must face up

23.11 Lay the Plastigage strips (arrow) on the main bearing journals, parallel to the crankshaft centerline

the upper side rail in the same manner.
10   After the three oil ring components have been installed, check to make sure that both the upper and lower side rails can be turned smoothly in the ring groove.
11   The number two (middle) ring is installed next. It's usually stamped with a mark which must face up, toward the top of the piston. **Note:** *Always follow the instructions printed on the ring package or box - different manufacturers may require different approaches. Do not mix up the top and middle rings, as they have different cross sections.*
12   Use a piston ring installation tool and make sure the identification mark is facing the top of the piston **(see illustration)**, then slip the ring into the middle groove on the piston. Don't expand the ring any more than necessary to slide it over the piston.
13   Install the number one (top) ring in the same manner. Make sure the mark is facing up. Be careful not to confuse the number one and number two rings.
14   Repeat the procedure for the remaining pistons and rings.

---

23   Crankshaft - installation and main bearing oil clearance check

---

Refer to illustrations 23.11 and 23.15
1   Crankshaft installation is the first step in engine reassembly. It's assumed at this point that the engine block and crankshaft have been cleaned, inspected and repaired or reconditioned.
2   Position the engine with the bottom facing up.
3   Remove the main bearing cap bolts and lift out the caps. Lay them out in the proper order to ensure correct installation.
4   If they're still in place, remove the original bearing inserts from the block and the main bearing caps. Wipe the bearing surfaces of the block and caps with a clean, lint-free cloth. They must be kept spotlessly clean.

Main bearing oil clearance check

5   Clean the back sides of the new main bearing inserts and lay one in each main bearing saddle in the block. If one of the bearing inserts from each set has a large groove in it, make sure the grooved insert is installed in the block. Lay the other bearing from each set in the corresponding main bearing cap. Make sure the tab on the bearing insert fits into the recess in the block or cap. **Caution:** *The oil holes in the block must line up with the oil holes in the bearing insert. Do not hammer the bearing into place and don't nick or gouge the bearing faces. No lubrication should be used at this time.*
6   The flanged thrust bearing must be installed in the proper cap and saddle.
7   Clean the faces of the bearings in the block and the crankshaft main bearing journals with a clean, lint-free cloth.
8   Check or clean the oil holes in the crankshaft, as any dirt here can go only one way - straight through the new bearings.
9   Once you're certain the crankshaft is clean, carefully lay it in position in the main bearings.
10   Before the crankshaft can be permanently installed, the main bearing oil clearance must be checked.
11   Cut several pieces of the appropriate size Plastigage (they must be slightly shorter than the width of the main bearings) and place one piece on each crankshaft main bearing journal, parallel with the journal axis **(see illustration)**.
12   Clean the faces of the bearings in the caps and install the caps in their respective positions (don't mix them up) with the arrows pointing toward the front of the engine. Don't disturb the Plastigage.
13   Starting with the center main and working out toward the ends, tighten the main bearing cap bolts, in three steps, to the specified torque. Don't rotate the crankshaft at any time during this operation.
14   Remove the bolts and carefully lift off

23.15 Compare the width of the crushed Plastigage to the scale on the container to determine the main bearing oil clearance (always take the measurement at the widest point of the Plastigage); be sure to use the correct scale - standard and metric scales are included

the main bearing caps. Keep them in order. Don't disturb the Plastigage or rotate the crankshaft. If any of the main bearing caps are difficult to remove, tap them gently from side to side with a soft-face hammer to loosen them.
15   Compare the width of the crushed Plastigage on each journal to the scale printed on the Plastigage envelope to obtain the main bearing oil clearance **(see illustration)**. Check the Specifications to make sure it's correct.
16   If the clearance is not as specified, the bearing inserts may be the wrong size (which means different ones will be required). Before deciding that different inserts are needed, make sure that no dirt or oil was between the bearing inserts and the caps or block when the clearance was measured. If the Plastigage was wider at one end than the other, the journal may be tapered (refer to Section 19).

24.3 Use a wood hammer handle for installing the rear main bearing seal - fabric (rope) type seals

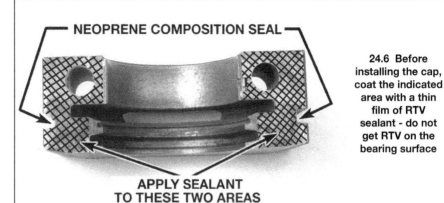

NEOPRENE COMPOSITION SEAL

24.6 Before installing the cap, coat the indicated area with a thin film of RTV sealant - do not get RTV on the bearing surface

APPLY SEALANT TO THESE TWO AREAS

17 Carefully scrape all traces of the Plastigage material off the main bearing journals and/or the bearing faces. Use your fingernail or the edge of a credit card - don't nick or scratch the bearing faces.

Final crankshaft installation

18 Carefully lift the crankshaft out of the engine. If the engine is equipped with a two piece rear main oil seal refer to Section 24 and install the seal halves into the cylinder block and the rear main bearing cap.
19 Clean the bearing faces in the block, then apply a thin, uniform layer of moly-base grease or engine assembly lube to each of the bearing surfaces. Be sure to coat the thrust faces as well as the journal face of the thrust bearing.
20 Make sure the crankshaft journals are clean, then lay the crankshaft back in place in the block.
21 Clean the faces of the bearings in the caps, then apply lubricant to them.
22 Install the caps in their respective positions with the arrows pointing toward the front of the engine.
23 Install the bolts.
24 Tighten all except the thrust bearing cap bolts to the specified torque (work from the center out and approach the final torque in three steps).
25 Tighten the thrust bearing cap bolts to 10-to-12 ft-lbs.
26 Tap the ends of the crankshaft forward and backward with a lead or brass hammer to line up the main bearing and crankshaft thrust surfaces.
27 Retighten all main bearing cap bolts to the specified torque, starting with the center main and working out toward the ends.
28 On manual transmission equipped models, install a new pilot bearing in the end of the crankshaft (see Chapter 8).
29 Rotate the crankshaft a number of times by hand to check for any obvious binding.
30 The final step is to check the crankshaft end play with a feeler gauge or a dial indicator as described in Section 14. The end play

should be correct if the crankshaft thrust faces aren't worn or damaged and new bearings have been installed.
31 If you are working on an engine with a one-piece rear main oil seal, refer to Section 24 and install the new seal, then bolt the housing to the block.

---

24 Rear main oil seal installation

Two-piece fabric (rope) type seal

Refer to illustrations 24.3 and 24.6
1 Braided fabric seals pressed into grooves formed in the crankcase and rear bearing cap are used to seal against oil leakage around the crankshaft. The crankshaft must be removed for this operation.
2 With the bearing caps and the crankshaft removed place the new seals in the grooves of the cylinder block and the rear main bearing cap with both ends projecting above the cap parting surface.
3 Use a handle of a hammer or similar tool to force the seal into the groove by rubbing down until the seal projects above the groove not more then 1/16-inch **(see illustration)**. Cut the ends of the seal flush with the surface of the cap with a single-edged razor blade.
4 Soak the neoprene seals (if equipped), which go into the grooves in the sides of the bearing cap in kerosene for one to two minutes.
5 Install the neoprene seals (if equipped) in the groove between the bearing cap and the crankcase. The seals are slightly undersized and swell in the presence of heat and oil. They are slightly longer than the groove in the bearing cap and must not be cut to fit.
6 Apply a small amount of RTV sealer at the joint where the bearing cap meets the crankcase to help eliminate oil leakage **(see illustration)**. A very thin coat is all that is necessary.
7 Install the bearing cap in the crankcase. Force the seals up into the bearing cap with a blunt instrument to be sure of a good seal at the upper parting line between the cap and case.

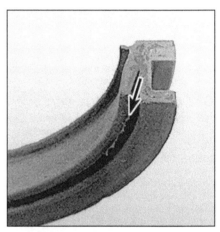

24.9 The rear main oil seal may have two lips - the oil seal (arrow) must point toward the front of the engine, which means that the dust seal will face out, toward the rear of the engine

Two-piece neoprene type seal

Refer to illustration 24.9
8 Inspect the rear main bearing cap and engine block mating surfaces, as well as the seal grooves, for nicks, burrs and scratches. Remove any defects with a fine file or deburring tool.
9 Install one seal section in the block with the lip facing the front of the engine (if the seal has two lips, the one with the helix must face the front) **(see illustration)**. Leave one end protruding from the block approximately 1/4- to 3/8-inch and make sure it's completely seated.
10 Repeat the procedure to install the remaining seal half in the rear main bearing cap. In this case, leave the opposite end of the seal protruding from the cap the same distance the block seal is protruding from the block.
11 During final installation of the crankshaft (after the main bearing oil clearances have been checked with Plastigage) as described in Section 23, apply a thin, even coat of anaerobic-type gasket sealant to the area of the cap adjacent to the seal **(see illustration 24.6)**. Don't get any sealant on the bearing

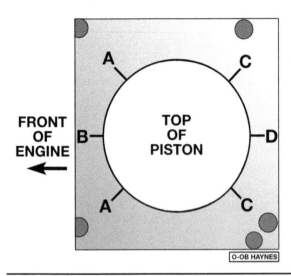

25.5 Ring end gap positions

A   Oil ring rail gaps
B   Second compression ring gap
C   Oil ring spacer gap (position in-between marks)
D   Top compression ring gap

25.9 The notch in each piston must face the FRONT of the engine as the pistons are installed

face, crankshaft journal, seal ends or seal lips. Also, lubricate the seal lips with moly-base grease or engine assembly lube.

One piece neoprene type seal

12   Some models are equipped with a one-piece seal that fits into a housing attached to the block. The crankshaft must be installed first and the main bearing caps bolted in place, then the new seal should be installed in the housing and the housing bolted to the block.
13   Before installing the crankshaft, check the seal contact surface very carefully for scratches and nicks that could damage the new seal lip and cause oil leaks. If the crankshaft is damaged, the only alternative is a new or different crankshaft.
14   The old seal can be removed from the housing with a screwdriver by prying it out from the front **(see illustration 17.23 in Chapter 2B)**. Be sure to note how far it's recessed into the housing bore before removing it; the new seal will have to be recessed an equal amount. Be very careful not to scratch or otherwise damage the bore in the housing or oil leaks could develop.
15   Make sure the housing is clean, then apply a thin coat of engine oil to the outer edge of the new seal. The seal must be pressed squarely into the housing bore, so hammering it into place is not recommended. If you don't have access to a press, sandwich the housing and seal between two smooth pieces of wood and press the seal into place with the jaws of a large vise. The pieces of wood must be thick enough to distribute the force evenly around the entire circumference of the seal. Work slowly and make sure the seal enters the bore squarely.
16   The seal lips must be lubricated with moly-base grease or engine assembly lube before the seal/housing is slipped over the crankshaft and bolted to the block. Use a new gasket - no sealant is required - and make sure the dowel pins are in place before installing the housing.
17   Tighten the screws a little at a time until they're all at the specified torque.

25   Piston/connecting rod assembly - installation and rod bearing oil clearance check

Refer to illustrations 25.5, 25.9 and 25.11

1   Before installing the piston/connecting rod assemblies, the cylinder walls must be perfectly clean, the top edge of each cylinder must be chamfered, and the crankshaft must be in place.
2   Remove the cap from the end of the number one connecting rod (refer to the marks made during removal). Remove the original bearing inserts and wipe the bearing surfaces of the connecting rod and cap with a clean, lint-free cloth. They must be kept spotlessly clean.

Connecting rod bearing oil clearance check

3   Clean the back side of the new upper bearing insert, then lay it in place in the connecting rod. Make sure the tab on the bearing fits into the recess in the rod. Don't hammer the bearing insert into place and be very careful not to nick or gouge the bearing face. Don't lubricate the bearing at this time.
4   Clean the back side of the other bearing insert and install it in the rod cap. Again, make sure the tab on the bearing fits into the recess in the cap, and don't apply any lubricant. It's critically important that the mating surfaces of the bearing and connecting rod are perfectly clean and oil-free when they're assembled.
5   Position the piston ring gaps at 120-degree intervals around the piston **(see illustration)**.
6   Slip a section of plastic or rubber hose over each connecting rod cap bolt.
7   Lubricate the piston and rings with clean engine oil and attach a piston ring compressor to the piston. Leave the skirt protruding about 1/4-inch to guide the piston into the cylinder. The rings must be compressed until they're flush with the piston.

8   Rotate the crankshaft until the number one connecting rod journal is at BDC (bottom dead center) and apply a coat of engine oil to the cylinder walls.
9   With the mark or notch on top of the piston **(see illustration)** facing the front of the engine, gently insert the piston/connecting rod assembly into the number one cylinder bore and rest the bottom edge of the ring compressor on the engine block.
10   Tap the top edge of the ring compressor to make sure it's contacting the block around its entire circumference.
11   Gently tap on the top of the piston with the end of a wooden hammer handle **(see illustration)** while guiding the end of the connecting rod into place on the crankshaft journal. The piston rings may try to pop out of the ring compressor just before entering the cylinder bore, so keep some downward pressure on the ring compressor. Work slowly, and if any resistance is felt as the piston enters the cylinder, stop immediately. Find out what's hanging up and fix it before proceeding. Do not, for any reason, force the piston into the cylinder - you might break a ring and/or the piston.

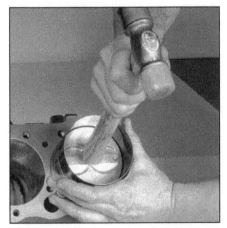

25.11 The piston can be driven (gently) into the cylinder bore with the end of a wooden hammer handle

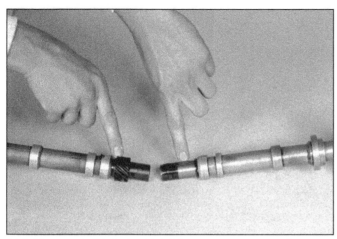

26.3 The pre-oil distributor (right) has the gear ground off and the advance weights (if equipped) removed

26.5 A drill motor connected to the modified distributor shaft drives the oil pump

12   Once the piston/connecting rod assembly is installed, the connecting rod bearing oil clearance must be checked before the rod cap is permanently bolted in place.

13   Cut a piece of the appropriate size Plastigage slightly shorter than the width of the connecting rod bearing and lay it in place on the number one connecting rod journal, parallel with the journal axis.

14   Clean the connecting rod cap bearing face, remove the protective hoses from the connecting rod bolts and install the rod cap. Make sure the mating mark on the cap is on the same side as the mark on the connecting rod.

15   Install the nuts and tighten them to the specified torque, working up to it in three steps. **Note:** *Use a thin-wall socket to avoid erroneous torque readings that can result if the socket is wedged between the rod cap and nut. If the socket tends to wedge itself between the nut and the cap, lift up on it slightly until it no longer contacts the cap. Do not rotate the crankshaft at any time during this operation.*

16   Remove the nuts and detach the rod cap, being very careful not to disturb the Plastigage.

17   Compare the width of the crushed Plastigage to the scale printed on the Plastigage envelope to obtain the oil clearance. Compare it to the Specifications to make sure the clearance is correct.

18   If the clearance is not as specified, the bearing inserts may be the wrong size (which means different ones will be required). Before deciding that different inserts are needed, make sure that no dirt or oil was between the bearing inserts and the connecting rod or cap when the clearance was measured. Also, recheck the journal diameter. If the Plastigage was wider at one end than the other, the journal may be tapered (refer to Section 19).

Final connecting rod installation

19   Carefully scrape all traces of the Plastigage material off the rod journal and/or

bearing face. Be very careful not to scratch the bearing; use your fingernail or the edge of a credit card.

20   Make sure the bearing faces are perfectly clean, then apply a uniform layer of clean moly-base grease or engine assembly lube to both of them. You'll have to push the piston into the cylinder to expose the face of the bearing insert in the connecting rod - be sure to slip the protective hoses over the rod bolts first.

21   Slide the connecting rod back into place on the journal, remove the protective hoses from the rod cap bolts, install the rod cap and tighten the nuts to the specified torque. Again, work up to the torque in three steps.

22   Repeat the entire procedure for the remaining pistons/connecting rods.

23   The important points to remember are:

a) *Keep the back sides of the bearing inserts and the insides of the connecting rods and caps perfectly clean when assembling them.*

b) *Make sure you have the correct piston/rod assembly for each cylinder.*

c) *The notch or mark on the piston must face the front of the engine.*

d) *Lubricate the cylinder walls with clean oil.*

e) *Lubricate the bearing faces when installing the rod caps after the oil clearance has been checked.*

24   After all the piston/connecting rod assemblies have been properly installed, rotate the crankshaft a number of times by hand to check for any obvious binding.

25   As a final step, the connecting rod end play must be checked. Refer to Section 13 for this procedure.

26   Compare the measured end play to the Specifications to make sure it's correct. If it was correct before disassembly and the original crankshaft and rods were reinstalled, it should still be right. If new rods or a new crankshaft were installed, the end play may be inadequate. If so, the rods will have to be removed and taken to an automotive machine shop for resizing.

26   Pre-oiling engine after overhaul

Refer to illustrations 26.3 and 26.5

1   After an overhaul it is a good idea to pre-oil the engine before it is installed in the vehicle and started for the first time. Pre-oiling will reveal any problems with the lubrication system at a time when corrections can be made easily and will prevent major engine damage. It will also allow the internal engine parts to be lubricated thoroughly in the normal fashion without the heavy loads associated with combustion placed on them.

2   The engine should be completely assembled with the exception of the distributor and rocker arm covers. The oil filter and oil pressure sending unit must be in place and the specified amount of oil must be in the crankcase (see Chapter 1).

3   An old distributor will be needed for this procedure - a salvage yard should be able to supply one for a reasonable price. In order to function as a pre-oil tool, the distributor must have the gear on the lower end of the shaft ground off **(see illustration)** and, if equipped, the advance weights on the upper end of the shaft removed.

4   Install the pre-oil distributor in place of the original distributor and make sure the lower end of the shaft mates with the upper end of the oil pump driveshaft. Turn the distributor shaft until they are aligned and the distributor body seats on the block. Install the distributor hold-down clamp and bolt.

5   Mount the upper end of the shaft in the chuck of an electric drill and use the drill to turn the pre-oil distributor shaft, which will drive the oil pump and circulate the oil throughout the engine **(see illustration)**. **Note:** *The drill must turn in a clockwise direction on Chevrolet built engines. On Pontiac and Oldsmobile-built engines, the shaft must be turned counterclockwise as viewed from above.*

6   It may take two or three minutes, but oil should soon start to flow out of all of the rocker arm holes, indicating that the oil pump

is working properly. Let the oil circulate for several seconds, then shut off the drill motor.

7   Remove the pre-oil distributor, then install the rocker arm covers. The distributor should be installed after the engine is installed in the vehicle, so plug the hole with a clean cloth.

27 Initial start-up and break-in after overhaul

Warning: *Have a fire extinguisher handy when starting the engine for the first time.*

1   Once the engine has been installed in the vehicle, double-check the engine oil and coolant levels.

2   With the spark plugs out of the engine and the ignition system disabled (see Section 3), crank the engine until oil pressure registers on the gauge or the indicator light goes out.

3   Install the spark plugs, hook up the plug wires and restore the ignition system functions (see Section 3).

4   Start the engine. It may take a few moments for the fuel system to build up pressure, but the engine should start without a great deal of effort. **Note:** *If backfiring occurs, recheck the valve timing and ignition timing.*

5   After the engine starts, it should be allowed to warm up to normal operating temperature. While the engine is warming up, make a thorough check for fuel, oil and coolant leaks.

6   Shut the engine off and recheck the engine oil and coolant levels.

7   Drive the vehicle to an area with minimum traffic, accelerate at full throttle from 30 to 50 mph, then allow the vehicle to slow to 30 mph with the throttle closed. Repeat the procedure 10 or 12 times. This will load the piston rings and cause them to seat properly against the cylinder walls. Check again for oil and coolant leaks.

8   Drive the vehicle gently for the first 500 miles (no sustained high speeds) and keep a constant check on the oil level. It is not unusual for an engine to use oil during the break-in period.

9   At approximately 500 to 600 miles, change the oil and filter.

10   For the next few hundred miles, drive the vehicle normally. Do not pamper it or abuse it.

11   After 2000 miles, change the oil and filter again and consider the engine broken in.

Chapter 3
Cooling system

Contents

Specifications

General

System type	Pressurized, with thermostatic control, and pump and fan assistance
Pressure cap setting	15 lbf/in2
Thermostat type	Wax pellet
Thermostat rating	195°F
Water pump	Impeller type
Radiator type	Crossflow
Cooling fan	Belt driven from engine
	Automatic fluid clutch fan on later models

Coolant capacity*		U.S. quarts
1970	W/350 cu in engine	19.6
	W/400 cu in engine	18.0
	W/455 cu in engine	17.2
1971-1972	W/350 cu in engine	19.5
	W/400 cu in engine	18.6
	W/455 cu in engine	18.0
1973	W/350 cu in engine	22.3
	W/400 cu in engine	22.3
	W/455 cu in engine	20.8
1974-1975	W/350 cu in engine	22.0
	W/400 cu in engine	22.0
	W/455 cu in engine	19.3
1976	W/350 cu in engine	21.2
	W/400 cu in engine	21.2
	W/455 cu in engine	23.3
1977	W/301 cu in engine (standard cooling)	19.1
	W/301 cu in engine (H.D. cooling)	20.1
	W/305 cu in engine	17.2
	W/350 cu in engine (VIN code R)	15.6
	W/350 cu in engine (VIN code P)	20.3
	W/400 cu in engine	20.4
	W/403 cu in engine	16.8
1978	W/305 cu in engine	17.2
	W/350 cu in engine	17.2
	W/400 cu in engine	19.7
	W/403 cu in engine	17.4
1979	W/301 cu in engine	19.9
	W/305 cu in engine	17.2
	W/350 cu in engine	17.2
	W/400 cu in engine	19.7
	W/403 cu in engine	17.4
1980	W/265 cu in engine	20.4
	W/301 cu in engine	20.4
	W/305 cu in engine	16.4

* with air conditioning add approximately 1 quart

Torque specifications

	Ft-lbs
Water outlet bolts	30
Water pump bolts	30
Temperature sender unit	20
Radiator mounting bolts	20
Fan fluid hub bolts	25

1   General description

The engine cooling system is of the pressurized type with pump and fan assistance. It comprises a radiator, flow and return water hoses, water pump, thermostat and vehicle interior heater.

The system is pressurized by means of a spring loaded radiator filler cap which prevents premature boiling by increasing the boiling point of the coolant. If the coolant temperature goes above this increased boiling point, the extra pressure in the system forces the radiator cap internal spring loaded valve off its seat and exposes the overflow pipe down which displaced coolant escapes.

It is important to check that the radiator cap is in good condition and that the spring behind the sealing washer has not weakened or corroded. Most service stations have a machine for testing that the cap operates at the specified pressure.

On vehicles built after 1972, a coolant recovery system is provided. This consists of a plastic reservoir into which the coolant which normally escapes down the overflow pipe is retained. When the engine cools and the coolant contracts, coolant is drawn back into the radiator and thus maintains the system at full capacity.

This is a continuous process and provided the level in the reservoir is correctly maintained, no topping up of the radiator or cooling system will be necessary.

The cooling system functions in the following manner. The water pump discharges engine coolant to each bank of cylinders; this flows from the front of each bank around each cylinder and towards the rear of the block. Passages in the block and cylinder head direct coolant around the inlet and exhaust ports and around the exhaust valve guide inserts. A metered amount of coolant is also diverted to cool the spark plug region.

When the thermostat is closed, coolant is re-directed through a small passage in the front right-hand cylinder head and block to a mating hole in the bottom of the water pump runner. At normal running temperature, the thermostat is open and coolant is directed from the intake manifold through the coolant outlet and thermostat to the radiator.

The radiator is of the crossflow type. Hot engine coolant enters the radiator at the top left-hand side, is cooled by the inrush of cold air through the core (this is created by the fan and ram-effect of air, resulting from forward motion of the vehicle) and returns to the engine via the outlet at the right-hand side.

Later models are fitted with a fluid-type fan coupling. This is a sealed unit, thermostatically controlled which " slips" the fan blades according to engine temperature and speed, to avoid overcooling with consequent loss of fuel economy.

2   Coolant level

Warning: *If the radiator cap has to be removed when the engine is hot, rotate the cap slowly counter-clockwise to the detent and allow the residual pressure to escape. Do not press the cap down until all hissing has stopped and keep the cap wrapped in a towel to protect your hand.*

Vehicles without expansion reservoir

1   The level of the coolant in the radiator should be maintained at 3 inches below the bottom of the filler neck. Carry out this check when the engine and coolant are cold.

Vehicles with expansion reservoir

Refer to illustration 2.2

2   The level of the coolant in the expansion reservoir should be maintained at the " FULL HOT" mark **(see illustration)**. Any checking and topping-up should be carried out with the engine and cooling system at normal operating temperature.

3   Antifreeze and inhibiting solutions

Warning 1: *Do not allow antifreeze to come in contact with your skin or painted surfaces of the vehicle. Flush contaminated areas immediately with plenty of water. Don't store new coolant or leave old coolant lying around where it's accessible to children or pets – they're attracted by its sweet smell. Ingestion of even a small amount of coolant can be fatal! Wipe up garage floor and drip pan spills immediately. Keep antifreeze containers covered and repair cooling system leaks as soon as they're noticed. Check with local authorities about disposing of used antifreeze. Many communities have collection centers which will see that antifreeze is disposed of safely. Never dump used antifreeze on the ground or pour it into drains.*

Warning 2: *DO NOT remove the radiator cap or the coolant recovery cap while the cooling system is hot as escaping steam could cause serious injury.*

1   It is recommended that the cooling sys-

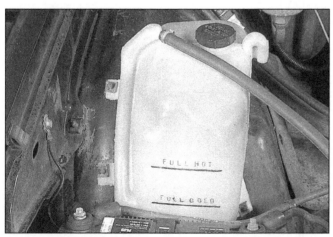
2.2 Maintain the coolant level at FULL HOT

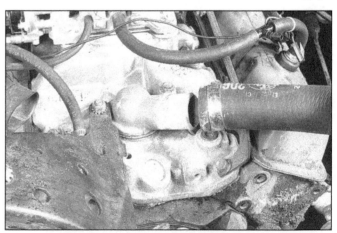
4.5 Disconnecting the upper radiator hose from the thermostat housing

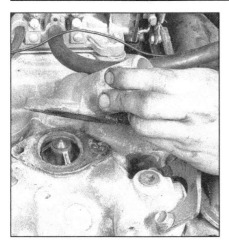

4.6 As the housing is lifted away from the engine, the thermostat becomes visible

4.7 Lift the thermostat out of its bore, noting how it is installed

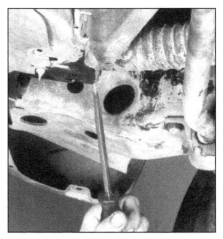

6.3 Disconnecting the lower radiator hose from the bottom of the radiator

tem be filled with a water/ethylene glycol based antifreeze solution which will give protection down to at least -20°F at all times. This provides protection against corrosion and increases the coolant boiling point. When handling antifreeze, take care that it is not spilled on the vehicle paintwork, since it will invariably cause damage if not removed immediately.

2   The cooling system should be drained, flushed and refilled every alternate Fall. The use of antifreeze solutions for periods of longer than two years is likely to cause damage and encourage the formation of rust and scale due to the corrosion inhibitors gradually losing their efficiency.

3   Before adding antifreeze to the system, check all hose connections.

4   The exact mixture of antifreeze to water which you should use depends upon the relative weather conditions. The mixture should contain at least 50 percent antifreeze, offering protection to -34°F. Under no circumstances should the mixture contain more than 70 percent antifreeze.

4   Thermostat- removal and installation

Refer to illustrations 4.5, 4.6 and 4.7

1   The thermostat is basically a restriction valve which is actuated by a thermostatic element. It is mounted inside a housing on the engine and is designed to open and close at predetermined temperatures to allow coolant to warm-up the engine or cool it.

2   To remove the thermostat for replacement or testing, begin by disconnecting the negative battery cable.

3   Remove the air cleaner for better working access.

4   Drain the coolant into a suitable container for disposal. See Chapter 1 for more information on this. It is not necessary to drain the coolant from the engine.

5   Disconnect the upper radiator hose from

the thermostat housing **(see illustration)**.

6   Remove the thermostat housing bolts and the housing from the engine **(see illustration)**. On some models, the alternator mounting bracket will have to be disconnected first, as this bracket is attached to the housing mounting stud. Also, late model vehicles may have a TVS switch installed in the thermostat housing. If this is the case, disconnect each of the vacuum hoses on the switch (noting their installed positions) and then unscrew the switch from the housing.

7   After lifting the thermostat housing from the engine, the thermostat can be removed from the engine. Note how the thermostat sits in the recess, as it must be replaced in this same position **(see illustration)**.

8   Before installation, use a gasket scraper or putty knife to carefully remove all traces of the old gasket on the thermostat housing and the engine sealing surface. Do not allow the gasket particles to drop down into the intake manifold.

9   Place a 1/8 inch bead of RTV or equivalent sealer around the sealing surface on the engine and place the thermostat into its recess.

10   Immediately place the thermostat housing with sealer and a new gasket into position and torque-tighten the attaching bolts.

11   Where applicable, install the alternator brace and/or the TVS switch and vacuum hoses.

12   Connect the upper radiator hose and tighten the hose clamp securely.

13   Connect the negative battery cable and fill the radiator with the proper amount of antifreeze and water (see Chapter 1).

14   With the radiator cap removed, start the engine and run, until the upper radiator hose becomes hot. When this hose is hot, the thermostat should be in the open position. At this point, add more coolant if necessary to reach the top of the filler neck.

15   Install the radiator cap, making sure the arrows are aligned with the overflow hose.

5   Thermostat - testing

1   The only way to test the operation of the thermostat is with the unit removed from the engine. In most cases if the thermostat is suspect it is more economical to merely buy a replacement thermostat as they are not very costly.

2   To test, first remove the thermostat as described in Section 4.

3   Inspect the thermostat for excessive corrosion or damage. Replace the thermostat with a new one if either of these conditions is found.

4   Place the thermostat in hot water 25 degrees above the temperature stamped on the thermostat. Since nearly all Pontiac V8 engines use a 195-degree thermostat. The water temperature will be approximately 220. When submerged in this water (which should be agitated thoroughly), the valve should fully open.

5   Now, remove the thermostat using a piece of bent wire and place it in water which is 10 degrees below the temperature on the thermostat. In most cases this cooler water temperature should be 185 degrees. At this temperature the thermostat valve should close fully.

6   Reinstall the thermostat if it checks out OK, or purchase a new thermostat of the same temperature rating. See Section 4 for installing the thermostat.

6   Radiator - removal and installation

Refer to illustrations 6.3, 6.4a, 6.4b, 6.5a, 6.5b, 6.6a and 6.6b

1   Disconnect the negative battery cable.

2   Drain the radiator referring to Chapter 1.

3   Disconnect the radiator upper and lower hoses and the automatic transmission cooling lines if applicable **(see illustration)**.

4   Disconnect the radiator shroud and

6.4a Screws secure the fan shroud to the radiator

6.4b With the shroud disconnected, hang it over the fan, away from the radiator

hang it over the fan. The shroud is attached with screws going into the radiator with clips or staples across the bottom **(see illustrations)**.

5   Remove the upper metal panel at the top of the radiator **(see illustrations)**.

6   Lift the radiator straight up and out of the engine compartment **(see illustrations)**. Be careful not to scratch the paint on the front nosepiece. If coolant drips on any body paint, immediately wash it off with clear water as the antifreeze solution can damage the finish.

7   With the radiator removed, it can be inspected for leaks or damage. If in need of repairs, have a professional radiator shop or dealer perform the work as special welding techniques are required.

8   Bugs and dirt can be cleaned from the radiator by using compressed air and a soft brush. Do not bend the cooling fins as this is done.

9   Inspect the rubber mounting pads which the radiator sits on and replace as necessary.

10   Lift the radiator into position making sure it is seated in the mounting pads.

11   Install the upper panel, shroud and hoses in the reverse order of removal.

12   Connect the negative battery cable and fill the radiator as described in Chapter 1.

13   Start the engine and check for leaks. Allow the engine to reach normal operating temperature (upper radiator hose hot) and add coolant until the level reaches the bottom of the filler neck.

14   Install cap with arrows aligned with the overflow tube.

7   Water pump - testing

Refer to illustrations 7.4

1   A failure in the water pump can cause serious engine damage due to overheating. The pump will not be able to circulate cooled water through the engine.

2   There are three ways in which to check the operation of the water pump while it is still installed on the engine. If the pump is suspect, it should be replaced with a new or factory-rebuilt unit.

3   With the engine warmed up to normal operating temperature, squeeze the upper

radiator hose. If the water pump is working properly, a pressure surge should be felt as the hose is released.

4   Water pumps are equipped with " weep" or vent holes **(see illustration)**. If a failure occurs to the seal of the pump, small amounts of water will leak from these "weep" holes. In most cases it will be necessary to use a flashlight from under the car to see evidence of leakage from this point in the pump body.

5   If the water pump shaft bearings fail there may be a squealing sound at the front of the engine while it is running. Shaft wear can be felt if the water pump pulley is forced up and down. Do not mistake drive belt slippage, which also causes a squealing sound, for water pump failure.

8   Water pump - removal and installation

Refer to illustrations 8.3, 8.7, 8.8, 8.10, 8.11, 8.12, 8.13a, 8.13b, 8.14, 8.15 and 8.16
Note: *It is not economical or practical to overhaul a water pump. If failure occurs, a*

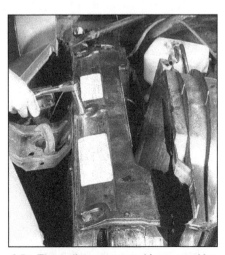

6.5a The radiator top panel is secured by bolts across the top

6.5b Lifting the radiator top plate away from the radiator

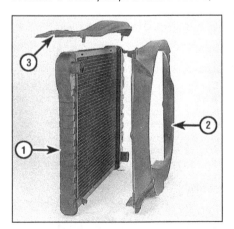

6.6a Typical radiator mount and shroud

1   *Radiator*
2   *Radiator shroud*
3   *Mounting panel*

6.6b With the top plate removed, the radiator can be lifted from the engine compartment

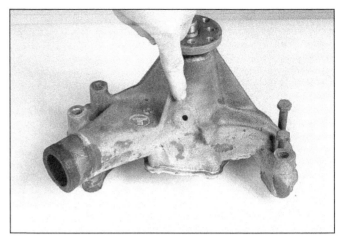

7.4 The " weep" hole out of which water leaks when the internal seal has failed

8.3 Removing the fan from the engine compartment

8.7 Lifting the drive belt pulley from the water pump shaft

new or rebuilt unit should be purchased to replace the faulty water pump.

1   Disconnect the negative battery cable.
2   Drain the radiator, referring to Chapter 1 if necessary.
3   Reaching inside the radiator shroud, remove the bolts which secure the fan to the water pump hub. Remove the fan and spacer (if equipped) **(see illustration)**. A thermostatic fan clutch must remain in the " in- car" position.
4   Remove the bolts which secure the radiator shroud to the radiator and lift the shroud up and out of the engine compartment (see Section 6).
5   Loosen the two mounting bolts for the alternator. There is an adjusting strap bolt located in the slotted bracket and a long pivot bolt under the alternator.
6   Push the alternator inward to relieve tension on the drive belt and then remove the drive belt from the alternator and water pump pulleys.
7   Remove the water pump pulley from the hub **(see illustration)**.
8   Completely remove the alternator strap bolt and pivot the alternator away from the water pump. Now remove the alternator

mounting bracket which is secured at the thermostat housing on the top of the engine with one of the water pump bolts. Remove the negative battery cable and then lift the mounting bracket off the engine **(see illustration)**.

9   Disconnect the wiring at the rear of the alternator using identifying pieces of tape if necessary to help in reinstallation.
10   Remove the alternator pivot bolt and lift the alternator off the engine **(see illustration)**.

8.8 The alternator bracket must be removed for access to the water pump

8.10 Removing the alternator from its brackets

8.11 This bracket for the AIR pump mounts to the water pump and so must be removed

8.12 The long pivot bolt for the power steering pump also mounts to the water pump

11   Loosen the two mounting bolts for the AIR pump. Completely remove the bracket which is attached to the water pump, then pivot the AIR pump away from the engine **(see illustration)**. On some models, the AIR pump pulley must first be removed from the

pump to gain access to the bracket bolts.
12   If equipped with power steering, loosen the adjusting bolt and completely remove the pivot bolt which passes through the water pump **(see illustration)**. Swing the pump away from the engine as far as possible with-

out crimping the hoses.
13   Disconnect the lower radiator hose, heater hose and by-pass hose (if equipped) from the water pump housing **(see illustrations)**.
14   Remove the remaining bolts which

8.13a Disconnecting the lower radiator hose from the water pump

8.13b Disconnecting the heater hose from the top of the water pump

8.14 Removing the water pump from the engine

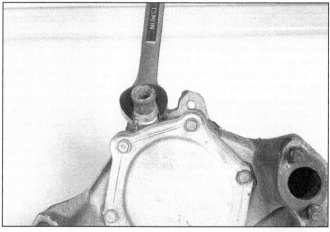

8.15 If a replacement pump is used, transfer all hose fittings from the old pump to the new

8.16 The gasket surfaces must be perfectly clean before the replacement water pump is installed

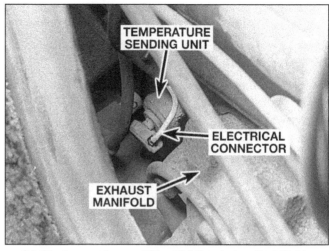

9.1 The temperature sending unit is located on the left side between the number one and number three spark plugs (Chevrolet engine shown)

secure the water pump to the front of the engine block. Lift the water pump away from the engine and out of the engine compartment **(see illustration)**.

15 If installing a new or rebuilt water pump, transfer the heater hose fitting from the old pump to the new one **(see illustration)**.

16 Clean the gasket surfaces of the engine of all excess gasket material using a gasket scraper or putty knife **(see illustration)**.

17 Use a thin coat of gasket sealer on the new gaskets and install to the new pump. Place the pump into position on the engine and secure with the bolts. Do not torque-tighten these bolts until the power steering pump bracket and air pump brackets have been installed, as these brackets are secured with the water pump bolts.

18 Install the engine components in the reverse order of removal, tightening the appropriate fasteners to torque specifications.

19 Adjust all drive belts to the proper tension (see Chapter 1).

20 Connect the negative battery cable and fill the radiator with a mixture of ethylene glycol antifreeze and water in a 50/50 mixture. Start the engine and allow to idle until the upper radiator hose gets hot. Check for leaks. With engine hot, fill with more coolant mixture until the level is at the bottom of the filler neck. Install radiator cap and check coolant level periodically over the next few miles of driving.

9 Water temperature sender - fault diagnosis and replacement

Refer to illustration 9.1

1 The indicator system comprises a lamp mounted on the instrument panel and a sender unit which is located on the left-hand cylinder head or on the front of the intake manifold **(see illustration)**.

2 In the event of an unusual indication or a fault developing, check the coolant level in the system and then ensure that the connecting wiring between the gauge and the sender unit is secure.

3 When the ignition switch is turned on and the starter motor is turning, the indicator lamp should be illuminated (overheated engine indication). If the lamp is not on, the bulb may be burned out, the ignition switch may be faulty or the circuit may be open.

4 As soon as the engine starts, the lamp should go out and remain so unless the engine overheats. Failure of the lamp to go out may be due to the wiring being grounded between the lamp and the sender unit, a defective temperature sender unit or a faulty ignition switch.

5 If the sender unit is to be replaced it is simply unscrewed from the left-hand cylinder head and a replacement installed. There will be some coolant spillage, so check the level after the replacement has been installed.

10 Heater components - removal and installation

Blower assembly

1970 to 1976

1 The blower assembly is located between the inner fender panel and the fire-wall, on the right side of the vehicle. The only way to gain access for service is to use an air chisel to cut a portion of the inner fender panel. Due to this, the procedure is not recommended for the home mechanic.

1977 to 1981

2 On the right side of the firewall in the engine compartment, disconnect the blower motor feed wire and the ground wire where they connect to the blower assembly.

3 Remove the screws and nuts that

secure the assembly to the firewall.

4 Pry the blower assembly away from the firewall.

5 When reinstalling, use new strip caulking all the way around for an airtight seal.

Air distribution ducts and core (models without air-conditioning)

6 Disconnect the negative battery cable.

7 Drain the radiator, referring to Chapter 1 if necessary.

8 Disconnect the heater hoses where they are connected to the core. Temporarily plug the core tubes to prevent coolant from spilling.

9 Remove the nuts from the heater distribution studs on the engine side of the firewall.

10 Remove the nuts from the glove box door and the glove box.

11 Disconnect any wires or cables connected to the heater assembly, along with the air distribution ducts.

12 Pull the assembly away from the firewall from under the dashboard and remove it from the vehicle. Separate the core from the assembly.

Air distribution duct and core (air-conditioned models)

13 Initially follow Steps 6 through 10 above.

14 Raise the vehicle and remove the right side rocker panel trim and forward trim bracket screws.

15 Inside the right front fender opening, remove the fender attaching bolts (rear only), the four fender to fender-liner bolts and two fender-liner bolts near the blower motor attaching area.

16 Pry the inner fender-liner outward and use a block of wood to keep it out.

17 Through this opening, disconnect the water valve-to-core hose from the heater core.

18 Remove the bolts securing the heater

case on the inside of the vehicle.

19   Disconnect all wiring, cables and ducts from the heater case.

20   Remove the right side kick panel and heater assembly.

21   After disconnecting the various vacuum hoses, the core can be separated from the case.

Control head

22   Disconnect the negative battery cable.

23   Lower the steering column trim panel.

24   Remove the glove box, radio or gauge cluster as necessary to gain access to the rear of the heater control unit.

25   Disconnect the air-defrost cable and temperature control cable where they connect to the air distribution assembly under the dashboard.

26   Disconnect all electrical connectors attached to the control head.

27   Remove the attaching screws and pull the control head assembly out from the dashboard.

28   Installation is the reverse of the removal procedure.

11   Air conditioner - general description

1   Three types of systems may be encountered. The Four-Season System in which both the heating and cooling functions are performed by the one system. Air entering the vehicle, passes through the cooling unit (evaporator) and then around the heating unit so following the " reheat" system principle.

2   The evaporator cools the air passing through it and by means of its built-in thermostatic switch, controls the operation of the compressor.

3   The system operates by air (outside or recirculated) entering the evaporator core by the action of the blower, where it receives maximum cooling if the controls are set for cooling. When the air leaves the evaporator, it enters the heater/air conditioner duct assembly and by means of a manually controlled deflector, it either passes through or bypasses the heater core in the correct proportions to provide the desired vehicle interior temperature.

4   Distribution of this air is then regulated by a vacuum actuated deflector and passes through the various outlets according to requirements.

5   When during the cooling operation, the air temperature is cooled too low for comfort, it is warmed to the required level by the heater. When the controls are set to " HEATING ONLY" , the evaporator will cease to function and ambient air will be warmed by the heater in a similar manner to that just described.

6   The main units of the system comprise the evaporator, an engine driven compressor and the condenser.

7   In view of the toxic nature of the chemicals and gases employed in the system, no part of the system must be disconnected by the home mechanic. Due to the need for specialized evacuating and charging equipment, such work should be left to a refrigeration specialist.

8   The Comfortron System is essentially the same as the Four Season System except that it is fully automatic in operation.

9   The air conditioner is a dealer installed unit and operates independently of the vehicle heater using only recirculated air.

12   Air conditioner - checks and maintenance

1   Regularly inspect the fins of the condenser (located ahead of the radiator) and if necessary, brush away leaves and bugs.

2   Clean the evaporator drain tubes free from dirt.

3   Check the condition of the system hoses and if there is any sign of deterioration or hardening, have them replaced by your dealer.

4   At similar intervals, check and adjust the compressor drive belt as described in Chapter 1.

Chapter 4
Fuel and exhaust systems

Contents

Specifications

System	Rear mounted fuel tank, mechanically operated fuel pump and 2 or 4 barrel carburetor
Fuel type	Unleaded or low leaded fuels (vehicles without a catalytic converter)

Fuel tank capacity

1970	19.0 gals
w/Evaporative control system	18.0 gals
1971	17.0 gals
1972-1973	18.0 gals
1974-1978	21.0 gals
1979-1980	20.8 gals

Note: *Unless otherwise specified, all measurements are in inches.*

1970 Carburetor specifications											
Carburetor model		Usage	Float Setting	Float Drop	Pump Rod	Choke Rod	Vacuum Break	Unloader	Metering Rod	Choke Coil Rod	Air Valve lock-out	Air Valve dash-pot
49-State	California											
Rochester 2GV										Refer To Choke Adjustment		
7040060	7040460	400 A.T.	11/16"	1-3/4"	1-11/32"	.085"	.150"	.180"			N.A.	N.A.
7040060	7040461	400 A.T. A/C	11/16"	1-3/4"	1-11/32"	.085"	.150"	.180"				
7040062	7040462	350 A.T.	9/16"	1-3/4"	1-11/32"	.085"	.150"	.180"				
7040062	7040463	350 A.T. A/C	9/16"	1-3/4"	1-11/32"	.085"	.150"	.180"	N.A.			
7040064		400 Altitude A.T.	11/16"	1-3/4"	1-11/32"	.085"	.150"	.180"				
7040066	7040466	400 M.T.	11/16"	1-3/4"	1-11/32"	.085"	.170"	.180"				
7040071	7040471	350 M.T.	9/16"	1-3/4"	1-11/32"	.085"	.160"	.180"				
7040072		350 Altitude A.T.	9/16"	1-3/4"	1-11/32"	.085"	.150"	.180"				
Rochester 4MV										Center Notch		
7040263	7040563	400 M.T. (All exc. Ram-Air)	9/32"				.400"				.015"	.025"
7040264	7040564	400 A.T. (All exc. Ram-Air)	9/32"				.400"				.015"	.025"
7040267	7040567	455 M.T. (All)	9/32"				.400"				.015"	.025"
7040268	7040568	455 A.T. (All)	9/32"	N.A.	N.A.	.100"	.400"	N.A.	N.A.		.015"	.025"
7040270	7040570	400 A.T. (Ram-Air III & IV)	9/32"				.245"				.015"	.025"
							.245"				.015"	.025"
7040273	7040573	400 M.T. (Ram-Air III & IV)	9/32"				.245"				.015"	.025"
							.245"				.015"	.025"
7040274		455 Altitude A.T. (Small Valve)	9/32"				.400"				.015"	.025"

1970 carburetor specifications

1971 Carburetor specifications											
Carburetor model See Section 8	Usage	Float Setting	Float Drop	Pump Rod	Choke Rod	Vacuum Break	Unloader	Metering Rod	Choke Coil Rod	Air Valve Lock out	Air Valve Dash-pot
Rochester 2GV									Refer To Choke Adjustment		
7041060	400 A.T. (All exc. "F" with A/C)	11/16"	1-3/4"	1-11/32"	.085"	.125"	.180"			N.A.	N.A.
7041061	400 A.T. "F" with A/C		1-3/4"	1-11/32"	.085"	.125"	.180"				
7041062	350 A.T. (All exc. "F" with A/C)		1-3/4"	1-11/32"	.085"	.105"	.180"				
7041063	350 A.T. "F" with A/C	9/16"	1-3/4"	1-11/32"	.085"	.105"	.180"	N.A.			
7041064	455 A.T.		1-3/4"	1-11/32"	.085"	.130"	.180"				
7041070	400 A.T. (Altitude)	11/16"	1-3/4"	1-11/32"	.085"	.125"	.180"				
7041171	350 M.T.		1-3/4"	1-11/32"	.085"	.140"	.180"				
7041072	350 A.T. (Altitude)	9/16"	1-3/4"	1-11/32"	.085"	.105"	.180"				
7041074	455 A.T. (Altitude)	11/16"	1-3/4"	1-11/32"	.085"	.130"	.180"				
Rochester 4MV											
7041262	455 A.T. (All exc. Ram-Air)	9/32"			.100"	.240"				.015"	.025"
7041263	400 M.T. (All exc. Ram-Air)	9/32"			.100"	.240"				.015"	.025"
7041264	400 A.T. (All exc. Ram-Air)	9/32"			.100"	.240"			None	.015"	.025"
7041267	455 H.O. M.T. (All exc. Ram-Air)	9/32"			.100"	.370"				.015"	.025"
7041268	455 H.O. A.T. (All exc. Ram-Air)	9/32"	N.A.	N.A.	.100"	.430"	N.A.	N.A.	Center Notch	.015"	.025"
7041270	455 H.O. A.T. (All exc. Ram-Air)	9/32"			.100"	.430"				.015"	.025"
7041271	400 & 455 A.T. (Altitude)	9/32"			.100"	.240"			None	.015"	.025"
7041273	455 H.O. M.T. (All exc. Ram-Air)	9/32"			.100"	.370"			Center Notch	.015"	.025"

1971 carburetor specifications

Note: *Unless otherwise specified, all measurements are in inches.*

1972 Carburetor specifications											
Carburetor model See Section 8	Usage	Float Setting	Float Drop	Pump Rod	Choke Rod	Vacuum Break	Unloader	Meter-ing Rod	Choke Coil Rod	Air Valve Lock-out	Air Valve Dash-pot
Rochester 2GV									Refer To Choke Adjust-ment		
7042060	400 A.T.	5/8"	1-9/32"	1-11/32"	.085"	.122"	.180"				
7042061	400 A.T.	5/8"	1-9/32"	1-11/32"	.085"	.122"	.180"				
7042062	350 A.T.	9/16"	1-9/32"	1-11/32"	.085'	.105"	.180"	N.A.		N.A.	N.A.
7042064	455 A.T.	5/8"	1-9/32"	1-11/32"	.085"	.150"	.180"				
7042100	307 A.T.	25/32"	1-31/32"	1-5/16	.040"	.080"	.215"				
7042101	307 M.T.	25/32"	1-31/32"	1-5/16"	.075"	.100"	.215"				
Rochester 4MV											
7042262	455 A.T. (All exc. Ram-Air)	1/4"		13/32"	.100"	.290"	.310"			.015"	.025
7042263	400 M.T. (All exc. Ram-Air)	1/4"		13/32"	.100"	.290"	.310"			.015"	.025
7042264	400 A.T. (All exc. Ram-Air)	1/4"	N.A.	13/32"	.100"	.290"	.310"	N.A.	N.A.	.015"	.025
7042270	455 H.O. A.T. (Ram-Air)	1/4"		7/16"	.100"	.290"	.310"			.015"	.025
7042273	455 H.O. M.T. (Ram-Air)	1/4"		7/16"	.100'	.290"	.310"			.015"	.025

1972 carburetor specifications

1973 Carburetor specifications													
Carburetor model (see Section B)	Usage	Float Setting	Float Drop	Pump Rod	Choke Rod	Vac-um Break	Un-load-er	Meter-ing Rod	Air Valve Lock out	Air Valve Dash pot	Air Valve Spring Wind Up	Choke Set-ting	Pump Rod Locat-ion
Rochester 2GC													
7043062	350 A.T. Non CA	21/32"	1-9/32"	1-5/16"	.085"	.167"	.180"					1NL	
7043063	350 A.T. CA	21/32"	1-9/32"	1-5/16"	.085"	.167"	.180"					1NL	
7043071	350 M.T. Both	23/32"	1-9/32"	1-5/16"	.085"	.195"	.180"					1NL	
7043072	350 A.T. ALT.	23/32"	1-9/32"	1-5/16"	.085"	.167"	.180"					1NL	
7043060	400 A.T. Non CA	21/32"	1-9/32"	1-5/16"	.085"	.157"	.180"					1NL	
7043061	400 A.T. CA	21/32"	1-9/32"	1-5/16"	.085"	.157"	.180"	N.A.	N.A.	N.A.	N.A.	1NL	N.A.
7043066	400 A.T. Non CA	21/32"	1-9/32"	1-5/16"	.085"	.180"	.180"					1NL	
7043067	400 A.T. Non CA	21/32"	1-9/32"	1-5/16"	.085"	.180"	.180"					1NL	
7043067	400 A.T. CA	21/32"	1-9/32"	1-5/16"	.085"	.180	.180"					1NL	
7043070	400 A.T. Alt.	23/32	1-9/32"	1-5/16"	.085"	.157"	.180"					1NL	
Rochester 4MC													
7043263	400 M.T. Both	13/32"		13/32"	.205"	.290"	.310		.015	.025	5/8	Index	Inner
7043264	400 A.T. Both	13/32"		13/32"	.205"	.290"	.310		.015	.025	1/2	Index	Inner
7043274	400 A.T. Alt.	13/32"		13/32"	.205"	.290"	.310		.015	.025	9/16	Index	Inner
7043262	455 A.T. Both	13/32"	N.A.	13/32"	.205"	.290"	.310	N.A.	.015	.025	3/8	Index	Inner
7043265	455 M.T. Both	13/32"		13/32"	.205"	.290"	.310		.015	.025	9/16	Index	Inner
7043272	455 A.T. Both	13/32"		13/32"	.205"	.290"	.310		.015	.025	3/8	Index	Inner
7043270	455 S.D.A.T. Both												
7043273	455 S.D.M.T. Both												

1973 carburetor specifications

Note: *Unless otherwise specified, all measurements are in inches.*

1974 Carburetor specifications												
Carburetor model	Usage	Float Set-ting	Float Drop	Pump Rod	Choke Rod	Vacu-um Break	Unload-er	Air Valve Lock-out	Air Valve dash-pot	Choke Setting	Air Valve Spring Wind Up	Pump Rod Locat-ion
Rochester 2GC												
7043060	Non-CA 400 A.T.	.670"	1-3/4"	1-5/16"	.085"	.157"	.180"			1NL		
7043062	350 A.T. Non-CA	.670"	1-3/4"	1-5/16"	.085"	.167"	.180"			1NL		
7043070	400 A.T. Alt,	.670"	1-3/4"	1-5/16"	.085"	.157"	.180"			1NL		
7043071	350 A.T. Non-CA	.670"	1-3/4"	1-5/16"	.085"	.195"	.180"	N.A.	N.A.	1NL		
7043072	350 A.T. Alt.	.670"	1-3/4"	1-5/16"	.085"	.167"	.180"			1NL		
7044063	350 A.T. CA	.670"	1-3/4"	1-5/16"	.085"	.157"	.180"			1NL		
7044066	400 A.T. Non-CA	.670"	1-3/4"	1-5/16"	.085"	.177"	.180"			1NL		
7044067	400 A.T. CA	.670"	1-3/4"	1-5/16"	.085"	.177"	.180"			1NL		
Rochester 4MC												
7043263	400 M.T. Non-CA	.390"		.410"	205"	.290"	.310"	.015	.025	Index	5/8	Inner
7044262	455 A.T. Nationwide	.390"		.410"	.205"	.260"	.310"	.015	.025	Index	3/8	Inner
7044266	455 A.T. Nationwide	.390"		.410"	.205"	.260"	.310"	.015	.025	Index	1/2	Inner
7044267	455 A.T. H.D.	.390"	N.A.	.410"	.205"	.260"	.310"	.015	.025	Index	3/8	Inner
7044268	350 A.T. Non-CA	.390"		.410"	.205"	.260"	.310"	.015	.025	Index	1/2	Inner
7044269	350 M.T. Non-CA	.390"		.410"	.205"	.290'	.310"	.015	.025	Index	1/2	Inner
7044270	455 A.T. S.D.	.390"		.410"	.205"	.290"	.310"	.015	.025	Index	3/4	Inner
7044272	455 A.T. Alt.	.390"		.315"	.205"	.290"	.310"	.015	.025	Index	3/8	Inner
7044273	455 M.T. S.D.	.390"		.410"	.205"	.290"	.310"	.015	.025	Index	3/4	Inner
7044274	400 A.T. Alt.	.390"		.315"	.205"	.290"	.310"	.015	.025	Index	9/16	Inner
7044560	455 A.T. CA	.390"		.410"	.205"	.260"	.310"	.015	.025	Index	3/8	Inner
7044568	350 A.T. CA	.390"		.410"	.205"	.260"	.310"	.015	.02	Index	1/2	Inner

1974 carburetor specifications

1975 Carburetor specifications													
Carburetor model (See Section 8)	Usage	Float Set-ting	Float Drop	Choke Rod Cam Adj.	Vacu-um Break	Vacu-um Break	Un-load-er	Air Valve Dash-pot	Pump Rod	Choke Set-ting	Air Valve Spring Wind-up	Pump Rod Locat-ion	Idle Vent	Air Valve Spring Adj.
Rochester 2GC													
7045160	400 A.T. Fed.	9/16	1-7/32	.085	.145	.265	.180		1-3/4	1NR			.025	
7045162	350 A.T. Fed.	9/16	1-7/32	.085	.145	.260	.180	N.A.	1-13/16	1NR			.025	
7045171	350 A.T. Fed.	9/16	1-7/32	.085	.145	.260	.180		1-13/16	1NR			.025	
7045143	350 A.T. Fed	15/32	1-7/32	.080	.140	.120	.180		1-13/16	1NR			.025	
Rochester M4MC													
7045246	350 A.T. Fed	5/16		.095	.130	.115	.240	.015	15/32	1NR		Outer hole		.015
7045546	350 A.T. CA	5/16		.095	.145	.130	.240	.015	15/32	1NR		Outer hole		.015
7045263	400 M.T. Fed	1/2		.130	.150	.260	.230	.030	9/32	Index	.500	Inner hole		
7045264	400 A.T. Fed	1/2	N.A.	.130	.150	.260	.230	.030	9/32	Index	.375	Inner hole	N.A.	
7045268	350 A.T. Fed	1/2		.130	.150	.260	.230	.030	9/32	Index	.375	Inner hole		
7045269	350 M.T. Fed	1/2		.130	.160	.265	.230	.030	9/32	Index	.500	Inner hole		
7045274	400 A.T. Fed	1/2		.130	.150	.260	.230	.030	9/32	Index	.500	Inner hole		

1975 carburetor specifications (1 of 2)

Note: *Unless otherwise specified, all measurements are in inches.*

Carburetor model (See Section 8)	Usage	Float Setting	Float Drop	Choke Rod Cam Adj.	Vacuum Break	Vacuum Break	Unloader	Air Valve Dashpot	Pump Rod	Choke Setting	Air Valve Spring Windup	Pump Rod Location	Idle Vent	Air Valve Spring Adj.
1975 Carburetor specifications (continued)														
Rochester M4MCA														
7045260	455 A.T. Fed	1/2		1.30	.150	.260	.230	.030	9/32	Index	.500	Inner hole		
7045262	455 A.T. Fed	1/2		1.30	.150	.260	.230	.030	9/32	Index	.500	Inner hole		
7045266	400 A.T. Fed	1/2		1.30	.150	.260	.230	.030	9/32	Index	.500	Inner hole		
7045562	455 A.T. CA	1/2	N.A.	1.30	.150	.260	.230	.030	9/32	Index	.500	Inner hole	N.A.	N.A.
7045564	400 A.T. CA	1/2		1.30	.150	.260	.230	.030	9/32	Index	.500	Inner hole		
7045568	350 A.T. CA	1/2		1.30	.150	.260	.230	.030	9/32	Index	.500	Inner hole		
7045566	455 A.T. CA	1/2		1.30	.150	.260	.230	.030	9/32	Index		Inner hole		

Note 1: Auxiliary vacuum break and unloader set at top of choke valve
Note 2: 2MC choke valve settings at bottom of valve
* Set choke coil lever 7045263 M4MC thru 7045274 M4MC to 0.120 inch
**Set choke coil lever 7045260 M4MCA thru 7045564 M4MCA to 0.120 inch

1975 carburetor specifications (2 of 2)

Carburetor model	Usage	Float Setting	Float Drop	Choke Rod Cam. Adj.	Vacuum Break Point	Vacuum Break Point	Choke Unloader	Air Valve Dashpot Rod	Accel. Pump Rod	Choke Index Setting	Air Valve Spring Windup	Pump Rod Location	Choke Coil Lever
1976 Carburetor specifications													
Rochester 2GC													
350 & 400 C.I.D	Fed A.T.	9/16	1-9/32	.085	.165	.285	.180		1-11/32	1 NR			.120
Rochester M4MC													
350 C.I.D.	CA A.T.	17/32	N.A.	.125	.160	.250	.230	.030	3/8	1 NR	1/2	Outer	.120
400 C.I.D	Fed A.T.	17/32		.125	.160	.250	.230	.030	3/8	1 NR	1/2	Outer	.120
400 C.I.D	Fed A.T.	17/32		.125	.170	.250	.230	.030	3/8	1 NR	5/8	Outer	.120
400 C.I.D.	CA A.T.	17/32		.130	.150	.260	.230	.030	3/8	1 NR	1/2	Outer	.120
455 C.I.D.	Fed M.T.												

*Refer to the vehicle emission tune-up label to determine if the vehicle is certified for California or Federal
1 Choke blade specifications have the following tolerances: 2MC & M4MC +/- 0.015; 2GC +/- 0.012
2 Float setting specification has a tolerance of +/- 3/32

1976 carburetor specifications

Carburetor model and usage (See Section 8)	Float Setting	Float Drop	Choke Rod Cam. Adj.	Vacuum Break Point	Vacuum Break Point	Choke Unloader	Air Valve Dashpot	Accel. Pump Rod	Choke Index Setting	Air Valve Spring Windup	Pump Rod Location	Choke Coil Lever
1977 Carburetor specifications												
Rochester 2GC												
17057143	7/16"	1-5/32"	.080	.130"	.100"	.140"		1 19/32"	1 NR			.120"
17057144	7/16"	1-5/32"	.080	.130"	.100"	.140"		1 19/32"	1 NR			.120"
17057145	7/16"	1-5/32"	.080	.110"	.040"	.140"		1 19/32"	1 NR			.120"
17057146	7/16"	1-5/32"	.080	.110"	.040"	.140"		1 9/16"	1 NR			.120"
17057148	7/16"	1-5/32"	.080	.110"	.030"	.140"	N.A.	1 9/16"	1 NR	N.A.	N.A.	.120"
17057446	7/16"	1-5/32"	.080	.130"	.110"	.140"		1 19/32"	1 NR			.120"
17057447	7/16"	1-5/32"	.080	.130"	.110"	.140"		1 19/32"	1 NR			.120"
17057448	7/16"	1-5/32"	.080	.130"	.110"	.140"		1 19/32"	1 NR			.120"
17057108	5/8"	1 1/4"	.260	.130"		.325"		1 5/8"	Index			.120"
17057110	5/8"	1 1/4"	.026	.130"		.325"		1 5/8"	Index			.120"
Rochester M2MC				Front	Rear							
17057172 / 17057173	11/32"		23.5° (.129)	26° (.149)	36° (.225)	38° (.240)		3/8	2 NR		Outer	.120
Rochester M4MC				Front	Rear							
17057250	13/32"		19° (0.95)	24° (.125)	30.5° (.170)	35° (.205)	.030	9/32	2 NR	1/2	Inner	.120
17057253	13/32"		19° (0.95)	24° (.125)	30.5° (.170)	35° (.205)	.030	9/32	2 NR	1/2	Inner	.120
17057255	13/32"		19° (0.95)	24° (.125)	30.5° (.170)	35° (.205)	.030	9/32	2 NR	1/2	Inner	.120
17057256	13/32"	N.A.	19° (0.95)	24° (.125)	30.5° (.170)	35° (.205)	.030	9/32	2 NR	1/2	Inner	.120
17057258	13/32"		19° (0.95)	26° (.150)	30.5° (.215)	35° (.205)	.030	9/32	2 NR	1/2	Inner	.120
17057262	17/32"		23.5° (.130)	26° (.150)	38° (.240)	35° (.220)	.030	3/8	1 NR	1/2	Outer	.120
17057263	17/32"		23.5° (.130)	28° (.165)	38° (.240)	35° (.220)	.030	3/8	1 NR	5/8	Outer	.120

1977 carburetor specifications (1 of 2)

Note: *Unless otherwise specified, all measurements are in inches.*

Carburetor model and usage (See Section 8)	Float Setting	Float Drop	Choke Rod Cam. Adj.	Vacuum Break Point	Vacuum Break Point	Choke Unloader	Air Valve Dashpot	Accel. Pump Rod	Choke Index Setting	Air Valve Spring Windup	Pump Rod Location	Choke Coil Lever
1977 Carburetor specifications (continued)												
Rochester M4MC				Front	Rear							
17057266	17/32"		23.5º (.130)	26º (.150)	38º (.240)	.35º (.220)	.030	3/8	1 NR	1/2	Outer	.120
17057274	17/32"		23.5º (.130)	26º (.150)	38º (.240)	35º (.220)	.030	3/8	1 NR	1/2	Outer	.120
17057502	15/32"		46º (.325)	28.5º (.165)		42º (.280)	.030	9/32	2 NL	1/2	Inner	.120
17057504	15/32"	N.A.	46º (.325)	28.5º (.165)		42º (.280)	.030	9/32	2 NL	1/2	Inner	.120
17057550	13/32"		19º (.095)	24º (.125)	36.5º (.215)	34.5º (.200)	.030	9/32	2 NR	1/2	Inner	.120
17057553	13/32"		19º (.095)	24º (.125)	36.5º (.215)	34.5º (.200)	.030	9/32	2NR	1/2	Inner	.120
17057582	15/32"		46º (.325)	28.5º (.165)		42º (.280)	.030	3/8	2NL	1/2	Outer	.120
17057584	15\32"		46º (.325)	28.5º (.165)		42º (.280)	.030	3/8	2NL	1/2	Outer	.120

1 Choke blade specifications have the following tolerances: 2MC and M4MC +/- 0.015; 2GC +/- 0.012
2 Float setting specification has a tolerance of +/- 3/32

1977 carburetor specifications (2 of 2)

Carburetor model (See Section 8)	Float Setting	Float Drop	Choke Rod Fast Idle Cam Adj.	Vacuum Break	Vacuum Break	Choke Unloader Rod	Air Valve Rod	Acell. Pump	Choke Index Setting	Air Valve Spring Wind-up	Pump Rod Location
1978 Carburetor specifications											
Rochester 2G				Primary	Secondary						
17058102, 103, 126, 128	19/32"	1-9/32"	.260"	.130"		.325"		1-17/32"	Index		
17058108, 110, 112, 114	19/32"	1-9/32"	.260"	.130"		.325"		1-21/32"	Index		
17058111, 113, 121, 123	19/32"	1-9/32"	.260"	.130"		.325"		1-5/8"	Index		
17058404, 410, 412, 414	21/32"	1-9/32"	.260"	.140"		.325"		1-21/32"	1/2 NL		
17058145	7/16"	1-5/32"	.080"	.145	.060"	.160"		1-5/8"	1 NL		
17058147, 444, 446	7/16"	1-5/32"	.080"	.140"	.100"	.140"	N.A.	1-5/8"	1 NR	N.A.	N.A.
17058182, 183	7/16"	1-5/32"	.080"	.110"	.080"	.140"		1-5/8"	1 NR		
17058447	7/16"	1-5/32"	.080"	.150"	.110"	.140"		1-5/8"	1 NR		
17058448	7/16"	1-5/32"	.080"	.140"	.100"	.140"		1-5/8"	1 NR		
17058185	7/16"	1-5/32"	.080"	.110"	.050"	.140"		1-19/32"	1 NR		
17058187, 189	7/16"	1-5/32"	.080"	.110"	.080"	.140"		1-19/32"	1 NR		
Rochester M2MC				Front	Rear						
17058160	11/32"		23.5º (.129)	26º (.149)	40º (.260)	35º (.220)	N.A.	9/32	2 NR	N.A.	Inner
Rochester M4MC											
17058274, 276, 266	17/32"		23.5º (.129)	26º (.149)	40º (.260)	35º (.220)	.030	3/8	Index	1/2	Outer
17058502, 504	15/32"		46º (.314)	28º (.164)		42º (.277)	.015	9/32	2NL		Inner
17058202, 204	15/32"		46º (.314)	27º (.157)		42º (.277)	.015	9/32	2 NL		Inner
17058582, 584	15/32"		46º (.314)	30º (.179)		42º (.277)	.015	9/32	2 NL	7/8	Inner
17058263	17/32"		23º (.129)	28º (.164)	40º (.260)	35º (.220)	.030	3/8	Index	5/8	Outer
17058250, 253	13/32"		18º (.088)	23º (.119)	30.5º (.167)	35º (.203	.030	9/32	2 NR	1/2	Inner
17058258, 553	13/32"		19º (.092)	24º (.126)	36.5º (.212)	35º (.203)	.030	9/32	2NR	1/2	Inner
17058264, 278	17/32"		23.5º (.129)	26º (.149)	40º (.260)	35º (.220)	.030	3/8	1 NR	1/2	Outer
17058272	15/32"		14.5º (.071)	24º (.126)	32º (.195)	36º (.227)	.030	3/8	2 NR	5/8	Outer
17058241	5/16"		18º (.096)	21.5º (.117)	19º (.103)	38º (.243)	.015	3/8	1 NR	3/4	Outer

1978 carburetor specifications

Note: *Unless otherwise specified, all measurements are in inches.*

1979 Carburetor specifications											
Carburetor model (See Section 8)	Float Setting	Float Drop	Choke Rod Fast Idle Cam Adj.	Vacuum Break (Front)	Vacuum Break	Choke Unloader Rod	Air Valve Rod	Acell. Pump Rod	Choke Index Setting	Air Valve Spring Wind-up	Pump Rod Location
Rochester M2MC/M2ME											
17059134, 135, 136, 137	13/32"		38°	.27°		38°		9/32	1 NL		Inner
17059180, 190, 191	11/32"		24.5°	19°	17°	38°		1/4	2 NCC		Inner
17059160	11/32"		20°	23°	33°	32°		9/32	2 NCC		Inner
17059196	11/32"	N.A.	24.5°	23°	21°	42°	N.A.	1/2	1 NCC	N.A.	Inner
17059434, 436	13/32"		38°	28°		38°		9/32	2NL		Inner
17059492, 498	11/32"		24.5°	23°	21°	42°		9/32	2NCC		Inner
17059430, 432	9/32"		38°	29°		38°		9/32	1NL		Inner
17059491	11/32"		24.5°	23°	21°	42°		9/32	1NCC		Inner
Rochester M4MC											
17058263	17/32"		23°	28°	38°	35°	.030	3/8	Index	5/8	Outer
17059250, 253	13/32"		18°	23°	30.5°	35°	.030	9/32	2 NR	1/2	Inner
17059241	5/16"		18°	21.5°	20.5°	38°	.030	3/8	INCC	3/4	Outer
17059271	9/16"		20°	25°	36°	33°	.030	3/8	1 NRL	5/8	Outer
17059272	15/32"	N.A.	14.5°	24°	32°	35°	.030	3/8	2 NR	5/8	Outer
17059502, 504	15/32"		38°	28°		38°	.015	1/4	2 NLR	7/7	Inner
17059553	13/32"		19°	24°	36.5	35°	.030	9/32	2 NR	1/2	Inner
17059582, 584	15/32"		38°	33°		46°	.015	11/32	1 NL	7/8	Outer

1979 carburetor specifications

1980 Carburetor specifications											
Carburetor model (See Section 8)	Float Setting	Float Drop	Choke Rod Fast Idle Cam	Vacuum Break (Front)	Vacuum Break (Rear)	Choke Unloader	Air Valve Rod	Acell. Pump Rod	Choke Index Index Setting	Air Valve Wind-up	Pump Rod Location
M2MC/M2ME											
17090130, 131, 132, 133, 146, 147, 148, 149	11/32"		20°	25°	NA	38°		1/4"	TR		Inner
17080160	5/16"	N.A.	14.5°	28.5°	33.5°	37.5°	N.A.	1/4"	TR	N.A.	Inner
17080190, 192	9/32"		24.5°	22°	20°	38°		1/4"	TR		Inner
17080191	11/32"		24.5°	18°	18°	38°		1/4"	TR		Inner
17080195, 197	9/32"		24.5°	19°	14°	38°		1/4"	TR		Inner
E2MC/E2ME											
17080490, 492, 496, 498	5/16"		24.5°	21°	33°	38°		3/8"	TR		TR
17080491, 493, 495	5/16"	N.A.	24.5°	21°	30°	38°	N.A.	3/8"	TR	N.A.	TR
M4MC/M4ME											
17080249	7/16"		18°	23°	20.5°	38°	.025"	9/32"	TR	3/4"	Inner
17080270	15/32"		14.5°	26°	34°	35°	.025"	3/8	TR	5/8"	Outer
17080272	15/32"		14.5°	23°	29.5°	33°	.025"	3/8"	TR	5/8"	Outer
17080274	15/32"	N.A.	16°	20°	28°	33°	.025"	5/16"	TR	5/8"	Inner
E4MC/E4ME											
17080502, 504, 517	1/2"	N.A.	20°	24°	30°	38°	.025"	TR	TR	7/8"	TR
17080553	15/32"	N.A.	17°	25°	35°	35°	.25"	9/32"	TR	1/2"	TR

1980 carburetor specifications

Note: *Unless otherwise specified, all measurements are in inches.*

1981 Carburetor specifications							
Carburetor model (See Section 8, Chapter 4)	Float Setting	Accel. Pump Rod	Pump Rod Location	Choke Rod Fast Idle Cam Ad.	Vacuum Break (Front)	Vacuum Break (Rear)	Choke Unloader
E2MC, E2ME							
17080185, 187	9/32"	1/4"	Inner	24.5º	19º	14º	38º
17080191	11/32"	1/4"	Inner	24.5º	18º	18º	38º
17080491	5/16"			24.5º	21º	35º	38º
17080496, 498	5/16"			24.5º	21º	33º	38º
17081130, 132	13/32"		Inner	20º	25º		38º
17081131, 133	13/32"		Inner	20º	25º		38º
17081138, 140	13/32"		Inner	20º	25º		40º
17081150, 152	13/32"			14º	24º	36º	35º
17081160	11/16"			14.5º	24º	37º	35º
17081191, 194	5/16"			24.5º	28º	24º	38º
17081196	5/16"			24.5º	28º	24º	38º
17081192, 197	3/8"			24.5º	28º	24º	38º
17081198	3/8"			24.5º	28º	24º	38º
17081199	3/8"			18º	28º	24º	38º

1981 Carburetor specifications							
Carburetor model (See Section 8, Chapter 4	Float Setting	Choke Rod Fast Idle Cam Ad.	Air Valve Rod	Vacuum Break (Front)	Vacuum Break (Rear)	Air Valve Windup	Choke Unloader
E4MC, E4ME							
17081202, 204	11/32"	20º	.025	27º		7/8	38º
17081203, 207	11/32"	20º	.025	27º		7/8	38º
17081216, 217, 218	11/32"	20º	.025	27º		7/8	38º
17081242	3/8"	24.5º	.025	17º	15º	9/16	38º
17081243	5/16"	24.5º	.025	19º	17º	9/16	38º
17081245, 247	3/8"	24.5º	.025	28º	24º	5/8	38º
17081248, 249	3/8"	24.5º	.025	28º	24º	5/8	38º
17081253, 254	15/32"	14º	.025	25º	36º	1/2	35º
17081270	7/16"	14.5º	.025	24º	34º	5/8	35º
17081272	7/16"	14.5º	.025	24º	40º	5/8	35º
17081274	7/16"	16º	.025	24º	35º	5/8	35º
17081289	13/32"	24.5º	.025	28º	24º	5/8	38º

1981 carburetor specifications

Torque specifications

	Lb-in

Two barrel carburetor

Throttle body to bowl	72
Bowl cluster	46
Fast idle cam	58
Metering jet	40
Choke lever	14
Choke housing to throttle body	46
Choke housing cover	26
Air horn to bowl	46
Vacuum break unit	26
Choke shaft	14
Fuel inlet nut	40
Fuel inlet needle seat	45

Four barrel carburetor

Throttle body to bowl	46
Choke lever	14
Choke housing	46
Choke housing cover	26
Air horn to bowl (large)	46
(small)	26
Air horn to throttle body	46
Choke lever	14
Vacuum break unit	26
Solenoid bracket	71
Fuel inlet nut	40
Manifold bolts	**Ft-lbs**
Intake	30
Exhaust except 350 engine inner bolts	20
350 engine inner bolts	30
Exhaust pipe to manifold bolts	15
Catalytic converter fill plug	50

1 General description

1   The fuel system of all models comprises a rear fuel tank, a mechanically operated fuel pump, a carburetor and an air cleaner.
2   The carburetor may be of dual or four barrel type depending upon the engine capacity and the date of production of the vehicle.
3   All models are equipped with some form of emission control equipment. The later the date of the vehicle, the more complex and sophisticated do the carburetor and the emission control system become.

2 Air cleaner - servicing

Non-temperature-controlled type (paper element)

1   At the intervals specified in Chapter 1, unscrew the top of the air cleaner cover and remove the cover.
2   Remove the cleaner element and discard it, then wipe clean the interior of the casing, insert a new element and install the cover.

Non-temperature-controlled type (oil bath)

3   With this type of air cleaner, release the clamp screw at the base of the reservoir and lift the cleaner assembly from the carburetor.
4   Remove the wing nut and take off the cover and element.
5   Release the clamp screw and remove the air intake horn from the carburetor. Loosen the stud wing nut to allow removal of the reservoir.
6   Drain the oil from the reservoir and clean all components in a suitable solvent.
7   Reassemble and install the air cleaner components. Fill the reservoir with SAE 50 engine oil when operating in above freezing temperatures, or SAE 20 below freezing.

Temperature-controlled (thermostatic) air cleaner (TAC)

8   If a plain paper air cleaner element is used, replace it as described in paragraphs 1 and 2 of this Section.
9   If a Polywrap element is used, remove the Polywrap band from the paper element and discard the element. If the band is in good undamaged condition, rinse it clean in kerosene and squeeze it dry. Dip the band in clean engine oil and gently squeeze out the excess. Install the band to a new paper element and reassemble.
10   Any malfunction in the temperature-controlled air cleaner should first be checked out by starting the engine (cold) and observing the position of the deflector flap valve, using a mirror to look up the intake nozzle of the cleaner. This should be closed to cold air but open to warm air. Conversely, once the

engine has warmed up, the flap should be open to cold and closed to warm. Both tests are carried out with the engine idling.
11   The vacuum unit can be removed from the air cleaner by drilling out the two spotwelds to remove the retaining strap. The new vacuum unit repair pack will contain the necessary sheet metal screws to hold the retaining strap in position when reassembling.
12   The sensor can be removed by prying up the tabs on the sensor retaining clip.

3 Fuel pump - description and testing

Warning: *Gasoline is extremely flammable, so take extra precautions when you work on any part of the fuel system. Don't smoke or allow open flames or bare light bulbs near the work area, and don't work in a garage where a natural gas-type appliance (such as a water heater or clothes dryer) with a pilot light is present. Since gasoline is carcinogenic, wear latex gloves when there's a possibility of being exposed to fuel, and, if you spill any fuel on your skin, rinse it off immediately with soap and water. Mop up any spills immediately and do not store fuel-soaked rags where they could ignite. When you perform any kind of work on the fuel system, wear safety glasses and have a Class B type fire extinguisher on hand.*

1   The fuel pump is a sealed type and is actuated from the engine camshaft. A pushrod is used between the camshaft and the pump rocker.
2   No servicing can be carried out as the unit is sealed, but if the pump is suspected of being faulty; carry out the following test.
3   Verify that gas is in the fuel tank. Disconnect the primary wire which runs between the coil and the distributor to prevent the engine firing when the starter motor is actuated (1970 - 1974 models only). For 1975 - 1980 models, disconnect the distributor wiring marked "BAT".

4   Disconnect the fuel inlet pipe from the carburetor and place its open end in a container.
5   Operate the starter motor and check that well-defined spurts of fuel are being ejected from the open end of the pipe. If so, the pump is operating correctly; if not, replace the pump as described in the following section.

4 Fuel pump - removal and installation

Warning: *Gasoline is extremely flammable, so take extra precautions when you work on any part of the fuel system. See the* **Warning** *in Section 3.*
Refer to illustrations 4.1, 4.2a, 4.2b, 4,3, 4.4, 4.5a and 4.5b
1   To remove the pump, remove the fuel inlet and outlet pipes. Use two wrenches to prevent damage to the pump and connections **(see illustration)**.
2   Remove the fuel pump mounting bolts, the pump, and the gasket **(see illustrations)**.

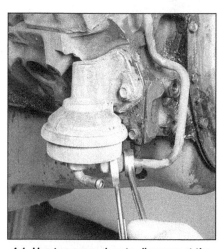

4.1 Use two wrenches to disconnect the fuel pipe from the fuel pump

4.2a Removing the fuel pump attaching bolts

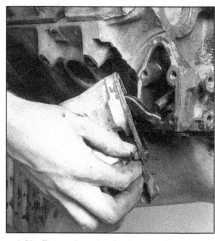

4.2b Removing the fuel pump from the engine block

4.3 The fuel pump push rod is located behind the fuel pump

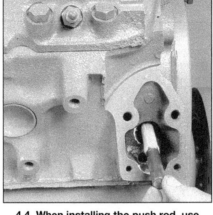

4.4 When installing the push rod, use heavy grease to keep it secure inside its bore

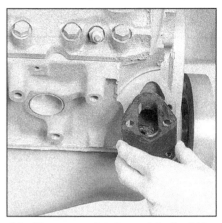

4.5a If a spacer plate is used, it should be installed after the push rod

4.5b Installing the fuel pump

6.10a Typical fuel tank mounting

A   Mounting strap bolts
B   Mounting strap hinges

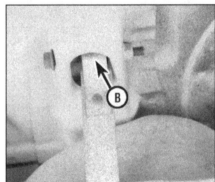

6.10b Close-up of mounting strap bolts (A) and hinges (B)

3   If the pushrod is to be removed, first remove the pipe plug or the pump adapter and gasket, as appropriate **(see illustration)**.
4   When installing, first install the pushrod using the gasket sealant on the pipe plug or gasket (where applicable). Retain the pushrod in position using heavy grease **(see illustration)**.
5   Install the pump using a new gasket. Use gasket sealant on the screw threads **(see illustrations)**.
7   Connect the fuel pipes, start the engine and check for leaks.

5   Fuel filters - replacement

1   See Chapter 1 for the step-by-step process.

6   Fuel tank- removal and installation

Warning: *Gasoline is extremely flammable, so take extra precautions when you work on any part of the fuel system. See the* **Warning** *in Section 3.*
Refer to illustrations 6.10a and 6.10b
1   The fuel tank located between the frame rails and behind the rear axle is held in place by two steel straps. These straps are hinged at either the front or the rear end (with a bolt through the hinge) and secured at the opposite end with a bolt and nut assembly.
2   Disconnect the battery before performing any servicing operations involving the fuel supply.
3   Disconnect the fuel gauge wiring to the top of the tank. On early models, the wire should be disconnected from inside the trunk and then fed through the trunk floorpan with the rubber grommet pushed out of place.
4   Raise the vehicle for access underneath the car.
5   Drain all fuel from the tank into a clean container. Since there are no drain plugs, it is necessary to siphon the fuel through the filler neck, or drain the fuel through the fuel feed line running to the carburetor. Do not start the siphoning process with your mouth as serious personal injury could result. Also make sure that no open flames, lighted cigarettes or sparks are in the area as they could ignite the fuel vapor.
6   Disconnect the fuel hose and/or vapor return hose at the top of the tank.

7   Remove the gauge ground wire attached to the underbody.
8   Disconnect the filler neck at the tank.
9   Support the bottom of the tank using an adjustable jack and a piece of wood to spread the load.
10   Remove the tank strap bolts and carefully lower the tank checking that all connections are free of the tank as it is lowered. Read the following section for important repair and storage information **(see illustrations)**.
11   Installation is a reversal of the removal process. Make sure all electrical connections are clean and properly installed and all hoses are tightened securely to the tank.

8.6 Exploded view of a typical Rochester 2G series carburetor

1	Pump Rod Retainer	40	Venturi Cluster Gasket
2	Pump Rod	41	Main Well Inserts
3	Fast Idle Cam Screw	42	Pump Return Spring
4	Fast idle Cam	43	Pump Check Ball
5	Trip Lever Screw	44	Pump Discharge Ball Guide
6	Trip Lever	45	Pump Discharge Ball Spring
7	Choke Lever and Collar	46	Pump Discharge Ball
8	Choke Rod	47	Power Valve Assembly
9	Idle Vent Valve Screw	48	Power Valve Assembly Gasket
10	Idle Vent Valve Shield	49	Main Metering Jets
11	Idle Vent Valve	50	Throttle Body To Bowl Screw & Lockwasher
12	Fuel Inlet Fitting	51	Throttle Body Gasket
13	Fuel Inlet Fitting Gasket	52	Throttle Body & Shaft Assembly
14	Fuel Filter Gasket	53	Idle Needles
15	Fuel Inlet Filter	54	Idle Needle Springs
16	Fuel Filter Spring	55	Flange Gasket
17	Stat Cover Retainer Screw	56	Idle Adjust Screw
18	Stat Cover Toothed Retainer	57	Idle Compensator Cover Screw
19	Stat Cover Plain Retainer	58	Idle Compensator Cover
20	Stat Cover & Spring Assembly	59	Idle Compensator Valve Screw
21	Stat Cover Basket	60	Idle Compensator Valve
22	Choke Baffle Plate	61	Idle Compensator Valve Gasket
23	Choke Housing Basket (Not Shown)	62	Hot Water Choke Assembly
24	Bowl Cover Screw & Lockwasher (Extra Long)	63	Hot Water Filter Retainer
25	Bowl Cover Screw & Lockwasher	64	Hot Water Filter
26	Bowl Cover Assembly	65	Vacuum Control Rod Retainer
27	Float Hinge Pin	66	Vacuum Control Rod
28	Float Assembly	67	Stat Rod Lever Screw
29	Rotary Inlet Valve & Gasket	68	Stat Rod Lever
30	Bowl Cover Gasket	69	Vacuum Control Attaching Screw
31	Pump Plunger Retainer	70	Vacuum Break Control Assembly
32	Pump Plunger Lock Ring	71	Vacuum Break Control Hose
33	Pump Plunger Washer	72	Idle Air Adjust Needle
34	Pump Plunger Spring	73	Idle Air Adjust Needle Spring
35	Pump Plunger Cup	74	Bowl Assembly
36	Power Piston Assembly		
37	Venturi Cluster Screw & Fiber Washer (Center)		
38	Venturi Cluster Screw & Lockwasher		
39	Venturi Cluster		

Illustration courtesy of
Tomco Industries

7   Fuel tank - repairs and storage

Warning: *Gasoline is extremely flammable, so take extra precautions when you work on any part of the fuel system. See the* **Warning** *in Section 3.*

1   Any repairs to the fuel tank or filler neck should be carried out by a professional who has experience in this critical and potentially dangerous work. Even after cleaning and flushing of the fuel system, explosive fumes can remain and ignite during the repairing of the tank.

2   If the fuel tank is removed from the vehicle, it should not be placed in any area where sparks, or open flames could ignite the fumes coming out of the tank. Be especially careful inside garages where a water heater is located as the pilot light of the heater could cause an explosion.

8   Carburetors - description

1   Reference should be made to the Specifications Section of Chapter 1 for the general application of the different types of carburetors installed during the production run of vehicles covered by this manual. It is emphasized that the information given is not intended to identify a particular carburetor with a specific vehicle, and the actual carburetor fitted to your engine should be checked out by recording the number stamped on the unit, and checking it with your partsman. It is very important not to use an incorrect unit, nor to modify the jets or internal components by substituting parts with different manufacturer's part numbers from those originally used.

2   All units have automatic chokes, either stove (hot air) heated from the manifold, or electrically heated.

3   Depending upon engine capacity, the carburetor may be of dual or four-barrel downdraft type.

4   Overhaul of a worn carburetor is not difficult, but always obtain a repair kit in advance, which will contain all the necessary gaskets and replaceable items.

5   If a carburetor has seen considerable use, and is obviously well worn, it will probably be more economical to replace it with a new, or factory reconditioned unit.

Rochester 2G series carburetor

Refer to illustration 8.6

6   This carburetor is a dual barrel, side bowl design **(see illustration)**.

7   Units fitted to manual and automatic transmission vehicles are similar but vary in calibration.

8.12 Exploded view of a typical Rochester 4MC/4MV series carburetor

1	Fuel Filter Nut (Inlet)
2	Filter Nut Gasket
3	Fuel Filter Gasket
4	Fuel Filter
5	Fuel Filter Spring
6	Idle Vent Valve Screw
7	Idle Vent Valve
8	Pump Rod Retainer
9	Pump Rod
10	Idle Vent Valve Lever
11	Choke Rod Retainer
12	Choke Rod
13	Air Horn Screw (4)
14	Air Horn Screw (3)
15	Air Horn Screw (2)
16	Bowl Cover Assembly
17	Dashpot Piston And Rod Assembly
18	Secondary Metering Rod (2)
19	Pump Assembly
20	Pump Return Spring
21	Air Horn Gasket
22	Primary Power Piston Assembly
23	Primary Metering Rods (2)
24	Power Piston Spring
25	Float Bowl Insert
26	Float Hinge Pin
27	Float And Lever Assembly
28	Float Needle Full Clip
29	Needle Diaphragm Retainer Screw (2)
30	Needle Diaphragm Retainer
31	Needle Diaphragm Assembly
31A	Needle Seat Gasket Assembly
32	Pump Discharge Ball Plug
33	Pump Discharge Ball
34	Primary Jets (2)
35	Idle Compensator Cover Screw (2)
36	Idle Compensator Cover
37	Idle Compensator Assembly
38	Idle Compensator Gasket
39	Throttle Body Screw (3)
40	Throttle Body Assembly
41	Idle Adjustment Needle (2)
42	Idle Adjustment Needle Spring (2)
43	Throttle Body Gasket
44	Vacuum Hose (4MV)
45	Vacuum Break Control Bracket Attaching Screw
46	Vacuum Break Control And Bracket Assembly (4MV)
47	Fast Idle Cam
48	Secondary Lockout Lever (4MV)
49	Intermediate Choke Lever
50	Stat Retainer Screw (3) (4MC)
51	Stat Cover Retainers (3) (4MC)
52	Stat Cover And Spring Assembly (4MC)
53	Stat Cover Gasket (4MC)
54	Choke Baffle Plate (4MC)
55	Stat Housing Attaching Screw
56	Choke Housing And Vacuum Break Assembly (4MC)
57	Choke Housing Gasket (4MC)
58	Float Bowl Assembly

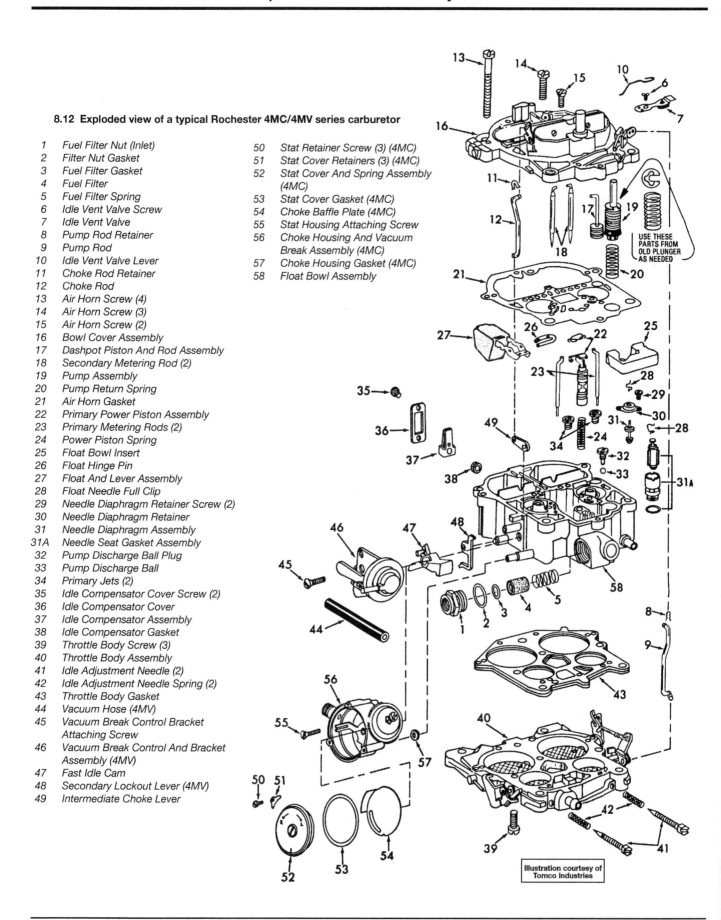

USE THESE PARTS FROM OLD PLUNGER AS NEEDED

Illustration courtesy of Tomco Industries

8.13 Exploded view of a typical Rochester M4MC/E4ME series carburetor

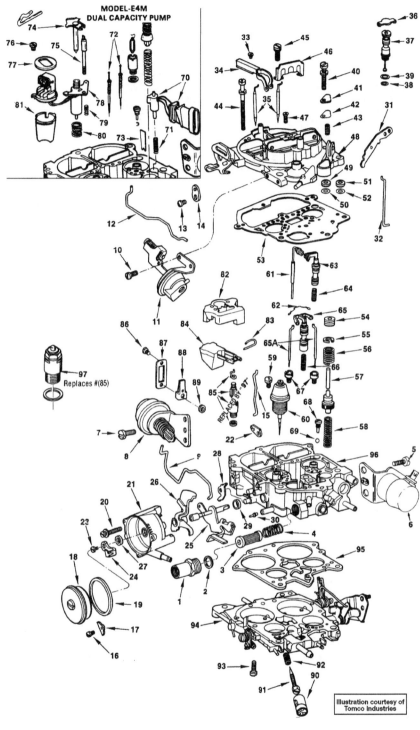

1   Fuel Filter Nut
2   Fuel Filter Nut Gasket
3   Fuel Filter
4   Fuel Filter Spring
5   Solenoid Screw
6   Idle Speed Solenoid
7   Rear Vacuum Break Screw
8   Rear Vacuum Break Assembly
9   Rear Vacuum Break Rod
10 Front Vacuum Break Screw
11 Front Vacuum Break Assembly
12 Front Vacuum Break Rod
13 Choke Lever Screw
14 Choke Lever
15 Choke Rod
16 Choke Cover Retainer Rivet
17 Choke Cover Retainer
18 Choke Cover Assembly
19 Choke Cover Gasket
20 Choke Housing Screw
21 Choke Housing Assembly
22 Intermediate Choke Lever
23 Choke Coil Lever Screw
24 Choke Coil Lever
25 Intermediate Choke Shaft
26 Fast Idle Cam
27 Choke Housing Seal
28 Secondary Metering Rod Holder
29 Intermediate Choke Shaft Seal
30 Vacuum Passage Tube
31 Pump Lever
32 Pump Rod
33 Secondary Metering Rod Holder Screw
34 Secondary Metering Rod Holder
35 Secondary Metering Rods
36 Air Bleed Valve Cover
37 Idle Air Bleed Valve
38 Lower Bleed Valve O-ring
39 Upper Bleed Valve O-ring
40 Vent Cover Screw
41 Vent Cover
42 Vent Cover Gasket
43 Vent Valve Spring
44 Airhorn Screw-long
45 Airhorn Screw-short
46 Air Baffle
47 Airhorn Screw-Special
48 Airhorn Assembly
49 Pump Stem Seal
50 Pump Stem Seal Retainer
51 T.P.S. Plunger Seal
52 T.P.S. plunger seal Retainer
53 Airhorn Gasket
54 Pump Stem Spacer
55 Pump Spring Retainer
56 Pump Spring
57 Pump Stem Assembly
58 Pump Return Spring
59 Aneroid Assembly Screw
60 Aneroid Assembly
61 Auxiliary Metering Rod
62 Metering Rod Spring
63 Auxiliary Power Piston
64 Auxiliary Power Piston Spring
65 Power Piston Assembly
66 Main Metering Rods
67 Main Jets
68 Pump Discharge Ball Screw
69 Pump Discharge Ball
70 Throttle Position Sensor Assembly
71 T.P.S. Spring
72 Main Metering Rod & Spring
73 Pump Well Baffle
74 Solenoid Plunger
75 Solenoid Lean Mixture Adjusting Screw
76 ECM Connector Screw
77 ECM Connector Gasket
78 ECM Connector & Solenoid Assembly
79 Lean Mixture Screw Spring
80 Solenoid Spring
81 Well Insert
82 Fuel, Bowl Inset
83 Float Hinge Pin
84 Float & Lever Assembly
85 Needle & Seat Assembly
86 Hot Idle Compensator Cover Screw
87 Hot Idle Compensator Cover
88 Hot Idle Compensator Assembly
89 Hot Idle Compensator Gasket
90 Idle Limiter Cap
91 Idle Needle
92 Idle Needle Spring
93 Throttle Body Screw
94 Throttle Body
95 Throttle Body Gasket
96 Main Body
97 Rotary Inlet Valve

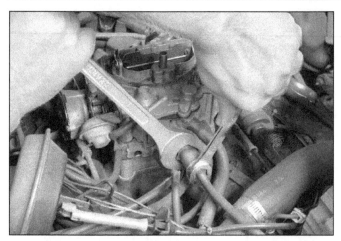

9.2 When removing the fuel line always use the correct size wrenches, preferably a "flare-nut" wrench to avoid stripping the tube nut, and a "backup" wrench to keep the carburetor inlet nut from turning

9.7 Remove the carburetor mounting bolts or nuts

8   The main metering jets are of a fixed type, calibration being accomplished through a system of air bleeds.

9   A power enrichment valve assembly is incorporated by which power mixtures are controlled by air velocity past the boost venturi according to engine demands.

10   On later model vehicles, an electrically-operated throttle closing solenoid (controlled through the ignition switch) is used to ensure that the throttle valve closes fully after the ignition is switched off, to prevent running-on (dieseling).

11   The choke is automatic and is operated by an exhaust manifold heated coil.

Rochester 4MV (Quadrajet) series carburetor

Refer to illustration 8.12

12   This is a downdraft two stage unit **(see illustration)**. The primary side uses a triple venturi system. The secondary side has two large bores and one metering system which supplements the primary main metering system and receives fuel from a common float chamber.

Rochester M4MC (Quadrajet) series carburetor

Refer to illustration 8.13

13   This is also downdraft two stage unit and is very similar to the 4 MV unit **(see illustration)**.

9   Carburetors - removal and installation

Warning: *Gasoline is extremely flammable, so take extra precautions when you work on any part of the fuel system. See the* **Warning** *in Section 3.*

Refer to illustrations 9.2 and 9.7

1   Remove the air cleaner.

2   Disconnect the fuel and vacuum pipes

from the carburetor **(see illustration)**.

3   Disconnect the choke rod or electrical wire (M4ME and M2ME carburetors).

4   Disconnect the accelerator linkage.

5   Disconnect the throttle valve linkage or downshift cable (automatic transmission)

6   Remove all hoses and electrical connections, making **very careful** note of where they were removed from. Tags or coded pieces of tape will help.

7   Remove the carburetor attaching nuts and/or bolts **(see illustration)**.

8   Lift away the carburetor.

9   Remove the gasket and/or insulator.

10   Installation is the reverse of the removal procedure, but the following points should be noted:

a) *By filling the carburetor bowl with fuel, the initial start-up will be easier and less drain on the battery will occur.*

b) *New gaskets should be used.*

c) *Idle speed and mixture settings should be checked, and adjusted if necessary.*

10   Carburetor (Rochester 2GV) - idle adjustment

1   Idle speed adjustment must be carried out after the engine has fully warmed up. The air cleaner must be fitted, except where otherwise specified, and it is essential that the ignition timing and dwell angle are correctly set. All emission control systems must also be functioning correctly. In order to check engine speed, an external tachometer must be connected, following the manufacturer's instructions. **Note:** *If the information given on the Decal label has superseded the information given in Specifications, the Decal label should be assumed to be correct.*

1970 models

Refer to illustration 10.3

2   Disconnect and plug the distributor vacuum line and disconnect the "Fuel Tank" line

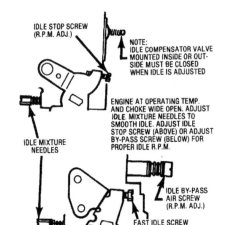

10.3 Rochester 2G carburetor idle speed and idle mixture adjustments

from the vapor canister.

3   Turn the mixture screws in gently until they seat and then back them out four turns **(see illustration)**.

4   Adjust the idle speed screw to obtain 800 rpm (manual transmission in neutral) or the solenoid screw to obtain 630 rpm (automatic transmission in "Drive").

5   Now adjust the two mixture screws equally to obtain 700 rpm (manual) or 600 rpm (automatic).

6   On vehicles with automatic transmission, disconnect the electrical lead from the solenoid and then set the idle speed screw on the carburetor to obtain 450 rpm.

7   Reconnect the distributor vacuum line and the solenoid lead.

1971 models

8   Disconnect and plug the distributor vacuum line.

9   Disconnect the "Fuel Tank" line from the vapor canister.

10   Adjust the idle speed screw on the carburetor to obtain 600 rpm (manual transmission in neutral) and air conditioning off (if fitted). With automatic transmission, adjust to 550 rpm (transmission in Drive) with the air conditioning (if fitted) on. Do not adjust the idle solenoid screw on automatic transmission vehicles.

11   The idle mixture screws on these carburetors are preset and should not be tampered with, which, in any event, cannot be accomplished without first breaking their limiter caps (refer to paragraph 24).

1972 models

12   The procedures are similar to those described in paragraphs 8 to 11 for 1971 models except that with air conditioning off, the idle stop solenoid screw should be adjusted to give an idle speed of 900 rpm (manual transmission in Neutral) or 600 rpm (automatic transmission in Drive).

1973 and 1974 models

13   Disconnect and plug the distributor vacuum pipe.
14   Disconnect the "Fuel Tank" line from the vapor canister.
15   With air conditioning off, adjust the idle stop solenoid screw to obtain 900 rpm (manual in Neutral) or 600 rpm (automatic in Drive).
16   Now de-energize the idle stop solenoid and with the idle cam screw on the low step of the cam, adjust the cam screw to obtain 400 rpm (automatic transmission in Drive) or 500 rpm (manual transmission in Neutral).
17   Reconnect the vacuum and fuel tank lines.

Idle mixture adjustment (1971 on)

18   The idle mixture screws are fitted with limiter caps as already described and any minor adjustment should be restricted to turning the screws within the extent of their travel (1/2 to 3/4 turn clockwise). Turning the screws in leans the mixture.
19   If after overhaul or replacement of carburetor internal components, it is essential to adjust the mixture screws, carry out the following operations:
20   Disconnect the fuel tank vent hose from the vapor canister.
21   Disconnect and plug the distributor vacuum line.
22   Switch off the air conditioning (if fitted).
23   Set transmission in Neutral (manual) or Drive (automatic).
24   Using a pair of pliers break off the tabs on the mixture screw limiter cap.
25   Refer to Specifications and set the engine idle speed to the initial idle speed (lean drop method) given in Specifications Section.
26   Now turn out the mixture screws equally until maximum idle speed is achieved. Readjust the initial speed to that given in the Specifications.

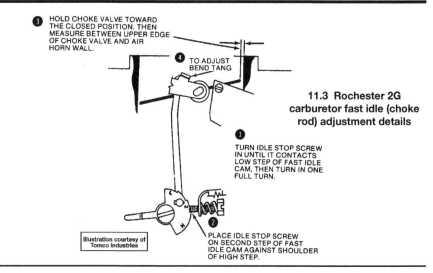

11.3 Rochester 2G carburetor fast idle (choke rod) adjustment details

27   Now turn both mixture screws in equally until the final idle speed is obtained as given in the Specifications Section.
28   Reconnect the hoses and fit new limiter caps with the cap stops at the fully rich (backed out) position.
29   An alternative method of setting the idle mixture adjustment is to connect a CO meter (exhaust gas analyzer) in accordance with the maker's instructions and then turn the mixture screws in or out until the CO level is within the maximum shown in the Specifications Section, consistent with smooth idling.

11   Carburetor (Rochester 2GV) - choke rod adjustment

Refer to illustration 11.3
Note: *The following adjustment will normally only be required after overhaul or repair of the carburetor.*
1   Turn the idle stop screw in until it just touches the bottom step of the fast idle cam, then screw it in exactly one full turn.
2   Position the idle screw so that it is on the second stop of the fast idle cam against the shoulder of the high step.
3   Hold the choke valve plate towards the closed position (using a rubber band to keep it in place) and check the gap between the upper edge of the choke valve plate and the inside wall of the air horn **(see illustration)**.
4   Adjust to the specified gap, if necessary, by bending the tang on the upper choke lever. The setting should provide the specified fast idle speeds.

12   Carburetor (Rochester 2GV) - choke vacuum break adjustment

Pre 1972 models

Refer to illustration 12.5
1   Remove the air cleaner and plug the air cleaner sensor vacuum take-off port in the carburetor.

2   Start the engine or apply suction to the diaphragm vacuum tube.
3   Remove the choke rod from the lever and install a rubber band to the lever to hold the choke towards the closed position.
4   Slowly open the accelerator until the choke is closed as far as the vacuum break link reaction will permit, and the idle is determined by the high step of the fast idle cam. Release the accelerator.
5   With the condition of paragraph 4 maintained, insert a gauge of the specified thickness between the air horn and the choke blade **(see illustration)**. Bend the rod or tang as necessary to obtain the specified dimension (see Specifications Section).

1972 models onwards

6   Remove the air cleaner and plug the air cleaner sensor vacuum take-off port in the carburetor.
7   Using an external suction source, apply suction to the vacuum break diaphragm until the plunger is fully seated.
8   With the diaphragm fully seated, push the choke valve towards the closed position and place a gauge of the specified thickness

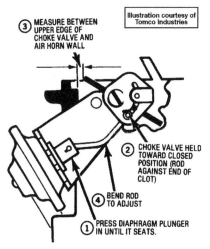

12.5 Rochester 2G carburetor vacuum break adjustment details

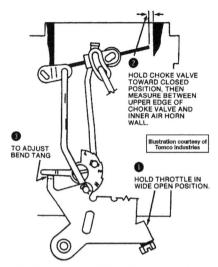

HOLD CHOKE VALVE TOWARD CLOSED POSITION, THEN MEASURE BETWEEN UPPER EDGE OF CHOKE VALVE AND INNER AIR HORN WALL.

TO ADJUST BEND TANG

HOLD THROTTLE IN WIDE OPEN POSITION.

Illustration courtesy of Tomco Industries

13.3 Rochester 2G carburetor choke unloader adjustment details

between the air horn and the choke blade.

9   Bend the vacuum break rod if necessary to obtain the specified dimension (see Specifications Section).

13 Carburetor (Rochester 2GV) - choke unloader adjustment

Refer to illustration 13.3

1   Hold the throttle valve plates in the fully open position.
2   Hold the choke valve plate towards the closed position using a rubber band to keep it in place.
3   Check the gap between the upper edge of the choke valve plate and the inside wall of the air horn **(see illustration)**.
4   Bend the tang on the throttle lever to adjust the gap to the specified value if necessary, as given in Specifications Section.

14 Carburetor (Rochester 2GV) - choke coil rod adjustment

Pre-1972 models

1   Hold the choke valve open then pull down on the coil rod to the end of its travel.
2   The top of the rod end which slides in the hole in the choke lever, should be even with the bottom of the choke lever hole. Bend the rod at the point shown to adjust.
3   Connect the rod to the choke lever and install the retaining clip. Check that the choke operates freely.

1972 models onwards

Refer to illustration 14.6

4   Hold the choke valve plate fully open.
5   Disconnect the thermostatic coil rod from the upper lever and push down on the rod as far as it will go. The top of the rod

should be level with the bottom of the hole in the choke lever.
6   Adjust if necessary by bending the rod **(see illustration)**.

15 Carburetor (Rochester 2GV) - accelerator pump adjustment

Refer to illustration 15.3

1   Unscrew the idle speed screw.
2   Close both throttle valve plates completely and measure from the top surface of the air horn ring to the top of the pump rod.
3   Bend the rod to obtain the specified dimension **(see illustration)**.

16 Carburetor (Rochester 2GV) - overhaul

1   When a carburetor develops faults after a considerable mileage, it is usually more economical to replace the complete unit, rather than to completely dismantle it and replace individual components. Where, however, it is decided to strip and rebuild the unit, first obtain a repair kit which will contain all the necessary gaskets and other needed items, and proceed in the following sequence.
2   Bend back the lockwasher tabs then remove the idle stop solenoid (where applicable) from the carburetor.
3   Remove the choke lever from the vacuum break diaphragm link and the vacuum break link from the diaphragm plunger. The diaphragm plunger stem spring need not be removed.
4   Disconnect the vacuum break hose from the tube then remove the diaphragm from the air horn by unscrewing two retaining screws.
5   Remove the fuel inlet filter nut, filter, spring and two gaskets.
6   Remove the pump rod from the throttle lever after removing the retaining clip. Rotate the upper pump lever counter-clockwise, then remove the pump rod from the lever by aligning the rod "pip" with the lever notch.
7   Remove the fast idle cam retaining screw, rotate the cam and remove it from the rod.
8   Hold the choke open, rotate the upper end of the choke rod towards the pump lever and remove the rod from the upper choke lever.
9   Remove the air horn from the float bowl (8 screws).
10   Remove the float hinge pin, float, splash shield and float needle.
11   Unscrew the float needle seat and remove the gasket.
12   Remove the air horn to float bowl gasket.
13   Depress the power piston shaft, and allow the spring to snap sharply and eject the piston from the casting.
14   Remove the inner pump lever retaining screw then remove the outer pump lever and plastic washer from the air horn. Place the

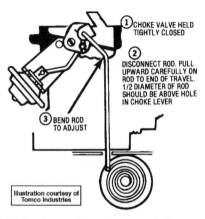

PRESS DOWNWARD ON ROD TO LIMIT OF TRAVEL. TOP OF ROD ENDS SHOULD BE EVEN WITH BOTTOM OF HOLE IN LEVER.

① CHOKE VALVE HELD TIGHTLY CLOSED

② DISCONNECT ROD. PULL UPWARD CAREFULLY ON ROD TO END OF TRAVEL. 1/2 DIAMETER OF ROD SHOULD BE ABOVE HOLE IN CHOKE LEVER

③ BEND ROD TO ADJUST

Illustration courtesy of Tomco Industries

14.6 Rochester 2G carburetor choke coil rod adjustment details

plunger in gasoline to prevent the rubber from drying out.
15   Rotate the pump plunger stem out of the hole in the inner lever if it is required to remove it. Do not bend the tang on the inner lever.
16   If the choke shaft or the valve need replacement, remove the two staked screws, remove the valve, then remove the shaft and lever from the air horn.
17   Remove the pump plunger return spring from the pump well, followed by the inlet check ball (where applicable).
18   Remove the pump inlet screen from the bottom of the float bowl (where applicable).
19   Unscrew the main jets, power valve and gaskets.
20   Remove the cluster and gasket (3 screws and washers). Note the fiber washer on the center screw.
21   Remove the pump discharge spring retainer, the spring and the check ball.
22   Remove the throttle body to bowl attaching screws. Remove the body and gasket.

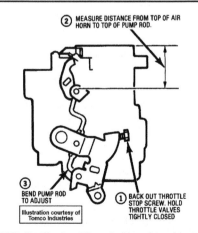

② MEASURE DISTANCE FROM TOP OF AIR HORN TO TOP OF PUMP ROD.

③ BEND PUMP ROD TO ADJUST

① BACK OUT THROTTLE STOP SCREW. HOLD THROTTLE VALVES TIGHTLY CLOSED

Illustration courtesy of Tomco Industries

15.3 Rochester 2G carburetor accelerator pump rod adjustment details

23 Further dismantling is not recommended. If it is essential to remove the idle mixture needles, pry out the plastic limiter caps, then count the number of turns to bottom the needles and fit replacements in exactly the same position. New limiter caps should be fitted after running adjustments have been made.

24 Clean all metal parts in a suitable cold solvent. Do not immerse rubber parts, plastic parts, the vacuum break assembly, or the idle stop solenoid, or permanent damage will result. Do not probe the jets, but blow them through with clean, dry compressed air. Examine all fixed and moving parts for cracks, distortion, wear and other damage; replace as necessary. Discard all gaskets and fuel inlet filter.

25 Assembly is essentially the reverse of the removal procedure, but the following points should be noted:

   a) *If new idle mixture screws are used, and the original setting was not noted, install the screws finger-tight to seat them, then back-off 4 full turns (3 full turns for 1970 models).*

   b) *installing the choke valve on the seat, the letters "RP" face upwards. Ensure that there is 0.020 inch clearance between the choke kick lever on the air horn before tightening the choke valve screws.*

   c) *Brass float: With the air horn inverted and the air horn gasket installed, measure the distance from the gasket to the edge of the float seam at the outer edge of the float pontoon. Adjust the float level to the specified dimension by bending the float arm. With the air horn assembly upright and float freely suspended, measure from the gasket to the bottom of the float pontoon. Adjust the float drop to the specified dimension by bending the tang adjacent to the float need/e.*

   d) *Plastic float: Refer to the procedure for the brass float, but note that for float level and float drop, the dimension is taken from the lip at the toe of the float in both instances.*

   e) *Install and tighten the air horn screws evenly in the order shown.*

   f) *After reassembly, carry out all the settings and adjustments listed previously in this Chapter.*

17 Carburetor (Rochester 2GC) - idle adjustment

Note: *If the information given on the VECI Decal label has superseded the information given in the Specifications, the Decal label should be assumed to be correct.* **Note:** *Refer to the illustration in Section 10.*

Idle speed - 1975 models

1 Have the engine at normal operating temperature with the ignition settings correct.

2 Disconnect the fuel tank hose from the vapor canister.

3 Connect a tachometer to the engine and switch the air conditioning off.

4 Turn the idle speed screw until the engine is running at the speeds specified in Specifications Section with manual transmission in Neutral and automatic transmission in Drive.

Idle mixture - 1975 models

5 The mixture screws are fitted with limiter caps which restrict their movement between 1/2 and 3/4 turn lean. Any adjustment should be kept to this but where the carburetor has been overhauled or new components fitted then the caps should be broken off and the following operations carried out.

6 Have the engine at normal operating temperature with air conditioning off and a tachometer connected to the engine.

7 Disconnect the fuel tank hose from the vapor canister.

8 Adjust the idle speed screw until the initial idle speed (see Specifications Section) is obtained.

9 Now unscrew the mixture screws equally until maximum idle speed is achieved. Readjust the idle speed screw again to obtain initial idle speed.

10 Screw in the mixture screws equally until final idle speed (lean drop) is obtained.

Idle speed - 1976 models and later

11 Have the engine at normal operating temperature with ignition settings correct and emission control systems operating correctly.

12 Set the idle speed screw on the low step of the fast idle cam.

13 Turn the idle speed screw to set the curb (initial idle speed) to specification (see Specifications Section or vehicle Decal).

14 Where a solenoid is fitted to the carburetor, carry out the operations described in paragraphs 11 and 13 and then with (I) the solenoid energized, (ii) the lead disconnected from the air conditioner compressor, (iii) the air conditioner on, open the throttle to allow the solenoid plunger to extend fully. Turn the solenoid hexagonal headed bolt until the idle speed is 700 rpm (manual) or 650 rpm (automatic). Reconnect the compressor lead on completion.

15 2GC carburetors are fitted with a solenoid when the vehicle is equipped with automatic transmission or air conditioning.

Idle mixture - 1976 models and later

16 Refer to paragraphs 5 to 10 of this Section.

18 Carburetor (Rochester 2GC) - accelerator pump rod adjustment

1 The procedure is as for 2GV carburetor (Section 15).

19 Carburetor (Rochester 2GC) - choke coil lever adjustment

Note: *Refer to the illustration in Section 14.*

1 Remove three screws and retainers and remove the thermostatic coil cover, gasket and inside baffle plate assembly.

2 Place the idle speed screw on the highest step of the fast idle cam.

3 Close the choke valve by pushing up on the intermediate choke lever.

4 The edge of the coil lever inside the choke housing must align with the edge of the gauge.

5 If necessary, bend the choke rod to adjust.

20 Carburetor (Rochester 2GC) - fast idle cam adjustment

Note: *Refer to the illustration in Section 10*

1 Place the idle speed screw on the second step of the cam, against the high step.

2 Check the dimension between the upper edge of the choke valve and the air horn wall.

3 If adjustment is necessary to obtain the specified dimension, bend the choke lever tang.

21 Carburetor (Rochester 2GC) - choke unloader adjustment

Note: *Refer to the illustration in Section 13.*

1 Hold the throttle valve open with the fingers.

2 Using a suitable gauge, check that the clearance between the edge of the choke valve plate and the air horn wall is as specified (see Specifications Section).

3 If necessary, bend the tang to adjust.

22 Carburetor (Rochester 2GC) - vacuum break adjustment

Note: *Refer to the illustration in Section 12.*

1 Using a separate source of suction, such as the mouth or a small hand pump, seat the vacuum break diaphragm.

2 Cover the vacuum break bleed hole with a piece of masking tape.

3 Place the idle speed screw on the high step of the fast cam idle.

4 Hold the choke coil lever inside the choke housing towards the closed choke position.

5 Check the dimension between the upper edge of the choke valve and the air horn wall. If adjustment is required to obtain the specified dimension (see Specifications Section) bend the vacuum break rod.

6 Remove the masking tape on the vacuum unit bleed hole and reconnect the vacuum hose.

23 Carburetor (Rochester 2GC) - automatic choke coil adjustment

Note: *Refer to the illustration in Section 14.*
1   Place the idle speed screw on the highest step of the fast idle cam.
2   Loosen the choke coil cover retaining screws.
3   Rotate the cover against the coil tension until the choke begins to close. Continue rotating until the index mark aligns with the specified point on the choke housing, which is between the center and 1/2 notch lean.
4   Tighten the choke cover retaining screws.

24 Carburetor (Rochester 2GC) - overhaul

Warning: *Gasoline is extremely flammable, so take extra precautions when you work on any part of the fuel system. See the* **Warning** *in Section 3.*
Note: *When a carburetor develops faults after a considerable mileage, it is usually more economical to replace the complete unit rather than to completely dismantle it and replace individual components. However, if it is decided to strip and rebuild the unit, first obtain a repair kit which will contain all the necessary gaskets and other needed items, and proceed in the following sequence.*
1   If the carburetor is fitted with a solenoid (automatic transmission or air conditioning) this should be removed before dismantling the carburetor. To do this, bend back the lockwasher tabs and unscrew the large nut which holds the solenoid to the bracket. Avoid immersion of the solenoid in cleaning solvent.
2   Remove the fuel inlet filter nut, gasket. filter and spring.
3   Disconnect the lower end of the pump rod from the throttle lever.
4   Remove the upper end of the pump rod from the pump lever.
5   Remove the vacuum break diaphragm hose.
6   Remove the vacuum break diaphragm assembly (2 screws) and disconnect it from the lever on the end of the choke shaft.
7   Remove the vacuum break lever from the end of the choke shaft (1 screw), then remove the intermediate choke rod from the vacuum break lever on the coil housing.
8   Remove the fast idle cam retaining screw, then remove the cam from the end of the choke rod. The upper end of the rod cannot be removed until the air horn has been removed from the float bowl.
9   Remove the 8 air horn attaching screws and lockwashers, then lift off the air horn.
10   Remove the float hinge pin and lift off the float. The float needle and pull clip (where applicable) can now be removed from the float arm.

11   Unscrew the float needle seat and remove the gasket.
12   Depress the power piston and release it to allow it to snap free.
13   Remove the pump plunger assembly and inner pump lever from the shaft by loosening the set screws on the inner lever.
14   If the pump assembly is to be overhauled, break off the flattened end of the pump plunger stem; the service pump uses a grooved pump plunger stem and retaining clip. After removing the inner pump lever and pump assembly, remove the outer lever and shaft assembly from the air horn. Remove the plastic washer from the pump plunger shaft.
15   Remove the gasket from the air horn.
16   Remove the fuel inlet baffle (next to the needle seat).
17   Taking care not to bend the choke shaft, remove the choke valve. The retaining screws may need to be suitably dressed to permit removal.
18   Remove the choke valve shaft. Remove the fast idle cam rod and lever from the shaft.
19   Remove the pump plunger return spring from the float bowl pump well, then invert the bolt and remove the aluminum ball.
20   Remove the main metering jets, power valve and gasket from inside the float bowl.
21   Remove the three screws which retain the venturi cluster; remove the cluster and gasket.
22   Use needle-nosed pliers to remove the pump discharge spring retainer, then remove the spring and check ball from the discharge passage.
23   Remove the three large throttle body to bowl attaching screws and lockwashers. Remove the throttle body and gasket.
24   Remove the thermostatic choke coil cover (3 screws and retainers) and gasket from the choke housing. Do not remove the cap baffle from beneath the coil cover.
25   Remove the choke housing baffle plate.
26   From inside the choke housing, remove the 2 attaching screws; remove the housing and gasket.
27   Remove the screw from the end of the intermediate choke shaft, then remove the choke lever from the shaft. Remove the inner choke coil lever and shaft assembly from the choke housing, followed by the rubber dust seal.
28   Further dismantling is not recommended, particularly with regard to the throttle valves or shaft since it may be impossible to reassemble the valves correctly in relation to the idle discharge orifices. If it is essential to remove the idle mixture needles, break off the plastic limiter caps then count the number of turns to bottom the needles and fit replacements in exactly the same position. New limiter caps should be fitted after running adjustments have been made.
29   Clean all metal parts in a suitable cold solvent. Do not immerse rubber parts. plastic parts, diaphragm assemblies or pump plungers, as permanent damage will result. Do not probe the jets, but blow through with clean, dry compressed air. Examine all fixed

and moving parts for cracks, distortion, wear and other damage; replace as necessary. Discard all gaskets and the fuel inlet filter.
30   Assembly is essentially the reverse of the removal procedure, but the following points should be noted:

a) *If new idle mixture screws were used, and the original setting was not noted, install the screws finger-tight to seat them, then back off 4 full turns*
b) *When installing the rubber dust seal in the choke housing cavity, the seal lip faces towards the carburetor after the housing is installed.*
c) *Before installing the choke cover coil and baffle plate assembly, carry out the Choke Coil lever adjustment (Section 19).*
d) *When installing the choke coil and cover assembly, the end of the coil must be below the plastic tang on the inner choke housing lever. At this stage carry out the Automatic Choke Coil adjustment (Section 23).*
e) *When installing the venturi cluster, ensure that a gasket is fitted on the center screw.*
f) *Install the choke valve with the letters "RP" or the part number, facing upwards.*
g) *Carry out float level and float drop checks as specified for the 2GV carburetor in Section 16 for plastic floats.*
h) *Install and tighten the air horn screws as shown for 2GV carburetors.*
j) *After reassembly, carry out the relevant settings and adjustments listed previously in this Chapter.*

25 Carburetor (M2ME) - idle adjustment

Refer to the illustrations 25.3a and 25.3b
1   Idle speed adjustment must be carried out after the engine has fully warmed up. The air cleaner must be fitted, except where otherwise specified, and it is essential that the ignition timing and dwell angle are correctly set. All emission control systems must also be functioning correctly. In order to check engine speed, an external tachometer must be connected, following the manufacturer's instructions. **Note:** *If the information given on the VECI Decal label has superseded the information given in Specifications, the Decal label should be assumed to be correct.*
2   Disconnect the electrical lead from the idle speed solenoid (if so equipped).
3   Adjust the base idle speed screw to the rpm specified on the emission label **(see illustrations)**. The shift selector on automatic transmissions should be in Drive, and manual transmissions should be in Neutral.
4   The idle mixture screws have been preset at the factory and sealed. The only time the mixture screws will need adjusting is in the case of a major carburetor overhaul, throttle body replacement or in the case of a high emissions reading by official inspections. Because the mixture screws are

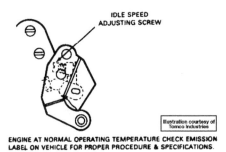

ENGINE AT NORMAL OPERATING TEMPERATURE CHECK EMISSION
LABEL ON VEHICLE FOR PROPER PROCEDURE & SPECIFICATIONS.

25.3a On non-feedback models without an idle-stop solenoid,
after the engine is warmed to normal operating temperature and
the idle mixture is adjusted, turn the idle speed screw, as
necessary, to adjust the idle speed to the specification listed on
the VECI label under the hood

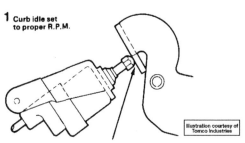

2 With A/C on. Solenoid energized. (stem extended) Adjust stem screw
to obtain proper R.P.M.

25.3b If your non-feedback carburetor is equipped with an idle-
stop solenoid, as shown, set the curb idle speed, then follow the
steps shown in this illustration to adjust the solenoid idle speed to
the specification listed on the VECI label under the hood

---

sealed, an artificial enrichment procedure using propane gas is required to check the mixture. Adjusting the mixture by any other means may be a violation of law.

26 Carburetor (M2ME) - fast idle adjustment

Refer to illustration 26.1

1   With the engine turned off, place the throttle on the high step of the fast idle cam **(see illustration)**.
2   Disconnect and plug the vacuum hose at the EGR valve.
3   Disconnect and plug the vacuum hose at the distributor.
4   Start the engine in "Park" or "Neutral" without touching the accelerator pedal.
5   Adjust the fast idle speed screw to the rpm specified on the emission Decal.
6   Open the throttle to release the fast idle cam and turn off the engine.
7   Unplug and reconnect the vacuum hoses to the EGR valve and distributor.

27 Carburetor (M2ME) - overhaul

Warning: *Gasoline is extremely flammable, so take extra precautions when you work on any part of the fuel system. See the* **Warning** *in Section 3.*
Note: *Refer to the Haynes Rochester Carbu-*

retor Manual for detailed information on carburetor overhauls and adjustment procedures.
1   When a carburetor develops faults after a considerable mileage, it is usually more economical to replace the complete unit, rather than to completely dismantle it and replace individual components. Where, however, it is decided to strip and rebuild the unit, first obtain a repair kit which will contain all the necessary gaskets and other needed items and proceed in the following sequence.
2   Remove the solenoid (if equipped) from the float bowl. Screws secure the solenoid and bracket assembly. Do not immerse the solenoid in any type of carburetor cleaner.
3   Remove the choke lever at the top of the carburetor by removing the retaining screw. Then rotate the choke lever to remove the choke rod from its slot in the lever.
4   To remove the choke rod from the lower lever, hold the lower lever outward and twist the choke rod in a counterclockwise direction.
5   Note the position of the accelerator pump rod on its lever. Then remove the pump lever by driving the pivot pin inwards slightly until the lever can be removed from the air horn.
6   Remove the seven screws which attach the top air horn assembly to the bowl. Two of them are countersunk near the center of the carburetor. Lift the air horn straight up and off the float bowl.
7   From the air horn assembly, remove the vacuum break hose followed by the vacuum break control and bracket assembly. Do not

immerse the vacuum break assembly in carburetor cleaner.
8   Lift the air horn gasket from the top of the float bowl assembly being careful not to distort the spring holding the main metering rods in place.
9   Remove the pump plunger from the pump well. Following the plunger from the well will be the plunger return spring.
10   Remove the power piston and metering rods from the well. Do this by pressing down on the piston and releasing it quickly with a snap. This procedure may have to be repeated many times. Do not remove the piston with pliers on the metering rod hanger. The A.P.T. metering rod adjustment screw is pre-set and should not be changed. If float bowl replacement is necessary the new float bowl will be supplied with a new A.P.T. metering screw.
11   Remove the metering rods from the power piston by disconnecting the spring from the top of each rod. Rotate the rod to remove from the hanger.
12   Remove the plastic filler block over the float valve.
13   Remove the float assembly and float needle by pulling up on the retaining pin. Also remove the needle, seat and gasket.
14   Remove the main metering jets only if necessary to replace.
15   Remove the pump discharge check ball retainer and check ball.
16   Remove the pump well fill slot baffle.
17   The choke cover is held in place with rivets to discourage tampering. It is removed by drilling out the rivet heads with a .159-inch drill bit.
18   Remove the choke assembly retainers, cover gasket and choke cover assembly from the main housing. Do not remove the baffle beneath the choke cover coil.
19   The choke housing can be removed from the float bowl by removing the retaining screw inside the housing.
20   Remove the rear vacuum break rod from the intermediate choke lever.
21   To remove the intermediate choke shaft, remove the retaining screw inside the choke housing and the coil lever from the flats on the

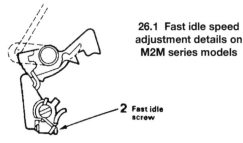

26.1 Fast idle speed adjustment details on M2M series models

shaft. Slide the intermediate shaft outward and remove the fast idle cam from the shaft.

22   Remove the cup seal from the float bowl insert. Do not remove the cup seal from the float bowl insert. Do not remove the insert itself.

23   Turn the float bowl upside down and remove the choke lever from inside the cavity.

24   From the float bowl assembly, remove the fuel inlet nut, gasket, check valve filter and spring.

25   The throttle body can be separated from the float bowl by removing the attaching screws.

26   Remove the pump rod from the throttle lever.

27   Do not remove the plugs covering the idle mixture needles unless it is necessary to replace the mixture screws. The mixture passages should clean with normal soaking and air pressure.

28   Clean all metal parts in a suitable cold solvent. Do not immerse rubber parts, plastic parts, the vacuum break assembly or the idle stop solenoid. Do not probe the jets, but blow them through with clean, dry compressed air. Examine all fixed and moving parts for cracks, distortion, wear and other damage. Replace parts as necessary. Discard all gaskets and the fuel inlet filter.

29   Assembly is essentially the reverse of the removal procedure, but the following points should be noted:

a) *Do not install the choke coil cover assembly until the inside coil lever is adjusted. With the fast idle cam follower on the high step, push up on the coil tang until the choke valve is closed. Insert a .120-inch plug gauge and bend the choke rod near the lever until the lower edge of the lever just contacts the plug gauge.*

b) *With the float bowl components assembled, adjust the float level. Hold down the float retainer firmly and push the float down tightly against the needle. Measure from the top of the float bowl (without gasket) to the top of the float, about 3/16" back from the toe. Bend the float arm as necessary.*

c) *Tighten the seven air horn attaching screws evenly in the sequence given.*

28   Carburetor (E2ME) - idle speed

1   The procedure for setting idle speed on the E2ME carburetor is the same as that for the M2ME. Refer to Section 25.

29   Carburetor (E2ME) - fast idle adjustment

1   The procedure for adjusting the fast idle on the E2ME is the same as that for the M2ME. Refer to Section 26.

30   Carburetor (E2ME) - overhaul

Warning: *Gasoline is extremely flammable, so take extra precautions when you work on any part of the fuel system. See the* **Warning** *in Section 3.*

Note: *Refer to the Haynes Rochester Carburetor Manual for detailed information on carburetor overhauls and adjustment procedures.*

Refer to illustration 30.33

1   When a carburetor develops faults after a considerable mileage, it is usually more economical to replace the complete unit, rather than to completely dismantle it and replace individual components. Where, however, it is decided to strip and rebuild the unit, first obtain a repair kit which will contain all the necessary gaskets and other needed items, and proceed in the following sequence:

2   Remove the screws holding the wide open throttle and idle solenoid and bracket assembly to the float bowl. Do not immerse these parts in carburetor cleaner.

3   Remove the upper choke lever from the end of the shaft by removing the retaining screw and rotating the lever.

4   Remove the choke rod from the lower lever inside the float bowl casting. Do this by holding the lever outward and twisting the rod counterclockwise.

5   Use a drift to drive the pump lever pivot pin inward until the lever can be removed from the air horn. Note the position of the accelerator pump rod in the lever and then remove the pump lever from the pump rod.

6   Remove the vacuum break hose from the tube on the float bowl.

7   Remove the nine air horn attaching screws. Two of them are countersunk near the center of the carburetor. Lift the air horn straight up and off the float bowl.

8   From the air horn assembly, remove the vacuum break control with its bracket. Do not immerse this in carburetor cleaner.

9   Remove the pump plunger stem seal by inverting the air horn and using a small screwdriver to remove the staking. Remove and discard the retainer and seal.

10   The air horn assembly includes an idle air bleed valve which is preset at the factory. The air valve and seals should not be removed from the air horn unless replacement is necessary. The air horn assembly should not be immersed or cleaned in carburetor cleaner in the normal manner as this may damage the O-rings which seal the idle air bleed valve.

11   Holding down on the pump plunger stem, raise the corner of the air horn gasket still attached to the float bowl and remove the pump plunger from its well.

12   Remove the solenoid metering rod plunger by lifting straight up.

13   Remove the rubber seal from around the mixture control solenoid plunger.

14   Remove the air horn gasket from the float bowl.

15   Remove the pump return spring from the well.

16   Remove the plastic filler block over the float valve.

17   Carefully lift out each metering rod assembly. Make sure the return spring comes with the assembly.

18   Remove the mixture control solenoid from the float bowl. Do this by first removing the two attaching screws. Do not remove the solenoid connector at this time. Turn the mixture control screw counterclockwise and remove the screw. Carefully lift the solenoid and connector assembly from the float bowl. The solenoid and connector are serviced as an assembly only.

19   Remove the plastic insert from the cavity in the float bowl under the solenoid connector.

20   Remove the solenoid screw tension spring next to the float hanger clip.

21   Remove the float assembly and float needle by pulling up on the retaining clip. Remove the needle and seat.

22   Remove the large mixture control solenoid spring from the bottom of the float bowl.

23   Remove the main metering jets, if necessary.

24   Remove the pump discharge check ball retainer and check ball.

25   Remove the pump well fill slot baffle, if necessary for replacement.

26   Remove the rear vacuum break control, along with its attaching bracket. Do not immerse this in carburetor cleaner.

27   The non-adjustable choke is designed to be a permanent fixture. Rivets are used to secure the cover. If disassembly is necessary, see the overhaul instructions for the M2ME, as the choke mechanisms are the same.

28   Remove the fuel inlet nut, gasket, check valve filter assembly and spring from the float bowl.

29   Remove the four throttle body attaching screws and remove the throttle body assembly.

30   Remove the pump rod from the throttle lever by rotating the rod until the tang aligns with the slot in the lever.

31   Do not remove the plugs covering the idle mixture needles unless they must be replaced, which is not common in a standard overhaul.

32   Clean all metal parts in a suitable cold solvent. Do not immerse rubber parts, plastic parts, the vacuum break assembly, wide-open throttle switch, solenoid or air horn assembly. Do not probe the jets, but blow them through with clean, dry compressed air. Examine all fixed and moving parts for cracks, distortion, wear and other damage. Replace parts as necessary. Discard all gaskets and the fuel filter.

33   Assembly is essentially the reverse of the removal procedure, but the following points should be noted:

a) *To make the float level adjustment, hold the float retaining clip firmly in place and*

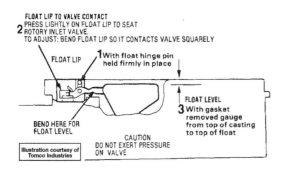

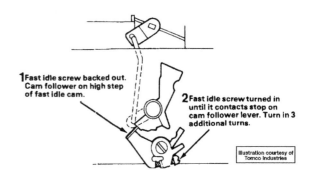

30.33 Rochester E4ME/E4MC carburetor float level adjustment details

31.10 The fast-idle speed screw is in a slightly different location on 4MV models, but the procedure is essentially the same as shown in the previous illustration

push down lightly on the float arm. Measure from the top of the float bowl casting (without gasket) to the top of the float about 3/16" back from the toe. Bend the float arm as necessary for adjustment **(see illustration)**.

b) Tighten the nine air horn attaching screws securely in a crossing pattern starting with the inner screws and working to the outer screws.

31 Carburetor (Rochester 4MV) - idle adjustment

Note: *Refer to the illustration in Section 10.*

1970 models (350, 402 cu in engines)

Note: *If the information given on the VECI Decal label has superseded the information given in the Specifications, the Decal label should be assumed to be correct.*

1   Have the engine at the normal operating temperature with a tachometer connected.
2   Disconnect and plug the distributor vacuum line.
3   Gently seat the mixture screws and then unscrew four turns.
4   Adjust the idle speed screw to obtain 775 rpm (manual transmission in Neutral) or 630 rpm (automatic transmission in Drive).
5   Adjust the mixture screws equally until the engine speed is 700 rpm (manual) 600 rpm (automatic).

1971 and 1972 models (350, 402 cu in engines)

Refer to illustration 31.10

6   Disconnect the distributor vacuum line from the distributor and plug the line. Connect a tachometer to the engine.
7   Disconnect the fuel tank line from the vapor canister.
8   Switch the air conditioning off.
9   With the engine at the normal operating temperature, adjust the idle stop solenoid screw to obtain 900 rpm (manual transmission in Neutral) or 600 rpm

(automatic transmission in Drive).
10   Place the fast idle cam follower on the second step of the cam and adjust the fast idle to 1,350 rpm (manual) or 1,500 rpm (automatic in Park) **(see illustration)**.
11   The mixture screws fitted to these vehicles have limiter caps which restrict their movement to between 1/2 and 3/4 turn lean. Any adjustment should be confined to this but where the carburetor has been overhauled or new components fitted, then the caps should be broken off and the following operations carried out.
12   Have the engine at the normal operating temperature with the air conditioning off and a tachometer connected.
13   Disconnect the fuel tank hose from the vapor canister.
14   Adjust the idle speed crew until the initial idle speed (see Specifications Section) is obtained.
15   Now unscrew the mixture screws equally until maximum idle speed is achieved. Readjust the idle speed screw again to obtain the initial idle speed.
16   Screw in the mixture screws equally until the final idle speed (lean drop) is obtained (see Specifications Section).
17   If an Air Injection Reactor System is fitted, now turn the mixture screws 1/4 turn out equally.
18   If the carburetor is fitted with a solenoid, the final idle speed should be adjusted to complete the turning procedure by de-energizing the solenoid and turning the solenoid

Allen screw to attain 450 rpm.
19   An alternative method of adjusting the mixture is to connect a CO meter /exhaust gas analyzer) in accordance with the maker's instructions and adjust the screws equally until the emission level is within the maximum permitted (see Specifications Section).
20   Install new limiter caps to the mixture screws so that any travel will be in the lean direction (screw in) only.

1973 and 1974 models (350, 400 cu in engines)

21   The operations are similar to those described in the preceding paragraphs except to refer to Specifications Section for initial, final and fast idle settings.

32 Carburetor (Rochester 4MV) - choke rod adjustment

Refer to illustration 32.3

1   Place the cam follower on the second step of the fast idle cam and against the high step.
2   Rotate the choke valve towards the closed position by turning the external lever counterclockwise.
3   Check that the dimension between the lower edge of the choke valve and the air horn wall (at the lever end) is as specified **(see illustration)**. Bend the choke rod if adjustment is required.

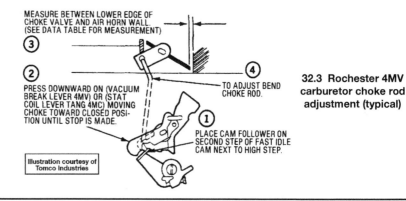

32.3 Rochester 4MV carburetor choke rod adjustment (typical)

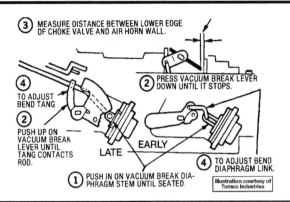

33.4 Rochester 4MV carburetor choke vacuum break adjustment (typical)

33   Carburetor (Rochester 4MV) - choke vacuum break adjustment

Pre- 1972 models

1   Refer to Section 12.

1972 models onwards

Refer to illustration 33.4

2   Using an external source of suction, seat the choke vacuum break diaphragm.

3   Open the throttle slightly so that the cam follower clears the fast idle cam steps, then rotate the vacuum break lever towards the closed direction. Ensure that the vacuum break rod is in the outer end of the slot in the diaphragm plunger. A rubber band can be used to hold the vacuum break lever in position.

4   Measure the distance from the lower edge of the choke valve to the air horn wall **(see illustration)**. If adjustment is needed, bend the link rod.

34   Carburetor (Rochester 4MV) - choke coil rod adjustment

Pre-1972 models

Refer to illustration 34.2

1   Hold the choke valve closed then pull down on the coil rod to the end of its travel. The rod should contact the bracket surface.

2   Bend the choke coil rod, if necessary, so that the top of the rod aligns with the bottom of the holes **(see illustration)**.

3   Connect the coil rod to the choke lever and install the retaining clip. Check that the choke operates freely over its full range of travel.

1972 models onwards

4   Rotate the choke coil lever counter-clockwise to fully close the choke.

5   With the coil rod disconnected and the cover removed, push down on the rod until it contacts the bracket surface.

6   The coil rod must fit in the choke lever notch; bend the rod to adjust if necessary.

7   Install the choke coil cover.

8   Install the coil rod in the choke coil lever slot and install the retaining clip.

9   Check that the choke operates freely over its full range of travel.

35   Carburetor (Rochester 4MV) - air valve dashpot adjustment

Pre-1972 models

1   Seat the vacuum break diaphragm, and check that the specified clearance exists between the dashpot and the end of the slot in the air valve lever, when the air valve is fully closed.

2   If adjustment is necessary, bend the rod at the air valve end.

1972 models onwards

Refer to illustration 35.5

3   Seat the choke vacuum break diaphragm using an outside source of suction, then measure the dimension between the end of the slot in the vacuum break plunger lever and the air valve when the air valve is fully closed.

4   If adjustment is necessary, bend the rod at the air valve end.

5   Some models are equipped with adjustable air valve dashpots **(see illustration)**. Be sure the curb idle speed is set before loosening the air valve dashpot.

36   Carburetor (Rochester 4MV) - overhaul

Warning: *Gasoline is extremely flammable, so take extra precautions when you work on any part of the fuel system. See the* **Warning** *in Section 3.*

1   When a carburetor develops faults after a considerable mileage, it is usually more economical to replace the complete unit rather than to completely dismantle it and replace individual components. However, if it is decided to strip and rebuild the unit, first obtain a repair kit which will contain all the necessary gaskets and other needed items, and proceed in the following sequence.

2   Bend back the lockwasher tabs, then remove the idle stop solenoid.

3   Remove the larger idle stop solenoid bracket screw from the float bowl .

4   Remove the clip from the upper end of the choke rod, disconnect the rod from the upper choke shaft lever and remove the rod from the lower lever in the bowl.

5   Drive the pump lever pivot inwards to remove the roll pin then remove the pump lever from the air horn and pump rod.

6   Remove 2 long screws, 5 short screws and 2 countersunk head screws retaining the air horn to the float bowl.

7   Remove the vacuum break hose, and the diaphragm unit from the bracket.

8   Disconnect the choke assist spring.

9   Remove the metering rod hanger and secondary rods after removing the small screw at the top of the hanger.

10   Lift off the air horn, but leave the gasket in position. Do not attempt to remove the air bleed tubes or accelerating well tubes.

11   If the choke valve is to be replaced, remove the valve attaching screws, then measure the valve and shaft.

12   The air valves and air valve shaft are calibrated and should not be removed. A shaft spring repair kit is available, and contains all the necessary instructions, if these parts require replacement.

13   Remove the pump plunger from the well.

14   Carefully remove the air horn gasket.

15   Remove the pump return spring from the pump well.

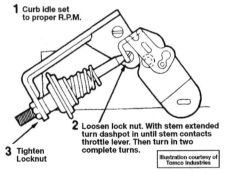

35.5 Rochester 4MV carburetor air valve dashpot adjustment (typical)

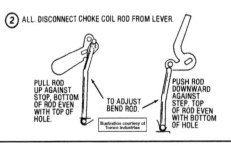

34.2 Rochester 4MV carburetor choke coil rod adjustment (typical)

16 Remove the plastic filler over the float valve.

17 Press the power piston down and release it to remove it. Remove the spring from the well. Note the power piston plastic retainer which is used for ease of assembly.

18 Remove the metering rods from the power piston by disconnecting the spring from the top of each rod, then rotating the rod to remove it from the hanger.

19 Remove the float assembly by pulling up on the retaining pin until it can be removed, then sliding the float towards the front of the bowl to carefully disengage the needle pull clip.

20 Remove the pull clip and the fuel inlet needle, then unscrew the needle seat and remove the gasket.

21 Unscrew the primary metering jets; do not attempt to remove the secondary metering jets.

22 Remove the discharge ball retainer and the check ball.

23 Remove the baffle from the secondary side of the bowl.

24 Remove the choke assembly after removing the retaining screw on the side of the bowl. Remove the secondary locknut lever from the cast boss on the bowl.

25 Remove the fast idle cam and the choke assembly.

26 Remove the intermediate choke rod and actuating lever from the float bowl.

27 Remove the fuel inlet filter nut, gasket, filter and spring.

28 Remove the throttle body to bowl screws. Remove the throttle body.

29 Remove the throttle body to bowl insulator gaskets.

30 Remove the pump rod from the throttle lever by rotating the rod out of the primary lever.

31 Further dismantling is not recommended. If it is essential to remove the idle mixture needles, pry out the plastic limiter caps then count the number of turns to bottom the needles and fit replacements in exactly the same position. New limiter caps should be fitted after running adjustments have been made (see Section 31).

32 Clean all metal parts in a suitable cold solvent. Do not immerse rubber parts, plastic parts, the vacuum break assembly or the idle stop solenoid, or permanent damage will result. Do not probe the jets, but blow them through with clean dry compressed air. Examine all fixed and moving parts for cracks, distortion, wear and other damage: replace as necessary. Discard all gaskets and the fuel inlet filter.

33 Assembly is essentially the reverse of the removal procedure, but the following points should be noted:

a) *If new idle mixture screws are used, and the original setting was not noted, install the screws finger-tight to seat them, then back off 4 full turns (see Section 31).*

b) *Having installed the float, measure from the top of the float bowl gasket surface (gasket not fitted) to the top of the float at a point 3/16 inch from the toe. Bend the float up, or down, to obtain the specified dimension.*

c) *Tighten the air horn retaining screws in the sequence shown.*

d) *When connecting the pump lever to the upper pump rod, install the rod in the inner hole.*

e) *After reassembly, carry out all the relevant settings and adjustments listed previously in this chapter.*

37 Carburetor (Rochester M4MC/M4MCA/M4ME) - idle adjustment

Note: *If the information given on the VECI Decal label has superseded the information given in Specifications, the Decal label should be assumed to be correct.*

1975 on

1 Have the engine at normal operating temperature, air cleaner in position and air conditioning off. Connect a reliable tachometer to the engine.

2 Disconnect the fuel tank hose from the vapor canister.

3 Disconnect the lead from the idle stop solenoid.

4 With automatic in Drive or manual in Neutral, turn the idle speed screw to obtain the curb (final) idle speed shown in the Specifications Section **(see illustrations 25.3a and 25.3b).**

5 Reconnect the solenoid, crack open the throttle slightly to extend the solenoid plunger.

6 Now turn the solenoid plunger screw to set the curb (initial) idle speed shown in Specifications Section.

7 Remove the tachometer and reconnect the fuel tank hose.

8 The idle mixture screws are pre-set and fitted with limiter caps which allow them to be turned about one turn lean to rectify uneven idling. If after carburetor overhaul or replacement of components, the mixture must be adjusted beyond the limit of travel of the caps, carry out the following operations:

9 Repeat the procedure described in paragraphs 1 and 2.

10 Break off the cap on the mixture screws.

11 Set the idle speed to the curb (initial) figure using the solenoid plunger.

12 Unscrew each of the mixture screws equally until the highest idle speed is achieved. Reduce the speed if necessary to curb (initial) specifications using the solenoid plunger.

13 Now screw in each of the mixture screws equally until the curb (final) idle speed is obtained.

14 Reconnect the fuel tank hose and switch off the engine.

38 Carburetor (Rochester M4M series) - accelerator pump rod adjustment

Refer to illustration 38.4

1 With the fast idle cam follower off the steps of the fast idle cam, back out the idle speed screw until the throttle valves are completely closed in the bore. Make sure that the secondary actuating rod is not restricting movement; bend the secondary closing tang if necessary then readjust it after pump adjustment.

2 Place the pump rod in the inner hole in the lever.

3 Measure from the top of the choke valve wall (next to the vent stack) to the top of the pump stem.

4 If necessary, adjust to obtain the specified dimension (see Specifications Section) by bending the lever while supporting it with a screwdriver **(see illustration)**.

5 Adjust the idle speed (Section 47).

39 Carburetor (Rochester M4M Series) - fast idle adjustment

Refer to illustration 39.7

Carburetor removed

1 Place the cam follower lever on the highest step of the fast idle cam.

2 Turn the fast idle screw out until the primary throttle valves are closed.

3 Turn in the fast idle screw to contact the lever then screw in a further 3 full turns.

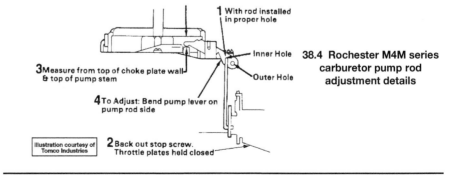

1 With rod installed in proper hole

3 Measure from top of choke plate wall & top of pump stem

4 To Adjust: Bend pump lever on pump rod side

Inner Hole

Outer Hole

2 Back out stop screw. Throttle plates held closed

Illustration courtesy of Tomco Industries

38.4 Rochester M4M series carburetor pump rod adjustment details

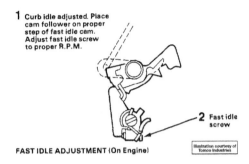

39.7 Rochester M4M series carburetor fast idle adjustment details

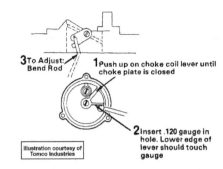

40.4 Rochester M4M series carburetor choke coil lever adjustment details

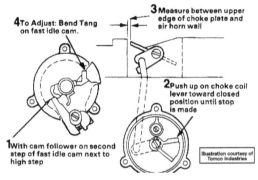

41.4 Rochester M4M series carburetor choke rod (fast idle cam) adjustment details

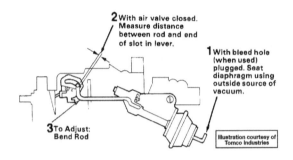

42.2 Rochester M4M series carburetor air valve rod adjustment details

Carburetor in vehicle

4   Connect a tachometer to the engine which should be at the normal operating temperature.
5   Place the transmission in Park or Neutral.
6   Disconnect and plug the vacuum hose at the EGR valve.
7   Position the cam follower on the highest step of the fast idle cam **(see illustration)**.
8   Turn the fast idle screw to achieve the specified fast idle (see Specifications Section).
9   Remake the original connections, remove the tachometer and switch off the engine.

40 Carburetor (Rochester M4M Series) - choke coil lever adjustment

Refer to illustration 40.4
1   Loosen the 3 retaining screws and remove the cover and coil assembly from the choke housing.
2   Push up on the thermostatic coil tang (counterclockwise) until the choke valve is closed.
3   Check that the choke rod is at the bottom of the slot in the choke lever.
4   Insert a plug gauge (an unmarked drill shank is suitable) of the specified size in the hole in the choke housing **(see illustration)**.
5   The lower edge of the choke coil lever should just contact the side inside of the plug gauge.

6   If necessary, bend the choke rod at the point shown.

41 Carburetor (Rochester M4M Series) - fast idle cam (choke rod) adjustment

Note: *Always adjust choke coil lever before carrying out the following operations.*
Refer to illustration 41.4
1   Turn the fast idle screw in until it contacts the fast idle cam follower lever, then turn in 3 full turns more.
2   Place the lever on the second step of the fast idle cam against the rise of the high step.
3   Push upwards on the choke coil lever inside the housing to close the choke valve.
4   Measure between the upper edge of the choke valve and the air horn wall **(see illustration)**.
5   If necessary, bend the tang on the fast idle cam to adjust, but ensure that the tang lies against the cam after bending.
6   Re-check the fast idle adjustment.

42 Carburetor (Rochester M4M Series) - air valve dashpot adjustment

Refer to illustration 42.2
1   Using an external source of suction,

seat the front vacuum break diaphragm. Suction from the mouth or a small hand pump is normally adequate.
2   Ensure that the air valves are completely closed then measure between the air valve dashpot and the end of the slot in the air valve lever **(see illustration)**. This dimension should be 0.015 in.
3   Bend the air valve dashpot rod at the point shown, if adjustment is necessary.

43 Carburetor (Rochester M4M Series) - front vacuum break adjustment

Refer to illustration 43.4
1   Loosen the 3 retaining screws and remove the choke coil cover and coil assembly from the choke housing.
2   Place the cam follower lever on the highest step of the fast idle cam.
3   Using an outside source of suction, seat the diaphragm unit.
4   Push up on the inside choke coil lever until the tang on the vacuum break lever contacts the tang on the plunger **(see illustration)**.
5   Measure between the upper edge of the choke valve and the inside of the air horn wall.
6   Turn the adjustment screw on the vacuum break plunger to obtain the specified dimension.
7   Install the vacuum hose on completion.

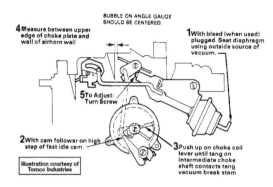

43.4 Rochester M4M series carburetor vacuum break adjustment details

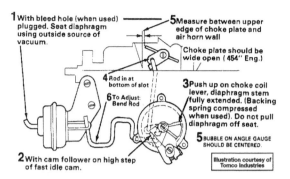

44.4 Rochester M4ME carburetor rear vacuum break adjustment details

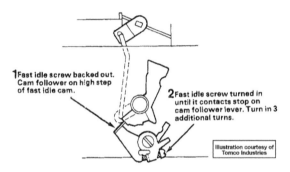

45.2 Rochester M4MC/M4MCA carburetor automatic choke coil adjustment details

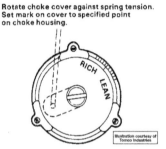

46.3 Rochester M4ME carburetor automatic choke coil adjustment details (early models)

44 Carburetor (Rochester M4M Series) - rear vacuum break adjustment

Refer to illustration 44.4

1   Initially follow the procedure of Paragraphs 1 through 3 in the previous Section, but additionally plug the bleed hose in the end cover of the vacuum break unit using adhesive tape.

2   Push up on the choke coil lever inside the choke housing towards the closed choke position.

3   With the choke rod in the bottom of the slot in the choke lever, measure between the upper edge of the choke valve and the air horn wall.

4   If necessary, bend the vacuum break rod at the point shown to obtain the specified dimension **(see illustration)**.

5   On completion, remove the adhesive tape and install the vacuum hose.

45 Carburetor (Rochester M4MC and M4MCA) - automatic choke coil adjustment

Refer to illustration 45.2

1   With the hot air heater type of choke, install the choke coil and cover assembly with a gasket between the cover and housing. The tang in the coil must be installed in the slot inside the choke coil lever pick-up arm.

2   Place the fast idle cam follower on the highest step of the fast idle cam then rotate the cover counterclockwise until the choke just closes **(see illustration)**.

3   Align the index mark on the cover with the specified point (2 notches lean) on the choke housing then tighten the retaining screws.

46 Carburetor (Rochester M4ME) - automatic choke coil adjustment

Refer to illustrations 46.3 and 46.4

1   With this type of electrically heated automatic choke, make sure that with the coil assembly inside the choke housing, the coil tang contacts the bottom side of the inner face of the choke coil lever pick-up arm.

2   Position the fast idle cam follower on the high step of the cam.

3   Rotate the cover and coil assembly counterclockwise until the choke valve just closes **(see illustration)**.

4   Align the index marks (center) and install the cover and screws **(see illustration)**.

Note: *The ground contact for the electrically heated choke is through a metal plate at the rear of the choke assembly. Do not install a gasket between the cover and housing or this will interrupt the circuit.*

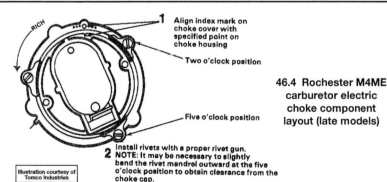

46.4 Rochester M4ME carburetor electric choke component layout (late models)

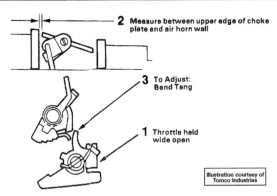

47.3 Rochester M4MC/M4MCA carburetor choke unloader adjustment details

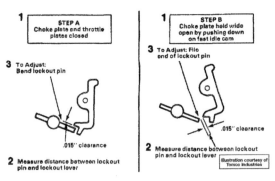

48.2 Rochester M4MC/M4MCA carburetor secondary throttle lockout adjustment details

47 Carburetor (Rochester M4M Series) - unloader adjustment

Refer to illustration 47.3

1   Adjust the choke coil, as described in the previous section.
2   Hold the throttle valves wide open and the chokes fully closed. A rubber band can be used on the tang of the intermediate choke lever if the engine is warm.
3   Measure between the upper edge of the choke valve and the air horn wall **(see illustration)**.
4   If adjustment is necessary, bend the tang on the fast idle lever to obtain the specified dimension. Ensure that the tang on the fast idle cam lever contacts the center point of the fast idle cam after adjustment.

48 Carburetor (Rochester M4M Series) - secondary throttle valve lock-out adjustment

Lock-out lever clearance

Refer to illustration 48.2

1   Hold the choke valves and secondary lock-out valves closed then measure the clearance between the lock-out pin and lock-out lever.

2   If adjustment is necessary, bend the lock-out pin to obtain the specified clearance (0.015 inch) **(see illustration)**.

Opening clearance

3   Push down on the tail of the fast idle cam to hold the choke wide open.
4   Hold the secondary throttle valve partly open then measure between the end of the lock-out pin and the toe of the lock-out lever. (This should be 0.015 inch).
5   If adjustment is necessary, file the end of the lock-out pin but ensure that no burrs remain afterwards.

49 Carburetor (Rochester M4M Series) - secondary closing adjustment

Refer to illustration 49.3

1   Adjust the engine idle speed as described previously in this Chapter.
2   Hold the choke valve wide open with the cam follower lever off the steps of the fast idle cam.
3   Measure the clearance between the slot in the secondary throttle valve pick-up lever and the secondary actuating rod **(see illustration)**.
4   If adjustment is necessary, bend the secondary tang on the primary throttle lever to obtain the specified clearance (0.020 inch).

50 Carburetor (Rochester M4M Series) - secondary opening adjustment

Refer to illustration 50.2

1   Lightly open the primary throttle lever until the link just contacts the tang on the secondary lever.
2   Bend the tang on the secondary lever **(see illustration)**, if necessary, to position the link in the center of the secondary lever slot.

51 Carburetor (Rochester M4M Series) - air valve spring wind-up adjustment

Refer to illustration 51.3

1   Remove the front vacuum break diaphragm unit and the air valve dashpot rod.
2   Using a suitable hexagonal wrench loosen the lock screw then turn the tension adjusting screw counterclockwise until the air valve is partly open.
3   Hold the air valve closed then turn the tension adjusting screw clockwise the specified number of turns after the spring contacts the pin **(see illustration)** (Air Valve Spring Wind-up, see Specifications Section).
4   Tighten the lockscrew and install the air

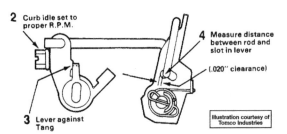

49.3 Rochester M4M series carburetor secondary closing adjustment details

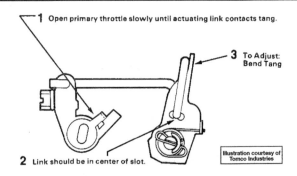

50.2 Rochester M4M series carburetor secondary opening adjustment details

valve dashpot rod, and the front vacuum break diaphragm unit and bracket.

52   Carburetor (Rochester M4M Series) - overhaul

Warning: *Gasoline is extremely flammable, so take extra precautions when you work on any part of the fuel system. See the* **Warning** *in Section 3.*

1   When a carburetor fault develops after a considerable mileage, it is usually more economical to replace the complete unit rather than to completely dismantle it and replace individual components. However, if it is decided to strip and rebuild the unit, first obtain a repair kit which will contain all the necessary gaskets and other needed items, and proceed in the following manner.

2   If the carburetor has an idle stop solenoid, remove the bracket retaining screws and lift away the solenoid and bracket assembly.

3   Remove the upper choke lever from the end of the choke shaft (1 screw) then rotate the lever to remove it, and disengage it from the choke rod.

4   Remove the choke rod from the lower lever inside the float bowl by holding the lever outwards with a small screwdriver and twisting the rod counterclockwise.

5   Remove the vacuum hose from the front vacuum break unit.

6   Remove the small screw at the top of the metering rod hanger, and remove the secondary metering rods and hanger.

7   Using a suitable drift,. drive the small pump lever pivot roll pin inwards to permit removal of the lever.

8   Remove 2 long screws, 5 short screws and 2 countersunk head air horn screws to detach the float bowl. Remove the secondary air baffle deflector (where applicable) from beneath the 2 center air horn screws.

9   Remove the float bowl but leave the gasket in position at this stage. Do not attempt to remove the small tubes protruding from the air horn.

10   Remove the front vacuum break bracket screws and lift off the unit. Detach the air valve dashpot rod from the diaphragm assembly and the air valve lever.

11   If considered necessary, remove the staked choke valve attaching screws then remove the choke valve and shaft from the air horn. Do not remove the air valve and the air valve shaft. The air valve closing spring or center plastic cam can be replaced by following the instructions in the appropriate repair kit.

12   Remove the air horn gasket from the float bowl taking care not to distort the springs holding the main metering rods.

13   Remove the pump plunger and pump return spring from the pump well.

14   Depress the power piston stem and allow it to snap free, withdrawing the metering rods with it. Remove the power piston spring from the well.

15   Taking care to prevent distortion, remove the metering rods from the power piston by disconnecting the tension springs then rotating the rods.

16   Remove the plastic filler block over the float valve then remove the float assembly and needle by pulling up on the pin. Remove the needle seat and gasket.

17   Remove the 2 cover screws and carefully lift out the metering rod and filler spool (metering rod and aneroid on M4MCA carburetors) from the float bowl. **Note:** *The adjustable part throttle (APT) metering rod assembly is extremely fragile and must not be interfered with. If replacement is necessary, refer to Paragraphs 35 through 44.*

18   Remove the primary main metering jets. Do not attempt to remove the APT metering jet or secondary metering orifice plates.

19   Remove the pump discharge check ball retainer and the ball.

20   Remove the rear vacuum break hose and the bracket retaining screws. Remove the vacuum break rod from the slot in the plunger head.

21   Press down on the fast idle cam and remove the vacuum break rod. Move the end of the rod away from the float bowl, then disengage the rod from the hole in the intermediate lever.

22   Remove the choke cover attaching screws and retainers. Pull off the cover and remove the gasket.

23   Remove the choke housing assembly from the float bowl by removing the retaining screw and washer.

24   Remove the secondary throttle valve lock-out lever from the float bowl .

25   Remove the lower choke lever by inverting the float bowl.

26   Remove the plastic tube seal from the choke housing.

27   If it is necessary to remove the intermediate choke shaft from the choke housing, remove the coil lever retaining screw and withdraw the lever. Slide out the shaft and (if necessary), remove the fast idle cam.

28   Remove the fuel inlet filter nut, gasket and filter from the float bowl .

29   If necessary, remove the pump well fill slot baffle and the secondary air baffle.

30   Remove the throttle body attaching screws and lift off the float bowl. Remove the insulator gasket.

31   Remove the pump rod from the lever on the throttle body.

32   If it is essential to remove the idle mixture needles, pry out the plastic limiter caps then count the number of turns to bottom the needles and fit replacements in exactly the same position. New limiter caps should be fitted after running adjustments have been made.

33   Clean all metal parts in a suitable cold solvent. Do not immerse rubber parts, plastic parts, pump plungers, filler spools or aneroids, or vacuum breaks. If the choke housing is to be immersed, remove the cup seal from inside the choke housing shaft hole. If the bowl is to be immersed remove the cup seal from the plastic insert; do not attempt to remove the plastic insert. Do not probe the jets, but blow through with clean, dry compressed air. Examine all fixed and moving parts for cracks, distortion, wear and other damage; replace as necessary. Discard all gaskets and the fuel inlet filter.

34   Assembly is essentially the reverse of the removal procedure, but the following points should be noted:

   a)   *If new idle mixture screws were used, and the original setting was not noted, install the screws finger-tight to seat them, then back off 4 full turns.*

   b)   *The lip on the plastic insert cup seal (on the side of the float bowl) faces outward.*

   c)   *The lip on the inside choke housing shaft hole cup seal faces inwards towards the housing.*

   d)   *When installing the assembled choke body install the choke rod lever into the cavity in the float bowl. Install the plastic tube seal into the housing cavity before installing the housing. Ensure that the intermediate choke shaft engages into the lower choke lever. The choke coil is installed at the last stage of assembly.*

   e)   *Where applicable. the notches on the secondary float bowl air baffle are towards the top, and the top edge of the baffle must be flush with the bowl casting.*

   f)   *To adjust the float, hold the retainer firmly in place and push down lightly against the needle. Measure from the top of the float bowl casting (air horn*

TO ADJUST LOOSEN ALLEN LOCK SCREW. AIR VALVES HELD CLOSED, TURN ADJUSTING SCREW CLOCKWISE UNTIL TORSION SPRING CONTACTS PIN ON AIR VALVE SHAFT. THEN TURN ADDITIONAL SPECIFIED TURNS AND TIGHTEN ALLEN LOCK SCREW. (SEE DATA TABLE).

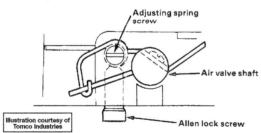

51.3 Rochester M4M series carburetor air valve spring adjustment details

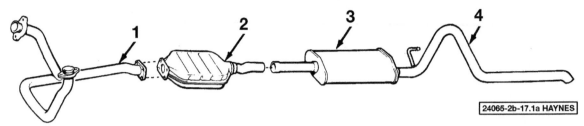

24065-2b-17.1a HAYNES

53.1 Typical exhaust system with catalytic converter

| 1 | Exhaust crossover pipe | 2 | Catalytic converter | 3 | Muffler | 4 | Exhaust pipe |

gasket removed to a point on the top of the float 7/16-inch back from the toe. Bend the float arm to obtain the specified dimension by pushing on the pontoon.

g) Tighten the air horn screws in a crossing pattern, starting with the inner screws and working to the outer screws.

h) On completion of assembly. adjust the front and rear vacuum breaks. fast idle cam (choke rod) choke coil /ever and automatic choke coil.

APT metering rod replacement

35   Replacement of the metering rod must only be carried out if the assembly is damaged or the aneroid has failed.

36   Lightly scribe the cover to record the position of the adjusting screw slot.

37   Remove the cover screws then carefully lift out the rod and cover assembly.

38   Hold the assembly upright then turn the adjusting screw counterclockwise, counting the number of turns until the metering rod bottoms in the cover.

39   Remove the E-clip from the threaded end of the rod then turn the rod clockwise until it disengages from the cover.

40   Install the tension spring on the new metering rod assembly and screw the rod and spring assembly into the cover until the assembly bottoms.

41   Turn the adjusting screw clockwise the number of turns noted at Paragraph 38.

42   Install the E-clip. **Note:** *It will not matter if the scribed line (Paragraph 36) does not align exactly provided that the assembly sequence has been followed.*

43   Carefully install the cover and metering rod assembly onto the float bowl, aligning the tab on the cover assembly with the float bowl slot closest to the fuel inlet nut.

44   Install the cover attaching screws and nut.

53   Exhaust system - general description

Refer to illustration 53.1

1   The exact exhaust system installed will depend on a number of factors, most notably the engine size, geographic area where the car will be driven and the year of production. Typical components of an exhaust system are: the exhaust manifold connected to the engine, a muffler, a catalytic converter (1975 and later) and exhaust pipe to route the gases through the components and out the rear of the car **(see illustration)**.

2   Information concerning the catalytic converter can be found in Chapter 6 dealing with the emission system.

3   The exhaust system should be periodically checked for leaks which could prove hazardous to persons inside the car. Leaks can be detected by placing your hand along the pipes before the system has warmed up. After driving, the exhaust system can cause injury if touched. A leaking exhaust system can also become apparent by excessive noise during operation.

4   As a general rule, the components of the exhaust system are secured by U-shaped clamps. After removing the clamps, the exhaust pipes (which are of a slightly different diameter) can be pulled away from each other. Due to the high temperatures and exposed location of the exhaust pieces, rust and corrosion can "freeze" the parts together. Liquid penetrating oils are available to help loosen the connections; however, it is often necessary to cut the parts with a hack saw or cutting torch. The later method should be employed only by a person experienced in this work.

5   The exhaust system is often a cause of mysterious rattles and noises heard from inside the car. The rubber-insulated hangers which suspend the system should be checked for deterioration and damage. No exhaust components should come in contact with other vehicle parts.

6   When replacing exhaust system parts, do not tighten the clamp bolts until the complete system has been installed and clearances checked. Then tighten from the front to the rear.

Chapter 5
Engine electrical systems

Contents

Specifications

Distributor type

1970 through 1974	Mechanical contact breaker
1975 on	Breakerless. Designated High Energy Ignition (HEI)
Distributor direction of rotation	Clockwise
Point gap	0.019 inch
Firing order	1-8-4-3-6-5-7-2
Condenser capacity (thru 1974)	0.18 to 0.23 mfd

Coil (with breaker type distributor)

Primary resistance	1.77 to 2.05 Ohms
Secondary resistance	3,000 to 20,000 Ohms
Resistor	1.35 Ohms

Coil (with HEI distributor)

Primary resistance	0.41 to 0.51 Ohms
Secondary resistance	3,000 to 20,000 Ohms
Resistor	0.43 to 0.68 Ohms

Alternator (generator)

Type (according to year of manufacture)	Delcotron Series 1 D, 10SI, 15SI or 1ODN Series 100B
Field current	2.2 to 2.6 amps at 80°F (pre-1973)
	4.0 to 4.5 amps at 80°F (1973 and later)
Output current	Varies according to vehicle specification and alternator type

Voltage regulator (used with Series 1D and 10DN Series 100B Delcotron)

Type	Double contact

Field relay

Air gap	0.015 in
Point opening	0.030 in
Closing voltage	1.5 to 3.2 volts

Regulator

Air gap	0.067 in
Point opening	0.014 in
Voltage setting	13.8 to 14.8 V at 85°F

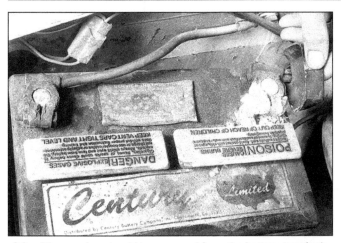

2.3a   All corrosion should be removed from the battery terminals   **2.3b   Removing the cable connector from the terminal**

1   General description - ignition system

In order that the engine can run correctly it is necessary for an electrical spark to ignite the fuel/air mixture in the combustion chamber at exactly the right moment in relation to engine speed and load. The ignition system is based on feeding low tension (LT) voltage from the battery to the coil where it is converted to high tension (HT) voltage. The high tension voltage is powerful enough to jump the spark plug gap in the cylinders many times a second under high compression pressures, providing that the system is in good condition and that all adjustments are correct.

The ignition system fitted to all pre-1975 cars as standard equipment is the conventional distributor with mechanical contact breaker and coil type. For 1975 models a breakerless high energy ignition (HEI) system is used.

Pre-1975 ignition systems

The ignition system is divided into two circuits: the low tension circuit and the high tension circuit. The low tension (sometimes known as the primary) circuit consists of the battery lead to the starter motor, lead to the ignition switch, calibrated resistance wire from the ignition switch to the low tension or primary coil winding, and the lead from the low tension coil windings to the contact breaker points and condenser in the distributor.

The high tension circuit consists of the high tension or secondary coil windings, the heavy ignition lead from the center of the coil to the center of the distributor cap. the rotor, and the spark plug leads and spark plugs.

The system functions in the following manner. Low tension voltage is changed in the coil into high tension voltage by the opening and closing of the contact breaker points in-the low tension circuit.

High tension voltage is then fed via the brush in the center of the distributor cap to the rotor arm of the distributor cap, and each time it comes in line with one of the 8 segments in the cap, which are connected to the spark plug leads, the opening and closing of the contact breaker points causes the high tension voltage to build up, jump the gap from the rotor arm to the appropriate segment and so, via the spark plug lead to the spark plug, where it finally jumps the spark plug gap before going to ground.

The ignition advance is controlled both mechanically and by a vacuum operated system. The mechanical governor mechanism comprises two weights, which move out from the distributor shaft as the engine speed rises due to centrifugal force. As they move outwards they rotate the cam relative to the distributor shaft, and so advance the spark. The weights are held in position by two light springs and it is the tension of the springs which is largely responsible for correct spark advancement.

The vacuum control consists of a diaphragm, one side of which is connected via a small bore tube to the carburetor, and the other side to the contact breaker plate. Vacuum in the intake manifold and carburetor, which varies with engine speed and throttle opening, causes the diaphragm to move, so moving the contact breaker plate, and advancing or retarding the spark. A fine degree of control is achieved by a spring in the vacuum assembly.

On some models, a Transmission Controlled Spark (TCS) system has an effect on vacuum advance. Further information on this system can be found in Chapter 6.

1975 and later ignition systems

The high energy ignition (HEI) system is a pulse triggered, transistor controlled, inductive discharge system.

A magnetic pick-up inside the distributor contains a permanent magnet, pole-piece and pick-up coil. A time core, rotating inside the pole piece, induces a voltage in the pick-up coil, and when teeth on the timer and pole piece line up, a signal passes to the electronic module to open the coil primary circuit. The primary circuit current decreases and a high voltage is induced in the coil secondary winding: this is then directed to the spark plugs by the distributor rotor as with the conventional system. A capacitor is fitted to suppress radio interference.

The system features a longer spark duration and the dwell period automatically increases with engine speed. These features are desirable for firing lean and EGR diluted mixtures (refer to Chapter 6).

The ignition coil, somewhat smaller than the coil in a conventional system, and the electronic module are both housed in the distributor cap. The distributor does not require routine servicing.

Spark advancement is by mechanical and vacuum means, as described for conventional systems. The TCS system is not used.

If the need arises for the vehicle to be cranked remotely using jumper cables from another battery source, the distributor BAT terminal must be disconnected.

2   Battery - maintenance

Refer to illustrations 2.3a, 2.3b, 2.3c and 2.3d

1   Every week, check the level of the battery electrolyte. The method of doing this depends upon the type of battery. Some batteries have a "Delco eye" which glows if the level is low. Others have a split ring in the filler opening with which the electrolyte should be level.

2   On later vehicles (1977) a "Freedom" battery is used which does not require topping up.

3   Clean the top of the battery, removing all dirt and moisture **(see illustrations)**. As well as keeping the terminals clean and covered with petroleum jelly, the top of the battery, and especially the top of the cells, should be kept clean and dry. This helps prevent corrosion and ensures that the battery does not become partially discharged by

2.3c A special wire-brush cleaning tool is used here to clean the battery terminal

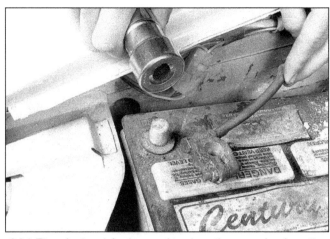

2.3d The wire brush is also used to clean the corrosion from the inside of the cable connector

leakage through dampness and dirt. On some models a felt ring is used under the battery terminals. This should be oiled.

4   Once every three months, remove the battery and inspect the battery securing bolts, the battery clamp plate, and battery leads for corrosion (white fluffy deposits on the metal which are brittle to touch). If any corrosion is found, clean off the deposits with an ammonia or soda solution. After cleaning, smear petroleum jelly on the battery terminals and lead connectors. Application of a zinc-base primer and/or underbody paint will help to prevent recurrence of corrosion on body panel metal.

5   If topping-up the battery becomes excessive and the case has been inspected for cracks that could cause leakage, but none are found, the battery is being over-charged and the alternator will have to be tested and if necessary serviced as described later in this Chapter.

6   If any doubt exists about the state of charge of a battery, a hydrometer should be used to test it by withdrawing a little electrolyte from each cell in turn.

7   The specific gravity of the electrolyte at the temperature of 80°F (26.7°C) will be approximately 1.270 for a fully charged battery. For every 10°F (5.5°C) that the electrolyte temperature is above that stated, add 0.04 to the specific gravity or subtract 0.04 if the temperature is below that stated.

8   A specific gravity reading of 1.240 with an electrolyte temperature of 80°F (26.7°C) indicates a half-charged battery.

9   With the "Freedom" type of battery, a charge indicator is built into it which uses a color system to relay the state of charge of the battery.

3   Battery charging

1   In winter time when heavy demand is placed upon the battery, such as when starting from cold. and much electrical equipment is continually in use. it is a good idea to occasionally have the battery fully charged from an external source at the rate of 3.5 to 4 amps.

2   Continue to charge the battery at this rate until no further rise in specific gravity is noted over a four hour period.

3   Alternatively, a trickle charger charging at the rate of 1.5 amps can be safely used overnight.

4   Special rapid boost charges which are claimed to restore the power of the battery in 1 to 2 hours are most dangerous as they can cause serious damage to the battery plates. This type of charge should only be used in a "crisis" situation.

5   On vehicles equipped with the "Freedom" type battery, do not charge the battery if the built-in hydrometer on the top of the battery is a clear or light yellow color. This coloring indicates that the battery needs replacement.

4   Battery - removal and installation

1   The battery is located at the front of the engine compartment. It is held in place by either a hold-down rod running across the top of the battery or a clamp near the bottom of the battery case.

2   As hydrogen gas is produced by the battery, keep open flames or lighted cigarettes away from the battery at all times.

3   Avoid spilling any of the electrolyte battery fluid on the vehicle or yourself. Always keep the battery in the upright position. Any spilled electrolyte should be immediately flushed with large quantities of water. Wear eye protection when working with a battery to prevent serious eye damage from splashed fluid.

4   Always disconnect the negative (-) battery cable first, followed by the positive (+) cable.

5   After the cables are disconnected from the battery, remove the hold-down mechanism, be it a rod or bottom clamp.

6   Carefully lift the battery from its tray and out of the engine compartment.

7   Installation is a reversal of removal, however make sure that the hold-down clamp or rod is securely tightened. Do not over-tighten, however, as this may damage the battery case. The battery posts and cable ends should be cleaned prior to connection.

5   Condenser (capacitor) - testing, removal and installation (1970 - 1974)

1   The condenser ensures that when the contact breaker points open, the sparking between them is not excessive to cause severe pitting. The condenser is fitted in parallel and its failure will automatically cause failure of the ignition system as the points will be prevented from interrupting the low tension circuit.

2   Testing for an unserviceable condenser may be done by switching on the ignition and separating the contact points by hand. If this action is accompanied by a blue flash then condenser failure is indicated. Difficult starting, missing of engine after several miles running or badly pitted points are other indications of a faulty condenser.

3   The surest test is by substitution with a new unit.

4   To replace the condenser, remove the distributor cap, rotor and RFI shield.

5   Disconnect the condenser lead and remove the condenser retaining screw. Slide the condenser from the bracket.

6   Installation is the reverse of the removal procedure.

6   Distributor cap - replacement (1970-1974)

Note: *It is imperative that the spark plug wires be installed in the correct order on the distributor cap.*

1   Purchase a replacement distributor cap

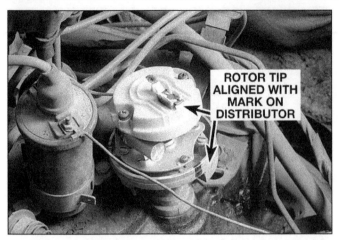

7.3 After turning the rotor until it is pointing at the terminal for the number 1 spark plug, paint or scribe a mark on the edge of the distributor base directly beneath it

7.6a A special distributor wrench is available for loosening the distributor lock bolt

for the particular model year and engine size.

2   Release the old cap from the distributor body by pushing downward on the slotted latches and then turning the latches 1/4 turn.

3   Place the new cap next to the old one. Use the metal window and the two latches as reference points to get the new cap in the same relative position.

4   Begin transferring the spark plug wires one at a time from the old cap to the new one. Do not pull on the wire insulation, but rather grab the rubber boot, twist slightly and then pull the plug wire free by the boot.

5   Push the plug wires and boots firmly onto the new distributor cap.

6   Place the new cap and plug wires into position over the top of the distributor and lock it in place by pushing and turning the latches. Make sure the cap is firmly seated.

7   Distributor- removal and overhaul (1970-1974)

Refer to illustrations 7.3, 7.6a, 7.6b, 7.7 and 7.9

1   Release the two latches on the distributor cap by pressing them downward with a screwdriver and then turning them 1/4 turn. Move the cap (with the spark plug wires still attached) out of the way Use wire or tape if necessary.

2   Disconnect the distributor primary wiring lead from the coil terminal.

3   At this point it is important to mark the position of the rotor and distributor housing for easier reassembly. At the very bottom of the distributor, scribe a mark on the distributor base and another mark in line with the base mark on the engine block **(see illustration)**. Also note the direction in which the rotor contact is pointed. Make a mark on the distributor housing in-line with the rotor contact strip.

4   Disconnect the vacuum line at the distributor.

5   Note the position of the vacuum

7.6b The hold-down bolt and retainer used at the base of the distributor

advance mechanism (canister from which vacuum hose was just disconnected) relative to the engine.

6   Remove the distributor hold-down bolt and clamp from the base of the distributor. A special curved distributor wrench is best for this purpose **(see illustrations)**.

7   Lift the distributor straight up and out of the engine **(see illustration)**.

8   Avoid rotating the engine with the distributor removed as the ignition timing will be changed.

9   To disassemble, remove the rotor (2 screws), the advance weight springs and the weights **(see illustration)**. Where applicable, also remove the radio frequency interference (RFI) shield.

10   Drive out the roll pin retaining the gear to the shaft then pull off the gear and spacers.

11   Ensure that the shaft is not burred, then slide it from the housing.

12   Remove the cam weight base assembly.

13   Remove the screws retaining the vacuum unit and lift off the unit itself .

14   Remove the spring retainer (snap-ring) then remove the breaker plate assembly.

7.7 Once the bottom retainer is removed, the distributor can be lifted straight out of the engine. Carefully note position of rotor as described in text

15   Remove the contact points and condenser, followed by the felt washer and plastic seal located beneath the breaker plate.

16   Wipe all components clean with a solvent moistened cloth and examine them for wear, distortion and scoring. Replace parts as necessary. Pay particular attention to the rotor and distributor cap to ensure that they are not cracked.

17   Fill the lubricating cavity in the housing with general purpose grease then fit a new plastic seal and felt washer.

18   Install the vacuum unit, the breaker plate in the housing and the spring retainer on the upper bushing.

19   Lubricate the cam weight base and slide it on the mainshaft; install the weights and springs.

20   Insert the mainshaft in the housing then fit the shims and drive-gear. Install a new roll-pin.

21   Install the contact point set (Chapter 1).

22   Install the rotor, aligning the round and square pilot holes.

23   Install the distributor as described in Section 8.

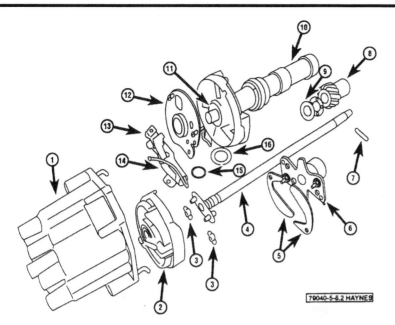

7.9 Exploded view of a typical contact breaker type distributor

1	Distributor cap	9	Washer and shim
2	Rotor	10	Distributor housing
3	Advance weight springs	11	Plastic washer
4	Mainshaft	12	Breaker plate
5	Advance weights	13	Contact point assembly
6	Cam and advance weight base	14	Condenser
7	Drive gear roll pin	15	Retaining ring
8	Distributor drive gear	16	Felt washer

8   Distributor - installation (1970 - 1974)

If engine was not rotated after removal

1   Turn the rotor about 1/8 turn in a clockwise direction past the mark made on the distributor housing upon removal.
2   Lower the distributor down into the engine, positioning the vacuum advance mechanism in the approximate position as removal. To mesh the gears at the bottom of the distributor it may be necessary to turn the rotor slightly.
3   With the base of the distributor all the way down against the engine block, the rotor should be pointed to the mark made on the distributor housing. If these two marks are not in alignment, repeat the previous steps.
4   Now turn the distributor housing until the scribed marks at the bottom of the distributor are in alignment.
5   Place the clamp into position and tighten the clamp bolt securely.
6   Connect the vacuum hose to the distributor and connect the primary wire to the coil terminal.
7   Install the distributor cap.
8   Check the ignition timing as described in Chapter 1.

If engine was rotated after removal

9   Turn the crankshaft by applying a wrench to the crankshaft pulley bolt at the front of the engine until the number 1 piston is at top-dead-center (TDC). This can be ascertained by removing the number 1 spark plug and feeling the compression being generated. If you are careful not to scratch the cylinder, you can also use a length of stiff wire to Feel the piston come to the top of the cylinder.
10   With the number 1 piston at TDC (as indicated by the timing marks on the front cover), the distributor should be firing this cylinder.
11   Hold the distributor over its recess with the vacuum advance unit in its "installed" position. It should be pointed towards the front of the right-hand cylinder head.
12   Point the metal contact on the rotor towards the number 1 cylinder and lower the distributor into place.
13   With the distributor fully seated to the engine (it may be necessary to turn the rotor slightly to mesh the gears), the rotor contact should be in-line with the number 1 spark plug wire in the distributor cap. To find out if this is true, temporarily install the cap to the distributor, checking the rotor contact and the number 1 spark plug terminal.
14   Install the clamp and the hold-down bolt at the bottom of the engine. Leave the bolt loose enough to enable you to turn the distributor.

15   Start the engine and adjust the timing as described in Chapter 1.
16   On Mark IV engines, there is a punch mark on the drive gear which represents the position of the contact end of the rotor. This enables the distributor to be installed with the cap in place.
17   Once installed, turn the distributor until the contact points are just about to open and tighten the clamp bolt.
18   Tighten all connections and install the distributor caps.
19   Check and adjust the dwell angle and the timing as soon as the engine has been run to normal operating temperature.

9   Distributor - removal and installation (1975-1980)

1   The procedures for removing and installing the breakerless distributor are basically the same as for the conventional unit described in Sections 7 and 8. Follow the sequence given in Sections 7 and 8 with the following exceptions:

a) Disconnect the wiring connector on the outside of the distributor.
b) The spark plug wires are connected to a ring around the top of the distributor cap. This retaining ring can be removed once the latches are disengaged.
c) Ignore all references to the contact points and setting the dwell angle as this does not apply to the breakerless distributor.
d) Set the ignition timing after installation.

10   Distributor (breakerless type) - overhaul

Refer to illustrations 10.2, 10.3, 10.4, 10.5, 10.6, 10.9a and 10.9b
1   Remove the distributor as previously described.
2   Remove the rotor (2 screws) **(see illustration)**.

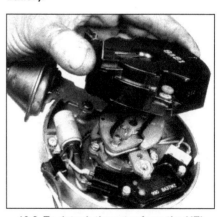

10.2 To detach the rotor from the HEI distributor, remove the two screws on top that attach it to the centrifugal advance mechanism

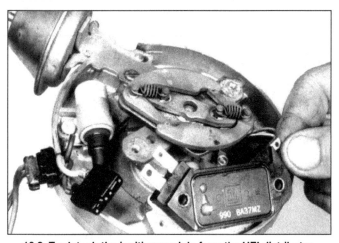

10.3 To detach the ignition module from the HEI distributor, remove the two mounting screws and unplug the connector from the B and C terminals

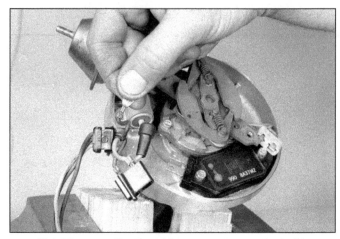

10.4 Disconnecting the wiring connectors on the inside of the distributor

10.5 Using a hammer and punch to drive out the roll pin from the bottom of the distributor shaft

10.6 The shaft, gear, shim and tanged washer removed from the distributor

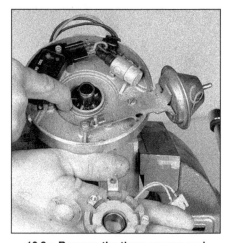

10.9a Remove the three screws and separate the pole-piece and washer from the upper end of the distributor body (early models)

3   Remove the 2 screws retaining the module. Move the module aside and remove the connector from the "B" and "C" terminals. **(see illustration).**
4   Remove the connections from the "W" and "G" terminals **(see illustrations).**
5   Carefully drive out the roll pin from the drive gear **(see illustration).**
6   Remove the gear, shim and tanged washer from the distributor shaft **(see illustration).**
7   Ensure that the shaft is not burred, then remove it from the housing.
8   Remove the washer from the upper end of the distributor housing.
9   Remove the pole-piece, magnet and pick-up coil **(see illustrations).**
10   Remove the lock ring, then take out the pick-up coil retainer, shim and felt washer.
11   Remove the vacuum unit (2 screws).
12   Disconnect the capacitor lead and remove the capacitor (1 screw).
13   Disconnect the wiring harness from the distributor housing.
14   Wipe all components clean with a solvent moistened cloth and examine

them for wear, distortion and other damage. Replace parts as necessary.
15   To assemble, position the vacuum unit to the housing and secure with the 2 screws.
16   Position the felt washer over the lubricant reservoir at the top of the housing then position the shim on top of the felt washer.
17   Position the pick-up coil retainer to the housing. The vacuum advance arm goes over the actuating pin of the advance mechanism. Secure it with the lock-ring.
18   Install the pick-up coil magnet and pole-piece. Loosely install the 3 screws to retain the pole-piece.
19   Install the washer to the top of the housing. Install the distributor shaft then rotate it and check for equal clearance all round between the shaft projections and pole-piece. Secure the pole-piece when correctly positioned.
20   Install the tanged washer, shim and drivegear. Align the gear and install a new roll pin.
21   Loosely install the capacitor with one screw.
22   Install the connector to the "B" and "C"

terminals on the module with the tab at the top.
23   Apply silicone grease to the base of the module and secure it with 2 screws. This

10.9b The pick-up coil and pole piece assembly can be removed after prying out the retaining ring (late models)

11.1 1970 - 1974 ignition coil being lifted away from the top of the engine

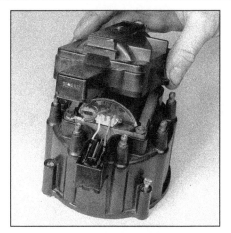

11.3 The coil cover being lifted off the top of the distributor cap (1975 - 1980)

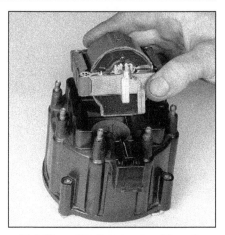

11.4 The coil is then removed from its recess in the top of the distributor cap

grease is essential to ensure good heat conduction.

24 Position the wiring harness with the grommet in the housing notch then connect the pink wire to the capacitor stud and the black wire to the capacitor mounting screw. Tighten the screw.

25 Connect the white wire from the pick-up coil to the module "W" terminal and the green to the "G" terminal.

26 Install the advance weights, weight retainer (dimple downwards), and springs.

27 Install the rotor and secure with the 2 screws. Ensure that the notch on the side of the rotor engages with the tab on the cam weight base .

28 Install the distributor as previously described.

---

11 Ignition coil - removal and installation

Thru 1974

Refer to illustration 11.1

1 This is a straightforward operation, requiring only the removal of the electrical connections and the two mounting screws **(see illustration)**. It is a good policy to mark the connections before removal to ensure that they are re-installed correctly.

1975 on

Refer to illustrations 11.3, 11.4, 11.5a and 11.5b

2 Disconnect the battery wire and harness connector from the distributor cap.

3 Remove the coil cover (3 screws) and the coil assembly (4 screws) from the distributor cap **(see illustration)**.

4 Note the position of each wire, duly marking them if necessary. Remove the coil ground wire then push the leads from the underside of the connectors. Remove the coil from the distributor cap **(see illustration)**.

5 Installation is the reverse of the removal procedure, but ensure that the leads are con-

11.5a Before installing new coil, ensure that center electrode is in good condition

nected to their original positions **(see illustrations)**.

---

12 Spark plugs

1 Properly functioning spark plugs are a necessity if the engine is to perform properly. At the intervals specified in Chapter 1 or your owner's manual, the spark plugs should be replaced with new ones. Removal and installation information can be found in the Tune-up and Basic Maintenance Chapter.

2 It is important to replace spark plugs with new ones of the same heat range and type. A series of numbers and letters are stamped on the spark plug to help identify each variation.

3 The spark plug gap is of considerable importance as, if it is too large or too small the size of the spark and its efficiency will be seriously impaired. To set it, measure the gap with a feeler gauge, and then bend open, or close, the outer plug electrode until the correct gap is achieved. The center electrode should never be bent as this may crack the insulation and cause plug failure, if nothing worse.

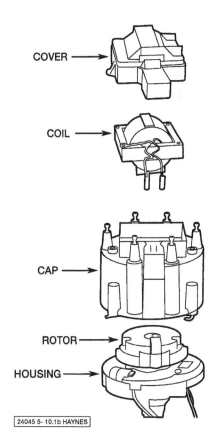

11.5b Typical late model HEI coil installation details

4 The condition and appearance of the spark plugs will tell much about the condition and tune of the engine. If the insulator nose of the spark plug is clean and white with no deposits, this is indicative of a weak mixture, or too hot a plug (a hot plug transfers heat away from the electrode slowly - a cold plug transfers it away quickly.

5 If the tip and insulator nose is covered with hard black looking deposits, then this is

15.2 The first step in alternator removal is disconnecting all electrical leads (which will vary somewhat with alternator type and year of manufacture)

15.3a To remove the drivebelt, loosen the alternator mounting bolt . . .

15.3b . . . then loosen the adjustment bolt and slip off the belt - finally, remove the mounting and adjusting bolts and remove the alternator

indicative that the mixture is too rich. Should the plug be black and oily, then it is likely that the engine is fairly worn as well as the mixture being too rich.

6   If the insulator nose, is covered with light tan to greyish brown deposits, then the mixture is correct and it is likely that the engine is in good condition.

7   If there are any traces of long brown tapering stains on the outside of the white portion of the plug, then the plug will have to be replaced with a new one, as this shows that there is a faulty joint between the plug body and the insulator, and compression is being allowed to leak away.

8   Always tighten a spark plug to the specified torque - no tighter.

13   General description - charging system

The charging system is made up of the alternator, voltage regulator and the battery. These components work together to supply electrical power for the engine ignition, lights, radio, etc.

The alternator is turned by a drive belt at the front of the engine, Thus, when the engine is operating, voltage is generated by the internal components of the alternator to be sent to the battery for storage.

The purpose of the voltage regulator is to limit the alternator voltage to a pre-set value. This prevents power surges, circuit overloads, etc. during peak voltage output. 1970 - 1972 vehicles have an external voltage regulator mounted to the inner fender panel. 1973 and later models have the voltage regulator built into the alternator housing.

The charging system does not ordinarily require periodic maintenance. The drive belts, electrical wiring and connections should, however, be inspected during normal tune-ups (see Chapter 1).

14   Alternator - maintenance and special precautions

1   The alternator fitted to all models is a Delco-Remy Delcotron. Three types have been used, the 5.5 inch Series 1D, 10DN Series 100B and the Series 10SI. The first types require a separate voltage regulator; the last type has an integral regulator.

2   Alternator maintenance consists of occasionally wiping away any dirt or oil which may have collected.

3   Check the tension of the driving belt (refer to Chapter 1, Section 41).

4   No lubrication is required as alternator bearings are grease sealed for the life of the unit.

5   Take extreme care when making circuit connections to a vehicle fitted with an alternator and observe the following. When making connections to the alternator from a battery always match correct polarity. Before using electric-arc welding equipment to repair any part of the vehicle, disconnect the connector from the alternator and disconnect the positive battery terminal. Never start the car with a battery charger connected. Always disconnect both battery leads before using a charger. If boosting from another battery, always connect in parallel using heavy cable. It is not recommended that testing of an alternator should be undertaken at home due to the testing equipment required and the possibility of damage occurring during testing. It is best left to automotive electrical specialists.

15   Alternator - removal and installation

Refer to illustrations 15.2, 15.3a and 15.3b

1   Disconnect both leads from the battery terminals.

2   Disconnect the leads from the rear face of the alternator. marking them first to ensure correct installation **(see illustration)**.

3   Loosen the alternator mounting and adjuster link bolts, push the unit in towards

the engine as far as possible and slip off the drivebelts **(see illustrations)**.

4   Remove the mounting bolts and lift the alternator from the engine compartment.

5   Installation is a reversal of removal; adjust the drivebelt tension. **Note:** *New alternators are not usually supplied with pulleys. The old one should therefore be removed if a new unit is to be purchased. To do this, hold the alternator shaft still with an Allen wrench while the pulley nut is unscrewed.*

16   Alternator- overhaul

Note: *Due to the critical nature of the disassembly and testing of the various alternator components it may be advisable for the home mechanic to simply replace a faulty unit with a new or factory rebuilt model. If it is decided to perform the overhaul procedure make sure that replacement parts are available before proceeding.*

Refer to illustrations 16.3a and 16.3b

1   Remove the alternator and pulley as described in the preceding Section.

2   Secure the alternator in the jaws of a vice, applying the pressure to the mounting flange.

3   Remove the four through-bolts **(see illustration)**, and separate the slip-ring, end frame and stator assembly from the drive-end and rotor assembly. Use a screwdriver to lever them apart and mark the relative position of the end frames to facilitate reassembly **(see illustration)**.

4   Remove the stator lead securing nuts and separate the stator from the end frame.

1D series

Refer to illustration 16.6

5   Extract the screws and remove the brush holder assembly.

6   Remove the heat sink from the end frame after extracting the BAT and GRD terminals **(see illustration)** and single securing screw.

10 SI series

Refer to illustrations 16.7a and 16.7b

7   Continue dismantling, by removing the rectifier bridge, securing screw and the BAT terminal screws **(see illustration)**. Disconnect the capacitor lead and remove the rectifier bridge from the end-frame **(see illustration)**.
8   Unscrew the two securing screws and remove the brush holder and regulator. Carefully retain the insulating sleeves and washers.
9   Remove the capacitor lone screw from the end-frame.

All models

Refer to illustrations 16.17a, 16.17b and 16.7c

10   If the slip ring end frame bearing is dry or noisy when rotated, it must be replaced

16.3a Paint an alignment mark on the alternator body between each end frame

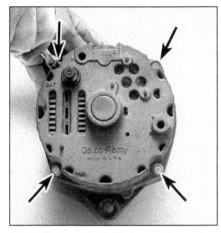

16.3b Remove the bolts (arrows) securing the rear end frame to the drive end frame

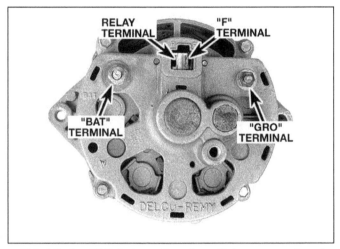

16.6 A Series 1D Delcotron alternator, which uses an external voltage regulator (Series 10DN and 100B types are similar)

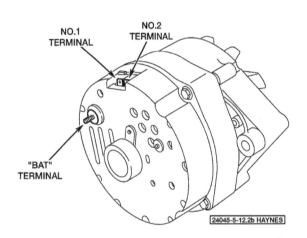

16.7a A Series 10SI Delcotron alternator, which uses an internal voltage regulator

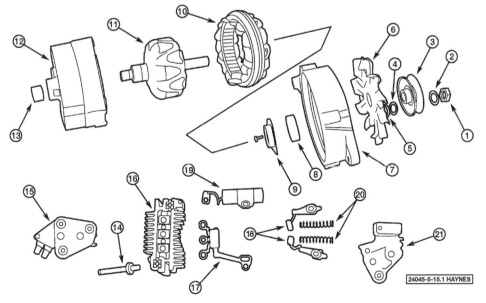

16.7b An exploded view of the 10SI alternator

1   Nut
2   Washer
3   Pulley
4   Washer
5   Collar
6   Fan
7   Drive end frame
8   Bearing
9   Plate
10   Stator
11   Rotor
12   Slip-ring end frame
13   Bearing
14   Terminal component stud
15   Voltage regulator
16   Rectifier bridge
17   Diode trio
18   Brushes
19   Capacitor
20   Brush springs
21   Brush holder

16.17a Apply a small amount of grease to the bearing surface

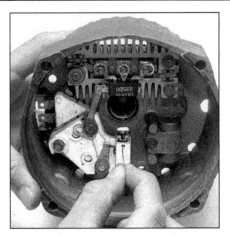

16.17b Press the two brushes into the holder and slide a paper clip through the eyelet to keep the brushes in the holder assembly

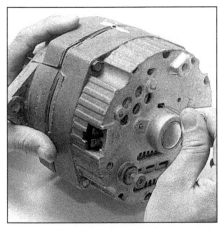

16.17c After the alternator is completely assembled remove the wire or paper clip to release the brushes

(not greased). Greasing will not extend its service life. Press out the old bearing and discard the oil seal. Press in the new bearing, squarely, until the bearing is flush with the outside of the end frame. Install a new oil seal. During these operations, support the end- frame adequately to prevent cracking or distorting the frame.

11   Now insert a 5/16 inch Allen wrench into the socket in the center of the shaft at the drive pulley end. Using this to prevent the shaft from rotating, unscrew the pulley retaining nut and remove the washer, pulley, fan and the spacer.

12   Remove the rotor and spacers from the drive end-frame.

13   If the bearing in the drive end-frame is dry or noisy it must be replaced. Do not grease it in the hope that this will extend its life. Access to the bearing is obtained after removing the retainer plate bolts and separating the plate/seal assembly. Press the bearing out using a piece of tube applied to the inner race and press the new one in by applying the tube to the outer race. Make sure that the slinger is correctly located and recommended grease is applied to the bearing before installation.

14   With the alternator completely dismantled, wipe all components clean (do not use solvent on the stator or rotor windings), and examine for wear or damage. Purchase new components as necessary.

15   If the slip rings are dirty they should be cleaned by spinning the rotor and holding a piece of 400 grain abrasive paper against them. This method will avoid the creation of flat spots on the rings. If the rings are badly scored, out-of-round or otherwise damaged, the complete rotor assembly must be replaced.

16   Check the brushes for wear. If they are worn halfway or more in length, do not re-use them. Purchase new springs only if they appear weak or are distorted.

17   Reassembly is a reversal of dismantling but observe the following points:

(a) Tighten the pulley nut to the specified torque. Take great care to position the

insulating washers and sleeves correctly on the brush clip screws **(see illustration)**.

(b) Clean the brush contact surfaces before installing the slip ring end-frame and hold the brushes up in their holders by passing a thin rod through the opening in the slip ring end-frame to permit the brushes to pass over the slip rings **(see illustrations)**.

(c) Finally make sure that the marks on the slip ring and drive end-frame {which were made before dismantling) are in alignment.

---

17   Voltage regulator (externally mounted type) - removal, servicing and installation

---

Refer to illustration 17.9

1   A discharged battery will normally be due to a fault in the voltage regulator but before testing the unit, check the following:

2   Check the drivebelt tension.

3   Test the condition of the battery.

4   Check the charging circuit for loose connections and broken wires.

5   Make sure that lights or other electrical accessories have not been left switched on inadvertently.

6   Check the generator indicator lamp for normal illumination with the ignition switched on and off, and with the engine idling and stationary.

7   Disconnect the battery ground cable and the harness connector. Remove the screws securing the unit to the vehicle.

8   Under no circumstances should the voltage regulator contacts be cleaned since any abrasive materials will destroy the contact material. Relay point and air-gap adjustments can be checked using a feeler gauge to obtain approximate settings if they are thought to be requiring attention.

9   The field relay point opening may be adjusted by bending the stop. The air gap is checked with the points just touching and is adjusted by bending the flat contact spring **(see illustration)**. **Note:** *The field relay will normally operate satisfactorily even if the air-gap is outside the specified limits, and should be adjusted when the system is functioning satisfactorily.*

10   Installation is the reverse of the removal procedure, but ensure that the rubber gasket is in place on the regulator base.

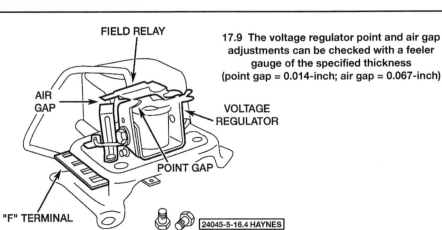

17.9 The voltage regulator point and air gap adjustments can be checked with a feeler gauge of the specified thickness (point gap = 0.014-inch; air gap = 0.067-inch)

FIELD RELAY

AIR GAP

VOLTAGE REGULATOR

POINT GAP

"F" TERMINAL

24045-5-16.4 HAYNES

20.4a Removing the bolts which secure the starting motor to the engine block

20.4b The starter motor and solenoid being drawn away from flywheel

18 General description - starting system

The function of the starting system is to crank the engine. This system is composed of a starting motor, solenoid and battery. The battery supplies the electrical energy to the solenoid which then completes the circuit to the starting motor which does the actual work of cranking the engine.

The solenoid and starting motor are mounted together on a pad at the side of the engine. No periodic lubrication or maintenance is required to the starting system components.

The electrical circuitry of the vehicle is arranged so that the starter motor can only be operated when the clutch pedal is fully depressed (manual transmission) or the transmission selector lever is at "P" or "N" (automatic transmission).

The starter motor fitted to the Firebird models has remained almost unchanged throughout the production run of the vehicle. However, with the introduction of the HEI ignition system in 1975, the "R" terminal on the solenoid was removed.

19 Starter motor - testing in vehicle

1   If the starter motor does not rotate at all when the switch is operated, check that the speed selector lever is in "N" or "P" (automatic transmission) and that the front seat belts are connected (starter interlock system) and also that the clutch pedal is depressed (where applicable).
2   Check that the battery is well charged and all cables, both at the battery and starter solenoid terminals, are secure.
3   If the motor can be heard spinning but the engine is not being cranked, then the overrunning clutch in the starter motor is slipping and the assembly must be removed from the engine and dismantled.

4   If, when the switch is actuated, the starter motor does not operate at all but the solenoid plunger can be heard to move with a loud "click" then the fault lies in the main solenoid contacts or the starter motor itself.
5   If the solenoid plunger cannot be heard to move when the switch is actuated then the solenoid itself is defective or the solenoid circuit is open.
6   To check out the solenoid, connect a jumper lead between the battery (+) terminal and the terminal on the solenoid to which the purple cable is attached. If the starter motor now operates, the solenoid is OK and the fault must lie in the ignition or neutral start switches or in their interconnecting wiring.
7   If the starter motor still does not operate, remove the starter/solenoid assembly for dismantling, testing and repair.
8   If the starter motor cranks the engine at an abnormally slow speed, first ensure that the battery is fully charged and all terminal connections are tight, also that the engine oil is not too thick a grade and that the resistance is not due to a mechanical fault within the power unit.
9   Run the engine until normal operating temperature is attained, shut it off and disconnect the coil to distributor LT wire or "BAT" connection on HEI distributors so that the engine will not fire during cranking.
10   Connect a voltmeter positive lead to the starter motor terminal of the solenoid and then connect the negative lead to ground.
11   Actuate the ignition switch and take the voltmeter readings as soon as a steady figure is indicated. Do not allow the starter motor to turn for more than 30 seconds at a time. A reading of 9 volts, or more, with the starter motor turning at normal cranking speed proves it to be in good condition. If the reading is 9 volts, or more, but the cranking speed is slow, then the motor is faulty. If the reading is less than 9 volts and the cranking speed is slow, the solenoid contacts are probably at fault and should be replaced as described later in this Chapter.

20 Starter motor - removal and installation

Refer to illustrations 20.4a and 20.4b
1   Disconnect the ground cable from the battery.
2   Raise the vehicle to a satisfactory working height.
3   Disconnect the leads at the starter solenoid marking each with a coded piece of tape for easy identification upon reassembly. Temporarily replace each of the securing nuts to the terminals as they have various thread types which could cause damage to the stubs if not properly re-installed.
4   Loosen the starter motor front bracket nut and then remove the two mount bolts **(see illustrations)**.
5   Remove the front bracket bolt, rotate the bracket so that the starter motor can be withdrawn by lowering its front end.
6   Installation is a reversal of removal but tighten the mount bolts first to the specified torque and then tighten the front bracket bolt and nut.
7   Install each of the wires to the solenoid terminals using your identification coding.

21 Starter motor - dismantling and component testing

Note: *Due to the critical nature of the disassembly and testing of the starter motor it may be advisable for the home mechanic to simply purchase a new or factory-rebuilt unit. If it is decided to overhaul the starter, check on the availability of singular replacement components before proceeding.*

1   Disconnect the starter motor field coil connectors from the solenoid terminals.
2   Unscrew and remove the through bolts.
3   Remove the commutator end-frame, field frame assembly and the armature from the drive housing.
4   Slide the two-section thrust collar off the

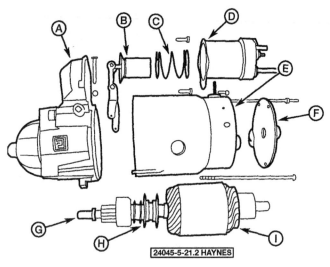

22.15 Exploded view of a typical starter motor and solenoid assembly

A   Drive gear housing
B   Solenoid plunger
C   Solenoid return spring
D   Solenoid
E   End frame insulator
F   Commutator end frame
G   Retainer assembly
H   Clutch and drive assembly
I   Armature

end of the armature shaft and then using a piece of suitable tube drive the stop/retainer up the armature shaft to expose the snap-ring.

5   Extract the snap-ring from its shaft groove and then slide the stop/retainer and overrunning clutch assembly from the armature shaft.

6   Dismantle the brush components from the field frame.

7   Release the V-shaped springs from the brushholder supports.

8   Remove the brushholder support pin and then lift the complete brush assembly upwards.

9   Disconnect the leads from the brushes if they are worn down to half their original length and they are to be replaced.

10   The starter motor is now completely dismantled except for the field coils. If these are found to be defective during the tests described later in this Section removal of the pole shoe screws is best left to a service station who will have the necessary pressure driver.

11   Clean all components and replace any obviously worn components.

12   On no account attempt to undercut the insulation between the commutator segments on starter motors having the molded type commutators. On commutators of conventional type, the insulation should be undercut (below the level of the segments) by 1/32 inch. Use an old hacksaw blade to do this and make sure that the undercut is the full width of the insulation and the groove is quite square at the bottom. When the undercutting is completed, brush away all dirt and dust.

13   Clean the commutator by spinning it while a piece of number "00" sandpaper is wrapped round it. On no account use any other type of abrasive material for this work.

14   If necessary, because the commutator is in such bad shape, it may be turned down in a lathe to provide a new surface. Make sure

to undercut the insulation when the turning is completed.

15   To test the armature for ground: use a lamp-type circuit tester. Place one lead on the armature core or shaft and the other on a segment of the commutator. If the lamp lights then the armature is grounded and must be replaced.

16   To test the field coils for open circuit: place one test probe on the insulated brush and the other on the field connector bar. If the lamp does not light, the coils are open and must be replaced.

17   To test the field coil/s for ground: place one test probe on the connector bar and the other on the grounded brush. If the lamp lights then the field coils are grounded.

18   The overrunning clutch cannot be repaired and if faulty, it must be replaced as a complete assembly.

22 Starter motor - reassembly and adjustment

Refer to illustration 22.15

1   Install the brush assembly to the field frame as follows:

2   Install the brushes to their holders.

3   Assemble the insulated and grounded brushholders together with the V-spring and then locate the unit on its support pin.

4   Push the holders and spring to the bottom of the support and then rotate the spring to engage the V in the support slot.

5   Connect the ground wire to the grounded brush and the field lead wire to the insulated brush.

6   Repeat the operations for the second set of brushes.

7   Smear silicone oil onto the drive end of the armature shaft and then slide the clutch assembly (pinion to the front) onto the shaft.

8   Slide the pinion stop/retainer onto the shaft so that its open end is facing away from the pinion.

9   Stand the armature vertically on a piece of wood and then position the snap-ring on the end of the shaft. Using a hammer and a piece of hardwood, drive the snap-ring onto the shaft.

10   Slide the snap-ring down the shaft until it drops into its groove.

11   Install the thrust collar on the shaft so that the shoulder is next to the snap-ring. Using two pairs of pliers, squeeze the thrust collar and stop/retainer together until the snap-ring fully enters the retainer.

12   Lubricate the drive housing bushing with silicone oil and after ensuring that the thrust collar is in position against the snap-ring, slide the armature and clutch assembly into the drive housing so that at the same time, the shift lever engages with the clutch.

13   Position the field frame over the armature and apply sealing compound between the frame and the solenoid case.

14   Position the field frame against the drive housing taking care not to damage the brushes.

15   Lubricate the bushing in the commutator end-frame using silicone oil: place the leather brake washer on the armature shaft and then slide the commutator end-frame onto the shaft **(see illustration)**.

16   Reconnect the field coil connectors to the MOTOR terminal of the solenoid.

17   Now check the pinion clearance. To do this, connect a 6 volt battery between the solenoid S terminal and ground and at the same time fix a heavy connecting cable between the MOTOR terminal and ground (to prevent any possibility of the starter motor rotating). As the solenoid is energized it will push the pinion forward into its normal cranking position and retain it there. With the fingers, push the pinion away from the stop/retainer in order to eliminate any slack and then check the clearance between the face of the pinion and the face of stop/retainer using a feeler gauge. The clearance should be between 0.010 and 0.140 inch to ensure correct engagement of the pinion with the flywheel (or driveplate - automatic transmission) ring-gear. If the clearance is incorrect, the starter will have to be dismantled again and any worn or distorted components replaced, no adjustment being provided for.

23 Starter motor solenoid - removal, repair and installation

Refer to illustration 23.2

1   After removing the starter/solenoid unit as described in Section 20 disconnect the connector strap from the solenoid MOTOR terminal.

2   Remove the two screws which secure the solenoid housing to the end-frame assembly **(see illustration)**.

3   Twist the solenoid in a clockwise direction to disengage the flange key and then withdraw the solenoid.

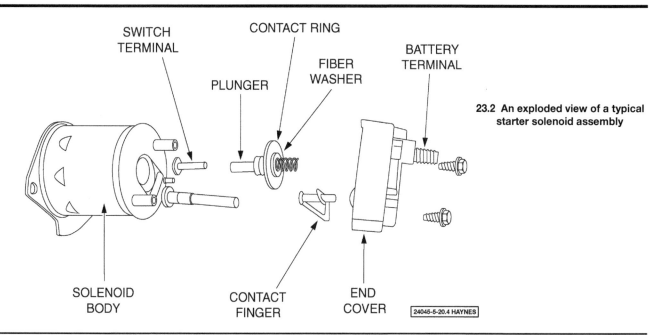

SWITCH TERMINAL
CONTACT RING
PLUNGER
FIBER WASHER
BATTERY TERMINAL
SOLENOID BODY
CONTACT FINGER
END COVER

24045-5-20.4 HAYNES

23.2 An exploded view of a typical starter solenoid assembly

4   Remove the nuts and washers from the solenoid terminals and then unscrew the two solenoid end-cover retaining screws and washers and pull off the end-cover.

5   Unscrew the nut washer from the battery terminal on the end- cover and remove the terminal.

6   Remove the resistor bypass terminal and contactor.

7   Remove the motor connector strap terminal and solder a new terminal in position.

8   Use a new battery terminal and install it to the end-cover. Install the bypass terminal and contactor.

9   Install the end-cover and the remaining terminal nuts.

10   Install the solenoid to the starter motor by first checking that the return spring is in position on the plunger and then insert the solenoid body into the drive housing and turn the body counterclockwise to engage the flange key.

11   Install the two solenoid securing screws and connect the MOTOR connector strap.

Notes

Chapter 6
Emissions systems

Contents

Specifications

Torque specifications	Ft-lb	In-lb
Diverter valve to air pump		90
Air pump mounting bolts	20 to 35	
Air pump pulley bolts	24	
Exhaust manifold		
inner bolts	20	
outer bolts	30	
Actuator mounting bolts	25	
Thermal vacuum switches	15	
Catalytic converter fill plug	28	

1 General description

1   Despite the general bad feelings towards emission controls, they play a necessary and integral role in the overall operation of the internal combustion engine. Your car is designed to operate with its pollution control systems, and disconnecting them or failing to properly maintain the components is illegal, not to mention being potentially harmful to the engine.

2   Through the years as smog standards have become more stringent, emission control systems have had to become more diverse and complex to keep pace. Where once the anti-pollution devices incorporated were installed as peripheral components to the main engine, later model engines work closely with, and in some cases are even controlled by, the emission control systems. Nearly every system in the make-up of a modern-day automobile is affected in some fashion by the emission systems.

3   This is not to say that the emission systems are particularly difficult for the home mechanic to maintain and service. You can perform general operational checks, and do most (if not all) of the regular maintenance easily and quickly at home with common tune-up and hand tools.

4   While the end result from the various emission systems is to reduce the output of pollutants into the air (namely hydrocarbons [HC] carbon Monoxide [CO], and oxides of Nitrogen [Nox]) the various systems function independently toward this goal. This is the way in which this chapter is divided.

2 Positive crankcase ventilation system (all 1970 - 1980)

General description

Refer to illustration 2.1

1 The positive crankcase ventilation, or PCV as it is more common called, reduces hydrocarbon emissions by circulating fresh air through the crankcase to pick up blow-by gases which are then re-routed through the carburetor or intake manifold to be returned by the engine **(see illustration)**.

2 The main components of this simple system are vacuum hoses and a PCV valve which regulates the flow of gases according to engine speed and manifold vacuum.

Positive crankcase ventilation system - checking

Refer to illustrations 2.6a, 2.6b and 2.9

3 The PCV system can be checked for proper operation quickly and easily. This system should be checked regularly as carbon and gunk deposited by the blow-by gases will eventually clog the PCV valve and/or system hoses. When the flow of the PCV system is reduced or stopped, common symptoms are rough idling or a reduced engine speed at idle.

4 To check for proper vacuum in the system, remove the top plate of the air cleaner and locate the small PCV filter on the inside of the air cleaner housing.

5 Disconnect the hose leading to this filter. Be careful not to break the molded fitting on the filter.

6 With the engine idling, place your thumb lightly over the end of the hose. Leave it there for about 30 seconds. You should feel a slight pull or vacuum **(see illustrations)**. The suction may be heard as your thumb is released. This will indicate that air is being drawn all the way through the system. If a vacuum is felt, the system is functioning properly. Check that the filter inside the air cleaner housing is not clogged or dirty. If in doubt, replace the filter with a new one, which is an inexpensive safeguard.

7 If there is very little vacuum, or none at all, at the end of the hose, the system is clogged and must be inspected further.

8 Shut off the engine and locate the PCV valve. Carefully pull it from its rubber grommet. Shake it and listen for a clicking sound. If the valve does not click freely, replace the valve with a new one.

9 Now start the engine and run it at idle speed with the PCV valve removed. Place your thumb over the end of the valve and feel for a suction **(see illustration)**. This should be a relatively strong vacuum which will be felt immediately.

10 If little or no vacuum is felt at the PCV valve, turn off the engine and disconnect the vacuum hose from the other end of the valve. Run the engine at idle speed and check for vacuum at the end of the hose just disconnected. No vacuum at this point indicates

that the vacuum hose or inlet fitting at the engine is plugged. If it is the hose which is blocked, replace it with a new one or remove it from the engine and blow it out sufficiently with compressed air. A clogged passage at the carburetor or manifold requires that the component be removed and thoroughly cleaned of carbon build-up. A strong vacuum felt going into the PCV valve, but little or no vacuum coming out of the valve, indicates a failure of the PCV valve requiring replacement with a new one.

11 When purchasing a new PCV valve make sure it is the proper one. Each PCV valve is metered for specific engine sizes and model years. An incorrect PCV valve may pull too much or too little vacuum, possibly causing damage to the engine.

12 Information on removing and installing the PCV valve can be found in Chapter 1.

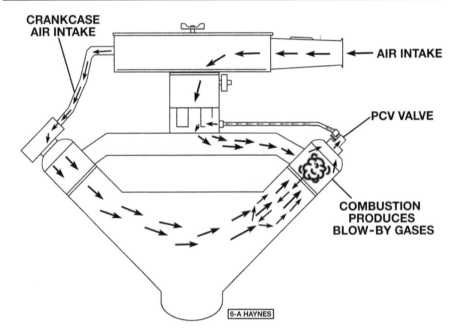

2.1 Typical components of a Positive Crankcase Ventilation (PCV) system

2.6a Typical late model PCV valve (arrow)

2.6b Checking for vacuum in the PCV hose where it connects to the air cleaner

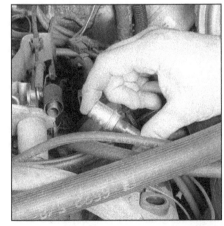

2.9 Checking for vacuum in the line at the PCV valve

3 Air injection reactor system (all 1970 - 1980)

General description

Refer to illustrations 3.3a and 3.3b

1   The function of the air injection reactor system is to reduce hydrocarbons in the exhaust. This is done by pumping fresh air directly into the exhaust manifold ports of each engine cylinder. The fresh oxygen-rich air helps combust the unburned hydrocarbons before they are expelled as exhaust.

2   This system operates at all engine speeds and will bypass air only for a short time during deceleration and at high speeds. In these cases the additional fresh air added to the over-rich fuel/air mixture may cause backfiring or popping through the exhaust.

3   This system as it is used on GM engines consists of the air injection pump (with supporting brackets and drivebelt) at the front of the engine, an air diverter valve attached to the pump housing, the manifold and injection tubes running into each port at the exhaust manifolds, and a check valve for each hose leading from the pump to the injection tubes on either side of the engine **(see illustrations)**. **Note:** *Many Pontiac-made engines will not have an AIR pump.*

Air injection reactor system - checking

Refer to illustrations 3.6, 3.7, 3.8 and 3.10

4   Properly installed and adjusted air injection systems are fairly reliable and seldom cause problems. However, a malfunctioning

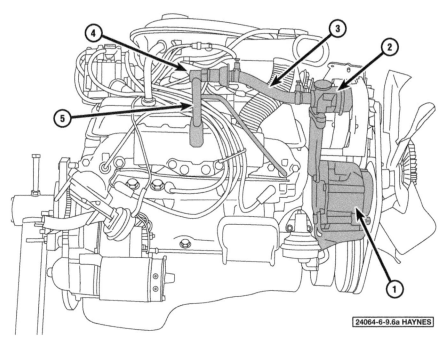

24064-6-9.6a HAYNES

3.3a Typical Air Injection Reaction (AIR) system component layout - (Right side)

1	Air pump	3	High temperature hose	5	Air injection pipe
2	Diverter valve	4	One way check valve		

system can cause engine surge, backfiring and over-heated spark plugs. The air pump is the most critical component of this system and the belt at the front of the engine which drives the pump should be your first check. If the belt is cracked or frayed, replace it with a new one. Check the tension of the drivebelt by pressing it with your finger. There should

be about 1/2 inch of play in the belt when pushed half-way between the pulleys.

5   The adjusting or replacement procedures for the drivebelt depend on the mounting of the air pump. On some models, a single belt is used for both the air pump and the alternator. If this is the case, loosen the mounting bolt and the adjusting bolt for the alternator and then push against the alternator to tighten the belt. Hold in this position while the two bolts are tightened. The procedure is basically the same for air pumps which use their own belt, except it will be the air pump which will be loosened.

6   To check for proper air delivery from the pump, follow the hoses from the pump to where they meet the injection tube/manifold assembly on each side of the engine **(see illustration)**. Loosen the clamps and disconnect the hoses.

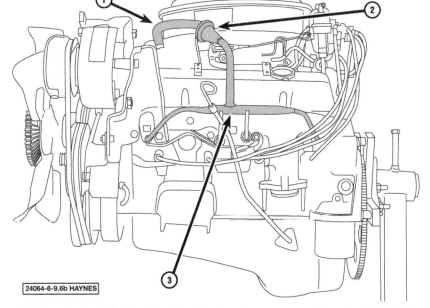

24064-6-9.6b HAYNES

3.3b Typical Air Injection Reaction (AIR) system component layout - (Left side)

1	High temperature hose	3	Air injection pipe
2	One way check valve		

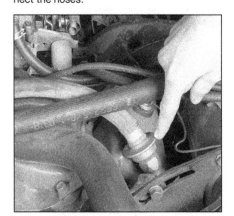

3.6 One of the two check valves used in the AIR system for V8 engines

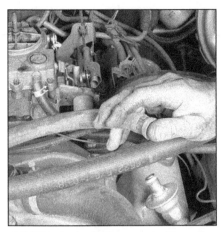

3.7 With the hose disconnected from the check valve, air should be felt with the engine running

3.8 The diverter valve with its by-pass muffler is mounted to the AIR pump at the front of the engine

3.10 A small diameter hose leads to the diverter valve. This is the vacuum signal hose to be disconnected during testing

7   Start the engine and with your fingers or a piece of paper, check that air is flowing out of these hoses **(see illustration)**. Accelerate the engine and observe the air flow, which should increase in relation to engine speed. If this is the case, the pump is working satisfactorily. If air flow was not present, or did not increase, check for crimps in the hoses, proper drivebelt tension, and for a leaking diverter valve which can be heard with the pump operating.

8   To check the diverter valve, sometimes called the "gulp" valve or anti-backfire valve, make sure all hoses are connected and start the engine. Locate the muffler on the valve which, is a canister unit with holes in it **(see illustration)**.

9   Being careful not to touch any of the moving engine components, place your hand near the muffler outlet holes and check that no air is escaping with the engine at idle speed. Now have an assistant depress the accelerator pedal to accelerate the engine and then quickly let off the pedal. A momentary blast of air should be felt discharging through the diverter valve muffler.

10   If no air discharge was felt, disconnect the smaller vacuum hose at the diverter valve **(see illustration)**. Place your finger over the end of the hose and again have your assistant depress the accelerator and let it off. As the engine is decelerating, a vacuum should be felt. If vacuum was felt, replace the diverter valve with a new one. If no vacuum was felt, the vacuum hose or engine vacuum source is plugged, requiring a thorough cleaning to eliminate the problem.

11   The check valves are located on the air manifold assembly and their function is to prevent exhaust gases from flowing back into the air pump. To find out if they are functioning properly, disconnect the two air supply hoses where they attach to the check valves. Start the engine, and being careful not to touch any moving engine components place your hand over the outlet of the check valve. The valve can be further checked by turning off the engine, allowing it to cool, and orally

3.17 Removing the AIR pump pulley

blowing through the check valve (toward the air manifold). Then attempt to suck back through it. If the valve is allowing you to suck back towards the air pump, the valve is bad and should be replaced.

12   Another check for this system is for leaks in the hose connection and/or hoses themselves. Leaks can often be detected by sound or feel with the pump in operation. If a leak is suspected, use a soapy water solution to verify this. Pour or sponge the solution of detergent and water on the hoses and connections. With the pump running, bubbles will form if a leak exists. The air delivery hoses are of a special design to withstand engine temperatures, so if they are replaced make sure the new hoses are of the proper standards.

Air pump - removal and installation

Refer to illustrations 3.17, 3.18a and 3.18b

13   As mentioned earlier, some air pumps share a common drivebelt with the alternator where others use their own belt. This will affect the removal and installation procedure somewhat.

3.18a The pump is held to the engine by brackets and attaching bolts

14   Disconnect the air delivery hoses at the air pump. Note the position of each hose for reassembly.

15   Disconnect the vacuum source hose at the diverter valve.

16   Compress the drivebelt to keep the air pump pulley from turning, and remove the bolts and washers securing the pulley to the pump.

17   To get some slack in the belt, loosen the alternator adjusting bolt and the pivot bolt. Push the alternator inward until the belt and air pump pulley can be removed from the pump **(see illustration)**.

18   Remove the bolts which secure the air pump to its brackets and then lift the pump and diverter valve assembly from the engine compartment **(see illustrations)**.

19   If the diverter valve is to be installed onto the new air pump, remove the bolts securing it to the pump and separate the two components.

20   Check the pump for evidence that exhaust gas has entered it, indicating a failure of one or both the check valves.

21   Install the diverter valve to the new air pump using a new gasket. Torque the attach-

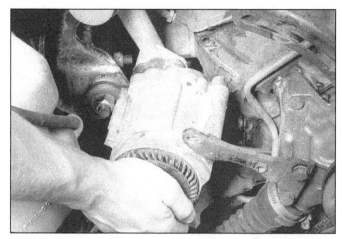

3.18b Lifting the pump and diverter valve away from the engine

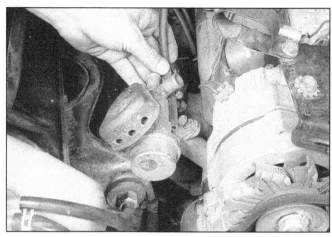

3.29 A slightly different type of diverter valve shown here with the air delivery hoses and vacuum hose disconnected

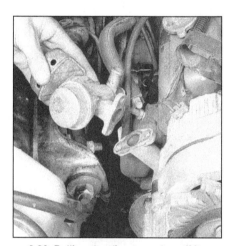

3.30 Pulling the diverter valve off its mounting base on the pump

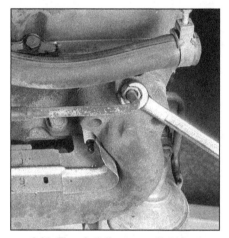

3.36 The air delivery manifold has threaded fittings in the exhaust manifold. Shown is a flare nut wrench which wraps around the fitting to prevent rounding off the flats

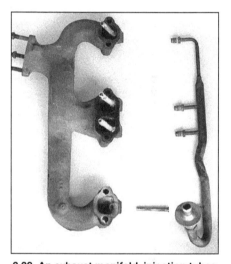

3.38 An exhaust manifold, injection tubes fitted inside the ports and the air delivery manifold

ing bolts to specifications.

22   Install the air pump to its engine mounting brackets with the attaching bolts loose. The exception to this is on models where the mounting bolts are inaccessible with the pulley installed. In this case, the pump mounting bolts should be fully tightened to specifications at this point.

23   Install the pump pulley with the bolts only hand tight.

24   Place the drive belt into position on the air pump pulley and adjust the belt by gently prying on the alternator until about 1/2 inch of play is felt in the belt when pushed with your fingers half-way between the pulleys. Tighten the alternator bolts, keeping the belt tension at this point.

25   Keep the pump pulley from turning by compressing the drive belt and torque the pulley bolts to specifications.

26   Connect the hoses to the air pump and diverter valve. Make sure the connections are tight.

27   Tighten the mounting bolts for the pump to specifications.

28   Check the operation of the air pump as outlined previously.

Diverter valve - removal and installation

Refer to illustrations 3.29 and 3.30

29   Disconnect the vacuum signal line and air delivery hoses at the diverter valve. Note the position of each for assembly (see illustration).

30   Remove the bolts which secure the valve to the air pump and remove the diverter valve from the engine compartment (see illustration).

31   When purchasing a new diverter valve, keep in mind that although many of the valves are similar in appearance, each is designed to meet particular requirements of various engines, therefore, be sure to install the correct valve.

32   Install the new diverter valve to the air pump or pump extension with a new gasket. Torque the securing bolts to specification.

33   Connect the air delivery and vacuum source hoses and check the operation of the valve as outlined previously.

Air manifold and injection tubes - removal and installation

Refer to illustrations 3.36 and 3.38

34   Due to the high temperatures at this area, the connections at the exhaust manifold may be difficult to loosen. Commercial penetrating oil applied to the threads of the injection tubes may help in the removal procedure.

35   Disconnect the air delivery hoses at the manifold check valves.

36   Loosen the threaded connectors on the exhaust manifold at each exhaust port (see illustration). Slide the connectors upwards on the injection tubes so the threads are out of the exhaust manifold.

37   Pull the injection tube/air manifold assembly from the engine exhaust manifold and out of the engine compartment. Depending on the model year, injection tube extensions leading inside the engine may come out with the assembly.

38   On models where the extension tubes

remain inside the exhaust manifold, they must be pressed out after the exhaust manifold is removed from the engine **(see illustration)**.

39 If the exhaust manifold was removed from the engine to clean or replace the extensions, reinstall the manifold with extensions to the engine using a new gasket. Torque to the proper specifications.

40 Thread each of the injection tube connectors loosely into the exhaust manifold, using an anti-seize compound on the threads. After each of the connectors is sufficiently started, tighten each securely.

41 Connect the air supply hoses to the check valves.

42 Start the engine and check for leaks as previously described.

Check valve - removal and installation

Refer to illustration 3.44

43 Disconnect the air supply hose at the check valve.

44 Using two wrenches on the flats provided, remove the check valve from the air manifold assembly **(see illustration)**. Be careful not to bend or twist the delicate manifold or injection tubes as this is done.

45 Installation is a reversal of the removal procedure.

---

4   Transmission controlled spark system (some 1970 - 1974)

General description

1   This system is designed to eliminate the vacuum advance at the distributor under certain driving conditions. The system is incorporated on most 1970 to 1980 Firebirds, though the specific makeup of the system varies considerably between the various makes of engines, from Chevrolet-built to Oldsmobile and Pontiac-built. In some years and on some engines, the TCS system is referred to as the CES, or combination emissions control system.

2   In most configurations, the vacuum for the advancing mechanism in the distributor is shut off until the transmission is in "Hi" gear or 3rd and 4th gears with the 4-speed transmission. Vacuum is also allowed in "Reverse" for the Turbo Hydramatic automatic transmissions.

3   This system generally consists of: a transmission switch; engine coolant temperature switch; time delay relay; vacuum advance solenoid; and an idle stop solenoid. Although this system is somewhat more difficult to service, check and maintain than the other emissions systems, when each component is examined individually the operation of the TCS system can be easily understood.
Transmission switch

4   On manual transmissions, the electrical switch is actuated by the internal shifter shaft. The switch is located on the outside of

3.44 Two wrenches should be used to loosen the check valve from the manifold

the transmission case, adjacent to the shifter shaft.

5   Automatic transmissions use a pressure-sensitive switch that is actuated by the fluid pressure as the transmission reaches "Hi" gear (and "Reverse" in the case of the Turbo Hydramatics). This switch is located on the outside of the transmission on Powerglide and Turbo Hydramatic 350 transmissions. Turbo Hydramatic 400 transmissions have the switch mounted internally in the transmission.

6   When activated in the proper transmission gears, the switch sends an electrical input to the vacuum advance solenoid. This TCS-component has remained basically unchanged through the four years in which it was used.

Temperature switch

7   The function of this switch is to sense the engine temperature and send a signal to the vacuum advance solenoid. It is the same switch that operates the dashboard-mounted warning light or water temperature gauge. The switch is located either on the side of the cylinder head, near the exhaust ports, or on the front of the intake manifold.

8   The temperature switch monitors engine coolant temperatures and sends electrical current to the vacuum advance solenoid. On earlier vehicles, the temperature switch reacts with the vacuum advance solenoid to allow full vacuum advance whenever the engine temperature is below 82 degrees, though this was raised to 93 degrees on later models. This means that regardless of the transmission gear or any other engine condition, the TCS system is not functional and should have no affect on engine operation until the engine has warmed up to these operating temperatures.

Time delay relay

9   This electrically operated relay has undergone some changes in the various TCS systems. In each model year, however, its

main function is to delay the operation of the vacuum advance solenoid.

10   In most years, the time delay relay will allow full distributor vacuum advance during the first 20 seconds of engine operation. This means that every time the ignition switch is turned on, no matter if the engine is warm or cold, the delay relay will render the TCS system inoperative for the first 20 seconds.

11   The 1972 relay is located under the dashboard, on the center reinforcement brace. For the other years, the relay is mounted inside the engine compartment, on the firewall.

Vacuum advance solenoid

12   This is the heart of the TCS system, with its function being to supply or deny vacuum to the distributor.

13   This canister-shaped unit is generally located on the right side of the engine, attached to the intake manifold. It can be readily located by simply following the vacuum hose out of the distributor vacuum advance unit.

14   In the energized position, the plunger inside the solenoid opens the vacuum port from the carburetor to the vacuum advance unit, and at the same time blocks off the clean air port at the other end. In the de-energized mode, the clean air port is uncovered which allows the distributor to vent to the atmosphere and shuts off vacuum to the distributor.

Idle stop solenoid

Refer to illustrations 4.15 and 4.16

15   This solenoid is attached to the right side of the carburetor with brackets. It can be identified by a wiring connector at one end and a bolt-head plunger on the other **(see illustration)**.

16   The idle stop solenoid is an electrically operated, two-position control. It is used to provide a predetermined throttle setting **(see illustration)**.

17   In the energized position, the plunger extends from the solenoid body and contacts the carburetor throttle lever. This prevents the carburetor throttle plates from closing fully. When de-energized (key off), the solenoid plunger retracts into the solenoid body to allow the throttle plates to fully close, which "starves" the engine and prevents run-on or "dieseling".

18   The system on some engines also incorporates a solid state timing device which allows the air conditioning compressor (if equipped) to come on when the ignition is turned off. The added load of the air conditioning compressor helps to shut off the engine to further prevent dieseling.

Transmission controlled spark - checking

19   This system is difficult to check due to the fact that the vehicle must be in full operation. This means that the checks must be made with the car travelling at speed. Such a test is easiest to perform on a chassis dynamometer.

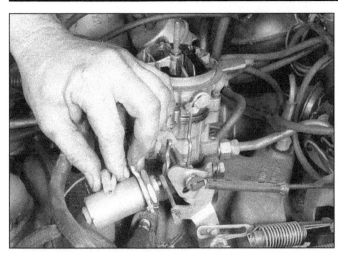

4.15 The idle solenoid is located on the left side of the carburetor and has an electrical connector attached

4.16 The solenoid has a bolt at one end that contacts the throttle linkage. Adjusting this bolt changes the engine idle speed

20   If a problem in this system is suspected, first check that all electrical wires and connections are in good condition and intact. Also inspect the vacuum hoses at the vacuum advance solenoid and the distributor vacuum advance unit. A blown fuse in the fuse box can also cause problems in this system.

21   To ascertain if the TCS system is in fact malfunctioning, connect a vacuum gauge in the hose between the solenoid and the distributor. A length of vacuum hose must be used to enable you to route the gauge inside the passenger's compartment. Make sure the hose is not crimped and will not be damaged by moving or hot engine parts.

22   If a dynamometer is not available, drive the car and have an assistant watch the vacuum gauge. Make a log of vacuum gauge readings and transmission gears. If the system is functioning properly, the following conditions will be met:

a) When the engine is cold, vacuum will show on the gauge until the engine has warmed to operating temperature.
b) Vacuum should be present on the gauge during the first 20 seconds after the engine is started, regardless of temperature.
c) At normal operating temperature there should be vacuum showing on the gauge in "Hi" gear only.

23   The system should be tested with the engine cold, and also after it has reached normal operating temperature. Don't forget about the time delay function and how it relates to your particular vehicle.

24   The above test will tell you if the system as a whole is functioning properly. The following are test procedures for the individual TCS components if a fault is detected in the driving test.

Idle stop solenoid

25   Have an assistant turn the ignition switch on as you watch the idle stop solenoid plunger. With the key on, the plunger should extend against the throttle linkage. With the key off, the plunger should retract into the solenoid.

Transmission switch

26   With the engine warm and running, have an assistant put the transmission in a low forward gear (make sure the front wheels are blocked, parking brake is on and the assistant has the brake pedal depressed). There should be no vacuum going to the distributor. If there is vacuum going to the distributor, remove the transmission switch connection. Replace the transmission switch if the vacuum stops when the transmission switch connection was removed.

Temperature switch

27   When the engine is cold, there should be vacuum going to the distributor. If this is not the case, ground the wire from the cold terminal of the temperature switch. If the vacuum advance solenoid energizes, replace the temperature switch with a new one.

28   A failure of the temperature switch may also show up on the driving test with the engine at different operating temperatures, as well as a malfunction of the temperature gauge or dash warning light.

Vacuum advance solenoid

29   Check the vacuum running into the solenoid from the intake manifold or carburetor. You should be able to feel this vacuum with the engine running.

30   Now reconnect the vacuum inlet hose and disconnect the vacuum hose leading to the distributor. Disconnect the electrical connectors at the solenoid and run a 12-volt jumper wire to the solenoid. The solenoid should be energized, allowing vacuum to reach the distributor.

Time delay relay (1972)

31   With the ignition on, check for 12 volts at the tan colored lead to the relay. Use a test light for this.

32   Install a 12-volt jumper wire to the terminal with the tan lead, and ground the terminal with the black lead. If, after 26 seconds, the advance solenoid does not energize (meaning vacuum to the distributor), replace the delay relay.

Time delay relay (except 1972)

33   Remove the temperature switch connector at the time delay relay.

34   Check to make sure the relay is cool, then turn the ignition to the on position.

35   The vacuum advance solenoid should energize for about 20 seconds and then de-energize. If it does not de-energize, remove the blue lead from the time relay. If this causes the solenoid to de-energize, the relay is bad.

---

5   Forced air pre-heat system (all 1970 - 1980)

General description

Refer to illustrations 5.5a and 5.5b

1   While coming under different names, the end result from this system is the same - to improve engine efficiency and reduce hydrocarbon emissions during the initial warm-up period of the car.

2   There are two different methods used to achieve this goal. First, a thermostatic air cleaner (Thermac) is used to draw warm air from the exhaust manifold directly into the carburetor. Second, some form of exhaust valve is incorporated inside the exhaust pipe to recirculate warm exhaust gases which are then used to pre-heat the carburetor and choke.

3   It is during the first few miles of driving (depending on outside temperature) when this system has its greatest effect on engine performance and emissions output. Once the engine has reached normal operating temperature, the flapper valves in the exhaust pipe and air cleaner open, allowing for normal engine operation.

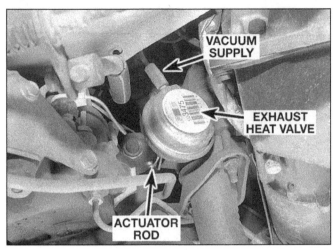

5.5a   Typical EFE heat valve and actuator

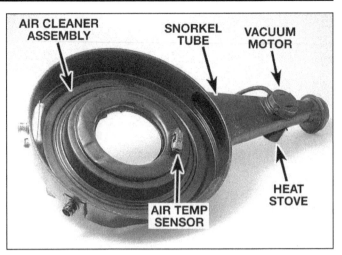

5.5b   Typical THERMAC system components

4   Because of this cold-engine only function, it is important to periodically check this system to prevent poor engine performance when cold, or over-heating of the fuel mixture once the engine has reached operating temperatures. If either the exhaust heat valve or air cleaner valve sticks in the ;no heat position, the engine will run poorly, stall and waste gas until it has warmed up on its own. A valve sticking in the "heat" position causes the engine to run as if it is out of tune due to the constant flow of hot air to the carburetor.

5   The components which make up this system include: a heat valve inside the exhaust pipe on the right side of the engine (called a heat riser on 1970 - 1974 models), an actuator and thermal vacuum switch (on 1975 - 1980 models to control the heat valve) **(see illustration)** and a thermostatic air cleaner consisting of a temperature sensor, vacuum diaphragm and heat stove (all models 1970 - 1980) **(see illustration)**. Initial checking procedures can be found in Chapter 1.

Forced air pre-heat system - checking

Refer to illustration 5.11

6   The conventional heat riser, installed on cars built up until 1975, should be checked often for free operation. Because of the high exhaust temperatures and its location which is open to the elements, corrosion frequently keeps the valve from operating freely, or even freezes it in position.

7   To check the heat riser operation, locate it on the exhaust manifold (it can be identified by an external weight and spring) and with the engine cold, try moving the counter-weight. The valve should move freely with no binding. Now have an assistant start the engine (still cold) while the counter-weight is observed. The valve should move to the closed position and then slowly open as the engine warms.

8   A stuck or binding heat riser valve often can be loosened by soaking the valve shaft

with solvent as the counter-weight is moved back and forth. Light taps with a hammer may be necessary to free a tightly stuck valve. If this proves unsuccessful the heat riser must be replaced with a new one after disconnecting it from the exhaust pipe.

9   In 1975, General Motors introduced a replacement for the heat riser which they called the Early Fuel Evaporation System. This system provides the same function, but uses manifold vacuum to open and close the heat valve.

10   To check this system, locate the actuator and rod assembly which is on a bracket attached to the right exhaust manifold. With the engine cold, have an assistant start the engine. Observe the movement of the actuator rod which leads to the heat valve inside the exhaust pipe. It should immediately operate the valve to the closed position. If this is the case, the system is operating correctly.

11   If the actuator rod did not move, disconnect the vacuum hose at the actuator and place your thumb over the open end **(see illustration)**. With the engine cold and at idle, you should feel a suction indicating proper vacuum. If there is vacuum at this point, replace the actuator with a new one.

12   If there is no vacuum in the line, this is an indication that either the hose is crimped or plugged, or the thermal vacuum switch threaded into the water outlet is not functioning properly. Replace the hose or switch as necessary.

13   To make sure the Early Fuel Evaporation System is disengaging once the engine has warmed, continue to observe the actuating rod as the engine reaches normal operating temperature (approximately 180 degrees depending on engine size). The rod should again move, indicating the valve is in the open position.

14   If after the engine has warmed, the valve does hot open, pull the vacuum hose at the actuator and check for vacuum with your thumb. If there is no vacuum, replace the actuator. If there is vacuum, replace the TVS switch on the water outlet housing.

Thermac assembly - checking

15   The thermostatic air cleaner components can be quickly and easily checked for proper operation. Routine checking procedures and illustrations can be found in Chapter 1.

16   With the engine off, observe the damper door inside the air cleaner snorkel. If this is difficult because of positioning, use a mirror. The valve should be open, meaning that in this position all air would flow through the snorkel and none through the exhaust manifold hot-air duct at the underside of the air cleaner housing.

17   Now have an assistant start the engine and continue to observe the flapper door inside the snorkel. With the engine cold and at idle the damper door should close off all air from the snorkel allowing heated air from the exhaust manifold to enter the air cleaner as intake. As the engine warms to operating temperature the damper door should move, allowing outside air through the snorkel to be included in the mixture. Eventually, the door should recede to the point where most of the

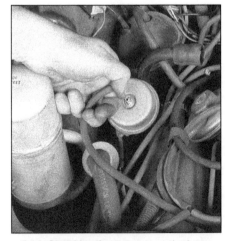

5.11   Checking for vacuum at the hose which leads to the actuator

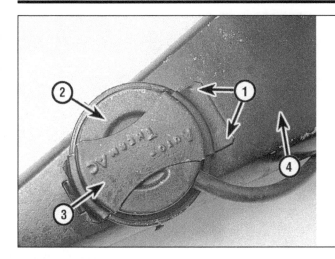

5.35 To remove the vacuum motor, drill out the spot welds and detach the retaining strap

1 Spot welds
2 Vacuum diaphragm motor
3 Retaining strap
4 Snorkel

5.44 The sensor retainer must be pried off with a screwdriver

incoming air is through the snorkel and not the exhaust manifold passage.

18   If the damper door did not close off snorkel air when the cold engine was first started, disconnect the vacuum hose at the snorkel vacuum motor and place your thumb over the hose end, checking for vacuum. If there is vacuum going to the motor, check that the damper door and link are not frozen or binding within the air cleaner snorkel. Replace the vacuum motor if the hose routing is correct and the damper door moves freely.

19   If there was no vacuum going to the motor in the above test, check the hoses for cracks, crimps or disconnections. If the hoses are clear and in good condition, replace the temperature sensor inside the air cleaner housing.

Actuator and rod assembly - replacement

20   Disconnect the vacuum hose from the actuator.
21   Remove the two nuts which attach the actuator to the bracket.
22   Disconnect the rod from the heat valve and remove the actuator and rod from the engine compartment.
23   Install the actuator and rod in the reverse order, tightening the attaching nuts to specifications.

Exhaust heat valve - replacement

24   Remove the crossover exhaust pipe.
25   Disconnect the actuating rod from the heat valve.
26   Remove the valve from inside the exhaust pipe.
27   Installation is a reversal of removal; however, make sure all attaching fasteners are tightened to proper specifications.

Thermal vacuum switch (TVS) - replacement

28   Drain the engine coolant until the fluid level is below the engine water outlet (thermostat} housing.
29   Disconnect the hoses from the TVS

switch making note of their positions for reassembly.
30   Using a suitable wrench, remove the TVS switch (see illustration 7.28).
31   Apply a soft setting sealant uniformly to the threads of the new TVS switch. Be careful that none of the sealant gets on the sensor end of the switch.
32   Install the switch and tighten to specifications.
33   Connect the vacuum hoses to the switch in their original positions and add coolant as necessary.

Air cleaner vacuum motor - replacement

Refer to illustration 5.35
34   Remove the air cleaner assembly from the engine and disconnect the vacuum hose from the motor.
35   Drill out the two spot welds which secure the vacuum motor retaining strap to the snorkel tube (see illustration).
36   Remove the motor attaching strap.
37   Lift up the motor, cocking it to one side to unhook the motor linkage at the control damper assembly.
38   To install, drill a 7/64 inch hole in the snorkel tube at the center of the retaining strap.
39   Insert the vacuum motor linkage into the control damper assembly.
40   Using the sheet metal screw supplied with the motor service kit, attach the motor and retaining strap to the snorkel. Make sure the sheet metal screw does not interfere with the operation of the damper door.
41   Connect the vacuum hose to the motor and install the air cleaner assembly.

Air cleaner temperature sensor - replacement

Refer to illustration 5.44
42   Remove the air cleaner from the engine and disconnect the vacuum hoses at the sensor.
43   Carefully note the position of the sensor. The new sensor must be installed in exactly the same position.

44   Pry up the tabs on the sensor retaining clip and remove the sensor and clip from the air cleaner (see illustration).
45   Install the new sensor with a new gasket in the same position as the old one.
46   Press the retaining clip on the sensor. Do not damage the control mechanism in the center of the sensor.
47   Connect the vacuum hoses and install the air cleaner to the engine.

6   Fuel evaporative system (all 1970 -1980)

General description

Refer to illustration 6.4
1   Although the evaporative control system is one of the most complex looking, it is in actuality one of the most basic and trouble-free portions of the emissions network. Its function is to reduce hydrocarbon emissions. Basically this is a closed fuel system which reroutes wasted fuel back to the gas tank and stores fuel vapors instead of venting them to the atmosphere.
2   Due to, its very nature of having few moving parts, the evaporative control system requires no periodic maintenance except for a replacement of the oiled fiberglass filter in the bottom of the charcoal canister at the recommended intervals.
3   A tip-off that this system is not operating properly is the strong smell of fuel vapors or if the engine starves from lack of fuel during acceleration.
4   A pressure vacuum gasoline filler cap must be used, as a standard cap may render the system ineffective and could possibly collapse the fuel tank. Other components which make up this system include: a special gas tank with fill limiters and vent connections, a charcoal canister (see illustration) with integral purge valve and filter which stores vapor from the fuel tank to be burned by the carburetor, a carburetor bowl vent valve and various hoses linking the main components.

6.4 Typical late model charcoal–filled canister

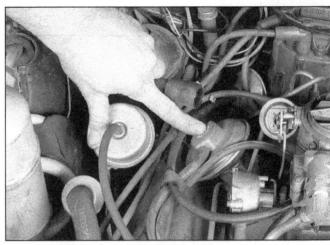

7.6 The EGR valve is a disc-shaped diaphragm bolted to the intake manifold, adjacent to the carburetor

Fuel evaporative system - checking

5   As mentioned. earlier, this system requires little maintenance, however, if a problem is suspected the system should be inspected.

6   With the engine cold, disconnect the fuel tank line at the charcoal canister. On most models the canister is located inside the engine compartment behind the left headlight. Each of the hose connections are duly labeled.

7   As this hose is disconnected, check for the presence of liquid fuel in the line. Fuel in this vapor hose is an indication that the vent controls or pressure-vacuum relief valve in the gas cap are not functioning properly.

8   Hook up a pressure suction device on the end of the fuel vapor line. Apply 15 psi pressure to the line and observe for excessive loss of pressure.

9   Check for a fuel vapor smell in the engine compartment and around the gas tank.

10   Remove the fuel filler cap and check for pressure in the gas tank.

11   If there is a large loss of pressure or a fuel odor, inspect all lines for leaks or deterioration.

12   With the fuel filler cap removed, apply pressure again and check for obstructions in the vent line.

13   To check the purge valve built into the canister, start the engine and disconnect the vacuum signal line running from the engine to the canister. With your thumb over the end of the hose, raise the engine speed to about 1500 rpm and check for vacuum. If there is no vacuum signal, check the EGR operation as described in this chapter. The vacuum signal for the canister and the EGR valve originate from the same source.

14   The purge line to the charcoal canister functions with the PCV vacuum source, so if there is no vacuum when this hose is disconnected from the canister check the PCV valve vacuum.

Charcoal canister and filter - replacement

15   Chapter 1 contains all information concerning the servicing of the fuel evaporation system, in particular the replacement of the canister filter.

---

7   Exhaust gas recirculation (EGR) system (all 1973 - 1980)

General description

1   This system is used to reduce oxides of nitrogen (Nox) emitted from the exhaust. Formation of these pollutants takes place at very high temperatures; consequently, it occurs during the peak temperature period of the combustion process. To reduce peak temperatures, and thus the formation of Nox, a small amount of exhaust gas is taken from the exhaust system and recirculated in the combustion cycle.

2   To tap this exhaust supply without an extensive array of pipes and connections in the exhaust system, additional exhaust passages are cast into the intricate runner system of the intake manifold. Because of this arrangement, most of the EGR routing components are hidden from view under the manifold.

3   Very little maintenance other than occasionally inspecting the vacuum hoses and the EGR valve is required. Besides the heart of the system - the EGR valve - the only moving part which can wear out is a thermal vacuum switch (TVS) which controls the vacuum signal to the EGR valve at varying engine temperatures.

4   The EGR system does not recirculate gases when the engine is at idle or during deceleration. The system is also regulated by the thermal vacuum switch which does not allow the system to operate until the engine has reached normal operating temperature.

5   Common engine problems associated with the EGR system are: rough idling or stalling when at idle, rough engine performance upon light throttle application and stalling on deceleration.

Exhaust gas recirculation system - checking

Refer to illustrations 7.6 and 7.13

6   Locate the EGR valve located on the right side of the intake manifold, adjacent to the carburetor **(see illustration)**. Initial checking with illustrations can be found in Chapter 12.

7   Place your finger under the EGR valve and push upwards on the diaphragm plate. The diaphragm should move freely from the open to the closed position. If it doesn't, replace the EGR valve.

8   Now start the engine and run at idle speed. With your finger, manually depress the EGR diaphragm. If the valve or adjacent accessories are hot, wear gloves to prevent burning your fingers. When the diaphragm is pressed (valve closed to recirculate exhaust), the engine should lose speed, stumble or even stall. If the engine did not change speed, the EGR passages should be checked for blockage. This will require that the intake manifold be removed (see Chapter 2 for engine strip-down).

9   Now allow the engine to reach normal operating temperature. Have an assistant depress the accelerator slightly and hold the engine speed constant above idle.

10   Pull off the vacuum signal line at the EGR valve and check for the diaphragm plate to move downward, accompanied by an increase in engine speed.

11   Reinstall the vacuum line to the valve and the diaphragm plate should move upward with a decrease in engine speed.

12   If the diaphragm did not move, make sure the engine was at operating temperature. Repeat the test if in doubt.

13   Your next check would be that vacuum is reaching the EGR valve. Pull off the vac-

7.13 Checking for vacuum at the end of the hose which attaches to the EGR valve

7.28 The thermal vacuum switch is threaded into the thermostat housing cover or intake manifold

1 EGR
2 Vacuum supply

uum hose at the valve and with the engine running and accelerator slightly pressed check for vacuum at the end of the hose with your thumb **(see illustration)**. If there is vacuum, replace the EGR valve with a new one. If there is no vacuum signal, follow the vacuum hose to its source, inspecting for disconnections, cracks, breaks or blockage in the lines.

14 On most models, the EGR system uses a thermal vacuum switch to regulate EGR valve operation in relation to engine temperature. Some 1973 vehicles have the vacuum source routed directly to the carburetor.

15 This vacuum switch opens as the coolant temperature increases, allowing vacuum to reach the EGR valve. The exact temperature varies from year to year, but is indicative of the normal operating temperature of the particular engine.

16 The best way to test the switch is with a vacuum gauge. checking the vacuum signal with the engine hot.

17 Disconnect the vacuum hose at the EGR valve, connect the vacuum gauge to the disconnected end of the hose and start the engine. Note the reading on the vacuum gauge with the engine at an idle and then have an assistant depress the accelerator slightly and note this reading. As the accelerator is depressed, the vacuum reading should increase.

18 If the gauge does not respond to the throttle opening, disconnect the hose which leads from the carburetor to the thermal vacuum switch. Repeat the test with the vacuum gauge installed in the vacuum hose end at the switch. If the vacuum gauge responds to accelerator opening, the thermal vacuum switch is defective and should be replaced with a new one.

19 If the gauge still does not respond to an increase in throttle opening, check for a plugged hose or defective carburetor.

EGR valve - replacement

20 Disconnect the vacuum hose at the EGR valve.
21 Remove the nuts or bolts which secure the valve to the intake manifold.
22 Lift the EGR valve from the engine.
23 Clean the mounting surfaces of the EGR valve. Remove all traces of gasket material.
24 Place the new EGR valve, with new gasket, on the intake manifold. Install the spacer, if used. Tighten the attaching bolts or nuts.
25 Connect the vacuum signal hose.

Thermal vacuum switch - replacement

Refer to illustration 7.28
26 Drain the engine coolant until the coolant level is beneath the switch.
27 Disconnect the vacuum hoses from the switch, noting their positions for reassembly.
28 Using a suitable wrench, remove the switch **(see illustration)**.
29 When installing the switch, apply thread sealer to the threads being careful not to allow the sealant to touch the bottom sensor.
30 Install the switch and tighten it to specifications.
31 Check the coolant level.

---

8 Catalytic converter (all 1975 -1980)

General description

1 The catalytic converter is an emission control device added to the exhaust system to reduce hydrocarbon and carbon monoxide pollutants. This converter contains beads which are coated with a catalytic substance containing platinum and palladium.
2 It is imperative that only unleaded gasoline be used in a vehicle equipped with a catalytic converter. Unleaded fuel reduces combustion chamber deposits, corrosion and prevents lead contamination of the catalyst.
3 Periodic maintenance of the catalytic converter is not required; however, if the car is raised for other service it is advisable to inspect the overall condition of the catalytic converter and related exhaust components.
4 If the catalytic converter has been proven by an official inspection station to be ineffective, the converter can be replaced with a new one. Physical damage or the use of leaded fuels are the main causes of a malfunctioning catalytic converter.
5 It should be noted that the catalytic converter can reach very high temperatures in operation. Because of this, any work performed to the converter or in the general area where it is located should be done only after the system has sufficiently cooled. Also, caution should be exercised when lifting the vehicle with a hoist as the converter can be damaged if the lifting pads are not property positioned.
6 There are no functional tests which the home mechanic can make to determine if the catalytic converter is performing its task.

Catalytic converter- replacement

Refer to illustration 8.9
7 While the removal of the catalytic converter will be a rare occurrence, it can be successfully separated from the exhaust system for replacement.
8 Raise the car and support firmly with jack stands. The converter and exhaust system should be cool before proceeding.
9 Disconnect the converter at the front and rear **(see illustration)**. On most models a flange is used with four bolts and nuts to secure the converter to its mating exhaust

8.9 Remove the catalytic converter flange bolts or U-bolts

pipes. If the fasteners are frozen in place due to the high temperatures and corrosion, apply a penetrating oil liberally and allow to soak in. As a last resort, the fasteners will have to be carefully cut off with a hacksaw.

10   Gently separate the inlet and outlet converter flanges from the exhaust pipes and remove the converter from under the vehicle.

11   Installation is a reversal of the removal process; however, always use new nuts and bolts.

Catalyst - replacement

12   There are two types of catalytic converters used on the covered vehicles. The monolith converter has coated rods which cannot be serviced. If failure occurs, the entire converter must be replaced with a new one. The catalyst in bead type converters can be changed by draining and filling the beads through a plug at the bottom of the converter.

13   With specialized equipment, the beads can be replaced with the converter still positioned under the car. This is definitely a job for a dealer who has the equipment and training necessary to perform this operation.

---

9   Troubleshooting - emission systems

Condition	Possible cause
Engine idles abnormally rough and/or stalls	EGR valve vacuum hoses misrouted Leaking EGR valve EFE valve malfunctioning PCV system clogged or hoses misrouted TCS system malfunctioning
Engine runs rough on light throttle acceleration	Malfunctioning EGR valve EFE valve malfunctioning TCS system malfunctioning
Engine stalls and/or backfires during deceleration	Restriction in EGR vacuum hoses Sticking EGR valve Malfunctioning AIR diverter valve Malfunctioning TCS system
Engine detonation	EGR control valve blocked or air flow restricted Binding EFE (heat riser) valve Malfunctioning or restricted operation of Thermac air cleaner Clogged PCV valve and/or hoses
Engine dieseling on shut-off	TCS idle stop solenoid improperly adjusted Thermac valve sticking
Excessive engine oil consumption	Clogged PCV valve and or hoses
Poor high gear performance	Malfunctioning TCS switch
Fuel odor	Evaporative emission system hoses clogged; hoses disconnected or cracked; charcoal canister filter in need of replacement

Chapter 7 Part A
Manual transmission

Contents

Specifications

Transmission type	3 or 4 forward speeds (all synchromesh) and reverse. Floor or steering column shift.

Application

1970 - 1980 3 speed	Saginaw
1970 - 1973 4-speed	Saginaw, Muncie
1974	Saginaw, Muncie, Warner
1975 4-speed	Warner
1976 4-speed	Saginaw
1977 - 1980 4-speed	Saginaw, Warner

Oil capacity

3 speed units	2.0 US pts
4 speed units	3.0 US pts

Torque specifications

Ft-lb

Three-speed Saginaw

Clutch gear retainer to case bolts	15
Side cover to case bolts	15
Extension to case bolts	45
Shift lever to shifter shaft bolts	25
Lubrication filler plug	18
Transmission case to clutch housing bolts	75
Crossmember to frame nuts	25
Crossmember to mount bolts	40
Mount to transmission bolts	32

Torque specifications   lb-ft

Four-speed Saginaw

Clutch gear retainer to case bolts	15
Side cover to case bolts	15
Extension to case bolts	45
Shift lever to shifter shaft bolts	25
Lubrication filler plug	18
Transmission case to clutch housing bolts	75
Crossmember to frame nuts	25
Crossmember to mount and mount to extension bolts	40
Mount to transmission bolts	32

Four-speed Muncie

Clutch gear bearing retainer to case bolts	25
Cover to case bolts	20
Extension and retainer to case bolts	
Upper	20
Lower	30
Lubrication filler plug	30
Shift lever to shifter shaft nut	20
Mount to transmission bolts	32

Four-speed Warner

Clutch gear retainer to case bolts	18
Side cover to case bolts	18
Extension to case bolts	40
Shift lever to shifter shaft bolts	20
Lubrication filler plug	15
Transmission case to clutch housing bolts	52
Crossmember to mount and mount to extension bolts	25
Rear bearing retainer to case bolts	25
Extension to rear bearing retainer bolts (short)	25
Retainer to case bolt	35
Transmission drain plug	20

1   General description

1   Manual transmissions have been available for the Firebird since its inception. The only exception to this is for cars built for California during the later years where the automatic is required.
2   Manual transmissions may be of the three or four-speed type manufactured by Muncie, Saginaw or Warner. Gearshift is by column or floor-mounted lever according to model.
3   The forward speeds on all versions are of the synchromesh type.
4   No provision is made for periodic oil changing but the oil level should be checked at the specified intervals and topped up as necessary.

2   Shift linkage - adjustment

Column shift

1   Place the shift lever in "Reverse" and the ignition switch in the "Lock" position.
2   Raise the vehicle for access beneath, then loosen the shift control swivel locknuts. Pull down slightly on the 1st/Reverse control rod attached to the column lever to remove

any slack, then tighten the locknut at the transmission lever.
3   Unlock the ignition switch and shift the column lever to Neutral. Position the column lower levers in the "Neutral" position, align the gauge holes in the levers and insert a 3/16 inch diameter gauge pin.
4   Support the rod and swivel to prevent movement, then tighten the 2nd/3rd shift control rod locknut.
5   Remove the alignment tool from the column lower levers and check the operation. Place the column shift lever in "Reverse" and check the interlock control. It must not be possible to obtain "Lock" except in "Reverse".
6   Lower the vehicle to the ground.

Floor shift

7   Switch the ignition to "Off" then raise the vehicle for access beneath.
8   Loosen the swivel locknuts on the shift rods. Check that the rods pass freely through the swivels.
9   Set the shift levers to "Neutral" at the transmission.
10   Move the shift control lever into the "Neutral" detent position, align the control assembly levers, and insert the locating gauge into the lever alignment slot.
11   Tighten the shift rod swivel locknuts

then remove the gauge.
12   Shift the transmission control lever into "Reverse" and place the ignition switch in the "Lock" position. Loosen the locknut at the back drive control rod swivel, then pull the rod down slightly to remove any slack in the column mechanism. Tighten the clevis jam nut.
13   Check the interlock control; the key should move freely to, and from, the "Lock" position when the adjustment is correct.
14   Check the transmission shift control and readjust if necessary.
15   Lower the vehicle to the ground.

3   Transmission mounts - checking

1   Raise the car for access beneath and support firmly with stands. Make sure the vehicle is secured, as you must jostle the vehicle somewhat to check the mounts.
2   Push upward and pull downward on the transmission extension housing and observe the transmission mount.
3   If the extension can be pushed upwards but cannot be pulled down, this is an indication that the rubber is worn and the mount is bottomed out.
4   If the rubber portion of the mount separates from the metal plate, this also means

that the mount should be changed.
5   Check that all of the attaching screws or nuts are tight on the crossmember and the transmission.

4   Floorshift transmission backdrive linkage - adjustment

1   Shift the transmission into "Reverse" and turn the ignition switch to the "Lock" position.
2   Raise the vehicle for access beneath.
3   Loosen the backdrive control rod swivel locknut, pull down on the column linkage to remove any slack, then tighten the clevis jam nut.
4   Check that the ignition key moves freely through the "Lock" position, readjust if necessary at the bellcrank.
5   Lower the vehicle to the ground.

5   Shift control assembly - removal and installation

Column shift models

1   Refer to Chapter 11 in conjunction with steering column dismantling.

Floor shift (3 and 4-speed)

2   With the shift lever in the Neutral position, remove the shift lever knob and center console trim plate.
3   Raise the vehicle and support firmly on stands.
4   Disconnect the shift rods from the shift control levers. They are secured with retaining clips. Mark each rod and its appropriate lever for easy reinstallation, and take care not to lose any special washers used.
5   Remove the bolts which secure the shift control unit to its support assembly.
6   Rotate the control assembly and pull it down past the crossmember and remove it from under the vehicle.
7   To reinstall, slide the control assembly up into the rubber boot and position it against the support. Install the retaining bolts.
8   Place the control levers in the Neutral position and insert a 1/4-inch gauge pin (see Section 2, *Shift linkage - adjustment*).
9   Connect the shift rods to the control levers and install the appropriate washers and retaining pins.
10   Lower the vehicle and check for proper operation. Make the necessary adjustment referring to the proper sections in this chapter.

6   Transmission oil seals - replacement

1   The following oil seals can be replaced without removing the transmission from the car.

6.11 Extension housing oil seal (arrow)

Speedometer gear seal

2   Raise the vehicle for access beneath. Set firmly on stands.
3   Disconnect the speedometer cable, remove the lockplate to extension bolt and lockwasher, then remove the lockplate.
4   Insert a screwdriver in the lockplate fitting, and pry the fitting gear and shaft from the extension.
5   Pry out the O-ring.
6   Installation is the reverse of removal, but lubricate the new seal with transmission lubricant and hold the assembly so that the slot in the fitting is towards the lockplate boss on the extension.

Extension oil seal

Refer to illustration 6.11
7   Remove the drive shaft, as described in Chapter 8. Remove any ancillary items necessary to provide additional clearance.
8   Carefully pry out the old seal.
9   Carefully clean the counterbore and examine for any damage.
10   Pre-lubricate between the lips of the new seal with transmission lubricant and coat the outer diameter with a suitable sealant.
11   Carefully install the seal, lips inwards, until the flange seats, ideally a tubular spacer should be used for this job **(see illustration)**.
12   Reinstall the drive shaft (refer to Chapter 8) and any other ancillary items removed.

7   Transmission side cover (3 speed Saginaw) - overhaul

1   Shift transmission into "Neutral" and raise the vehicle for access beneath. Set firmly on stands.
2   Disconnect the control rods from the levers on the side of the transmission.
3   Remove the cover assembly from the transmission case and allow the oil to drain.
4   Remove both shift forks from the shifter shaft assemblies and both shifter shaft assemblies from the cover.
5   Pry out shaft O-ring seals if replacement is required.

6   Remove the detent cam spring and pivot retainer C-clip. Remove both detent cams.
7   Inspect all parts for damage and wear, and replace as necessary.
8   With the detent spring tang projecting up over the 2nd/3rd shifter shaft cover opening, install the 1st/Reverse detent cam onto the detent cam pivot pin. With the detent spring tang projecting up over the first and reverse shifter shaft cover hole, install the 2nd/3rd detent cam.
9   Install the C-clip to the pivot shaft and hook the spring into the detent cam notches.
10   Install the shifter shaft assemblies carefully into the cover and the shift forks to the shifter shaft assemblies. Lift up the detent cam to allow the forks to seat properly.
11   Set the shifter levers into the Neutral detent (center position) and position the gasket on the case.
12   Carefully position the side cover, ensuring that the shift forks are aligned with their appropriate mainshaft clutch sliding sleeves.
13   Install and torque tighten the cover bolts to the specified value.
14   Top-up the oil in the transmission and lower the vehicle to the ground.

8   Transmission side cover (4 speed Saginaw and Muncie) - overhaul

1   Shift Saginaw models into "Neutral" and Muncie models into "Second" gear.
2   Raise the vehicle for access beneath. Set firmly on stands.
3   Remove the shift levers from the shifter shafts.
4   Remove the cover assembly and allow the oil to drain.
5   Remove the outer shifter levers.
6   Remove the shift forks from the shifter shaft assemblies, and the three shifter shaft assemblies from the cover.
7   If necessary, pry out the O-ring on the 1st/2nd and Reverse shafts.
8   On Saginaw models remove the Reverse shifter shaft detent ball and spring.
9   Remove the detent cam spring and the

10.1 Speedometer drive cable-to-transmission mounting bolt (arrow)

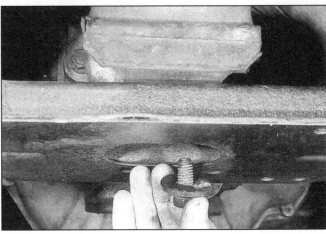

10.4 Transmission mount-to-crossmember bolt

pivot pin C-clip. Mark the cams for identification on reassembly, then remove them.
10 Inspect all the parts for damage and wear and replace as necessary.
11 With the detent spring tang projecting up over the 3rd/4th shifter shaft cover opening, install the 1st/2nd detent cam onto the detent cam pivot pin. With the detent spring tang projecting up over the 1st/2nd shifter shaft cover hole, install the 3rd/4th detent cam.
12 Install the detent cam C-clip to the pivot shaft and hook the spring into the cam notches.
13 Install the 1st/2nd and 3rd/4th shifter shaft assemblies carefully into the cover.
14 Install the shift forks to the shifter shaft assemblies, lifting up on the detent cam to permit the forks to seat.
15 Install the Reverse detent ball and spring, then install the Reverse shifter shaft assembly to the cover.
16 Move the shifter levers into "Neutral" (Saginaw) or "Second" (Muncie).
17 Position the cover gasket on the case and carefully position the side cover, ensuring that the shift forks are aligned with their appropriate mainshaft clutch sliding sleeves.
18 Screw in the side cover bolts and tighten to the specified torque.
19 Top-up the transmission oil and then lower the car to the ground.

9 Transmission side cover (4 speed Warner) - overhaul

1 Shift the transmission into 2nd gear.
2 Raise the car to provide access to the side cover. Set firmly on stands.
3 Disconnect the wiring from the TCS switch.
4 Remove the shift levers from the shifter shafts.
5 Unscrew and remove the nine cover screws, remove the cover and allow the oil to drain.
6 Remove the TCS from the cover.
7 Remove the outer shifter lever nuts and

pull the levers from the shafts.
8 Push the shifter shafts into the cover allowing the detent balls to fall free. Extract the shifter shafts.
9 Remove the interlock sleeve, the interlock pin and poppet spring.
10 Inspect and replace components as necessary.
11 Reassemble by reversing the overhaul procedure.
12 Before installing the side cover, move the shifter levers to 2nd gear position.
13 Locate a new gasket on the transmission.
14 Move the side cover into position making sure that the shift forks are aligned with their respective synchronizer sliding sleeve grooves.
15 Insert the cover bolts and tighten to specified torque wrench setting.
16 Connect the shift levers and the TCS switch wiring.
17 Add lubricant to level of the filler plug hole.
18 Lower the car to the ground.

10 Transmission - removal and installation

1970 through 1972

Refer to illustrations 10.1 and 10.4
1 Raise the vehicle for access beneath, then disconnect the speedometer cable, back-up lamp switch and TCS switch, as appropriate **(see illustration)**.
2 Remove the driveshaft assembly (refer to Chapter 8) and then support the engine/transmission by placing a jack under the oil pan. Use a block of wood as an insulator.
3 Remove the crossmember to frame attaching bolts. On 4-speed and floor shift transmission, also remove the crossmember to control lever support attaching bolts.
4 Remove the bolts retaining the transmission mount to the crossmember **(see illustration)**.

5 Raise the engine slightly until the crossmember can be moved rearwards.
6 Remove the shift levers at the transmission side cover. On 4-speed and floorshift transmissions, also remove the stabilizer to control lever assembly retaining nut. Push the bolt towards the transmission until the stabilizer can be disconnected.
7 Remove the transmission to clutch housing retaining bolts, install guide pins in the holes then remove the lower bolts.
8 Lower the engine until the transmission can be withdrawn rearwards and removed.
9 When installing, raise the transmission into position, then slide it forwards, piloting the clutch gear into the clutch housing.
10 Install the transmission retaining bolts and lockwashers, then torque-tighten to the specified value.
11 Install the shift levers and the stabilizer rod (where applicable).
12 Support the engine and raise it slightly until the crossmember can be repositioned. Install and torque-tighten the retaining bolts.
13 Remove the engine jack then install the transmission crossmember to mount retaining bolts and the crossmember to control lever support attaching bolts (where applicable).
14 Install the driveshaft (refer to Chapter 8).
15 Connect the speedometer cable, TCS switch and back-up switch wiring, as appropriate.
16 Fill the transmission with the correct quantity and grade of lubricant, then lower the vehicle to the ground.

1973 and later models

17 Remove the shift lever knob, and on 4-speed models the spring and T-handle.
18 Raise the vehicle for access beneath.
19 Disconnect the speedometer cable and TCS switch on the transmission.
20 Remove the driveshaft (refer to Chapter 8).
21 Support the engine/transmission by placing a jack and block of wood as an insulator under the oil pan.

11.13 Removing 2nd speed blocker ring and gear from front end of mainshaft (Saginaw 3-speed)

11.15 Extracting rear bearing snap-ring (Saginaw 3-speed)

22   Remove the transmission mount to crossmember bolts and crossmember to frame attaching bolts. Support the engine and remove the crossmember.

23   Disconnect the shift rods from the transmission and on floorshift models disconnect the backdrive rod at the bellcrank.

24   On floorshift models, remove the bolts attaching the shift control assembly to the support: then carefully pull the unit down until the shift lever clears the rubber boot. Remove the assembly from the vehicle.

25   Remove the transmission to clutch housing upper bolts. Install guide pins in the holes, then remove the lower bolts. **Note:** *On some later models it may be necessary to remove the catalytic converter to permit removal of the transmission. (Refer to Chapter 6 for further information).*

26   Lower the supporting jack until the transmission can be withdrawn rearwards and removed.

27   When installing, raise the transmission into position and slide it. forwards, guiding the clutch gear into the clutch housing.

28   Install the transmission clutch housing retaining bolts and lock-washers, and torque-tighten to the specified value.

29   Slide the shift lever into the rubber boot and position the shaft control to the support. Install and torque-tighten the retaining bolts.

30   Connect the shift rods to the transmission and torque-tighten the bolts. Connect the backdrive rod to the bellcrank.

31   Raise the engine and position the crossmember. Install and torque-tighten the transmission mount and crossmember retaining bolts.

32   Install the drive shaft (refer to Chapter 8).

33   Connect the speedometer cable and TCS switch wiring.

34   Install the T-handle and spring (4-speed), and the shift knob on floorshift models.

35   Fill the transmission with the correct quantity and grade of lubricant, then lower the vehicle to the ground.

11   Three-speed (Saginaw) transmission - overhaul

Disassembly

Refer to illustrations 11.13 and 11.15

1   Remove the transmission, drain the oil and remove the side cover assembly (refer to Section 7).

2   Remove the drive-gear bearing retainer and gasket.

3   Remove the drive-gear bearing stem snap-ring, then pull out the gear until a large screwdriver can be used to lever the drive-gear bearing from its location.

4   Remove the speedometer driven gear from the rear extension, then remove the extension retaining bolts.

5   Remove the reverse idler shaft E-ring.

6   Withdraw the drive-gear, mainshaft and extension assembly together through the rear casing.

7   From the mainshaft, detach the drive-gear, needle bearings and synchronizer ring.

8   Expand the snap-ring in the rear extension which retains the rear bearing and then withdraw the rear extension.

9   Using a dummy shaft or special tool, drive the countershaft (complete with Woodruff key) out of the rear of the transmission case. Carefully remove the dummy shaft and extract the countergear, bearings and thrust washers from the interior of the transmission case.

10   Drive the reverse idler shaft out of the rear of the transmission.

11   The mainshaft should only be dismantled if a press or bearing puller is available: otherwise take the assembly to your local machine shop. Be careful to keep all components separated and in order for easier reassembly.

12   Remove the 2nd/3rd synchro hub snap-ring from the mainshaft. Do not mix up the synchro unit components; although identical, the components of each unit are matched in production.

13   Remove the synchro unit, 2nd speed blocker ring and 2nd speed gear from the front end of the mainshaft **(see illustration)**.

14   Depress the speedometer drive-gear retaining clip and remove the gear from the mainshaft.

15   Remove the rear bearing snap-ring from its mainshaft groove **(see illustration)** .

16   Support the reverse gear and press the mainshaft out of the rear bearing, and snap-ring from the rear end of the mainshaft.

17   Remove 1st/reverse synchro hub snap-ring from the mainshaft and remove the synchro unit.

18   Remove the 1st speed blocker ring and 1st speed gear from the rear end of the mainshaft.

19   Clean all components in solvent and dry thoroughly. Check for wear or chipped teeth. If there has been a history of harsh or noisy gearshifts, then replace the appropriate synchro unit.

20   Extract the oil seal from the rear end of the rear extension and drive in a new one with a tubular drift.

21   Clean the transmission case inside and out and check for cracks, particularly around the bolt holes.

22   Extract the drive-gear bearing retainer seal and drive in a new one.

Reassembly

Refer to illustrations 11.32a, 11.32b, 11.32c, 11.32d, 11.33, 11.34, 11.35a, 11.35b, 11.36, 11.38a, 11.38b, 11.40, 11.41 and 11.42

23   Commence rebuilding the transmission by first reassembling the mainshaft. Install 2nd speed gear so that the rear face of the gear butts against the flange on the mainshaft.

24   Install the blocker ring, followed by the 2nd/3rd synchro assembly (shift fork groove nearer rear end of the mainshaft). Make sure that the notches of the blocker ring align with the keys of the synchro assembly.

25   Install the snap-ring which retains the synchro hub to the mainshaft.

26   To the rear end of the mainshaft, install

11.32a Installing rollers at the rear of the countergear (Saginaw 3-speed)

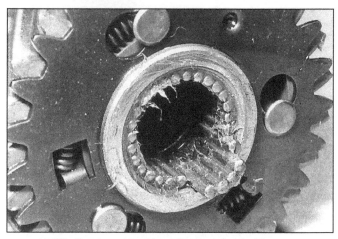

11.32b Front countergear rollers retained with grease (Saginaw 3-speed)

11.32c Countergear needle roller retaining washer in position (Saginaw 3-speed)

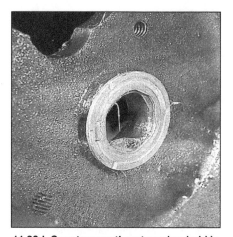

11.32d Countergear thrust washer held in position with grease (Saginaw 3-speed)

11.33 Reverse idler gear and shaft (Saginaw 3 -speed)

the 1st speed gear, followed by the blocker ring.

27   Install the 1st/reverse synchro unit (shift fork groove nearer the front end of the mainshaft), again making sure that the notches of the blocker ring align with the keys of the synchro unit.

28   Install the snap-ring, reverse gear thrust washer and spring washer.

29   Install the mainshaft rear ball bearing with the outer snap-ring groove nearer the front of the shaft.

30   Install the rear bearing shaft snap-ring.

31   Install the speedometer drive gear and retaining clip.

32   Insert a dummy shaft through the countergear, and stick the roller bearings (27 at each end), needle retainer washers and the transmission case thrust washers, in position using thick grease. Note that the tangs on the thrust washers are away from the gear faces. **Note:** *If no dummy shaft is available, carefully stick the roller bearings in place, but when installing the shaft {paragraph 34), take care that they are not dislodged* **(see illustrations)**.

33   Install reverse idler gear and shaft with

Woodruff key from the rear of the transmission case. Do not install the idler shaft E-ring at this time **(see illustration)**.

34   Install the countergear assembly from the rear of the transmission case and then insert the countershaft so that it picks up the

roller bearings and the thrust washers, at the same time displacing the dummy shaft or tool (if used). The countershaft should be inserted so that its slot is at its rear end when installed **(see illustration)**.

35   Expand the snap-ring in- the rear exten-

11.34 Installing countershaft (Saginaw 3-speed)

11.35a Mainshaft rear bearing outer snap-ring in position in extension housing (Saginaw 3-speed)

11.35b Expanding rear bearing outer snap-ring (Saginaw 3-speed)

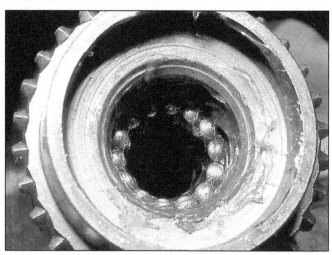

11.36 Mainshaft pilot bearings retained with grease (Saginaw 3-speed)

11.38a Installing clutch drive gear, mainshaft and extension (Saginaw 3-speed)

11.38b Countergear anti-lash plate (Saginaw 3-speed)

sion and locate the extension over the rear end of the mainshaft and onto the rear bearing. Make sure that the snap-ring seats in the rear bearing groove **(see illustrations)**.

36   Insert the mainshaft pilot bearings (14 of them) into the clutch gear cavity and then assemble the 3rd speed blocker ring onto the clutch drive gear **(see illustration)**.

37   Locate the clutch drive gear pilot bearings and 3rd speed blocker ring over the front of the mainshaft. Do not fit the drive gear bearing at this time; also make sure that the notches in the blocker ring align with the keys in the 2nd/3rd synchro unit.

38   Stick a new gasket (using grease) to the rear face of the transmission case and then, from the rear, insert the combined clutch drive gear mainshaft and rear extension. Make sure that the 2nd/3rd synchro sleeve is pushed fully forward so that the clutch drive gear engages with the countergear anti-lash plate **(see illustrations)**.

39   Install the rear extension to transmission case bolts. Torque tighten to specifications.

40   Install the outer snap-ring to the clutch drive gear bearing and install the bearing over the drive gear and into the front of the transmission case **(see illustration)**.

41   Install the clutch drive gear bearing shaft snap-ring **(see illustration)**.

11.40 Clutch drive gear bearing outer snap-ring (Saginaw 3-speed)

11.41 Installing clutch drive gear bearing shaft snap-ring (Saginaw 3-speed)

11.42 Installing clutch drive gear bearing retainer and gasket (Saginaw 3-speed)

12.5 Removing speedometer drive gear from mainshaft (Saginaw 4-speed)

42 Install the clutch drive gear bearing retainer and its gasket making sure that the oil return hole is at the bottom **(see illustration)**.

43 Now install the reverse idler gear "E" ring to the shaft.

44 With the synchronizer sleeves in the neutral position, install the side cover, gasket and fork assembly (Section 7). Torque-tighten all the bolts.

45 Install the speedometer driven gear in the rear extension.

12 Four speed (Saginaw) transmission - overhaul

Disassembly

Refer to illustrations 12.5, 12.6, 12.7, 12.8a, 12.8b, 12.8c and 12.9

1 Carry out the operations of paragraph 1 through 9 of Section 11 but note than an E-ring is not fitted to the reverse idler shaft.

2 Remove the reverse idler gear stop-ring (where applicable), then use a long drift to drive the reverse idler shaft gut of the rear of the transmission case.

3 Remove the 3rd/4th synchro hub snap-ring from the mainshaft. Do not mix up the synchro unit components, which although identical in appearance are matched in production.

4 Remove the synchro unit, 3rd gear blocker ring and 3rd speed gear from the front end of the mainshaft.

5 Depress the speedometer drive-gear retaining clip and remove the gear from the mainshaft **(see illustration)**.

6 Remove the rear bearing snap-ring from

12.6 Extracting rear bearing snap-ring from mainshaft (Saginaw 4-speed)

12.7 Removing wave washer, thrust washer and 1st gear from mainshaft (Saginaw 4-speed)

12.8a Removing 1st/2nd blocker ring (Saginaw 4-speed)

12.8b Extracting 1st/2nd synchro hub snap-ring (Saginaw 4-speed)

12.8c Removing 1st/2nd synchro sleeve (incorporating reverse gear) – (Saginaw 4-speed)

12.9 Removing 2nd speed blocker ring and gear (Saginaw 4-speed)

its mainshaft groove (see illustration).

7 Support 1st gear and press the mainshaft out of the rear bearing. Remove the snap-ring, the rear bearing, the wave washer, thrust washer and 1st gear from the rear end of the mainshaft (see illustration).

8 Remove the blocker ring and 1st/2nd synchro hub snap-ring from the mainshaft and remove the synchro unit/reverse gear (see illustrations).

9 Remove the 2nd speed blocker ring and 2nd speed gear from the rear end of the mainshaft (see illustration).

10 Carry out the operations of paragraphs 19 through 22 of Section 11.

Reassembly

Refer to illustrations 12.11a, 12.11b, 12.12a, 12.12b, 12.13, 12.15 and 12.21

11 Commence rebuilding the transmission by first reassembling the mainshaft. Install 3rd speed gear so that the rear face of the gear butts against the flange on the mainshaft (see illustrations).

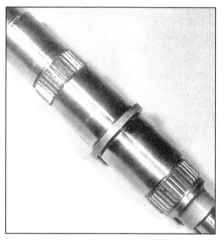

12.11a Mainshaft showing fixed shoulder (Saginaw 4-speed)

12.11b Installing 3rd speed gear to mainshaft (Saginaw 4-speed)

12 Install the blocker ring, followed by 3rd/4th synchro assembly (shift fork groove nearer mainshaft flange). Make sure that

the notches of the blocker ring align with the keys of the synchro assembly (see illustrations).

12.12a Installing 3rd/4th blocker ring (Saginaw 4-speed)

12.12b Installing 3rd/4th synchro assembly (Saginaw 4-speed)

12.13 Installing 3rd/4th synchro hub snap-ring (Saginaw 4-speed)

12.15 Installing 1st/2nd synchro assembly (Saginaw 4-speed)

13   Install the snap-ring which retains the synchro hub to the mainshaft **(see illustration)**.

14   To the rear end of the mainshaft, install the 2nd speed gear followed by the blocker ring.

15   Install the 1st/2nd synchro unit (shift fork groove nearer the front of the mainshaft), again making sure that the notches of the blocker ring align with the keys of the synchro unit. Install the snap-ring and blocker ring **(see illustration)**.

16   Install 1st gear, the steel thrust washer and the wave washer.

17   Install the mainshaft rear ball bearing with the outer snap-ring groove nearer the front of the shaft.

18   Install the rear bearing shaft snap-ring.

19   Install the speedometer drive-gear and retaining clip.

20   Carry out the operations of paragraphs 32 through 35 of Section 11 but ignore the reference to the E-ring.

21   Insert the mainshaft pilot bearings (14 of them) into the clutch cavity and then assemble the 4th speed blocker ring onto the clutch drive-gear **(see illustration)**.

22   Locate the clutch drive-gear, pilot bear-

12.21 Mainshaft pilot bearings retained with grease (Saginaw 4-speed)

ings and 4th speed blocker ring over the front of the mainshaft. Do not install the drive-gear bearing at this time; also make sure that the notches in the blocker ring align with the keys in the 3rd/4th synchro unit.

23   Carry out the operations of paragraphs 38 through 42 and paragraph 44 of Section 11. Note that the reference at paragraph 38 to 2nd/3rd synchro sleeve will now be 3rd/4th synchro sleeve.

13   Four speed (Muncie) transmission - overhaul

Disassembly

1   Remove the transmission, drain the oil and remove the transmission side cover (refer to Section 8).

2   Remove the bolts and lockstrips securing the front bearing retainer. Remove the retainer and gasket.

3   Lock-up the transmission by selecting 2 gears then use a suitable wrench designed for this purpose to remove the drive-gear retaining nut.

4   Select neutral, then drive out the lockpin from the reverse shifter lever boss. Pull the shifter shaft out about one inch to disengage the reverse shift fork.

5   Remove the 6 case extension retaining bolts then tap the extension rearwards using a soft hammer. Move the extension to the left when the reverse idler is out as far as it will go. This will permit the extension to be removed.

6   Remove the reverse idler, flat thrust washer, shaft and roll pin.

7   Remove the speedometer gear and reverse gear using a suitable extractor.

8   Slide the 3rd/4th synchronizer sleeve forwards into 4th gear position, then carefully remove the rear bearing retainer and mainshaft assembly from the case by tapping the retainer with a soft hammer.

9   Remove the 17 roller bearings from the main drive-gear, and the 4th speed synchro-

nizer blocker ring.

10   Lift the front half of the reverse idler and its thrust washer from the case.

11   Press the drive-gear from the front bearing into the case.

12   Tap out the front bearing and snap-ring from inside the case.

13   Using a dummy shaft or special tool, press out the countershaft, then remove the countergear and both tanged washers.

14   Remove the 112 rollers, six 0.070-inch spacers and the roller spacer from the countergear.

15   Remove the mainshaft front snap-ring and slide the 3rd/4th speed clutch assembly, 3rd gear and synchronizing ring from the mainshaft.

16   Remove the rear bearing snap-ring and press the mainshaft out of the retainer.

17   If no press or suitable extractor is available, this may be the limit of the dismantling and you may have to contact a transmission shop if you need to go further.

18   Remove the mainshaft rear snap-ring then, while supporting on the second speed gear, press on the rear of the mainshaft to remove the 1st gear and sleeve, 1st gear synchronizing ring, 1st/2nd speed synchronizing clutch assembly, 2nd speed synchronizing ring and second speed gear.

19   Remove the reverse shift fork from the shifter shaft, then carefully drive the shaft inwards to allow the detent ball to drop out. Remove the shaft and ball detent spring.

20   Carry out the operations of paragraphs 19 through 21 of Section 11.

21   Place the reverse shifter shaft detent spring into its hole in the extension then install the shifter shaft until the detent plate butts against the inside of the extension housing.

Reassembly

22   Commence reassembly by placing the detent ball on the spring and hold it down while moving the shifter shaft away from the ease until the ball drops into the detent on the shaft detent plate.

23 Install the fork but do not lock it at this stage.
24 To the rear of the mainshaft, assemble the 2nd gear, hub towards the rear of the shaft.
25 Install the 1st/2nd synchronizer clutch assembly to the mainshaft (hub towards the front), together with a synchronizing ring on each side. Align the keyways with the clutch keys.
26 Press the 1st gear sleeve onto the mainshaft using a 1 3/4 inch inside-diameter pipe or similar.
27 Install the 1st gear (hub towards the front) and, using a 1 5/8 inch inside-diameter pipe, press on the rear bearing.
28 Select a snap-ring to give 0 to 0.005 inch from the mainshaft groove to the rear face of the mainshaft rear bearing. New snap-rings are available in sizes of 0.087, 0.090, 0.093 and 0.096 inch.
29 Install the 3rd gear (hub to the front of the transmission) and the 3rd gear synchronizing ring (notches to the front of the transmission).
30 Install the 3rd/4th gear clutch assembly with the sleeve taper and hub towards the front. Ensure that the hub keys align with the synchronizing ring notches.
31 Install the snap-ring in the mainshaft groove in front of the 3rd/4th speed clutch assembly, with the ends seated behind the spline teeth.
32 Install the rear bearing retainer. Spread the snap-ring in the plate to allow it to drop around the rear bearing and press on the end of the mainshaft until it engages the groove in the rear bearing.
33 Install the reverse gear.
34 Install the speedometer gear, pressing it on to obtain a dimension of 4-7/8 inch from the forward side of the gear to the flat surface of the rear bearing retainer.
35 Install the tubular spacer in the counter gear.
36 Using heavy grease to retain the rollers, install one spacer, 28 rollers, one spacer, 28 rollers and one more spacer in each end of the counter gear.
37 Insert the dummy-shaft into the counter gear.
38 Lay the transmission case on its side with the cover opening towards you, then put the tanged washers in place, retaining them with grease.
39 Position the countergear, making sure that the thrust washers do not move, then position the transmission case so that it is resting on its front face.
40 Lubricate the countershaft with transmission oil and insert it in the rear of the case. Turn the countershaft so that the flat on the end is horizontal and facing the bottom of the case.
41 Align the countergear and shaft, and press in the shaft, ejecting the dummy-shaft out of the front of the case. Ensure that the thrust-washers are still in place.
42 Check the overall countergear endplay using a dial gauge or similar tool. If in excess

of 0.025 inch, new thrust washers must be used.
43 Install the cage and 17 rollers into the main drive-gear, retaining them with heavy grease. Install the oil slinger on the main drive-gear, concave side towards the gear.
44 Install the main drive-gear and pilot bearings through the side cover opening and into position in the transmission front bore.
45 Position the gasket on the front face of the rear bearing retainer.
46 Install the 4th speed synchronizing ring on the main drive-gear with the notches towards the rear of the transmission.
47 Position the reverse idler gear tanged thrust washer on the machined face of the ear cast in the case for the reverse idler shaft, and retain with heavy grease. Position the front reverse idler gear next to the thrust washer, with the hub facing towards the rear of the case.
48 Slide the 3rd/4th synchronizing clutch sleeve forward into the 4th speed detent position, then lower the mainshaft assembly into the case. Ensure that the notches on the 4th speed synchronizing ring align with the keys in the clutch assembly.
49 Align the rear bearing retainer guide pin with the hole in the rear of the case then tap the retainer into place with a soft faced hammer.
50 From the rear of the case, insert the rear reverse idler gear, engaging the splines with the portion of the front gear inside the case.
51 Use heavy grease to retain the gasket in position with the rear face of the bearing retainer.
52 Install the remaining flat thrust washer on the reverse idler shaft. If a new shaft is being used, drive out the old roll pin and press it into the new shaft.
53 Install the reverse idler shaft, roll pin and thrust washer into the gears and the front boss of the case, picking up the front thrust washer. The roll pin must be vertical.
54 Pull the reverse shifter shaft to the left side of the extension and rotate the shaft to bring the shift fork forwards to the reverse detent position. Move the extension onto the transmission case while slowly pushing in on the shifter shaft to engage the shift fork with the reverse gear shift collar. Now lead the reverse idler shaft into the extension housing, allowing the extension to slide onto the transmission case.
55 Install the 6 extension and retainer attaching bolts and torque tighten them.
56 Move the reverse shifter shaft to align the shaft groove with the holes in the boss, then drive in the lock pin. Install the shifter lever.
57 With the snap-ring groove to the front, press the main drive-gear bearing onto the shaft and into the case until at least 3 threads are exposed.
58 Lock the transmission in two gears at once, then install the main drive-gear retaining nut and draw it up tight, using the special wrench. With the bearing seating on the gear shoulder, torque-tighten the nut (40 lb ft) and

lock it by staking in several places. Take care not to damage the shaft screw threads.
59 Install the bearing retainer, gasket, 4 attaching bolts and 2 lockstrips, using a suitable sealant on the screw threads. Torque-tighten the bolts.
60 Shift the mainshaft 3rd/4th sliding clutch sleeve into neutral and 1st/2nd sliding clutch sleeve forward into the second gear detent. Shift the side cover 3rd/4th shifter lever into the neutral detent and the 1st/2nd shifter lever into the 2nd gear detent.
61 Install the side cover gasket and carefully position the side cover to ensure proper alignment. Install the attaching bolts and torque-tighten evenly to the specified value.

14 Four speed (Warner) transmission - overhaul

Disassembly

1 With the transmission removed from the car, clean away all external dirt.
2 Shift the transmission into 2nd gear, remove the drain plug and drain the lubricant.
3 Unscrew and remove the side cover bolts, then withdraw the cover and gasket. Remove the shift forks.
4 From the front of the transmission, unbolt and remove the drive gear bearing retainer and gasket.
5 Remove the lock pin from the reverse shifter lever boss, pull the shifter shaft partially out to disengage the reverse shifter fork from the reverse gear.
6 Remove the rear extension housing bolts and tap the extension to the rear with a soft-faced hammer, but only enough to start it moving.
7 Pull the extension until the reverse idler shaft clears the reverse idler gears. Rotate the extension to free the shift fork from the collar of reverse gear, and then withdraw the extension completely. Remove the gasket.
8 Extract the speedometer gear snap-ring, slide the speedometer gear from the mainshaft then extract the remaining snap-ring.
9 Slide the reverse gear from the mainshaft and then pull the reverse idler gear from the rear face of the transmission case.
10 Extract the snap-ring and spacer washer from the front bearing.
11 Using a suitable extractor, withdraw the front main drive gear bearing from the transmission case.
12 Remove the rear retainer lockbolt.
13 Move 1st/2nd and 3rd/4th synchronizer sleeves forward to provide enough clearance for removal of the mainshaft assembly.
14 Withdraw the mainshaft and rear bearing retainer from the transmission case.
15 Remove the front reverse idler gear and thrust washer from the case.
16 Using a dummy shaft drive the countershaft out of the transmission case, then remove the countergear and tanged thrust washers. Retrieve any needle bearings from the bottom of the case.

17   Unless a suitable press or extractors are available, dismantling the mainshaft should be left to a transmission specialist. If suitable tools are available, proceed in the following way.

18   Extract the snap-ring from the front of the 3rd/4th synchro unit. Slide the washer, synchro unit, synchro ring and 3rd speed gear from the mainshaft.

19   Expand the rear bearing retainer snap-ring and slide the retainer from the mainshaft.

20   Extract the snap-ring from the rear of the mainshaft rear bearing.

21   Support the front face of 2nd gear and press the mainshaft out of the rear bearing, 1st gear and sleeve, 1st/2nd synchro unit and 2nd gear.

22   With all components removed, inspect for wear or damage, and replace as necessary.

23   The synchronizer units should be dismantled only after having marked their hub to sleeve relationship.

24   Replace the extension housing and drive gear bearing retainer oil seals, as a matter of routine, at major overhaul.

25   To replace the reverse shifter shaft O-ring oil seal, remove the shift fork and carefully drive the shifter shaft into the extension housing allowing the detent ball to drop into the case. Remove the detent spring.

26   Extract the O-ring seal from the shaft.

Reassembly

27   When reassembling, place the detent spring into the hole and start the reverse shifter shaft into its hole in the boss. Hold the ball down and push the shaft into position turning it until the ball drops into place in the detent on the shaft detent plate.

28   Install a new O-ring and install the shift fork, but do not drive the shifter shaft lock pin into- place until the extension housing has been installed.

29   Replacement of the reverse idler shaft can be carried out if the welch plug and roll pin in the extension housing is first driven into the shaft, and the shaft then extracted.

30   Install the new idler shaft, drive in a new roll pin and finally tap in a new welch plug smeared with sealer.

31   Overhaul of the transmission side cover assembly is covered in Section 9.

32   The countergear end-play should be checked in the following way. Stick the thrust washers into the case using some thick grease.

33   Assemble the countergear rollers and spacers. Divide the rollers into four equal quantities, and then into each end of the countergear install rollers, spacer, rollers and spacer. Hold them in position using thick grease and insert the dummy shaft. Insert the

assembly into position in the case without disturbing the thrust washers and insert the countershaft from the rear end of the case. The dummy shaft will be displaced. Make sure that the slot for the Woodruff key is correctly aligned but do not install the key itself in case removal is required to change the thrust washers.

34   Using feeler gauges or a dial gauge check the end-float of the countergear. If it exceeds 0.025 in, new thrust washers are required. If the end-play is correct, the countershaft and gear can remain undisturbed pending reassembly of the transmission.

35   Commence reassembly of the mainshaft by installing the 2nd speed gear to its rear end so that the boss on the gear faces the rear end of the mainshaft.

36   Install the 1st/2nd synchronizer unit with a synchro ring on both sides. Make sure that the taper is towards the rear of the mainshaft.

37   Locate the 1st gear sleeve on the mainshaft and press the sleeve onto the shaft until the 2nd gear, the synchro unit and the sleeve contact the shoulder on the mainshaft.

38   Install the 1st speed gear (boss towards the front).

39   Apply pressure to the inner race of the mainshaft rear bearing and press the bearing into position. Make sure that the snap-ring groove in the outer race is towards the front end of the shaft.

40   Install the spacer and the thickest snap-ring which will fit behind the rear bearing.

41   Install the 3rd speed gear (boss towards the front of mainshaft) and the 3rd speed gear synchronizer ring (notches to front of mainshaft).

42   Install the 3rd/4th speed synchronizer unit (taper to front) making sure that the keys in the hub correspond with the notches in 3rd speed ring.

43   Install the thickest possible snap-ring into the groove in front of the 3rd/4th synchronizer unit.

44   Install the rear bearing retainer over the end of the mainshaft. Expand the snap-ring to drop it over the rear bearing and into its groove.

45   Install reverse gear to the mainshaft so that the shift collar is to the rear.

46   Install a snap-ring, the speedometer drive gear and the second snap-ring.

47   To reassemble the transmission, install the countergear and countershaft as described in paragraphs 32 and 33 (if not already done). Install the Woodruff key.

48   Install the front reverse idler gear (teeth facing forward) and thrust washer into the transmission case.

49   Using heavy grease, install the sixteen roller bearings and washer into the main drive gear. Engage the main drive gear with the

mainshaft assembly front end.

50   Push the 3rd/4th synchro sleeve forward.

51   Locate a new gasket for the rear bearing retainer on the rear of the transmission case and then carefully install the mainshaft/drive gear assembly into the transmission case.

52   Align the rear-bearing retainer with the transmission case, install the locating pin and retainer lockbolt. Tighten to the specified torque.

53   Locate a snap-ring around the outside of the front main bearing and then tap it into position in the front of the transmission case. Apply pressure to the inner race and make sure that the snap-ring is nearer the front of the bearing.

54   Install a spacer and the thickest snap-ring from the thicknesses available to secure the bearing.

55   Install the front bearing retainer and gasket. Smear the bolt threads with sealer and tighten to the specified torque.

56   Install the reverse idler gear up against the rear face of the transmission so that the splines engage with the reverse gear inside the transmission case.

57   Locate a new gasket on the rear bearing retainer.

58   Install the tanged thrust washer on the reverse idler shaft, so that the tang of the washer engages in the notch of the idler thrust face of the extension.

59   Place the 1st/2nd and 3rd/4th synchro unit sleeves in neutral. Pull the reverse shift shaft partially out of the extension housing and push the reverse shift fork as far forward as possible. Install the extension housing over the mainshaft, at the same time pushing the shifter shaft in to engage reverse shift fork with reverse gear shift collar.

60   When the fork engages, rotate the shifter shaft to move reverse gear rearward so enabling the extension to butt against the transmission case.

61   Install the reverse shifter shaft lock pin.

62   Install the extension housing retaining bolts and the shorter rear bearing retainer bolts. It is vital that these bolts have sealer applied to their threads before installation. Tighten all bolts to the specified torque.

63   Set the 1st/2nd speed synchro sleeve to the 2nd gear position and 3rd/4th to neutral.

64   Locate the forward shift forks in the sliding sleeves.

65   Set the 1st/2nd speed gear shifter shaft and detent plate on the transmission side cover in 2nd gear position and install the side cover, using a new gasket to which sealer has been applied on both sides.

66   Check the gear selection. Refill the transmission with oil after it has been installed in the car.

Chapter 7 Part B
Automatic transmission

Contents

Specifications

Transmission type	2-speed or 3-speed fully automatic depending upon model and engine. Shift control is by either a steering column mounted rod or by a floor-mounted, cable-operated shifter.

Applications

1970 - 1972	Powerglide (2-speed) Turbo Hydra-Matic 350 (3-speed) Turbo Hydra-Matic 400 (3-speed)
1973 - 1974	Turbo Hydra-Matic 350 (3-speed) Turbo Hydra-Matic 400 (3-speed)
1975 - 1980	Turbo Hydra-Matic 350 (3-speed)
1981	Turbo Hydra-Matic 200 (3-speed) Turbo Hydra-Matic 250 (3-speed)

Fluid capacities

Powerglide
Routine fluid change*	3.5 US qts
Filling from dry (overhaul)	10.0 US qts

Turbo Hydra-Matic 350
Routine fluid change*	3.1 US qts
Filling from dry (overhaul)	10.0 US qts

Turbo Hydra-Matic 400
Routine fluid change*	3.75 US qts
Filling from dry (overhaul)	9.5 US qts

Turbo Hydra-Matic 200
Routine fluid change*	3.5 US qts
Filling from dry (overhaul)	9.5 US qts

Turbo Hydra-Matic 250
Routine fluid change*	4.0 US qts
Filling from dry (overhaul)	10.75 US qts

* The small quantity required at routine fluid changing is due to the fact that the fluid in the torque converter cannot be drained unless dismantled.

Torque specifications

	Ft-lb	In-lb
Powerglide		
Transmission case to engine	35	
Transmission oil pan to case	8	
Transmission extension to case	25	
Speedometer driven gear fitting retainer	4	
Servo cover to transmission case bolts	20	
Front pump to transmission case bolts	15	
Front pump cover to body attaching bolts	20	
Pinion shaft lockplate attaching screws	2-1/2	
Governor body to hub attaching bolts	7	
Governor hub drive screw	8	
Governor support to transmission case bolts	10	
Valve body to transmission case bolts	15	
Valve body suction screen attaching screws	2-1/2	
Upper valve body plate bolts	5	
Lower to upper valve body attaching bolts	15	
Inner control lever Allen head screw	2-1/2	
Parking lock pawl reaction bracket attaching bolts	10	
Oil cooler plugs at transmission case	5	
Pressure test point plugs	5	
Low band adjustment locknut	15	
Converter to flexplate bolts	35	
Under pan to transmission case	7-1/2	
Oil cooler pipe connectors to transmission case or radiator	10	
Oil cooler pipe to connectors	10	
Vacuum modulator to transmission case	15	
Oil pan drain plug	20	
Parking brake lock and range selector inner lever Allen head screw	2-1/2	
Turbo Hydra-Matic 250/350		
Pump cover to pump body	17	
Pump assembly to case	18-1/2	
Valve body and support plate		130
Parking lock bracket	29	
Oil suction screen		40
Oil pan to case		130
Extension to case	25	
Modulator retainer to case		130
Inner selector lever to shaft	25	
Detent valve actuating bracket		52
Converter to flexplate bolts	35	
Under pan to transmission case		110
Transmission case to engine	35	
Oil cooler pipe connectors to transmission case or radiator	15	
Oil cooler pipe to connectors	10	
Gearshift bracket to frame	15	
Gearshift shaft to swivel	20	
Manual shaft to bracket	20	
Detent cable to transmission		75
Intermediate band adjust nut	15	
Turbo Hydra-Matic 400		
Pump cover bolts	18	
Parking pawl bracket bolts	18	
Center support bolts	23	
Pump to case attaching bolts	18	
Extension housing to case attaching bolts	23	
Rear servo cover bolts	18	
Detent solenoid bolts	7	
Control valve body bolts	8	
Bottom pan attaching screws	12	
Modulator retainer bolt	18	
Governor cover bolts	18	
Manual lever to manual shaft nut	8	
Manual shaft to inside detent lever	18	
Linkage swivel clamp nut	43	
Converter dust shield screws		93
Transmission to engine mounting bolts	35	

Torque specifications

	lb-ft
Converter to flexplate bolts	32
Rear mount to transmission bolts	40
Rear mount to cross-member bolt	40
Cross-member mounting bolts	25
Line pressure take-off plug	13
Strainer retainer bolt	10
Oil cooler pipe connectors to transmission case or radiator	14
Oil cooler pipe to connector	10
Gearshift bracket to frame	15
Gearshift shaft to swivel	20
Manual shaft to bracket	20
Downshift switch to bracket	30

Turbo Hydra-Matic 200

Pump cover bolts	18
Pump-to-case bolts	18
Parking pawl bracket bolts	18
Control valve body bolts	11
Oil screen retaining bolts	11
Oil pan bolts	12
Torque converter to flexplate bolts	35
Torque converter dust shield screws	8
Torque converter bracket-to-adapter	13
Transmission to engine mounting bolts	25
Transmission rear support bolts	40
Speedometer driven gear bolts	23
Fluid cooler line-to-transmission	25
Fluid cooler line-to-radiator	20
Linkage swivel clamp nut	30
Rear mounting support nuts	21
Support center nut	33
Adapter-to-transmission bolts	33

1 General description

1   Fully automatic transmissions have been available on Firebird models since their introduction. The type depends upon the year of manufacture, and the engine size and output.
2   *Powerglide* The Powerglide is a fully automatic 2-speed transmission which changes speed depending on load and throttle position. A forced downshift facility is provided for immediate change to low speed for rapid acceleration.
3   *Turbo Hydra-Matic* These are fully automatic 3-speed transmissions and although they differ in basic design. operate on the same principle as the Powerglide.

4   Automatic transmissions comprise a 3-element hydrokinetic torque converter coupling capable of torque multiplication in an infinitely variable ratio between approximately 2:1 and 1:1, and a torque/speed responsive hydraulically epicyclical gearbox.
5   In view of the need for special tools and equipment to carry out overhaul and repair operations to any of these automatic transmission units, the information in this chapter is restricted to maintenance and adjustment procedures; also the removal and installation of the transmission which will enable the home mechanic to install a new or rebuilt unit which, after a high mileage, is probably the most economical method of repair when a fault develops.

2 Identification

Refer to illustration 2.1
1   Besides checking the transmission serial number, there is a quick way to determine which of the three automatic transmissions a particular vehicle is equipped with. Read the following transmission oil pan descriptions **(see illustration)** to identify the various models.

Powerglide

2   The Powerglide transmission case is made of either cast iron or aluminum. The word "Powerglide" is plainly stamped on the case. The shift quadrant indicator is set up in one of two ways: P-N-D-L-R or P-R-N-D-L.

A

B

C

D

24045-7b-3.1 HAYNES

2.1 The oil pan gasket shape can help you determine which transmission your vehicle is equipped with

| A | THM400 | B | THM 250/350 | C | Powerglide | D | THM200 |

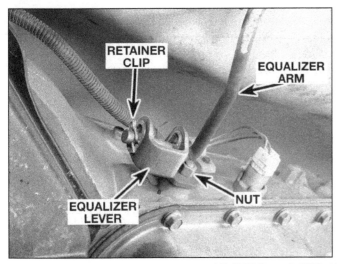 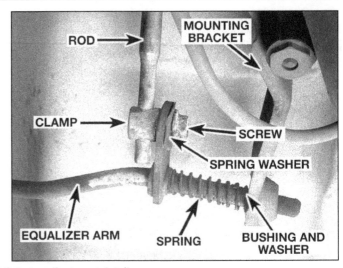

4.7 1974 through 1980 shift linkage adjustment details

Turbo Hydra-Matic 350

3   This transmission is a two-piece design with a downshift cable running from the accelerator to the right side of the transmission case. The oil pan has 13 bolts and is square-shaped with one corner angled (notched).

Turbo Hydra-Matic 400

4   The case of the 400 is also two-piece, but the downshifting is electrically controlled from a switch at the carburetor to the left side of the transmission. The oil pan also has 13 securing bolts. The shape of the pan is elongated and irregular.

Turbo Hydra-Matic 200/250

5   The Turbo Hydra-Matic 200/250 transmissions are new for 1981 models. The case of the 200/250 is also two-piece with a downshift cable running from the accelerator to the right side of the transmission case. The oil pan has 11 (200) or 13 (250) securing bolts. The shape of the pan is square with one corner angled.

---

3   Extension housing oil seal - replacement

---

1   This operation can be carried out without removing the transmission from the vehicle.
2   Place the vehicle over a pit or jack it up to gain access to the transmission. Support the vehicle with jack stands.
3   Disconnect the driveshaft from the transmission as described in Chapter 8.
4   Pry out the defective seal using a screwdriver or chisel as a lever.
5   Apply jointing compound to the outer edge of the new seal and drive it into position using a piece of tubing as a drift.
6   Install the driveshaft and check the fluid level in the transmission unit.

4   Column shift linkage - checking and adjustment

1   The selector linkage will be in need of adjustment if at any time "Low" or "Reverse" can be obtained without first having to lift the shift control lever to enable it to pass over the mechanical stop.

1970 through 1973 models

2   If adjustment is required, release the control rod swivel or clamp and set the lever on the side of the transmission in the "Drive" or L2 detent. This can be clearly defined by placing the lever in L or L1 and moving the lever back one detent (click).
3   Position the shift control lever up against the "Drive" stop and then tighten the swivel or clamp on the control rod.
4   Check all selector positions, especially "Park". In some cases, especially with worn linkage, it may be necessary to readjust slightly in order to ensure that the "Park" detent is fully engaged.

1974 through 1981 models

Refer to illustration 4.7

5   Place the shift lever in the Neutral position of the shift indicator.
6   Position the transmission shift lever in the Neutral detent.
7   Install the clamp spring and screw assembly on the equalizer lever control rod **(see illustration)**.
8   Hold the clamp flush against the equalizer lever and tighten the clamp screw finger tight. Make sure that no force is exerted in either direction on the rod or equalizer lever while the screw is tightened.
9   Tighten the screw securely.
10   Check that the ignition key can be moved freely to the "Lock" position when the shift lever is in "Park" and not in any other position.

5   Floor shift linkage - checking and adjustment

1   If the engine can be started in any of the Drive positions and the Neutral start switch is properly adjusted (Section 11), the shift linkage must be adjusted.

Powerglide

2   Set the shift lever in "Drive".
3   Working under the vehicle, disconnect the selector cable from the lever on the side of the transmission.
4   Move the lever on the side of the transmission to the "Drive" detent.
5   Measure the distance from the rear face of the cable mounting bracket to the center of the cable pivot stud. This should be 5-1/2 inches. Adjust the position of the stud if necessary to achieve this measurement.
6   Adjust the cable in its mounting bracket so that the cable end fits freely onto the pivot stud. Install the cable retaining clip.
7   Working inside the vehicle, remove the shift quadrant cover, plate and illumination bulbs.
8   Remove the selector cable clip and disconnect the cable from the shift lever.
9   Insert a gauge (0.07-inch thick) between the pawl and the detent plate, then measure the distance between the front face of the shifter assembly bracket and the center of the cable pivot pin. This should be 6-1/4 inches. If it is not, loosen bolt A and move the lever as necessary.
10   Adjust the cable mounting to the shifter bracket until the cable eye freely enters over the pivot pin. If at any time depressing the handle button does not clear the cut-outs in the detent plate, or conversely if the handle can be moved to P and R positions without depressing the button, raise or lower the detent plate after loosening the retaining bolt.

Turbo Hydra-Matic

Note: *Apply the parking brake and block the wheels to prevent the vehicle from rolling.*

7.1 Pry out the release tab with a screwdriver

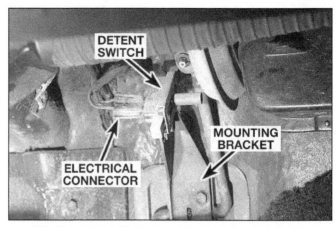

8.6 Turbo Hydra-Matic downshift (detent) switch details

11   Working under the vehicle, loosen the nut attaching the shift lever to the pin on the shift cable assembly.

12   Place the console shifter (inside the vehicle) in Park.

13   Place the manual shifting shaft on the transmission in Park.

14   Move the pin to give a "free pin" fit, making sure that the console shifter is still in the Neutral position, and tighten the pin-to-lever retaining nut to the specified torque.

15   Make sure the engine will start in the Park and Neutral positions only.

16   If the engine can be started in any of the drive positions (as indicated by the shifter inside the vehicle), repeat the steps above or have the vehicle examined by a dealer, because improper linkage adjustment can lead to band or clutch failure and possible personal injury.

6   Turbo Hydra-Matic 250 - on-vehicle adjustments

Intermediate band adjustment

1   This adjustment should be carried out every 24,000 miles or if the performance of the transmission indicates the need for it.

2   Raise the vehicle to gain access to the transmission, making sure to secure the vehicle on jackstands.

3   Place the speed selector lever in Neutral.

4   The adjusting screw and locknut for the intermediate band is located on the right-hand side of the transmission case.

5   Loosen the locknut 1/4-turn using a wrench or special tool. Hold the locknut In this position and tighten the adjusting screw to a torque of 30 in-lbs. Now back off the screw three complete turns exactly.

6   Without moving the adjusting screw, tighten the locknut to 15 ft-lbs.

Downshift (detent) cable adjustment

7   The cable will normally only require adjustment if a new one has been installed.

8   Depress the accelerator pedal fully. The ball will slide into the cable sleeve and automatically pre-set the cable tension.

7   Turbo Hydra-Matic 350 downshift (detent) cable - adjustment

Refer to illustration 7.1

1970 through 1980 models

1   Insert a screwdriver on each side of the snap-lock and pry out to release **(see illustration)**.

2   Compress the locking tabs and disconnect the snap-lock assembly from its bracket.

3   Manually set the carburetor in the fully open position with the throttle lever fully against its stop.

4   With the carburetor in the fully open position, push the snap-lock on the detent cable into the locked position and release the throttle lever.

1981 models

5   This will normally be required only after installation of a new cable.

6   Depress the accelerator pedal to the fully open position. The cable ball will slide into the sleeve of the cable and automatically adjust the setting of the detent cable.

8   Turbo Hydra-Matic 400 - downshift (detent) switch adjustment

1970 through 1971

1   Pull the detent switch driver rearwards until the hole in the switch body aligns with the hole in the driver. Insert a pin (0.092 inch diameter) into the holes to a depth of 0.10 inch to hold the driver in position.

2   Loosen the switch mounting bolt.

3   Depress the accelerator fully and then move the switch forward until the driver contacts the accelerator lever.

4   Tighten the switch bolt and extract the alignment pin.

1972 on

Refer to illustration 8.6

5   The switch is mounted on the pedal bracket as shown.

6   The switch is set by pushing the plunger as far forward as possible **(see illustration)**. At the first full depression of the accelerator pedal. the switch is automatically adjusted.

9   Turbo Hydra-Matic - neutral start switch adjustment (1970 through 1972)

Column shift

1   Set the shift lever in "Drive" and hold the lever tang against the selector plate. Release the switch screws.

2   Align the slot in the contact support with the hole in the switch and then insert a 3/32 inch diameter pin.

3   Place the contact support drive slot over the shifter tube drive tang and tighten the screws.

4   Withdraw the alignment pin.

Floor shift

5   Release the switch mounting screws and then set the shift lever in "Drive" and align the hole in the contact support with the one in the switch and then insert a 3/32 inch diameter pin.

6   Place the contact support drive slot over the drive tang and tighten the switch mounting screws.

7   Withdraw the alignment pin.

8   With both types of switch, check the operation with the ignition switched on. The starter should only operate in shift positions N or P.

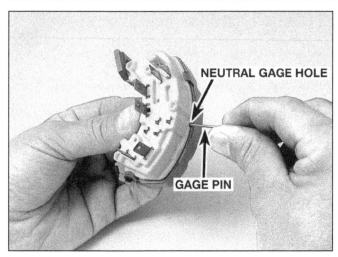

10.5a On earlier models, insert a pin into the gage hole to adjust the neutral start switch

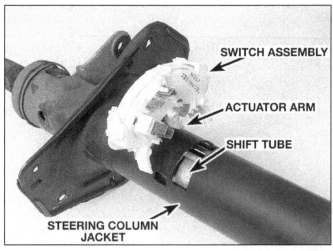

10.5b Later model neutral start switches are adjusted by moving the assembly housing to the Low gear position and then shifting into Park

10 Turbo Hydra-Matic - combined neutral start/back-up lamp/seat belt warning switch adjustment - 1973 on

Column shift

Refer to illustrations 10.5a and 10.5b

1   If a new switch is being installed, set the shift lever against the "Neutral" gate by rotating the lower lever on the shift tube in a counterclockwise direction as viewed from the driver's seat.

2   Locate the switch actuating tang in the shifter tube slot and then tighten the securing screws.

3   Connect the wiring harness and switch on the ignition and check that the starter motor will actuate.

4   If the switch operates correctly, move the shift lever out of neutral which will cause the alignment pin (installed during production of the switch) to shear.

5   If an old switch is being installed or readjusted, use a pin (0.093 to 0.097 in diameter) to align the hole in the switch with the actuating tang (see illustrations). Insert the pin to a depth of 1/4 inch. Remove the pin before moving the shift lever out of neutral.

Floor shift

6   This is similar to the procedure just described for column shift except that the shift lever should be set in "Park" not "Neutral".

7   Access to the switch is obtained after removal of the trim plate and shift control assembly.

11 Powerglide transmission - removal and installation

1   Raise the vehicle (and support it securely on jackstands). Drain the trans-

mission fluid.

2   Disconnect the oil cooler lines, vacuum modulator line, and speedometer cable.

3   Disconnect the throttle valve and manual control rods from the transmission.

4   Disconnect the driveshaft (refer to Chapter 8).

5   Support the weight of the transmission using a suitable jack and spacers.

6   Disconnect the rear mount on the transmission extension, then disconnect the transmission support crossmember and slide it rearward.

7   Remove the converter underpan, scribe the converter/flexplate relationship for assembly, then remove the flexplate to converter attaching bolts. These can be brought into view, one at a time if the crankshaft is turned using a wrench applied to the pulley bolt.

8   Support the engine at the oil pan rail with a suitable jack, then lower the rear of the transmission slightly so that the upper housing attaching bolts can be reached using a suitable socket and extension. Take care that the distributor does not touch the firewall as the transmission is being lowered.

9   Remove the upper attaching bolts first, then the remainder of the bolts.

10   Remove the transmission rearwards and downwards, and away from the engine. If necessary, pry it free from the flexplate. Keep the rear of the transmission downwards at all times or the converter will fall out. This can be retained using a holding strap.

11   When installing, remove the converter holding strap, keep the rear of the transmission slightly downwards then raise the transmission into place.

12   When the converter is aligned with the flywheel, install the upper attaching bolts, followed by the remaining bolts; torque-tighten to the specified value.

13   Remove the support from beneath the engine then raise the transmission into its installed position.

14   Torque-tighten the converter bolts to the specified value.

15   Install the converter underpan.

16   Install the support crossmember to the transmission and frame.

17   Remove the lifting equipment then connect the driveshaft (refer to Chapter 7).

18   Connect the manual and throttle valve control lever rods, the oil cooler lines, vacuum modulator line and speedometer drive cable.

19   Refill the transmission (Chapter 1), check for proper operation and examine for leaks.

20   Lower the vehicle and check the transmission fluid level.

12 Turbo Hydra-Matic transmission - removal and installation

Refer to illustrations 12.10a and 12.10b

1   Disconnect the battery ground cable and release the parking brake.

2   Raise the vehicle on a hoist or place it over an inspection pit.

3   Disconnect the speedometer cable, detent cable, electrical leads, modulator vacuum line and oil cooler pipes, as appropriate.

4   Disconnect the shift control linkage.

5   Disconnect the driveshaft (Chapter 8).

6   Support the transmission with a suitable jack, and disconnect the rear mount from the frame crossmember.

7   Remove the two bolts at each end of the crossmember then remove the crossmember.

8   Remove the converter underpan.

9   Loosen the exhaust downpipe bolts at the manifold and unscrew them about 1/4 inch.

10   Mark the relationship of the flexplate to the torque converter and then unscrew the connecting bolts (see illustrations).

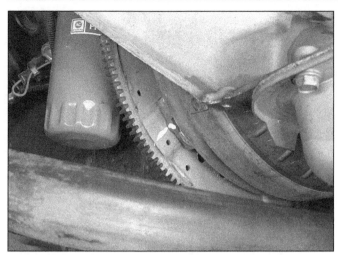

12.10a Mark the relationship of the torque converter to the flywheel

12.10b Remove the torque converter-to-flywheel retaining bolts (here, a flywheel wrench is being used to prevent the flywheel from turning, but a wrench on the crankshaft vibration damper will also work)

These are accessible through the front of the torque converter housing but will have to be brought into view one at a time by applying a wrench to the torsional damper center bolt.

11   Lower the transmission as far as possible without causing any engine or transmission components to come into contact with the engine compartment firewall.

12   Remove the transmission to engine connecting bolts and remove the oil filler tube at the transmission.

13   Raise the transmission to its normal position, support the engine with the jack and slide the transmission rearwards from the engine. Keep the rear of the transmission downwards so that the converter does not

fall off. Use a holding strap similar to the one described in Section 10.

14   Installation is the reverse of the removal procedure, but additionally ensure that the weld nuts on the converter are flush with the flexplate and that the converter rotates freely in this position. Tighten all bolts finger-tight before torque-tightening to the specified value.

Notes

Chapter 8
Clutch and driveline

Contents

Specifications

Clutch
Clutch type	Single dry plate, diaphragm spring
Clutch actuation	Mechanical by rod
Clutch pedal free-play (measured at center of pedal pad)	1 to 1-1/2 inches
Clutch throwout (release) bearing type	Grease sealed ball

Driveshaft
Driveshaft type	Open, single section, tubular steel with two universal joints and one slip joint

Rear axle
Rear axle type	Salisbury. semi-floating with cast carrier having overhung hypoid pinion and ring gear. Optional Positraction (limited slip) axle available on all models
Rear axle ring gear diameter	8 1/2 inch

Lubricant capacity
1970 through 1971
Light duty axle	4.5 pints
Heavy duty axle	4.9 pints
1973 through 1980	4.25 pints

B and O type axles (see Section 13, this Chapter)
Axleshaft end-play	0.001 to 0.022 in
Pinion bearing pre-load:	
New	15 to 30 in lbs
Used	10 to 15 in lbs

Torque specifications

Clutch   Ft-lb
Clutch pressure plate bolts   35
Transmission case to clutch bellhousing bolts   55
Clutch bellhousing to engine bolts...   30

Driveshaft
Universal joint strap bolts..   15
Universal joint U-bolt nuts...   15
Universal joint flange bolts (double Cardan type)   70

Rear axle

1970 through 1971
Differential carrier cover bolts   30
Ring gear bolts   85
Differential bearing cap bolts   60
Oil filler plug...   20
Differential pinion lock   20

1972
Differential carrier cover bolts   25
Ring gear bolts   85
Differential bearing caps...   60
Oil filler plug...   25
Differential pinion lock   20

1973 on
As 1972 except for
Ring gear bolts   90

1   General description - clutch

Refer to illustrations 1.1, 1.2 and 1.3

1   All models are fitted with a single dry plate, diaphragm spring type clutch. Operation is by means of a foot pedal and rod linkage. The unit comprises a pressure plate assembly which contains the pressure plate, diaphragm spring and fulcrum rings. The assembly is bolted to the rear face of the flywheel **(see illustration)**.

2   The driven plate (friction disc) is free to slide along the gearbox input shaft and it is held in place between the flywheel and pressure plate faces by the pressure exerted by the diaphragm spring. The friction lining material is riveted to the driven plate which incorporates a spring-cushioned hub designed to absorb transmission rotational shocks and to assist in ensuring smooth take-offs **(see illustration)**.

3   The circular diaphragm spring assembly is mounted on shouldered pins and held in place in the cover by fulcrum rings. The spring itself is held in place by spring steel clips. On high performance vehicles, or where a heavy duty clutch is required, the diaphragm spring has bent fingers, whereas the standard version has flat fingers. The bent finger design is used to gain a centrifugal boost to aid rapid re-engagement of the clutch at high rotational speeds **(see illustration)**.

4   Depressing the clutch pedal pushes the throwout-bearing, mounted on its hub retainer, forward to bear against the fingers of the diaphragm spring. This action causes the diaphragm spring outer edge to deflect and so move the pressure plate rearwards to disengage the pressure plate from the driven plate.

5   When the clutch pedal is released, the diaphragm spring forces the pressure plate into contact with the friction linings of the driven plate and at the same time pushes the drive plate fractionally forward on its splines to ensure full engagement with the flywheel. The driven plate is now firmly sandwiched between the pressure plate and the flywheel and so the drive is taken up.

1.1 After removal of the transmission, this will be the view of the clutch components

1   Pressure plate
2   Flywheel

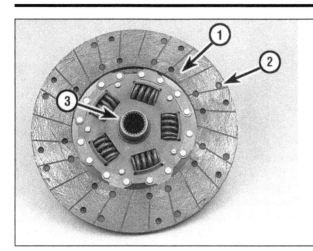

1.2 The clutch plate

1 **Lining** - this will wear down in use
2 **Rivets** - these secure the lining and will damage the flywheel or pressure plate if allowed to contact the surfaces
3 **Markings** - "Flywheel side" or something similar

1.3 The machined face of the pressure plate must be inspected for score marks and other damage - if damage is slight, a machine shop can make the surface smooth again

2 Clutch - adjustment

1 The free-play at the clutch pedal should be approximately 1 inch.
2 There is only one linkage adjustment to compensate for all normal clutch wear.
3 To check for correct adjustment, apply the parking brake, block the front wheels and start the engine. Hold the clutch pedal approximately 1/2-inch from the floor and move the shift lever between First and "Reverse" gears several times. If the shift is not smooth, clutch adjustment is necessary.
4 Raise the car to permit access to the clutch linkage under the car. Place firmly on jack stands.
5 Disconnect the return spring at the clutch fork.
6 Rotate the clutch lever and shaft assembly until the clutch pedal is firmly against the rubber bumper on the dashboard brace. If in doubt about this, have an assistant check this from inside the car.
7 Push the outer end of the clutch fork rearward until the release bearing lightly contacts the pressure plate fingers.
8 Keep the fork in this position while the push rod is removed from its holes in the shaft. Now place the rod in the gauge hole of the shaft, directly above the normal operating hole.
9 With the push rod in the gauge hole, loosen the locking nut and turn the rod to increase its length. Increase the length of the rod until all lash is removed from the system.
10 Remove the rod from the gauge hole and return it to the lower operating hole in the shaft. Install the retainer and then carefully tighten the nut, being sure the length of the rod is not changed.
11 Connect the return spring and check the pedal free-play as described previously. Lower the vehicle, then check for correct operation and free travel.

3 Clutch pedal - removal and installation

1 Disconnect the return spring for the clutch pedal.
2 Disconnect the clutch pedal push rod where it meets the pedal arm. This is held in place at the top of the pedal with a lock pin.
3 Disconnect the electrical coupler for the neutral start switch. Then remove the switch from the top of the clutch pedal.
4 The pivot shaft which runs through the clutch and brake pedals must now be removed. It is held in place with a retaining nut on one end. Remove the nut and slide the shaft until it clears the pedal support. Now insert a dummy shaft in the support to hold the brake pedal components in place while the pivot shaft is removed.
5 Remove the pivot shaft, pedal arm and bushings.
6 Inspect all parts and replace as necessary. Do not clean the nylon bushings with cleaning agent, simply wipe them clean with a cloth. Lubricate the bushings and all moving parts.
7 To reinstall the pedal, push the bushings into place and then the pivot shaft and pedal arm.
8 Install the retaining nut to the end of the shaft.
9 Install the neutral start switch and connect its wiring coupler.
10 Connect the push rod to the pedal arm. Make sure it is securely fastened.
11 Connect the return spring and check for free travel. Adjust the components as required.

4 Clutch cross-shaft - removal and installation

1 Remove the linkage return and lower linkage springs. Disconnect the clutch pedal and fork push rods from their respective cross-shaft levers.
2 Loosen the outboard ball stud nut and slide the stud out of the slot in the bracket.
3 Move the cross-shaft outboard far enough to clear the inboard ball stud, then lift it out and remove it from the vehicle.
4 Check the ball stud seats on the cross-shaft, the engine bracket ball stud assembly and the anti-rattle spring for damage and wear; replace parts as necessary.

5 When installing, reverse the removal procedure. Lubricate the ball studs and seat with graphite grease on assembly and finally adjust the clutch (Section 2).

5 Clutch - removal, servicing and installation

Refer to illustrations 5.4, 5.7, 5.19a, 5.19b, 5.24a, 5.24b and 5.24c

1 Access to the clutch is normally obtained by removing the transmission, leaving the engine in the car. If, of course, the engine is being removed for major overhaul, then the opportunity should always be taken to check the clutch assembly for wear at the same time.
2 Disconnect the clutch fork push rod and spring then remove the clutch housing from the engine cylinder block.
3 Slide the clutch fork from the ball stud and remove the fork from the dust boot.
4 If necessary, the ball stud can be removed from the clutch housing by unscrewing **(see illustration)**.

5.4 Front face of transmission showing the clutch fork ball stud (arrow)

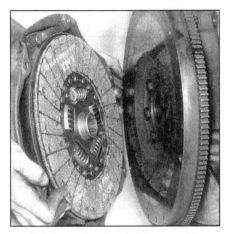

5.7 Removing the clutch assembly

5.19a Centralizing the clutch driven plate using an old clutch drive gear

5.19b A clutch alignment tool can be purchased at most auto parts stores and eliminates all guesswork when centering the clutch plate in the pressure plate

5   If there are no alignment marks on the clutch cover (an X-mark or white-painted letter), scribe or center-punch marks for indexing purposes during installation.

6   Unscrew the bolts securing the pressure plate and cover assembly one turn at a time in a diagonal sequence to prevent distortion of the clutch cover.

7   With all the bolts and lockwashers removed, carefully lift the clutch away from the flywheel, taking care that the driven plate does not fall or become damaged **(see illustration)**.

8   It is not practical to dismantle the pressure plate assembly and the term "dismantling" is usually used for simply installing a new clutch driven plate and pressure plate (if necessary).

9   If a new clutch driven plate is being installed it is a good idea to replace the throwout bearing at the same time.

10   If the pressure plate assembly requires replacement, an exchange unit must be purchased. This will have been accurately set up and balanced to very fine limits.

11   Examine the clutch plate friction linings for wear and loose rivets, and the disc for rim distortion, cracks, broken hub springs, and worn splines. The surface of the friction linings may be highly glazed, but as long at the

clutch material pattern can be clearly seen this is satisfactory. Compare the amount of lining wear with a new clutch disc at the stores in your local service station. If worn, the driven plate must be replaced.

12   Check the machined faces of the flywheel and the pressure plate. If either are grooved they should be machined until smooth, or replaced.

13   If the pressure plate is cracked or split, it is essential that an exchange unit is fitted; also if the pressure of the diaphragm spring is suspect, this should be checked and replaced if necessary.

14   Check the throwout bearing for smoothness of operation. There should be no harshness or slackness in it. It should spin reasonably freely bearing in mind it has been pre-packed with grease. If in doubt, replace the bearing with a new one.

15   It is important that no oil or grease gets on the clutch plate friction linings, or the pressure plate and flywheel faces. It is advisable to replace the clutch with clean hands and to wipe down the pressure plate and flywheel faces with a clean dry rag and brake cleaner before assembly begins.

16   Place the driven plate against the flywheel making sure that the longer splined

boss faces towards the flywheel (thicker torsional spring assembly projection towards the transmission).

17   Install the pressure plate and clutch cover assembly so that the marks made on dismantling are in alignment. Tighten the bolts only finger-tight so that the driven plate is gripped, but can still be slid sideways.

18   The clutch plate must now be centralized so that when the engine and transmission are mated, the clutch shaft splines will pass through the splines in the center of the driven plate hub.

19   Centering can be carried out quite easily by inserting a round bar or long screwdriver through the hole in the center of the clutch, so that the end of the bar rests in the small hole in the end of the crankshaft containing the input shaft pilot bushing. Ideally an old clutch drive gear or centering tool should be used **(see illustrations)**.

20   Using the clutch shaft bearing bushing as a fulcrum, moving the bar sideways or up and down will move the clutch plate in whichever direction is necessary to achieve centering.

21   Centering is easily judged by removing the bar and viewing the driven plate hub in relation to the hole in the center of the clutch cover plate diaphragm spring.

22   Tighten the clutch cover bolts firmly in a

5.24a Engagement of clutch fork with throwout bearing

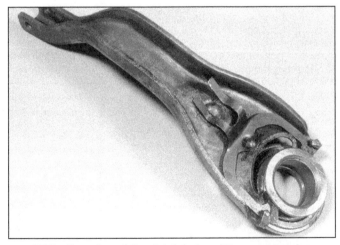

5.24b Rear view of the clutch fork and throwout bearing

5.24c Clutch fork and throwout bearing installed

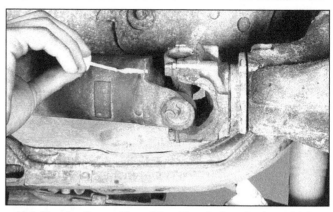

10.2 Marking the position of the drive shaft and universal joint components. All parts must be reinstalled in their original positions

diagonal sequence to ensure that the cover plate is pulled down evenly and without distortion to the flange. Torque the bolts to specifications.

23 Lubricate the clutch fork fingers at the throwout bearing end, and the ball and socket, with a high melting point grease. Also lubricate the throwout bearing collar and groove.

24 Install the clutch fork and dust boot into the clutch housing and install the throwout bearing to the fork **(see illustrations)**.

25 Install the clutch housing.

26 Install the transmission. Refer to Chapter 2 or Chapter 7, as necessary.

27 Connect the fork push rod and spring, lubricating the spring and push rod ends.

28 Adjust the shift linkage (Chapter 7) and the clutch linkage (Section 2).

6 Neutral start switch - removal and installation

1 This switch is a safety device intended to prevent the vehicle from being started without the clutch pedal being fully depressed. The small switch mounts to the clutch pedal mounting bracket and is activated by a plastic shaft which is part of the switch.

2 Disconnect the electrical coupler at the switch.

3 Compress the switch actuating shaft retainer and remove the shaft, with the switch attached, from the bracket.

4 To install, slide the switch onto the bracket and make sure the tab is fully seated. Then rotate the switch actuating shaft until it aligns with the hole in the clutch pedal arm and pop the shaft into the hole.

5 Connect the electrical coupler to the switch.

6 The switch is self-aligning, meaning that there is no need for adjustments.

7 General description - driveshaft

1 The driveshaft is of a one piece tubular steel construction having a universal joint at each end to allow for vertical movement of

the rear axle. At the front end of the shaft is a sliding sleeve which engages with the transmission unit splined output shaft.

2 Early models were fitted with Cleveland or Saginaw type universal joints. The Cleveland type is retained with snap-rings outboard of the universal joint but the Saginaw type is retained by a nylon material which is injected into a groove in the yoke during manufacture. The latter type of joint can be serviced by the use of a repair kit which utilizes snap-rings inboard of the yoke when the joint is reassembled. Some later models (1974 on) are equipped with a constant velocity joint at the axle end. The completed joint can be removed as an assembly by following the procedure given for the early type universal joint. The constant velocity joint has a centering ball which can be serviced (see Section 12).

3 Some driveshafts incorporate a vibration damper. This item is not serviced separately, and in the event of replacement being necessary, the damper and sleeves are to be replaced as an assembly.

4 The driveshafts are finely balanced during manufacture and it is recommended that an exchange unit is obtained rather than dismantling the universal joints when wear is evident. However, this is not always possible and provided care is taken to mark each individual yoke in relation to the one opposite, then the balance will usually be maintained. Do not drop the assembly during operations.

8 Universal joints - testing for wear

1 Wear in the needle roller bearings is characterized by vibration in the transmission, "clonks" on taking up the drive, and in extreme cases of lack of lubrication, metallic squeaking and ultimately grating and shrieking sounds as the bearings break up.

2 It is easy to check if the needle roller bearings are worn with the shaft in position, by trying to turn it with one hand, the other hand holding the rear axle flange when the rear universal joint is being checked, and the front half coupling when the front universal joint is being checked. Any movement

between the shaft and the couplings is indicative of considerable wear.

3 A further test for wear is to attempt to lift the shaft and note any movement between the yokes of the joints.

4 If wear is evident, either fit a new propeller shaft assembly complete or replace the universal joints, as described later in this chapter.

9 Driveshaft out-of-balance - correction

1 Vibration of the driveshaft at certain speeds may be caused by any of the following:

   a) Undercoating or mud on the shaft
   b) Loose rear strap attachment bolts
   c) Worn universal joints
   d) Bent or dented driveshaft

2 Vibrations which are thought to be emanating from the drive shaft are sometimes caused by improper tire balance. This should be one of your first checks.

3 If the shaft is in a good, clean, undamaged condition, it is worth disconnecting the rear end attachment straps and turning the shaft 180 degrees to see if an improvement is noticed. Be sure to mark the original position of each component before disassembly so the shaft can be returned to the same location.

4 If the vibration persists after checking for obvious causes and changing the position of the shaft, the entire assembly should be checked out by a professional shop or replaced.

10 Driveshaft - removal and installation

Refer to illustrations 10.2, 10.3a, 10.3b, 10.4 and 10.5

1 Raise the rear of the vehicle and support it securely on blocks or axle-stands.

2 Mark the relationship of the driveshaft to the companion flange on the rear axle pinion **(see illustration)**.

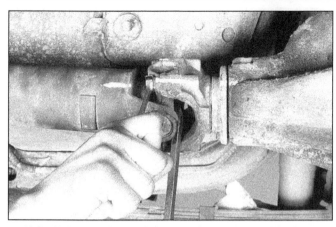

10.3a Hold the drive shaft from turning as the securing bolts are loosened

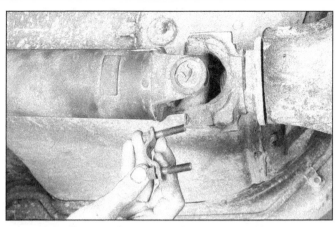

10.3b The securing strap and bolts removed from the rear axle assembly

10.4 Lower the rear of the driveshaft slightly and then pull front out of transmission

10.5 When reinstalling, be careful not to damage the seal at the rear of the transmission (screwdriver points to seal)

11.1 Removing the snap-rings from the bearing cup surface

3   Disconnect the rear universal joint by unscrewing and removing the nuts from the U-bolts or strap retaining bolts, or by removing the flange bolts. Where U-bolts or retaining straps are used, wrap adhesive tape around the bearing cups to prevent them

being displaced and the needle rollers dropping out **(see illustrations)**.
4   Lower the rear end of the driveshaft and then withdraw the complete shaft assembly to the rear. The front splined sliding sleeve section will be drawn off the transmission output shaft during the removal operation and a small amount of lubricant may be lost from vehicles equipped with manual trans-

mission **(see illustration)**.
5   Installation is a reversal of removal but remember to align the shaft to flange mating marks and take care not to damage the transmission extension oil seal with the sliding joint splines **(see illustration)**.
6   Check the transmission oil level when installation is complete.

---

11   Universal joints - dismantling and reassembly

Cleveland type joint
Refer to illustrations 11.1, 11.2, 11.3a, and 11.3b

1   Clean away all dirt from the ends of the bearings on the yokes so that the snap-rings can be removed using a pair of snap-ring pliers. If the snap-rings are very tight, tap the end of the bearing cup (inside the snap-ring) to relieve the pressure **(see illustration)**.
2   Support the trunnion yoke on a short piece of tube or the open end of a socket, then use a suitably sized socket to press out the cross (trunnion) by means of a vise **(see illustration)**.
3   Press the trunnion through as far as possible then grip the bearing cup in the jaws

11.2 Pressing out trunnion (cross) using a vise and sockets. One socket should be slightly smaller than the bearing cup and the socket on the other side slightly larger

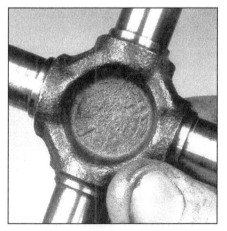

11.3a The trunnion (cross) removed from the driveshaft yoke

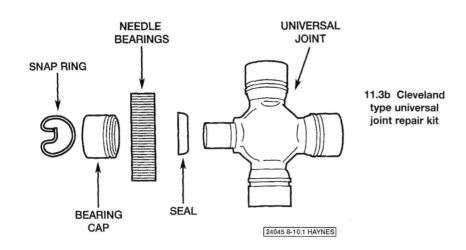

11.3b Cleveland type universal joint repair kit

of a vise to fully remove it. Repeat the procedure for the remaining cups (see illustrations).

4 On some models, the slip yoke at the transmission end has a vent hole. When dismantling, ensure that this vent hole is not blocked.

5 A universal joint repair kit will contain a new trunnion, seals, bearings, cups and snap-rings.

6 Commence reassembly by packing each of the reservoirs at the trunnion ends with lubricant.

7 Make sure that the dust seals are correctly located on the trunnion so that the cavities in the seals are nearer the trunnion.

8 Using a vise, press one bearing cup into the yoke so that it enters by not more than one quarter-inch.

9 Using a thick grease, stick each of the needle rollers inside the cup, making sure the bearings are all aligned and there are no gaps that would indicate missing bearings.

10 Insert the trunnion into the partially fitted bearing cup taking care not to displace the needle rollers.

11 Stick the needle bearings into the opposite cup and then holding the trunnion in cor-rect alignment, press both cups fully home in the jaws of the vise.

12 Install the new snap-rings.

13 Repeat the operations on the other two bearing cups.

14 In extreme cases of wear or neglect, it is possible that the bearing cup housings in the yoke will have worn so much that the cups are a loose fit in the yokes. In such cases, replace the complete driveshaft assembly.

15 Always check the wear in the sliding sleeve splines and replace the sleeve if worn.

Saginaw type joint

Refer to illustration 11.16

16 Where a Saginaw joint is to be disas-sembled, the procedure given in the previous section for pressing out the bearing cup is applicable. If the joint has been previously repaired it will be necessary to remove the snap-rings inboard of the yokes (see illustra-tion): if this is to be the first time that servic-ing has been carried out, there are no snap-rings to remove, but the pressing operation in the vise will shear the plastic molding mate-rial.

17 Having removed the cross (trunnion),

remove the remains of the plastic material from the yoke. Use a small punch to remove the material from the injection holes.

18 Reassembly is similar to that given for the Cleveland type joint except that the snap-rings are installed inside the yoke. If difficulty is encountered, strike the yoke firmly with a hammer to assist in seating.

12 Double cardan type constant velocity joint - overhaul

Refer to illustrations 12.1 and 12.3

1 An inspection kit containing two bearing cups and two retainers is available to permit the joint to be dismantled to the stage where the joint can be inspected. Before any dis-mantling is commenced, mark the flange yoke and coupling yoke so that they can be reassembled in the same relative position (see illustration).

2 Dismantle the joint by removing the bearing cups in a similar way to that described in the preceding section according to type.

3 Disengage the flange yoke and trunnion from the centering ball. Pry the seal from the ball socket and remove the washers, springs and the 3 ball seats (see illustration).

4 Clean the ball seat insert bushing and inspect for wear. If evident the flange yoke and trunnion assembly must be replaced.

5 Clean the seal, ball seats, spring and washers and inspect for wear. If excessive wear is evident or parts are broken, a replace-ment service kit must be used.

6 Remove all plastic material from the groove of the coupling yoke (if this type of joint is used).

7 Inspect the centering ball, if damaged it must be replaced.

8 Withdraw the centering ball from the stud using a suitable extractor. Provided that the ball is not to be re-used, it will not matter if it is damaged.

9 Press a new ball onto the stud until it seats firmly on the stud shoulder. It is extremely important that no damage to the

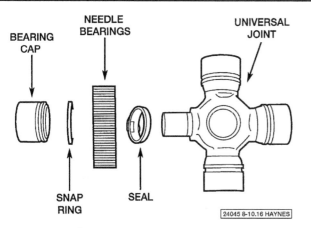

11.16 Saginaw type universal joint repair kit

12.1 CV joint alignment marks made before disassembly

ball occurs during this stage and suitable protection must be given to it.

10   Using the grease provided in the repair kit, lubricate all the parts and insert them into the ball seat cavity in the following order: spring, washer (small OD), 3 ball seats (largest opening outwards to receive the ball), washer (large OD) and the seal.

11   Lubricate the seal lips and press it (lip inwards) into the cavity. Fill the cavity with the grease provided.

12 Install the flange yoke to the centering ball, ensuring that the alignment marks are correctly positioned.

13   Install the trunnion caps as described previously for the Cleveland or Saginaw types.

13   General description and identification - rear axle

Refer to illustration 13.4

1   The rear axle is of hypoid, semi-floating type. The differential carrier is a casting with a pressed steel cover and the axle tubes are of steel construction.

2   Due to the need for special gauges and equipment and to the fact that individual differential components are no longer supplied (only a complete rear axle unit) the servicing and repair operations should be confined to those described in this chapter.

3   An optional "Positraction" (limited slip) differential unit has been available since the earliest models. Basically, the inclusion of clutch cones or plates and springs slow the rotation of the differential case when one wheel is on a firm surface and the other on a slippery one. This slowing action applies additional force to the pinion gears and through the medium of the cone which is splined to the axleshafts, exerts equalizing rotational power to the axleshaft which is

12.3 Place the companion flange in a vise as shown and remove the seal and centering ball

driving the wheel under traction.

4   In order to be able to undertake certain operations, particularly removal of the axleshafts, it is important to know the axle identification number. This is located on the front face of the right-hand axle tube about 3 inches from the differential cover. After the dirt and road grime has been brushed away, the code can be read **(see illustration)**. A typical General Motors axle code for 1971 and later models will read: CA C 150 N W.

5   The first two letters, in this case CA, are the axle code. By using the axle code and ratio chart which follows you can determine the gear ratios installed in the axle assembly.

6   The third letter of the code identifies the manufacturer of the axle. This is important, as axle design varies slightly between manufacturers. This single-letter code will be one of the following: B-Buick, C- Chevrolet (Buffalo), G-Chevrolet gear and axle, K-GM of Canada, M-GM of Canada, O-Oldsmobile or P-Pontiac. Manufacturers code letters B or

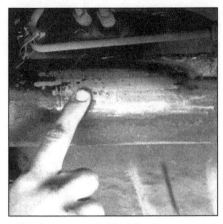

13.4 The rear axle identification number stamped onto the surface of the right axle tube

O, indicate that the wheel bearings are pressed onto the axleshafts whereas all other letters have bearings pressed into the axle tubes and the axleshafts are retained with C-locks.

7   Following the manufacturer's code letter will be varying numbers which indicate which day of the year that the axle was built. Letter D or N following the date code represents day or night shift.

8   The last letter of the code is a locking axle (Positraction) identification. Vehicles built with this type of axle will have one of the following code letters: E-Eaton, G-Chevrolet, O-Oldsmobile, or W- Borg-Warner.

9   The following axle code chart identifies the gear ratio and year of each axle assembly. Axle assemblies built for 1978 and later vehicles may have the axle ratio stamped on the housing rather than the two-letter axle code.

10   Two types of axles are used, those with a 4-bolt retainer plate at the brake end (called the Band O type), and axles retained with a C-clip inside the differential.

Axle code chart

CA	2.73 locking	1970-1974	PC	3.08 non-locking	1975-1978
CG	3.73 locking	1970-1972	PD	3.23 non-locking	1976-1978
CJ	3.42 locking	1970-1974	PE	3.42 non-locking	1976-1978
CK	3.42 non-locking	1970-1972	PH	2.56 non-locking	1977-1978
CL	3.42 non-locking	1973-1974	PJ	2.41 non-locking	1976-1978
CM	3.42 locking	1973-1974	PW	3.08 locking	1975-1978
GX	3.08 non-locking	1970-1974	PX	3.23 locking	1976-1978
GY	3.08 locking	1970-1974	PY	3.42 locking	1976-1978
GZ	2.73 non-locking	1970-1974	PT	2.56 locking	1977-1978
PA	2.73 non-locking	1975-1976	PS	2.41 locking	1976-1978

14   Axleshaft - removal and installation (except B and O type axles)

Refer to illustrations 14.4, 14.5 and 14.6

1   The following operations apply to rear axles which have the wheel bearings pressed

into the ends of the axle casing tubes (third letters of axle code - C, G, K, P, M).

2   Raise the rear of the vehicle and support securely and remove the wheel and brake drum.

3   Unscrew and remove the pressed steel cover from the differential carrier and allow the oil to drain into a suitable container.

4   Unscrew and remove the lock screw

from the differential pinion shaft. Remove the pinion shaft **(see illustration)**.

5   Push the outer (flanged) end of the axleshaft inwards and remove the C-ring from the inner end of the shaft **(see illustration)**.

6   Withdraw the axleshaft taking care not to damage the oil seal in the end of the axle housing as the splined end of the axleshaft passes through it **(see illustration)**.

14.4 The pinion shaft lock screw and the pinion shaft being removed from the differential assembly

14.5 The C-lock being withdrawn from the differential

14.6 Using a slide hammer to remove a B and O type axleshaft

15.2a After the brake components are removed, the oil seal is visible

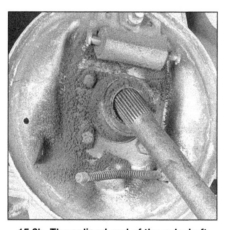

15.2b The splined end of the axleshaft can be used to pry the seal out of position

15.3 The new seal should be driven into place, flush with the axle casing

7   Installation is a reversal of removal but tighten the lock screw to the specified torque.
8   Always use a new cover gasket and tighten the cover bolts to the specified torque.
9   Refill the unit with the correct quantity and grade of lubricant.

15   Axleshaft oil seal - replacement (except B and O type axles)

Refer to illustrations 15.2a, 15.2b and 15.3
1   Remove the axleshaft as described in the preceding section.
2   Pry out the old oil seal from the end of the axle casing, using a large screwdriver or the inner end of the axleshaft itself as a lever **(see illustrations)**.
3   Apply high melting point grease to the oil seal recess and tap the seal into position so that the lips are facing inwards and the metal face is visible from the end of the axle housing. When correctly installed, the face of the oil seal should be flush with the end of the axle casing **(see illustration)**.

4   Installation of the axleshaft is as described in the preceding section .

16   Axleshaft bearing - replacement (except B and O type axles)

Refer to illustrations 16.3, 16.4 and 16.5
1   Remove the axleshaft (Section 14) and

the oil seal (Section 15).
2   A bearing extractor will now be required or a tool made up which will engage behind the bearing.
3   Attach a slide hammer and extract the bearing from the axle casing **(see illustration)**.
4   Clean out the bearing recess and drive in the new bearing using a piece of tubing *applied against the outer bearing track* **(see**

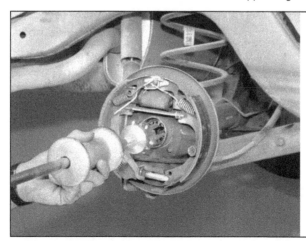

16.3 A slide hammer with a special bearing puller attachment is required to pull the axleshaft bearing from the axle housing

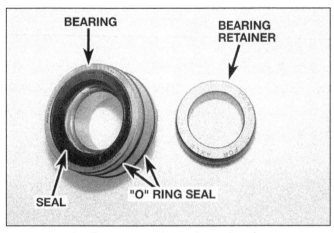

16.4 Typical rear axle bearing and retainer

16.5 A special bearing driver is needed to install the axleshaft bearing without damaging it

illustration). Lubricate the new bearing with gear lubricant. Make sure that the bearing is tapped in to the full depth of its recess and that the numbers on the bearing are visible from the outer end of the casing.

5   Discard the old oil seal and install a new one and install the axleshaft **(see illustration)**.

17   Axleshaft - removal, overhaul and installation (B and O type)

1   The usual reason for axleshaft removal on this type of axle is that the shaft end play has become excessive. To check this, remove the road wheel and brake drum and attach a dial gauge with its stylus against the axleshaft end flange. If the shaft is then moved in and out by hand, the end play should not exceed 0.022 inch. If the end play is excessive, carry out the following operations as the shaft bearing is probably worn.

2   Unscrew and remove the bolts which attach the axleshaft retainer plate to the brake backing plate.

3   Attach a slide hammer to the road wheel mounting studs and withdraw the axleshaft. Do not attempt to pull the axleshaft by hand from the housing as you will only succeed in pulling the vehicle off the support stands.

4   As the axleshaft is removed, it is possible that the bearing will become separated into three parts. This does not indicate that the bearing is unserviceable. If this happens, remove the two sections left behind from the axle tube.

5   With the axleshaft removed, hold it in the jaws of a vise so that the bearing retainer ring rests on the edges of the jaws.

6   Using a hammer and a sharp chisel, nick the retainer in two places. This will have the effect of spreading the retainer so that it will slide off the shaft. Do not damage the shaft in the process and never attempt to cut the retainer away with a torch as the temper of

the shaft will be ruined.

7   Using a suitable press or extractor, withdraw the bearing from the axleshaft.

8   Remove and discard the oil seal.

9   When installing the new bearing, make sure that the retainer plate and the seal are installed to the shaft first. Press on the bearing and the retaining ring tight up against it.

10   Before installing the axleshaft assembly. smear wheel bearing grease onto the bearing end and to the bearing recess in the axle-housing tube.

11   Apply rear axle oil to the axleshaft splines.

12   Hold the axleshaft horizontal and insert it into the axle housing. Feel when the shaft splines have picked up those in the differential side gears and then push the shaft fully into position, using a soft faced hammer on the end flange as necessary.

13   Bolt the retainer plate to the brake backplate, install the brake drum and wheel and lower the vehicle to the ground.

Chapter 9 Brakes

Contents

Specifications

System type .... Four wheel hydraulic, dual circuit. All models, 1970 - 1980, have front disc brakes as standard with rear drum brakes. Rear disc brakes were optional from 1978 to 1981. All brakes self-adjusting. Power booster option. Foot-operated parking brake by cables to the rear.

Drum size

Front	9.5 x 2.5 in
Rear	9.5 x 2.0 in
Maximum refinish internal diameter	9.560 in
Wear limit	9.590 in
Fluid type	DOT-3 brake fluid

Disc size

Diameter	11.00 inches
Width	1.030 inches
Minimum width (refinished)	0.980 inch
Minimum width (discard)	0.965 inch

Wheel cylinder piston diameter

Rear	0.9375 inch

Master cylinder piston diameter

Power assisted	1.125 inches
Manual	0.9375 inch

Brake pedal free travel (without booster) .... 1/16 to 1/4 in

Torque specifications

	Ft-lbs	in-lb
Master cylinder to dash	24	
Master cylinder to booster	24	
Booster to dash	25	
Brake line nuts		
1970 through 1980		150
1981	210	
Bleeder valves		110
Brake shoe anchor pin		120
Wheel cylinder to flange plate		110
Caliper mounting bolt	35	
Flexible hose to caliper		
1970 through 1980		22
1981	32	
Shield to steering knuckle		140
Brake pedal pivot bolt	30	

Component location

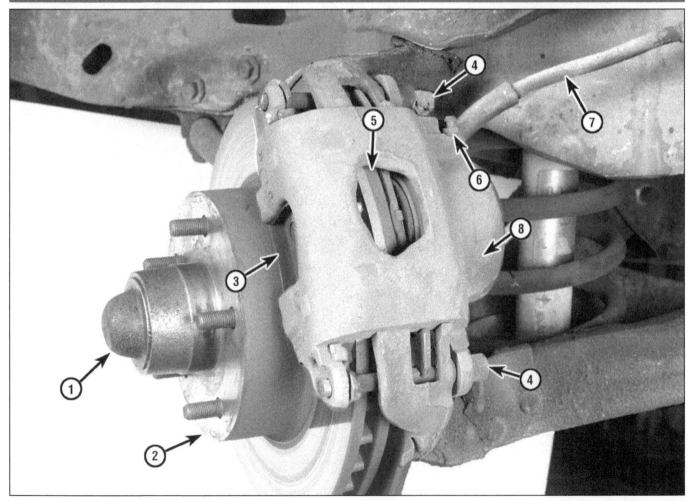

Typical front disc brake system

1	Dust cap	3	Outer brake pad	5	Inner brake pad	7	Brake hose
2	Brake rotor	4	Caliper mounting bolts	6	Bleeder Screw	8	Caliper housing

1 General description

The hydraulic system comprises two separate front and rear circuits.

The master cylinder is of tandem type with separate reservoirs for two circuits and in the event of a leak or failure in one hydraulic braking circuit, the other circuit will remain fully operative. A visual warning of circuit failure or air in the system is given by a warning lamp activated by displacement of the piston in the brake distribution (pressure differential warning) switch from its normal "in balance" position.

The parking brake operates mechanically to the rear brakes only. It is operated by a foot operated pedal to the left of the steering column.

A combination valve is fitted into the hydraulic circuit and provides the following three services:

Metering valve: This prevents the front disc brakes from operating until the rear shoes have contacted the drum.

Failure warning switch: This switch operates if either front or rear brakes fail to operate and a dash warning lamp then operates.

Proportioner: This reduces rear brake

system pressure during rapid deceleration, reducing the tendency for rear wheel skidding.

A power brake booster, which utilizes engine manifold vacuum and atmosphere pressure to provide assistance to the hydraulically operated brakes, is available as an option.

All brakes are self adjusting.

2 Maintenance and inspection

See Chapter 1 for maintenance and inspection procedures.

Component location

Typical rear drum brake system

1 Return spring	4 Primary brake shoe	6 Actuator lever	8 Actuator spring
2 Return spring	5 Adjuster screw assembly	7 Lever return spring	9 Hold-down spring
3 Hold-down spring			10 Secondary brake shoe

3.2 Pulling a brake drum off the axle studs

3.5 Measuring the thickness of the brake shoe lining

3   Drum brakes - lining inspection and replacement

Refer to illustrations 3.2, 3.5, 3.6a, 3.6b, 3.7a, 3.7b, 3.9, 3.10a, 3.10b, 3.14, 3.15a, 3.15b, 3.15c, 3.18, 3.19a, 3.19b, 3.20, 3.22, 3.23a and 3.23b

1   Jack up the rear of the vehicle and remove the wheel. Fully release the parking brake.

2   Mark the position of the brake drum in relation to one of the wheel studs so that the drum can be installed in the same relative attitude **(see illustration)**.

3   Remove the brake drums. If the brake drums are stuck tight due to severe wear (causing the shoes to be "locked" in grooves in the drum interior) and cannot be removed by gently tapping with a soft faced hammer or hardwood block, then the lanced area of the brake drum must be chiseled or knocked out. Rotate the drum until the adjuster lever can be released from the sprocket by pulling it outwards with a thin rod inserted through

the aperture. The sprocket can then be backed-off to release the drum. **Note:** *If the lanced area in the drum is knocked out, ensure that all metal is removed from the brake compartment Install a metal hole cover afterwards to prevent contamination of the brakes.*

4   Brush away any accumulations of dust, taking great care not to inhale it as it contains asbestos and is injurious to health.

5   Inspect the thickness of the friction material. If it has worn down to within 32 inches of the lining rivets or the metal backing plate of the shoe, then the shoes must be replaced **(see illustration)**. It is recommended that new or factory exchange shoes are obtained rather than attempt to reline the old ones yourself. Perform work on one brake assembly at a time, using the other side for reference.

6   Unhook the brake shoe pull-back springs from the anchor pin and link end **(see illustrations)**.

7   Remove the actuator return spring, the link, the hold-down pins and the springs **(see illustrations)**.

8   Remove the actuator assembly but do

3.6a A brake servicing tool is used here to disconnect the return spring for the primary brake shoe. A common screwdriver can also be used to pry the spring loose

not dismantle unless parts are broken.

9   Separate the brake shoes. This is achieved by removing the adjustment screw and spring. If the shoes are to be reinstalled,

3.6b The return spring for the secondary (rear) shoe also has a stiff wire link

3.7a To remove the anchor spring assemblies, compress the spring and then turn the end of the pin at the center of the spring

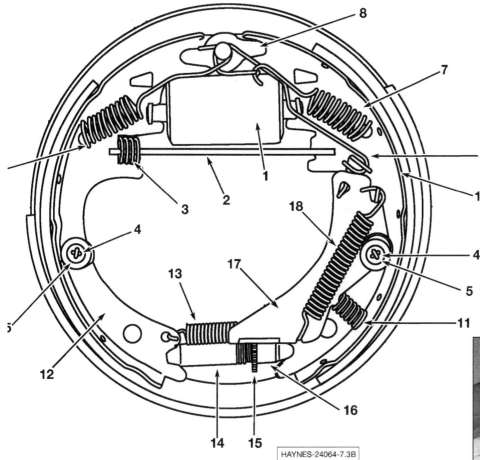

3.7b Exploded view of a typical drum brake assembly

1 Wheel cylinder
2 Parking brake strut
3 Strut spring
4 Hold-down pin
5 Hold-down spring and retainer
6 Return spring
7 Return spring
8 Shoe guide
9 Actuator link
10 Secondary shoe
11 Actuator lever return spring
12 Primary shoe
13 Adjuster screw spring
14 Pivot nut
15 Adjusting screw
16 Adjusting screw socket
17 Parking brake lever
18 Actuator spring

HAYNES-24064-7.3B

3.9 The primary shoe is held to the secondary shoe by a spring just behind the adjusting "starwheel"

mark the positions in which they are fitted **(see illustration)**.
10 Remove the parking brake lever from the secondary brake shoe **(see illustrations)**.
11 If there is any sign of hydraulic oil leakage at the wheel cylinders, the cylinder should be replaced or overhauled.
12 Check the flange plate attaching bolts

for tightness. Clean any rust and dirt from the shoe contact faces on the flange plate.
13 When installing, ensure that no grease or oil contact the linings and that they are free from nicks and burrs.
14 Lubricate the parking brake cable and the fulcrum end of the parking brake lever with brake lube. Attach the lever to the sec-

3.10a Removing the parking brake strut which runs between the shoes, behind the axle flange. Pay attention to how it is installed for reassembly

3.10b Pliers are used to disconnect the secondary shoe from the parking brake cable

3.14 After lubricating the parking brake cable, pull back the spring and connect the lever

3.15a Grease should be applied to the raised portions of the backing plate to prevent squeaks. These areas contact the brake shoes

3.15b Grease is also applied to the anchor pin

ondary shoe and ensure that it moves freely **(see illustration)**.

15   Put a smear of brake lube on the contact point of the pads and flange plate, and the threads of the brake adjusting screw **(see illustrations)**.

16   Connect the brake shoes together with the adjusting screw spring, then place the screw, socket and nut in position. **Note:** *Adjusting screws are marked "L" or "R" (left or right side of vehicle). The sprocket (star-wheel) should only be installed next to the secondary shoe and the adjusting screw spring inserted to prevent interference with the sprocket. Ensure that the sprocket lines up with the adjusting hole in the flange plate.*

17   Connect the parking brake cable to the lever.

18   Secure the primary shoe (short lining forward) first with the hold down pin and spring using pliers, and at the same time engage the shoes with the wheel cylinder connecting links **(see illustration)**.

19   Install the actuator assembly and secondary shoe with the hold down pin and spring using needle-nosed pliers. Position

3.15c The adjustment "starwheel" should be lubricated to ensure easy adjustments

the parking brake strut and strut spring **(see illustrations)**.

20   Install the guide plate over the anchor pin, then install the wire link. The wire link is connected to the actuator assembly first then

3.18 The primary shoe installed by the anchor spring assembly

placed over the anchor pin stud while holding the adjuster assembly fully down **(see illustration)**.

21   Install the actuator return spring, easing it in place with a screwdriver or similar tool.

3.19a The actuating spring is located just ahead of the parking brake lever

3.19b The parking brake strut has recesses in it to fit in the brake shoe cutouts

3.20 Use the brake tool or a screwdriver to force the wire link over the anchor pin

3.22 The installed position of the primary shoe return spring

3.23a The adjusting mechanism sprocket must be toward the rear shoe

3.23b The brakes are adjusted by lifting the lever away from the sprocket and then turning the adjusting mechanism. The brakes do this automatically when traveling in reverse

22   Hook the pull back springs into the shoes then install the spring from the primary shoe over the anchor pin and then the spring from the secondary shoe over the wire link end **(see illustration)**.
23   Ensure that the actuating lever functions by moving it by hand, then turn the sprocket back 1-1/4 turns to retract the shoes **(see illustrations)**.
24   Install the drum and wheel, ensuring that the drum locating tang is in line with the locating lobe in the hub.
25   Lower the vehicle to the ground.
26   Make numerous forward and reverse stops to finally adjust the brakes, until a satisfactory pedal action results.

4   Disc pads - inspection and replacement

Refer to illustrations 4.5, 4.6a, 4.6b, 4.7, 4.9, 4.10, 4.16, 4.17a, 4.17b, 4.18 and 4.23

1   At the intervals specified in Chapter 1, remove the front road-wheels and inspect the thickness of the pad material remaining. Check the ends of the outboard shoes by looking in at each end of the caliper. The inboard shoe can be checked by looking down through the inspection hole at the top of the caliper. Pads should be replaced when they are worn down to n inch thickness over the rivet heads.
2   In addition to the visual inspection, most models are equipped with an audible warning device which will indicate that the disc pads have worn down to their safe limit. The device is essentially a spring steel tang which emits a squeal by rubbing on the disc when the friction material has worn down to 0.030 in.
3   To replace the disc pads, first check that the brake fluid reservoir is no more than 1/3 full. Siphon off fluid above this level and discard it.
4   Raise the front end of the vehicle and remove the wheels. Perform disc pad replacement on one brake assembly at a time, using the assembled brake for reference if necessary.
5   Push the piston back into its bore. If necessary a C-clamp can be used but a flat

bar will usually do the job. As the piston is depressed to the bottom of the caliper bore, so the fluid in the master cylinder reservoir will rise. Ensure that it does not overflow **(see illustration)**.

4.5 A C-clamp is used to force the caliper piston back into its bore

4.6a An Allen head wrench is needed to remove the caliper mounting bolts from the inboard side

4.6b A caliper mounting bolt being removed from the caliper housing

4.7 Once the caliper is removed from the rotor, the pads are easily pulled from the caliper

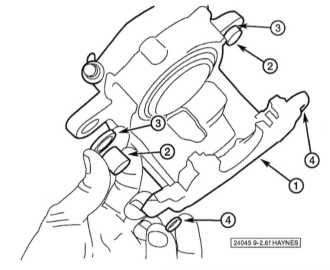

4.9 Push the mounting bolt sleeves out of the bores, remove the old bushings and install the new ones supplied with the brake pads

1   Caliper
2   Sleeves
3   Bushings
4   Bushings

6   Using an Allen key remove the two mounting bolts which attach the caliper to the support, then lift off the caliper **(see illustrations)**.

7   Remove the shoes, then position the caliper so that the brake hose will not have to support the caliper weight. If the disc pads are to be re-installed, mark their position **(see illustration)**.

8   Remove the shoe support spring from the piston.

9   Remove the 2 sleeves from the inboard ears of the caliper **(see illustration)**.

10   Remove the 4 rubber bushings from the grooves in each caliper ear **(see illustration)**.

11   Clean the holes and bushing grooves in the caliper ears.

12   Examine the inside of the caliper for signs of fluid leakage. If evident, the caliper should be overhauled.

13   When installing, ensure that the caliper is clean and that the dust boot is undamaged.

14   Lubricate new sleeves, rubber bushings, bushing grooves and the end of the mounting bolts using high temperature grease or equivalent.

15   Install the rubber bushings on the caliper ears.

16   Install the sleeves to the inboard ears so that the end towards the shoe is flush with the machine surface of the ear **(see illustration)**.

4.10 Rubber sleeves are located inside grooves and can be pried out with a screwdriver for replacement

17   Install the shoe support spring and inboard shoe in the center off the piston cavity. Push down until the shoe is flat against the caliper **(see illustrations)**.

18   Position the outboard shoe in the caliper

4.16 Lubricate the caliper bushings and push them into position

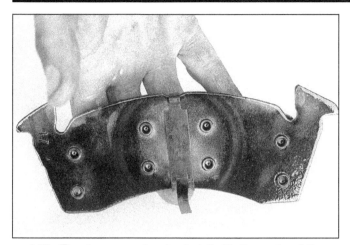

4.17a The shoe support spring installed in the center of the new disc pad

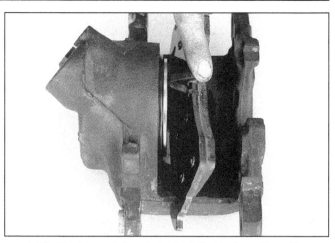

4.17b The inboard shoe being installed in the caliper. The extended portion of the support spring fits inside the piston

4.18 The outboard shoe is installed with its flange fitting in the caliper cutout area

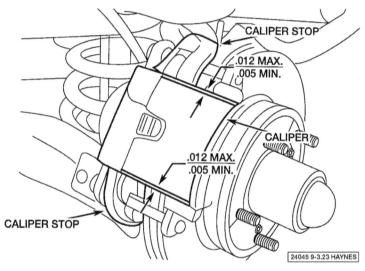

4.23 The dimension between each caliper stop and the caliper should be 0.005 to 0.012-inch

with the ears at the top of the shoe over the caliper ears and the tab at the bottom of the shoe engaged in the caliper cutout **(see illustration)**. If equipped with wear sensor, it will go towards the rear of the caliper abutment.

19 With the shoes installed, lift up the caliper and rest the bottom edge of the outboard lining on the outer edge of the disc to make sure that no clearance exists between the tab at the bottom and the caliper abutment.

20 Position the caliper over the disc, lining up the holes in the caliper ears and mounting bracket.

21 Install the mounting bolts, ensuring that they pass under the retaining ears of the inboard shoe and through the holes in the outboard shoe and caliper ears, then into the mounting bracket.

22 Torque-tighten the mounting bolts.

23 Pump the brake pedal to seat the linings on the disc then bend the upper ears of the outboard shoe until no radial clearance exists between the shoe and the caliper housing **(see illustration)**.

24 Install the front wheel and lower the vehicle.

25 Service the other side using the same procedures.

26 Add brake fluid to the master cylinder reservoir until It is 1/4 inch from the top.

27 Pump the brake pedal several times until a satisfactory pedal action is obtained then top up the master cylinder reservoir again (if necessary).

5   Wheel cylinder (drum brake) - removal, overhaul and installation

Refer to illustrations 5.5a, 5.5b and 5.7

1 Raise the vehicle and remove the wheel.

2 Remove the brake drum. See **Note** in Section 3.

3 Clean around the hydraulic connection to the wheel cylinder then disconnect the line. Plug the end of the line to prevent fluid loss and dirt contamination.

4 Remove the brake shoe pull back springs.

5 Remove the cylinder to flange plate securing screws and disengage the push rods from the brake shoes. Remove the cylinder **(see illustrations)**.

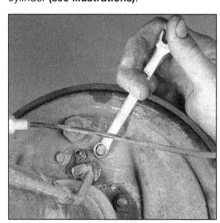

5.5a The two screws which mount the wheel cylinder are located on the inboard side of the backing plate

5.5b Removing the wheel cylinder from the backing plate

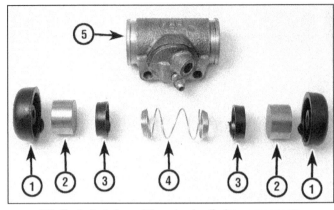

5.7 Exploded view of the wheel cylinder components

1	Dust boot	4	Spring
2	Piston	5	Wheel cylinder housing
3	Cup		

6   Using pliers, remove the boots from the cylinder and discard them.

7   Remove and discard the piston cups **(see illustration)**.

8   Inspect the cylinder bore and pistons for corrosion and pitting. Discard if pitted, but where there is staining, the surface may be polished with crocus cloth working around the circumference (not along the length).

9   Ensure your hands are clean, dry and free from grease, gasoline, kerosene or cleaning solvents then clean the metal parts in new brake fluid or denatured alcohol.

10   Shake off the surplus fluid for ease of handling.

11   Lubricate the cylinder with clean brake fluid and insert the spring expander assembly.

12   Insert new cups which must be clean and dry and not lubricated. The flat surface must be forward to enter ends of the cylinder. Use only the fingers to manipulate the cups.

13   Install the pistons, flat surface uppermost. Do not lubricate them before installation.

14   Press new boots into the cylinder counterbores. **Do not** lubricate them before installation.

15   When installing the wheel cylinder, position the wheel cylinder on the brake flange plate and install screws loosely.

16   Install the push rods and pull back springs, then connect the hydraulic line to the cylinder, moving the cylinder as necessary to prevent stripping the threads.

17   Tighten the cylinder mounting screws.

18   Install the brake drum and wheel.

19   Bleed the braking system (Section 10) then lower the vehicle to the ground.

6   Disc caliper - overhaul

Refer to illustrations 6.5, 6.11 and 6.13

1   Remove the disc pads as described in Section 4. Disconnect the brake flexible hose from the rigid brake line at the support bracket. Cap the line to prevent loss of fluid.

2   Unbolt and remove the caliper (also as described in Section 4) complete with flexible hose. Unscrew the hose from the caliper noting the copper sealing gaskets which should be replaced when the hose is reconnected.

3   To disassemble, clean the exterior of the caliper using brake fluid (never use gasoline,

kerosene or cleaning solvents) then place the assembly on a clean workbench.

4   Drain the fluid from the caliper and then place a cloth pad between the caliper piston and body then apply air pressure to the fluid inlet hole to free the piston; a small hand pump is adequate. If this method proves

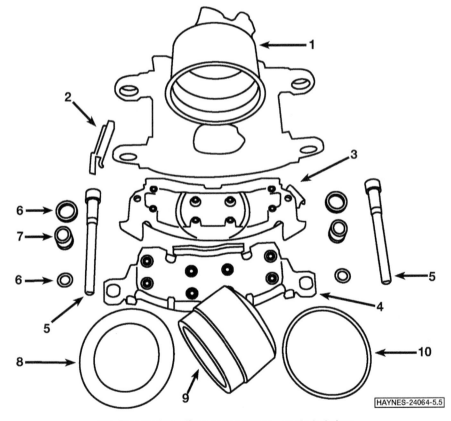

6.5 Disc brake caliper components - exploded view

1	Caliper assembly	5	Mounting bolts	8	Dust boot
2	Spring	6	Bushings2	9	Piston
3	Inner brake pad	7	Sleeves	10	Seal
4	Outer brake pad				

6.11 The piston boot should be installed in the groove, with the fold toward the open end of the piston

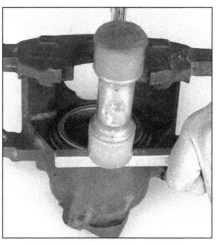

6.13 Tap the piston boot into the caliper evenly

7.2 It is best to use a flarenut wrench to disconnect the hydraulic lines at the master cylinder

unsuccessful at dislodging the piston, hydraulic fluid pressure must be used. With the brake pads removed, reconnect the caliper to the brake line on the vehicle and have an assistant slowly depress the brake pedal. The fluid will force the piston out of its bore. Be careful that the piston is not damaged.

5   Carefully pry the dust boot out of the caliper bore **(see illustration)**.

6   Using a small piece of wood or plastic, remove the piston seal from its groove in the caliper piston bore. Metal objects may cause bore damage.

7   Remove the caliper bleeder valve, then remove and discard the sleeves and bushings from the caliper ears. Also discard all rubber parts.

8   Clean the remaining parts in brake fluid. Allow them to drain and then shake them vigorously to remove as much fluid as possible.

9   Carefully examine the piston for scoring, nicks and burrs and loss of plating. if surface defects are present, parts must be replaced. Check the caliper bore in a similar way, but light polishing with crocus cloth is permissible to remove light corrosion and stains. Discard the mounting bolts if they are corroded or damaged.

10   When assembling, lubricate the piston bores and seal with clean brake fluid: position the seal in the caliper bore groove.

11   Lubricate the piston with clean brake fluid then assemble a new boot in the piston groove with the fold towards the open end of the piston **(see illustration)**.

12   Insert the piston squarely into the caliper bore then apply force to bottom the piston in the bore.

13   Position the dust boot in the caliper counterbore then use a suitable drift to drive it into its location **(see illustration)**. Ensure that the boot is installed below the caliper face and evenly all round.

14   Install the bleeder screw.

15   The remainder of the procedure for installation is the reverse of the removal procedure. Always use new copper gaskets

7.4 Removing the master cylinder. Be careful not to spill the fluid

when connecting the brake hose and finally bleed the system of air (Section 10).

7   Master cylinder - removal, overhaul and installation

Refer to illustrations 7.2, 7.4, 7.7, 7.8a, 7.8b, 7.8c, 7.8d, 7.11a, 7.11b, 7.12a, 7.12b, 7.14a, 7.14b, 7.14c and 7.15

1   As many types and sizes of master cylinders were installed on the Firebird, it may be wise to take all components with you to the auto parts store for proper fitting.

2   Remove the hydraulic lines at the master cylinder **(see illustration)**. Collect any fluid spillage with dry cloths and plug the ends of the hydraulic lines to prevent fluid loss or dirt from entering the system.

3   On manual brakes, disconnect the push rod at the brake pedal inside the car.

4   Unbolt and remove the master cylinder from the firewall or power booster **(see illustration)**. Be careful that no brake fluid is accidentally dripped on any painted surface as it will ruin the finish.

5   Drain all fluid from the master cylinder

and place the unit in a vise. Use wood blocks to cushion the jaws of the vise.

6   On manual brakes remove the push rod retaining ring.

7   Remove the secondary stop bolt from the bottom of the front fluid reservoir (Delco Moraine) or from the base of the master cylinder body (Bendix) **(see illustration)**.

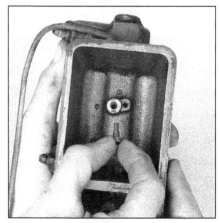

7.7 The stop bolt is located at the bottom of the reservoir

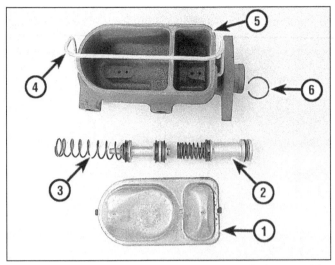

7.8a Exploded view of an early model master cylinder assembly

1 Reservoir cover
2 Primary piston assembly
3 Secondary piston assembly
4 Reservoir cover lock clip
5 Master cylinder body
6 Lock ring

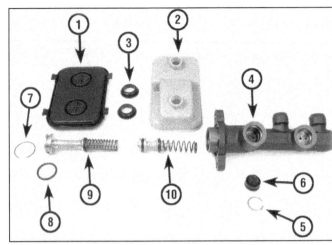

7.8b Exploded view of a later model master cylinder assembly

1 Reservoir cover and diaphragm
2 Reservoir
3 Reservoir grommets
4 Master cylinder body
5 Quick take-up valve circlip
6 Quick take-up valve
7 Lock ring
8 Primary piston O-ring
9 Primary piston assembly
10 Secondary piston assembly

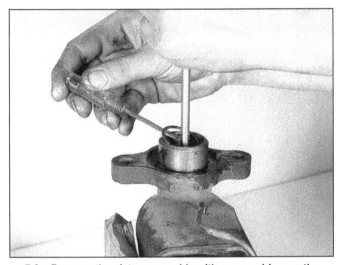

7.8c Depress the piston assembly with a screwdriver as the retaining ring is pried free with a screwdriver

7.8d A wire hook can be used to draw out the piston assembly

8 Remove the retaining ring from the groove **(see illustrations)** and take out the primary piston assembly **(see illustration)**. Following the primary piston out of the bore will be the secondary piston, spring and retainer. A piece of bent stiff wire can be used to draw these assemblies out of the cylinder bore **(see illustration)**.

9 Examine the inside surface of the master cylinder and the secondary piston. If there is evidence of scoring or "bright" wear areas, the entire master cylinder should be replaced with a new one.

10 If the components are in good condition, wash in clean hydraulic fluid. Discard all the rubber components and the primary piston. Purchase a rebuild kit which will contain all the necessary parts for the overhaul.

11 Inspect the tube seats which are located in the master cylinder body where the fluid pipes connect. If they appear damaged they

should be replaced with new ones which come in the overhaul kit. They are forced out of the body by threading a screw into the tube and then prying outwards **(see illustration)**.

The new ones are forced into place using a spare brake line nut **(see illustration)**. All parts necessary for this should be included in the rebuild kit.

7.11a After a screw is threaded into the tube seat, two screwdrivers are used to pry the tube seat out of its bore

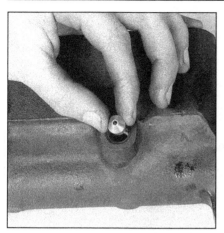

7.11b A new tube seat being installed

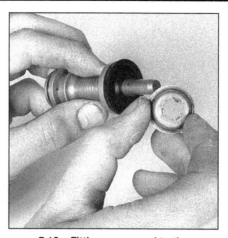

7.12a Fitting a new seal to the secondary piston

7.12b A new seal at the other end of the secondary piston

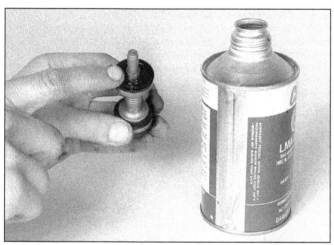

7.14a All parts should be liberally coated with fresh brake fluid during assembly

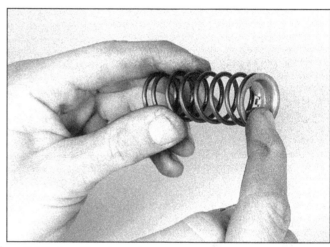

7.14b Installing the spring retainer to the end of the spring

12   Place the new secondary seals in the grooves of the secondary piston **(see illustrations)**.
13   Assemble the primary seals and seal protector over the end of the secondary piston.

14   Lubricate the cylinder bore and secondary piston with brake fluid **(see illustration)**. Insert the spring retainer into the spring then place the retainer and spring over the end of the secondary piston **(see illustrations)**. The retainer should locate

inside the primary seal lips.
15   With the master cylinder vertical, push the secondary piston into the bore to seat its spring **(see illustration)**.
16   Coat the seals of the primary piston with brake fluid and fit it into the cylinder bore.

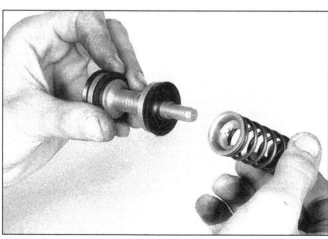

7.14c The spring assembly is then pushed onto the secondary piston assembly

7.15 The piston/spring assembly is then pushed into the master cylinder bore

Hold it down while the retaining ring is installed in the cylinder groove.

17 Continue to hold the piston down while the stop screw is installed.

18 Install the reservoir diaphragm into the reservoir cover plate making sure it is fully collapsed inside the recessed lid.

19 Install the master cylinder in the reverse order of removal, tightening the attaching nuts to specifications.

20 Fill the master cylinder with fresh brake fluid and bleed the master cylinder and complete hydraulic system as outlined in Section 10.

8 Hydraulic brake hoses - inspection, removal and installation

1 Periodically, examine all hydraulic brake lines, both rigid and flexible, for rusting, chafing and general deterioration. Also check the security of the connections.

2 If the hoses or pipes have to be disconnected, extensive loss of fluid can be avoided if the vent holes in the master cylinder fluid reservoir cap are taped over to create a vacuum.

Drum brakes

3 Using a back-up wrench on the hose fitting, unscrew the connector from the hose fitting.

4 Remove the U-shaped retainer from the hose fitting, withdraw the hose fitting from the support bracket, turn it out of the wheel cylinder and remove the copper gasket.

5 When installing, use a new copper gasket, moisten the screw threads with brake fluid and torque-tighten to the wheel cylinder.

6 With the weight on the suspension and the wheels "straight-ahead", insert the female end of the hose through the support bracket, allow it to seek its own position without kinking then install the U- shaped retainer and secure the hose in the bracket.

7 Turn the wheels from lock-to-lock to ensure that the hose does not contact other parts (reposition the female end if necessary).

8 Place the tubular steel connector in the hose fitting and torque- tighten, using a back-up wrench on the hose fitting.

9 Remove the tape from the master cylinder reservoir, top-up with new brake fluid and then bleed the system of air.

Disc brakes

10 To disconnect a rigid line from a flexible hose, unscrew the connector out of the hose end fitting. These connectors are located at the support brackets. Always hold the flexible hose and fitting quite still by using an open-ended wrench.

11 To remove the flexible hose, extract the retainer from the hose and fitting and pull the hose from the support bracket.

12 Remove the hose to caliper bolt, remove the center connector and the hose.

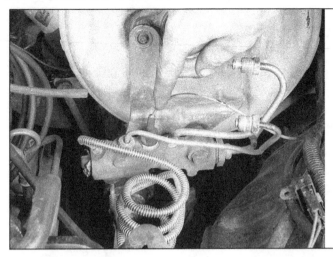

9.1 The combination valve is located just under the master cylinder in most models. The electrical wire is for the dashboard warning light

13 Installation is a reversal of removal but always use new copper gaskets in conjunction with the flexible hose end fittings and always let the flexible hose take up its natural curvature; never secure it in a twisted or kinked position.

Rigid lines

14 Rigid lines which need to be replaced can be purchased at many service stations. Take the old pipe as a pattern and make sure that the pipes are fitted with the correct connectors and that the ends are double-flared.

9 Hydraulic system pressure valves and switches

Refer to illustration 9.1

1 On all models a combination distribution block, or combination valve is installed in the hydraulic line **(see illustration)**. It is located adjacent to the master cylinder or on the inside of the body frame rail and its functions are as follows:

The metering valve holds off full pressure to the front disc brakes until a certain pressure level is reached. This allows the pressure in the rear brake circuit to build up sufficiently to overcome the force of the shoe retracting springs and ensure balanced braking between front and rear wheels.

The warning switch incorporates a piston which normally remains in a central position (in balance) when the front and rear independent hydraulic pressures are equal. In the event of a failure in either circuit, the piston is displaced and completes an electrical circuit through a switch terminal and lights a warning lamp in the vehicle interior.

The proportioning valve limits hydraulic pressure to the rear brakes to prevent them locking before full braking effort is obtained by the front disc brakes.

2 The following tests should be carried out periodically.

Brake warning lamp check

3 Disconnect the electrical lead from the switch terminal and connect the lead to ground.

4 Turn the ignition switch "ON" and the brake failure warning lamp should light up. If it does not, check for burned out bulb or faulty wiring.

Warning switch operation check

5 The operation of the switch can be checked by switching on the ignition and, with the help of an assistant, bleeding first a front caliper and then a rear wheel cylinder as described in the following Section. The warning lamp should light as soon as the bleeder valve is released and heavy pressure is applied to the brake foot pedal.

6 Any fault detected in the switch can only be rectified by replacement of the complete valve/switch assembly.

7 Bleed the hydraulic system (both circuits) on completion as described in the next Section.

10 Hydraulic system - bleeding

Refer to illustrations 10.3, 10.4 and 10.5

Note: *Never allow the hydraulic fluid to come in contact with the paint work of the vehicle as it acts as an efficient paint stripper.*

1 Whenever the hydraulic system is disconnected (to remove or install a component) air will enter the fluid lines and bleeding must be carried out. This is not a routine operation and if air enters the system without any repair operations having been carried out, then the cause must be sought and the fault rectified.

2 When applying the foot brake pedal, if the first application causes the pedal to go down further than usual but an immediate second or third application (pumping) reduces the pedal travel and improves the braking effect, this is a sure sign that there is air in the system.

3 Use only clean brake fluid (which has remained unshaken for 24 hours and has been stored in an airtight container) for topping-up the master cylinder reservoirs during

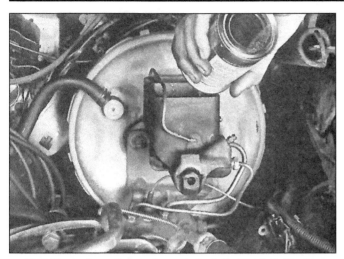

10.3 Always keep the master cylinder full of fresh fluid when bleeding the brakes

10.4 Most master cylinders are equipped with a bleeder valve. The procedure is the same

the following operations. Make sure that the reservoirs are kept topped-up during the whole of the bleeding operations otherwise air will be drawn into the system and the whole sequence of bleeding will have to be repeated **(see illustration)**. Where power brakes are fitted, depress the brake pedal several times to destroy any residual vacuum.

4   If the master cylinder is equipped with bleeder valves, do these valves first and then move to the wheel closest to the master cylinder **(see illustration)**. Proceed to each wheel, working away from the master cylinder.

5   Push a length of hose onto the bleeder valve and then immerse the open end of the hose in a jar containing sufficient brake fluid to keep the end of the hose well covered **(see illustration)**.

6   Unscrew the bleeder valve 3/4 turn and have an assistant depress the brake pedal. Just before the pedal reaches the floor, close the bleeder valve and allow the pedal to be released. Bubbles will flow from the tube as

air is expelled and the operation must be repeated until the bubbles cease.

7   Repeat the operation on the other front caliper then transfer operations to the rear brakes. At all times remember to maintain the fluid level as stated in paragraph 3.

8   On vehicles equipped with a combination valve the pin in the end of the metering part of the valve must be held in the open position. This can be carried out using the official tool or a similar device clamped under the mounting bolt which should have been temporarily loosened. The pin must be pushed, and held in.

9   If any difficulty is experienced in bleeding the hydraulic system or if the help of an assistant cannot be obtained, a pressure bleeding kit is a worthwhile investment. If connected in accordance with the makers' instructions, each bleed valve can be opened in turn to allow the system fluid to be pressure ejected until clear of air bubbles without the need to replenish the master cylinder reservoir during the process.

10   If the front or rear hydraulic circuit has been "broken" beyond the distribution block then only the particular circuit concerned need be bled. If the master cylinder has been removed and replaced or its connecting pipelines, then both circuits must be bled.

11 Disc and drum - inspection and renovation

Refer to illustrations 11.1, 11.3, 11.5 and 11.7

1   Whenever the disc brake pads are inspected for wear, take the opportunity to check the condition of the disc (rotor) surfaces. Light scoring or grooving is normal but deep grooves or severe erosion are not **(see illustration)**. 1974 and earlier models have a single deep groove in the rotor called a "squeal" groove. Do not be fooled into thinking this groove is due to damage.

2   If vibration has been noticed during application of the brake pedal, suspect disc runout.

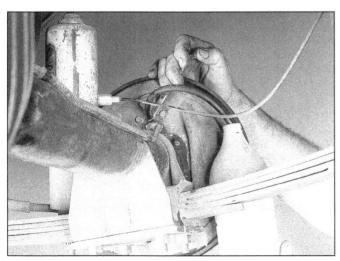

10.5 Bleeding the rear brake system

11.1 Check the rotor for deep grooves and score marks (be sure to inspect both sides of the rotor)

11.3 Check rotor runout with a dial indicator - if the reading exceeds the maximum allowable runout, the rotor will have to be resurfaced or replaced

11.5 A micrometer is used to measure rotor thickness - this can be done on the vehicle (as shown) or on the bench (the minimum thickness is cast into the inside of the rotor)

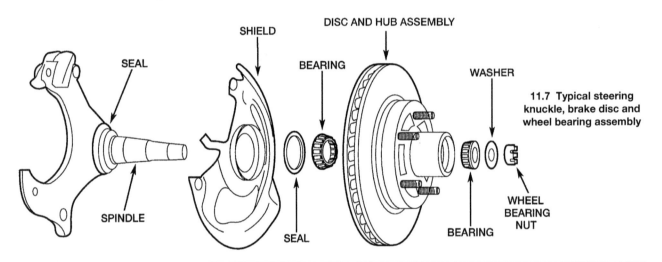

SEAL

SPINDLE

SHIELD

SEAL

DISC AND HUB ASSEMBLY

BEARING

WASHER

BEARING

WHEEL BEARING NUT

11.7 Typical steering knuckle, brake disc and wheel bearing assembly

3   To check this, a dial gauge will be required or the use of feeler blades between the disc and a fixed point **(see illustration)**.

4   Turn the disc slowly and check that the runout does not exceed 0.004 in.

5   Sometimes the different wearing characteristics of the disc material may cause it to wear to uneven thickness. Any variation in thickness over 0.0005 in will also cause vibration during brake application **(see illustration)**.

6   Discs usually have the wear limit and refinish thickness dimensions cast into them.

7   If your dealer cannot refinish a disc to come within the specified tolerances then a new disc must be installed **(see illustration)** (refer to front suspension, Chapter 11).

8   Whenever a brake drum is removed for lining inspection, check the drum for cracks, scoring or out of round.

9   An out of round drum will usually give rise to a pulsating feeling of the brake pedal as the brakes are applied. The internal diameter should be checked at several different points using an internal micrometer. Drums can be refinished internally provided the wear and refinish sizes cast into it are not exceeded.

12   Brake pedal - removal and installation

1   Disconnect the battery ground cable.

2   Disconnect the clutch pedal return spring if a manual transmission is fitted.

3   Remove the clip retainer from the push rod pin which travels through the pedal arm.

4   Remove the nut from the pedal shaft bolt. Slide the shaft out far enough to clear the brake pedal arm.

5   The brake pedal can now be removed, along with the spacer and bushing. The clutch pedal (if equipped) will remain in place.

6   When installing, lubricate the spacer and bushings with brake lube and tighten the pivot nut to specifications.

13   Stop lamp switch - replacement and adjustment

1   This switch is located on a flange or bracket protruding from the brake pedal support.

2   With the brake pedal in the fully released position, the plunger on the body of the switch should be fully pressed in. When the pedal is pushed in, the plunger releases and sends electrical current to the stop lights at the rear of the car.

3   Electrical contact should be made when the pedal is depressed .38 to .64 inches. If this is not the case, the switch can be adjusted by turning it in or out as required.

4   To replace the switch if it is faulty, disconnect the electrical coupler (two couplers if car is equipped with cruise control) and loosen the switch lock nut until the switch can be unscrewed from the bracket. Installation is a reversal of this procedure.

14   Parking brake - adjustment

Refer to illustration 14.3

1   The adjustment of the parking brake cable may be necessary whenever the rear brake cables have been disconnected or the parking brake cables have stretched due to age and stress.

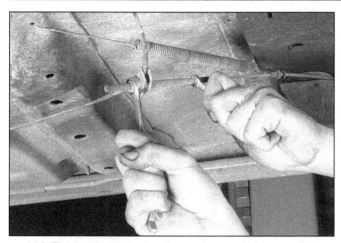
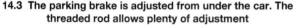

14.3 The parking brake is adjusted from under the car. The threaded rod allows plenty of adjustment

17.2 Disconnecting the vacuum hose to the power booster

2   Depress the parking brake pedal exactly two ratchet clicks and then raise the car for access underneath.
3   Tighten the adjusting nut until the left rear tire can just barely be turned in a rearward motion (see illustration). The tire should be completely locked from moving in a forward rotation.
4   Carefully release the parking brake pedal and check that the tire is able to rotate freely in either direction. It is important that there is no drag on the rear brakes with the pedal released.

15   Parking brake pedal - removal and installation

1   Disconnect the battery ground cable and the parking brake warning switch wire.
2   Remove the clip and ball from the clevis (if necessary, the equalizer nut can be slackened).
3   Remove the pedal rear mounting bolt and the nuts from the mounting studs at the front of the firewall (under the hood).
4   Remove the pedal assembly.
5   Installation is the reverse of the removal procedure, but the nuts and pedal rear mounting bolt must be torque tightened.

16   Power brake booster - general description

1   A power brake booster has been an option on all models since its introduction. The booster utilizes vacuum from the intake manifold.
2   In the event of a fault developing in the booster, enough vacuum is stored to provide sufficient assistance for two or three brake applications and after that the performance of the hydraulic part of the braking system is only affected in so far as the need for higher pedal pressures will be noticed. Alternative types of power brake boosters have been used; these are the Delco-Moraine and the

Bendix types. The principle of operation is similar in each case, and the descriptive cycle given in the following paragraph is applicable to both types.
3   Brakes released: In the "at rest" condition with the engine running, vacuum is present on both sides of the power piston. Air at atmospheric pressure, entering through the filter behind the push rod, is shut off at the air valve. The floating control valve is held away from the seat in the power piston insert. Any air in the system is drawn through a small passage in the power piston, past the power piston insert valve seat to the insert itself. It then travels through a drilling in the support plate, into the space in front of the power piston then to the intake manifold via a check valve. Vacuum therefore exists on both sides of the power piston which is held against the rear of the housing under spring action.
4   Brake application: When the pedal is depressed, the push rod carries the air valve away from the floating control valve. The floating control valve will follow until it contacts the raised seat in the power piston insert: vacuum is now shut off to the rear power piston and atmospheric air enters through the filter past the air valve seat and through a passage into the housing at the rear of the power piston. The power piston therefore moves forward to operate the floating piston assembly of the hydraulic master cylinder. As pressure increases on the end of the master cylinder piston, the hydraulic reaction plate is moved off its seat on the lower piston and contacts the reaction levers. These levers swing on their pivots and bear against the end of the air valve operating rod assembly to provide a feed back (approximately 30% of the master cylinder load) to the pedal. This enables the driver to "feel" the degree of brake application.
5   Brake holding: When the desired braking force is achieved the power piston moves forward until the floating control valve again seats on the air valve. The power piston will now remain stationary until there is a change in applied pedal pressure.

6   Brakes released: When the pedal pressure is released the air valve is forced back to contact the power piston under spring action. As it moves, the floating control valve is pushed off its seat on the power piston insert by the air valve. Atmospheric air is shut off by the air valve seating on the floating control valve. As the floating control cable lifts from its seat. it opens the rear of the power piston to intake manifold vacuum, and the power piston returns to the rear housing. The hydraulic pressure in the brake system is released as the floating piston assembly returns to the normal position.
7   Vacuum failure: In the event of vacuum failure, i.e.; engine switched off or failure of the vacuum line, application of the brake pedal moves the pedal push rod which in turn contacts the master cylinder push rod and the brakes are applied. This gives a condition as found in the standard braking system, and a correspondingly higher pedal pressure is required.
8   The power brake unit requires no special maintenance apart from periodic inspection of the hoses and inspection of the air filter beneath the boot at the pedal push rod end.
9   Dismantling of the power brake unit requires the use of special tools and in the event of a fault developing, it is recommended that a new or factory-exchange unit is fitted rather than attempt to overhaul the original booster.

17   Power brake booster - removal and installation

Refer to illustrations 17.2 and 17.3
1   Remove the securing nuts which hold the master cylinder to the power brake unit. Position the master cylinder out of the way, being careful not to strain the hydraulic lines leading to the master cylinder. If there is any doubt as to the flexibility of the fluid lines disconnect them at the cylinder and plug the ends.
2   Disconnect the vacuum hose leading to the front of the power brake booster (see illustration). Cover the end of the hose.

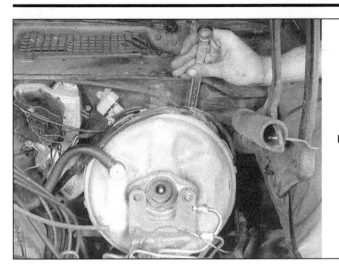

17.3 The attaching nuts for the booster assembly are between the booster and the firewall

3   Loosen the four nuts that secure the booster to the firewall **(see illustration)**. Do not remove these nuts at this time.

4   Inside the car, disconnect the power brake push rod from the brake pedal. Do not force the push rod to the side when disconnecting.

5   Now fully remove the four booster mounting nuts and carefully lift the unit out of the engine compartment.

6   When installing, loosely install the four mounting nuts and then connect the push rod to the brake pedal. Torque-tighten the attaching nuts and reconnect the vacuum hose and master cylinder. If the hydraulic brake fluid lines were disconnected, the master cylinder as well as the entire braking system should be bled to eliminate any air which has entered the system (see Section 10).

Chapter 10
Chassis electrical system

Contents

Specifications

Wiper motor

Type	2 speed, non-depressed park
Gear ratio	51 : 1
Current:	
low speed	6.0A
high speed	4.5A
Stall	18A max

Windshield washer

Type	Positive displacement, piston type
Mounting	Integral with wiper motor

Fuses

Circuit	Rating (amp)
1970	
Radio, tape player, accessories	10
Turn signal, heater back up lamps, cruise control	20
Instrument lamps	4
Tail, parking, side marker lamps	20
Stop, hazard warning lamps	20
Courtesy, dome, cigar lighter, clock lamps	20
Gauges, tell tale lamps	10
Windshield wiper motor	20
Air conditioning, TCS system	25

Fuses (continued)

Circuit	Rating (amp)
1971 through 1973	
Radio, TCS System, rear defogger Hydra-Matic downshift	10
Windshield wiper	25
Stop lamps, hazard flasher	20
Heater, air conditioner	25
Turn signal, back-up lamps, Cruise master, power windows	20
Instrument lamps, heater dial	3
Instrument panel lamps, gauges	10
Clock, courtesy lights, cigar lighter, anti-diesel valve, glove box lamp, light watch system	20
Tail, parking, rear license, dome and side marker lamp	20
Air conditioner high speed blower fuse	30
(in-line fuse located between horn relay and air conditioner relay)	

1974 on	
Radio, TCS system, anti-diesel valve, Hydra-Matic downshift, pulse wiper	10
Windshield wiper	25
Stop lamps, hazard flasher	20
Heater, air conditioner	25
Turn signal, back-up lamps, side marker, blocking relay (air conditioner), power windows	20
Instrument and floor shift lamps, heater dial	4
Gauges, instrument panel warning, rear defogger, Cruise control, seat belt buzzer	10
Clock, courtesy lamp, cigar lighter, trunk, glove box, dome lamp	20
Tail, rear license, side marker lamps	20
Air conditioner high speed blower fuse (in-line fuse located between horn relay and air conditioner relay)	30

Bulbs

Lamp	Candlepower/watts	Bulb No
1970 through 1973		
Headlamp outer		
high	60W	6014
low	50W	Sealed beam
Parking, directional (front and rear)	32/3	1157
Rear license plate	4	67
Back-up lamp	32	1156
Glove compartment	2	1895
Instrument panel lamps	2	194
Side marker	2	194
Heater control	27 (1972-on)	1895 1445 (1972-on)
Interior dome	12	211
Map lamp	4	563
Courtesy lamp	6	631
Radio dial	2	1893
(AM)	2	293
Washer fluid level indicator	3	168
Trunk lamp	15	1003
Underhood lamp	15	93
Radio dial (except stereo and tape player)	3	1816
Radio dial (stereo and tape player)	3	564
Rear seat courtesy	6	212
1974 on		
Headlamp		
high beam	60W	6014
low beam	50W	Sealed beam
Front turn and parking	24/2.2	1157 NA
Rear tail, stop, turn	32/3	1157
Rear license plate	33	168
Glove compartment	2	1891
Indicator and warning lamps	2	194
Instrument panel cluster lamps	3	168
Side marker	2	194

Lamp

Lamp	Candlepower/watts	Bulb No
Heater, air conditioner panel lamps	2	194
Interior dome lamp	12	561
Trunk lamp	15	1003
Underhood lamp	15	93
Courtesy lamp	6	631
Radio dial lamp (excluding stereo and tape)	1	1893
Radio dial lamp (stereo and tape)	2	1893
Reading lamp	15	1004
Radio indicator	+ LED	D5410

Torque specifications

	Ft-lb
Starter motor mountings bolts	30
Alternator pulley unit	45

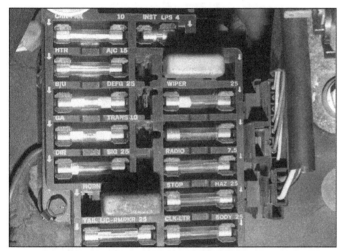

2.1a On most models the fuse block is located under the dash to the left of the driver (early style fuse block, with glass fuses shown)

2.1b Later models use miniaturized fuses in the fuse block

1   General description

The electrical system is of the 12 volt, negative ground type.

Power for the lighting system and all electrical accessories is supplied by a lead/acid type battery which is charged by an alternator.

This chapter covers repair and service procedures for the various lighting and electrical components not associated with the engine. Information on the battery, alternator, voltage regulator and starter motor can be found in Chapter 5.

It should be noted that whenever portions of the electrical system are worked on, the negative battery cable should be disconnected to prevent electrical shorts and/or fires.

2   Fuses

Refer to illustrations 2.1a, 2.1b and 2.4

The electrical circuits of the vehicle are protected by a combination of fuses, circuit breakers and fusible links. The fuse block is located under the instrument panel on the left

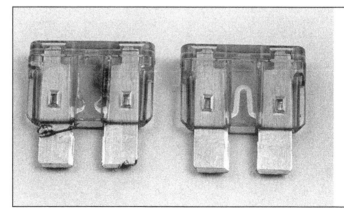

2.4 When a fuse blows, the element between the terminals melts - the fuse on the left is blown, the fuse on the right is good

side of the dashboard **(see illustrations)**.

Each of the fuses is designed to protect a specific circuit, and the various circuits are identified on the fuse panel itself.

A blown fuse on earlier models can be readily identified by inspecting the element inside the glass tube. If this metal element is broken, the fuse is inoperable and must be replaced with a new one.

On later models, miniaturized fuses are employed in the fuse block. These compact fuses, with blade terminal design, allow fingertip removal and replacement. If an electrical

component fails, always check the fuse first. The easiest way to check fuses is with a test light. Check for power at the exposed terminal tips of each fuse. If power is present on one side of the fuse but not the other, the fuse is blown. A blown fuse can also be confirmed by visually inspecting it **(see illustration)**.

Be sure to replace blown fuses with the correct type. Fuses of different ratings are physically interchangeable, but only fuses of the proper rating should be used. Replacing a fuse with one of a higher or lower value than specified is not recommended. Each electrical circuit needs a specific amount of protection. The amperage value of each fuse is indicated on the metal end of the fuse (glass body fuses) or is molded into the fuse body (miniturized fuses).

If the replacement fuse immediately fails, don't replace it again until the cause of the problem is isolated and corrected. In most cases, the cause will be a short circuit in the wiring caused by a broken or deteriorated wire.

3   Fusible links

1   In addition to fuses, the wiring system incorporates fusible links for overload protection. These links are used in circuits which are not ordinarily fused, such as the ignition circuit.
2   Although the fusible links appear to be of a heavier gauge than the wire they are protecting, this appearance is due to the heavy insulation. All fusible links are four wire gauges smaller than the wire they are incorporated into.
3   The exact locations of the four fusible links used may differ slightly but their protective circuits are the same. They are as follows:
  a) *A 14-gauge fusible link protecting the 10-gauge battery charging circuit. This may be located at the "Bat" terminal of the starter solenoid or as a pigtail lead at the battery positive cable.*
  b) *A 16-gauge link to protect all unfused wiring of 12-gauge or larger. This is located at the horn relay or junction block.*
  c) *A 20-gauge link is used to protect the generator warning light and the field circuitry which is of 16-gauge thickness. This link is also located at the junction block Later models also have another fusible link at the horn relay for this purpose.*
  d) *Two fusible links are used to protect the ammeter circuit. They are 20-gauge and located at the junction block and horn relay.*
4   The fusible links cannot be repaired, but rather a new link of the same wire size and Hypalon insulation can be put in its place. This process is as follows:
5   Disconnect the battery ground cable.
6   Disconnect the fusible link from the starter solenoid.
7   Cut the damaged fusible link out of the wiring system. Do this just behind the connector.
8   Strip the insulation from the circuit wiring approximately 1/2-inch.
9   Position connector on the new fusible link and crimp into place in the wiring circuit.
10   Use rosin core solder at each end of the new link to obtain a good solder joint.
11   Use plenty of electrical tape around the soldered joint. No exposed wiring should show.

7.2 Removing the decorative bezel around the headlamp

12   Connect the fusible link at the starter solenoid. Connect the battery ground cable. Test circuit for proper operation.

4   Circuit breakers

1   A circuit breaker is used to protect the headlight wiring, and located in the light switch. An electrical overload in the system will cause the lights to go on and off, or in some cases to remain off. If this happens, check the entire headlight wiring system immediately. Once the overload condition is corrected the circuit breaker will function normally.
2   Vehicles equipped with power windows and/or power door locks will also have a circuit breaker for protection of electrical overloads to these circuits. They are located on the interior fuse panel under the left end of the dash.

5   Turn signal and hazard flashers

1   Small canister-shaped flasher units are incorporated into the electrical circuits for the directional signals and hazard warning lights.
2   When the units are functioning properly an audible click can be heard with the circuit in operation. If the turn signals fail on one side only, and the flasher unit cannot be heard, a faulty bulb is indicated. If the flasher click can be heard, a short in the wiring is indicated.
3   If the turn signals fail on both sides, the fault may be due to a blown fuse, faulty flasher unit or switch, or a broken or loose connection. If the fuse has blown, check the wiring for a short before installing a new fuse.
4   The hazard warning lamps are checked in the same manner as paragraph 3 above.
5   The hazard warning flasher unit is located in the fuse box located under the dashboard on the left side. The turn signal flasher may be mounted in the fuse box or under the lower lip of the instrument panel.

7.4 Support the headlamp as the retaining ring screws are removed

6   When replacing either of these flasher units it is important to buy a replacement of the same capacity. Vehicles of model years 1970-1977 have 2-lamp turn signal flashers and 4-lamp hazard units. 1978 and later models have 2-lamp turn signal units and 6-lamp hazard flashers. Check the new flasher against the old one to be assured of the proper replacement.

6   Horns - fault testing

1   If the horn proves inoperable, your first check should be the fuse. A blown fuse can be readily identified at the fuse box under the lower left side of the dashboard.
2   If the fuse is in good condition, disconnect the electrical lead at the horn. Run a jumper wire from a 12-volt source (+ battery terminal) to the wiring terminal on the horn. If the horn does not blow, the fault lies in the grounding of the horn or the horn itself.
3   If current is not reaching the horn, indicated by the horn sounding from the above test, there is a failure in the circuit before the horn.
4   In most cases a failure of the horn relay is indicated if the circuit before the horn is at fault. Other checks would include bent metal contacts on the horn actuator or loose or broken wires in the system.
5   The horn relay is located in the wiring system, usually under the dashboard near the fuse box. When checking or replacing the horn relay be aware that the threaded stud is always hot and shorting of this stud to ground could destroy a fusible link, disabling the vehicle until the link is replaced.

7   Headlight sealed beam unit - removal and installation

Refer to illustrations 7.2, 7.4 and 7.5
1   Whenever replacing the headlight, do not turn the spring-loaded adjusting screws

7.5 Pull outwards on the headlamp until the electrical connector can be disconnected

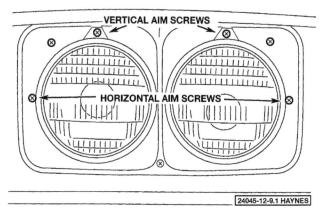

8.1 Typical headlight adjusting screw locations

of the headlight, as this will alter the aim.

2   Remove the headlight bezel screws and remove the decorative bezel **(see illustration)**.

3   Use a cotter pin removal tool or similar device to unhook the spring from the retaining ring.

4   Remove the two screws which secure the retaining ring and withdraw the ring. Support the light as this is done **(see illustration)**.

5   Pull the sealed beam unit outward slightly and disconnect the electrical connector from the rear of the light. Remove the light from the vehicle **(see illustration)**.

6   Position the new unit close enough to connect the electrical connector. Make sure that the numbers molded into the lens are at the top.

7   Install the retaining ring with its mounting screws and spring.

8   Install the decorative bezel and check for proper operation. If the adjusting screws were not altered, the new headlight will not need to have the aim adjusted.

8   Headlamps - adjustment

Refer to illustrations 8.1 and 8.2

Note: *The headlights must be aimed correctly. If adjusted incorrectly they could blind the driver of an oncoming vehicle and cause a serious accident or seriously reduce your ability to see the road. The headlights should be checked for proper aim every 12 months and any time a new headlight is installed or front end body work is performed. It should be emphasized that the following procedure is only an interim step which will provide temporary adjustment until the headlights can be adjusted by a properly equipped shop.*

1   Headlights have two spring loaded adjusting screws, one on the top controlling up-and-down movement and one on the side controlling left-and-right movement **(see illustration)**.

2   There are several methods of adjusting

the headlights. The simplest method requires a blank wall 25 feet in front of the vehicle and a level floor **(see illustration)**.

3   Position masking tape vertically on the

wall in reference to the vehicle centerline and the centerlines of both headlights.

4   Position a horizontal tape line in reference to the centerline of all the headlights.

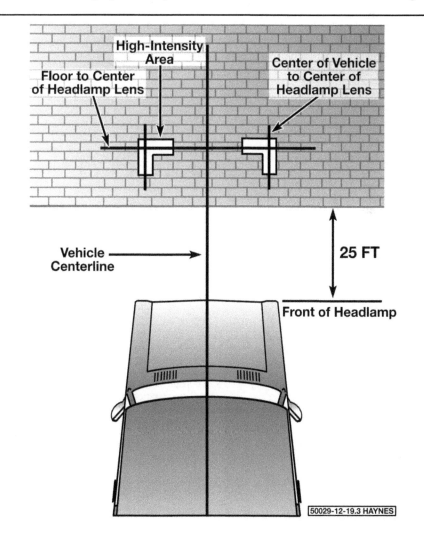

8.2 Headlight aiming details

9.1 On most models the entire parking light assembly is withdrawn from the body for access to the bulb

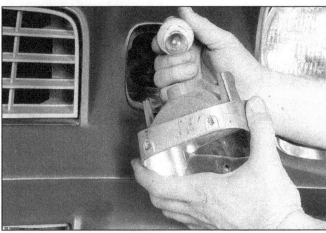

9.2 The bulb is located inside a socket which is twisted out of the light housing

Note: *It may be easier to position the tape on the wall with the vehicle parked only a few inches away.*

5   Adjustment should be made with the vehicle sitting level, the gas tank half-full and no unusually heavy load in the vehicle.

6   Starting with the low beam adjustment, position the high intensity zone so it is two inches below the horizontal line and two inches to the side of the headlight vertical line, away from the oncoming traffic. Adjustment is made by turning the top adjusting screw clockwise to raise the beam and counterclockwise to lower the beam. The adjusting screw on the side should be used in the same manner to move the beam left or right.

7   With the high beams on, the high intensity zone should be vertically centered with the exact center just below the horizontal line. **Note:** *It may not be possible to position the headlight aim exactly for both high and low beams. If a compromise must be made, keep in mind that the low beams are the most used and have the greatest effect on driver safety.*

8   Have the headlights adjusted by a dealer service department or service station at the earliest opportunity.

---

9   Bulb replacement - front end

Parking lamp

1970 - 1973

Refer to illustrations 9.1 and 9.2

1   Remove the screws which secure the lens to the body. Carefully extract the lens, being careful not to damage the fiber gasket **(see illustration)**.

2   Push in on the bulb and turn it 4 turn counterclockwise. Remove the bulb from the socket **(see illustration)**.

3   Check that the electrical contacts and wiring are in a useable condition and push the new bulb into place. This is done with a twisting motion.

4   Check the operation of the new bulb and if satisfactory, install the lens covering.

1974 - 1980

5   The bulb is housed in a metal socket which is located behind the grille.

6   Twist the socket out of the rear of the housing and replace the bulb as described for earlier vehicles.

Side marker lamps

All models

7   The bulb is located inside a twist socket at the rear of the housing. Twist the socket on the inner fender panel 1/4 turn and disengage the socket and bulb from the housing. The old bulb can then be released from the socket and a new one put in its place.

---

10   Bulb replacement - rear end

Refer to illustration 10.2

1   All the various bulbs for the rear end lighting are accessible from inside the trunk. The bulbs are located inside a metal socket which is secured to the rear of the particular housing.

2   The lamp bulb socket for all the lamps except the license plate is removed by twisting the socket 1/4 turn. The bulb inside the socket can then be replaced and the socket re-installed **(see illustration)**.

3   In most cases the license plate sockets must be pried out of the rear of the housing. Use a screwdriver to carefully lift the socket and bulb out of the hole in the housing. Replace the bulb and then push the socket back into position.

---

11   Bulb replacement - interior lamps

Center console lamps

1   Pry up the switch assembly from the console and remove the bulb from its socket.

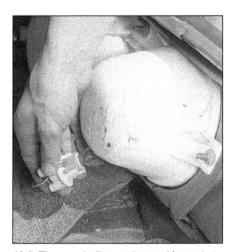

10.2 The rear bulbs are located in sockets which are twisted out of position. Access is through trunk

2   The courtesy lamp bulb is accessible after extracting the lens screws and removing the lens.

Automatic floor shift quadrant lamps

3   Remove the quadrant trim plate from the console and withdraw the lamp socket.

Interior (roof) lamp

4   Pinch the sides of the plastic lamp lens together and remove it.

5   The festoon type bulb can now be carefully pried from between the spring contacts.

---

12   Bulb replacement - instrument panel

---

1   All of the instrument illumination and telltale bulbs are mounted in twist sockets on the rear of the printed circuit instrument panel.

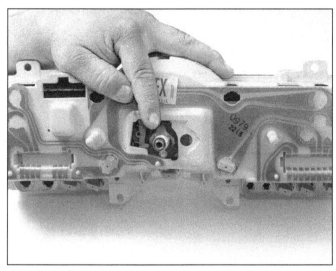

16.2 Reach behind the cluster and depress the clip to release the speedometer cable

16.4 Use pliers to pull the speedometer cable out of the housing

2   Most of the sockets can be reached without removing the instrument panel. For better access it is recommended that the steering column trim cover be removed from the lower portion of the dashboard. On most models there are a total of six screws retaining this panel. with two of those screws hidden above the ashtray. If, with the trim cover removed, the upper bulbs are still inaccessible, then the instrument cluster will have to be removed (See Section 17).

13 Headlamp switch - removal and installation

1   Disconnect the negative cable at the battery.
2   Remove the steering column cover from the bottom of the dashboard for better access.
3   With the headlights in the "full on" position, reach up under the dashboard and depress the lighting switch shaft retainer while pulling gently on the lighting knob. Remove the shaft and knob assembly.
4   Remove the nut which secures the lighting switch to the carrier.
5   For better access to the switch, remove the screws which secure the instrument cluster carrier and tilt the cluster.
6   Unplug the electrical connector at the switch and remove the switch .
7   Installation is a reversal of removal, however, make sure that all ground connections are refastened and that the switch shaft is fully seated in the switch. The shaft retainer should lock the shaft into place.

14 Windshield wiper-washer control - removal and installation

1   Remove the negative battery cable at the battery.

2   Remove the steering column trim cover with the air conditioning lap cooler attached to it. Two of the securing screws are hidden above the ash tray.
3   Remove the screws securing the instrument cluster and pull the cluster outward slightly to gain better access to the switch (see Section 17).
4   Disconnect the electrical connector from the rear of the switch.
5   Remove the screws securing the switch to the instrument cluster and remove the switch.
6   Installation is a reversal of removal, however, make sure that all ground wires are reconnected.

15 Cigar lighter assembly - removal and installation

1   Disconnect the negative cable at the battery.
2   Reach up under the dashboard and disconnect the electrical connector at the rear of the lighter housing. On some early models it may be necessary to remove the steering column trim panel at the bottom of the dashboard for better access.
3   Grip the retainer from the rear of the instrument carrier and unscrew the lighter housing from the front. A rubber thumb cover will help during this operation.
4   When installing make sure the grounding ring is between the lighter housing and the retainer.

16 Speedometer cable - replacement

Refer to illustrations 16.2 and 16.4
1   Disconnect the negative battery cable.
2   Reach up under the dashboard and dis-

connect the speedometer cable casing from the speedometer head **(see illustration)**. This is done by pressing the retaining spring clip towards the front of the instrument cluster and then pulling back on the speedometer cable casing.
3   Remove the dash panel sealing plug from the casing.
4   Using pliers, pull the old core out of the top of the casing **(see illustration)**. If the inner cable has broken, it will be necessary to remove the lower piece of cable from under the vehicle. Some models come equipped with a two-piece speedometer cable, while some have a single cable leading all the way from the speedometer head to the transmission. Ascertain which type you have and disconnect the lower end as necessary to pull out the remaining broken piece of inner cable.
5   When installing a new speedometer cable core always lubricate it the entire length with special lubricant designed for this purpose. Do not use oil.
6   Push the core into the casing, using a twisting motion when necessary. Make sure the end of the core is fully engaged in the pinion gear inside the transmission.
7   Reinstall the dash sealing plug and connect the casing to the rear of the instrument cluster. As in removal, push in on the retaining clip and then push the casing fully into the rear of the gauge.
8   Road test the vehicle and check for proper operation of the speedometer.

17 Instrument cluster - removal and installation

1970 - 1979

Refer to illustrations 17.2 and 17.9
1   Disconnect the battery ground cable.
2   Remove the steering column trim cover

17.2 Removing the steering column trim panel from under the dashboard

17.9 Tilting the instrument cluster outward from the dashboard opening

beneath the dashboard. This is held in place by six screws. Two of these screws are hidden above the ashtray **(see illustration)**.

3   Reach up under the dash and depress the headlamp switch shaft retainer button while gently pulling outward on the shaft and knob.

4   Remove the headlamp switch retaining nut.

5   Remove the cigar lighter element.

6   Reach up under the lower edge of the cluster and remove the two mounting screws. One is on each side of the steering column, about three inches from the column center.

7   Remove the four screws visible at the front side of the carrier.

8   Remove the ground screw for the wiper switch. If applicable, it will be located near the top left corner of the switch.

9   Tilt the carrier outwards for access to the electrical connectors for the wiper and headlamp switches. Disconnect the electrical connectors at these switches, as well as the cigar lighter **(see illustration)**.

10   Disconnect the transmission shift indictor from the steering column.

11   Disconnect the speedometer cable at the rear of the cluster. It is held in place by a tang which must be pushed forward as the cable is drawn away.

12   Disconnect the various electrical connectors attached to the rear printed circuit board and clock. Remove the wiring harness from its securing clips.

13   Remove the instrument cluster from the dash. Place on a bench for the remainder of the strip down (see following sections which are appropriate). The installation is a reversal of the removal procedure, however make sure that all ground connections are replaced in their original positions.

1980 models

14   Disconnect the battery ground cable.

15   Remove the six cluster bezel attaching screws.

16   Reach up under the dashboard and depress the headlamp retaining button while at the same time pulling gently on the headlamp switch knob.

17   Remove the headlamp switch retaining nut.

18   Disconnect the electrical couplers at the rear of the headlamp switch and windshield wiper switch. Remove the headlamp switch from the mounting hole in the bezel. Remove the windshield wiper switch which is held in place by two attaching screws.

19   Remove the cigar lighter element and disconnect the electrical connector. Unscrew the retainer from the housing and then remove the cigar lighter housing from the bezel.

20   The bezel is now free to be removed by pulling rearward.

21   Remove the cluster to carrier attaching screws and pull the instrument cluster rearward slightly for better access.

22   Disconnect the printed circuit electrical connector at the rear of the instrument cluster.

23   Disconnect the speedometer cable and wiring clips. The speedometer cable is held to the gauge by a retaining clip which must be pushed inward while the cable is pulled free.

24   Remove the instrument cluster.

25   Installation is a reversal of the removal procedure, however, make sure that all electrical connectors are firmly in place.

18   Gauge printed circuit board - replacement

1   Disconnect the negative battery cable.

2   Remove the instrument cluster as described in Section 17.

3   With the instrument cluster on a clean workbench, twist each of the illumination bulbs out of their sockets and remove the gauge securing nuts. Lift the printed circuit

off the rear of the instrument cluster.

4   Place the new printed circuit into position, securing it with the illumination bulbs and gauge nuts.

5   Reinstall the instrument cluster referring to Section 17.

6   Connect the negative battery cable.

19   Speedometer - removal and installation

1   Disconnect the negative battery cable.

2   Remove the instrument cluster as described in Section 17.

3   Remove the two screws which secure the speedometer case to the rear of the cluster. Lift the speedometer assembly from the cluster.

4   Installation is a reversal of the removal procedure. Use Section 17 as a guide if necessary when installing the instrument cluster.

20   Optional instrument cluster - servicing

1   All of the illumination bulbs, instruments (except the speedometer) and the printed circuit board are rear-loaded into the instrument cluster. This means that most of the servicing and replacement operations can take place with the cluster in position in the dashboard.

2   Vehicles equipped with air conditioning may require the cluster be removed for greater access. Follow the procedures outlined in Section 17 for removal of the instrument cluster.

Fuel, temperature and ammeter gauges

3   To remove these gauges, first disconnect the negative battery cable.

4   Remove the trim cover under the steering

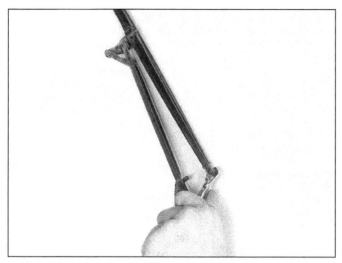

22.3 Using pliers to pinch the locking tabs on the windshield wiper blades

24.3 The splined windshield wiper arm and the small metal locking clip which must be depressed

column. This is held in place with six screws, two of them above the ash tray.

5   Remove the screws or nuts which secure the particular gauge to the rear of the cluster.

6   Remove the illumination bulbs which also are used to secure the printed circuit. They are removed by twisting them 1/4 turn and pulling outwards.

7   Carefully peel back the printed circuit enough to enable you to remove the faulty gauge from the instrument cluster.

8   Installation is a reversal of the removal operations.

Tachometer and speedometer

9   Disconnect the negative battery cable.

10   Remove the instrument cluster as described in Section 17.

11   Remove the nuts or screws which secure the tachometer and speedometer to the printed circuit.

12   Remove the illumination bulbs.

13   Carefully lay back the printed circuit and remove the attaching screws for the instruments. The tachometer can then be removed through the rear of the cluster and the speedometer pulled out through the front.

14   Installation is a reversal of removal.

Clock

15   Disconnect the negative battery cable.

16   Remove the trim cover beneath the steering column. Six screws are used, two of them above the ashtray.

17   Remove the clock set stem knob at the front of the instrument cluster lens.

18   Remove the electrical connector at the rear of the clock.

19   Remove the two screws securing the clock to the rear of the instrument cluster. It may be necessary to move the printed circuit away from the clock slightly.

20   Remove the clock through the rear of the cluster. Installation is a reversal of removal.

21 Windshield wiper system - general description

1   A two-speed wiper motor is installed as standard equipment and incorporates the gear train and the self-parking mechanism.

2   The wiper arms will only park when the motor is operating in low speed.

3   The drive from the wiper motor to the wiper arms is by means of a crank arm and a strut to the transmission shafts.

4   On all models, the windshield wiper motor incorporates the drive system for the windshield washers.

5   Two types of windshield wiper assemblies may be encountered according to vehicle model. On one type, the wiper arms park parallel with and about two inches above the windshield molding while on the other type, the blades park in a depressed position against a step on the windshield lower molding.

22 Wiper blade element - replacement

Refer to illustration 22.3

1   Two methods are used to retain the rubber wiper blade element to the blade assembly. This "refill", as it is sometimes called, can be replaced without removing or disassembling the wiper mechanism.

2   One method uses a press-type button, in most cases colored red. Depress the button and then slide the rubber element off of the wiper blade. To install a new element, press the button and slide the new piece into place. Once centered on the blade, it will lock into place.

3   The other method incorporates a spring-type retainer clip at the end of the removable element. When the retainer is pinched together, the element can slide out of the

blade assembly. A small pair of pliers can be used to squeeze the retainer. When installing a new element, be certain that the metal insert passes through all of the retaining tabs of the blade assembly **(see illustration)**.

23 Windshield wiper blades - removal and installation

1   Pull the wiper arm/blade assembly away from the windshield glass against the tension of the wiper arm spring.

2   Depress the small tab which lies just below the wiper arm at the blade connector socket and pull the blade from the arm. **Note:** *On some models a coil spring blade retainer is used. To remove the blade, insert a screwdriver on top of the spring and push downwards.*

3   Installation is a reversal of removal; make sure that the connector is pushed fully onto the arm so that the small locating "pip" is secure in the hole in the connector.

24 Windshield wiper arm - removal and installation

Refer to illustration 24.3

1   Make sure that the wiper arms are in the self-parked position, the motor having been switched off in the low speed mode.

2   Note carefully the position of the wiper arm in relation to the windshield lower reveal molding. Use tape on the windshield to mark the exact location of the wiper arm on the glass.

3   Using a suitable hooked tool or a small screwdriver, pull aside the small spring tang which holds the wiper arm to the splined transmission shaft and at the same time pull the arm from the shaft **(see illustration)**.

4   Installation is a reversal of removal but do not push the arm fully home on the shaft

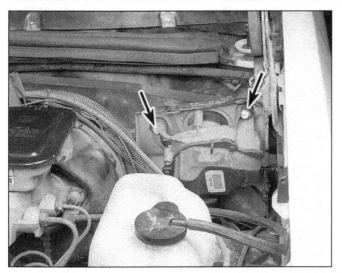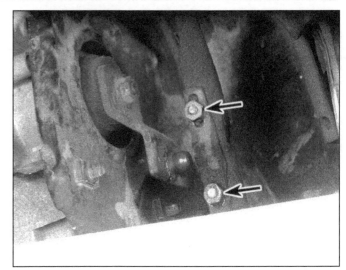

25.5 Typical windshield wiper motor installation details

until the alignment of the arm has been checked. If necessary, the arm can be pulled off again and turned through one or two serrations of the shaft to correct the alignment without the necessity of pulling aside the spring tang.

5   Finally, press the arm fully home on its shaft and then wet the windshield glass and operate the motor on low speed to ensure that the arc of travel is correct.

25   Wiper motor - removal and installation

Refer to illustration 25.5

1   Raise the hood and remove the cowl screen at the base of the windshield.
2   Reaching through the opening, loosen the transmission drive link to crank arm attaching nuts.
3   Remove the transmission drive links from the crank arm of the motor.
4   Disconnect the washer hoses and electrical wiring at the motor.
5   Remove the three bolts which secure the motor to the firewall cowling **(see illustration)**. Push the crank arm through its mounting hole and then withdraw the motor.
6   Installation is a reversal of removal, however, make sure that the motor is in the "Park" position.

26   Windshield wiper motor/transmission - servicing

1   The unit has a very long operating life and when it has finally worn so much that dismantling and repair is necessary, consideration should be given to the purchase of a new or reconditioned unit, particularly if the major components require replacement.

27   Washer assembly - removal servicing and installation

1970 through 1974 (rectangular motor type)

1   The washer pump can be removed independently, leaving the wiper motor in the vehicle. Disconnect the washer hoses and electrical wiring.
2   Remove the washer pump mounting screws and lift off the pump from the wiper motor.
3   Pull off the four lobe washer pump drive cam. This is a press fit and may require prying.
4   Remove the felt washer from the wiper shaft.
5   Remove the ratchet dog retaining screw, then hold the spring loaded solenoid plunger in position and lift the solenoid assembly and ratchet dog off the pump frame. Separate the dog from the mounting plate if necessary.
6   To remove the ratchet wheel, move the spring out of the shaft groove and slide the ratchet wheel off its shaft.
7   To separate the pump and pump actuator plate from the frame, pull the pump housing towards the valve end until the grooves in the housing clear the frame.
8   Reassembly is the reverse of the dismantling procedure.
9   Installation is the reverse of the removal procedure.

1970 on (round motor type)

10   Disconnect the washer hoses from the pump and disconnect the wires from the pump relay.
11   Remove the plastic pump cover.
12   Remove the frame screws and withdraw the pump and frame.
13   Extract the screw and lift the ratchet dog from the mounting plate.
14   Disengage the pawl spring from the

pawl and then slide the pawl from the cam follower pin.
15   Pry the ratchet spring out the slot in the shaft, hold the relay armature against the relay coil and slide the ratchet wheel off the shaft.
16   Pry off the retainer and slide the cam off the shaft.
17   Remove the relay armature and spring.
18   Chisel off the four tabs that secure the coil mounting bracket. Remove the relay coil and terminal board.
19   To remove the plastic pump housing, pull it towards the valve end until the grooves in the housing clear the base. Detach the assembly from the cam follower pin. The piston and plastic housing are serviced as an assembly.
20   The valve can be removed from the pump housing after extracting the four screws but make sure to mark the relative position of the valve to the housing before separating.
21   Reassembly is a reversal of dismantling but note that the wiper motor must be in the "Park" position before assembling the pump and the wiper motor.

28   Modified pulse (programmed) wiper/washer system - description, removal, dismantling reassembly, installation

1   This system which is fitted to some models as optional equipment is designed to provide (A) a low speed single wipe cycle delay of up to 10 seconds and (B) wash/wipe cycle comprising squirts, wiping and switching off in the "Park" position.
2   To remove the washer pump, first withdraw the complete wiper/washer assembly from the vehicle.
3   Remove the plastic tab from the opening under the terminals and pull the plastic

cover from the mounting post.

4   Disconnect the electrical leads and extract the three screws that attach the pump to the wiper transmission.

5   The valve assembly can be removed after extracting the four securing screws.

6   Slide the cam from the shaft after first removing the retainer.

7   Remove the pulse relay timing device, holding switch and override switch (one screw) from the washer frame.

8   Disconnect the red and yellow leads from the pulse relay and detach it from the locator pins.

9   Remove the dog spring assembly and the ratchet pawl retaining ring. Disconnect the pawl spring and slide the pawl from the cam follower shaft.

10   Disconnect the relay armature spring and remove the armature.

11   Release the ratchet gear spring from the groove in the shaft and slide the ratchet gear from the shaft.

12   To release the pump housing from its sheet metal hose, pull it towards the valve assembly until the grooves in the plastic pump housing clear the base. Detach the assembly from the cam follower pin.

13   Bend or chisel off the four bent over tabs that secure the coil mounting bracket to its base.

14   Reassembly is a reversal of dismantling but observe the following points.

15   When installing the pulse relay onto the switch base locator pins, rotate the drive cam counter clockwise and secure the complete assembly with the screw. Remember to insert the sealing rings between the housing and valve body.

29   Cruise master - description, adjustment and component r replacement

1   This cruising speed control system is optionally available on certain models and allows the driver to maintain a constant highway speed without the necessity of continual adjustment of foot pressure on the accelerator pedal.

2   The system employs a servo unit connected to the intake manifold, a speedometer cable-driven regulator and various switches.

3   An override capability is built in.

4   Any malfunction in the performance of the system should first be checked out by inspecting the fuse, the security of the leads and terminals, and the vacuum pipes and connections.

5   The following adjustments should then be checked and if necessary altered to conform to those specified.

6   The *servo operating rod* which connects to the carburetor throttle linkage should be adjusted by turning the link on the rod until there is 0.02 to 0.04 inches of free play at the carburetor.

7   The *regulator* can be adjusted by turning

the orifice tube in or out *(never remove it as it cannot be re-installed)*. If the vehicle cruises below the engagement speed, screw the orifice tube out. If the vehicle cruises above the engagement speed, screw the orifice tube in. Each 1/4 turn of the orifice tube will change the cruise speed by about 1 mph. Tighten the locknut after each adjustment.

8   *The brake release switch* contacts must open when the brake pedal is depressed between 0.38 and 0.64 inch measured at the pedal pad.

9   The vacuum valve plunger must clear the pedal arm when the arm is moved 5/16 inch measured at the switch.

10   *The column mounted engagement switch* is non-adjustable, and is serviced only as part of the complete turn signal lever assembly.

11   Faulty components should be replaced as complete assemblies after disconnecting electrical leads, vacuum hoses and control cables from them as necessary.

30   Power radio antenna - removal and installation

1   Lower the antenna mast fully by turning off the radio or ignition key switch. If the unit has failed with the antenna mast in the "up" position, it may be advisable to cut off the mast portion to make replacement easier.

2   Disconnect the negative battery cable.

3   Access to the power antenna motor is through the inner fender panel. Raise the vehicle and remove the front tire for better access if necessary.

4   Remove the fender skirt attaching screws and pull down on the rear edge of the skirt. Use a piece of 2x4-inch lumber as a spacer to keep the skirt pulled away as work is performed.

5   Remove the escutcheon nut at the fender.

6   Disconnect the electrical leads and remove the antenna and motor assembly through the fender skirt opening.

7   When installing a new unit, be sure that the mast is fully retracted and the lower bracket attachment is secured by the fender skirt attaching screw.

31   Seat belt warning systems

1972 through 1973

1   This system combined with the ignition key buzzer, provides for both visual and audible warnings if, with the weight of a person in either of the front seats, the following actions are taken without the seat belts having been fastened:

(A)   the ignition switched on
(B)   the parking brake released
(C)   forward gear (or speed - automatic transmission) selected

    Any faults in the system should be

checked out using the appropriate wiring diagrams. at the end of this Chapter.

1974 through 1976

2   Before the vehicle can be started, the belts must be fastened after the weight of the driver or passenger has been placed on their respective seats.

3   A warning system is actuated if any attempt is made to start the vehicle without the belts having been properly fastened.

4   The warning system will again be actuated if, after the engine has been started and the vehicle is in a forward gear or speed range, the occupied front seat belts are unfastened.

5   Once the engine has been started, the engine can be switched off and subsequently restarted with either or both front seat belts unfastened provided the driver only remains in his seat. Once the driver's weight is removed from his seat then the original starting procedure will again apply.

6   In order to facilitate vehicle maintenance and repair, a mechanic's start position is incorporated in the ignition switch. The engine will then start irrespective of the mode of the front seat belts or whether either front seat is occupied. Whenever the engine is started by this method, the warning buzzer can be terminated if the seat buckle switch is cycled.

7   An anti-bounce device is built into the system to prevent the non-start mode being re-established should a front seat occupant raise his weight from his seat (with seat belt fastened) for a period not exceeding ten seconds.

8   An override relay is incorporated in the system to permit starting the engine in the event of complete system failure. The relay is mounted within the engine compartment and to bring the relay into use, carry out the following operations:

9   Turn the ignition "ON".

10   Open the hood and depress and then release the button on the override relay. The engine can now be started and the vehicle driven until such time as the ignition key is turned to the "OFF" or "LOCK" position, when the override relay will return to its de-energized position.

1977 on

11   The system used on these later vehicles incorporates a timer-controlled buzzer and warning lamp which operate for a few seconds after the ignition is switched on without the seat belts having been fastened.

12   With this system, the fastening of safety belts is left to the driver and abandons the need for complicated starter interlock and other devices used in earlier systems.

32   Radio - removal and installation

Refer to illustrations 32.5 and 32.6

1   Disconnect the negative battery cable.

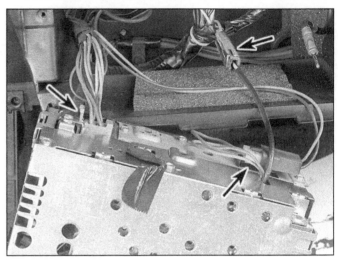

32.5 Remove the radio assembly mounting screws (later models)   **32.6 Pull the radio out from the dash and unplug the antenna and all electrical connectors (arrows)**

2   Pull off the radio control knobs and bezels. These are not held on with lock nuts, but are merely pushed onto the shafts.

3   Using a deep socket, remove the control shaft lock nuts now visible at the base of the shafts.

4   Look up under the dashboard, at the rear of the radio unit. Any obstructions, commonly a center air duct or hoses, should be disconnected and removed for access.

5   Remove the screws or nuts securing the rear mounting bracket to the radio **(see illustration)**.

6   Push the radio forward until the shafts are clear of the dashboard and then lower the unit enough to remove the electrical connections at the rear of the radio **(see illustration)**. Also disconnect the antenna lead-in cable.

7   Carefully lower the radio unit and remove.

8   Installation is a reversal of the removal operation, however, always attach the speaker wiring harness before applying power to the radio.

33 Power door lock system

1   This optional system incorporates a solenoid actuator inside each door. The solenoid is electrically operated from a control switch on the instrument panel and operates the lock through a linkage. Each actuator has an internal circuit breaker which may require one to three minutes to reset.

2   To remove the solenoid, raise the door window and remove the door panel trim pad as described in Chapter 12.

3   After prying away the water shield, the solenoid can be seen through the large access hole. The solenoid can be mounted to either the rear door lock pillar or the inner metal door panel.

4   Early models use attaching screws through the door panel and into the solenoid bracket. Later models use rivets to secure

the solenoid to the pillar. These must be drilled out using a 1/4 inch drill bit.

5   Once the securing devices are removed, disconnect the wiring harness at the solenoid and the actuating link held in place with a metal clip. Remove the solenoid from the door cavity.

6   To install, place the solenoid in position and connect the electrical connector and actuating link. If rivets were drilled out, new aluminum rivets (1/4 X 0.500" size) can be used upon reassembly. Optionally, 1/4-20 screws and U nuts can be used.

7   Check the operation of the door locks before installing the water shield and trim panel.

34 Power window system

1   This system incorporates an electric motor and an independent control switch for each of the door windows. The driver's door has a master control switch permitting operation of all the windows.

2   The electric motor which powers the window regulator is a reversible-direction motor and operates with 12 volts. It features an internal circuit breaker for protection. The motor is secured to the regulator with bolts.

3   The electrical motor can be removed from the regulator with the remainder of the window system intact only if the door glass is intact and attached to the regulator. If the door glass is broken or removed from the door, the motor must be separated after the regulator is removed from inside the door.

Glass intact and attached

4   Raise the window and remove the door trim panel and water shield as described in Chapter 12.

5   Reach inside the door access cavity and disconnect the wiring harness at the motor.

6   It is imperative at this point that the window glass be taped or blocked in the up

position. This will prevent the glass from falling into the door and possibly causing injury or damage.

7   Since the bolts used to secure the motor to the regulator are inaccessible, it is necessary to drill three large access holes in the metal door inner panel. The position of these holes is critical.

8   Use a center punch to dimple the panel at the center of the template access holes and then drill the 1-inch holes with a hole saw.

9   Reach in through the access hole and support the motor as the attaching bolts are removed. Remove the motor through the access hole, being careful that the window glass is firmly supported in the up position.

10   Before installation, the motor drive gear and regulator sector teeth should be lubricated.

11   Upon positioning of the motor, make sure that the drive gear properly engages with the regulator sector teeth. Install remaining components in the reverse order of removal. Waterproof tape can be used to seal the three access holes drilled in the metal inner panel.

Glass broken or not attached

12   Remove the window regulator as described in Chapter 12. Make sure that the wiring harness to the motor is disconnected first.

13   It is imperative that the regulator sector gear be locked into position before removing the motor from the regulator. The control arms are under pressure and can cause serious injury if the motor is removed without performing the following operation.

14   Drill a hole through the regulator sector gear and backplate. Install a bolt and nut to lock the gear in position. Do not drill closer than 1/2 inch to the edge of the sector gear or backplate.

15   Remove the three motor attaching bolts and remove the motor assembly from the regulator.

35.4 When measuring the voltage at the rear window defogger grid, wrap a piece of aluminum foil around the probe of the voltmeter and press the foil against the wire with your finger

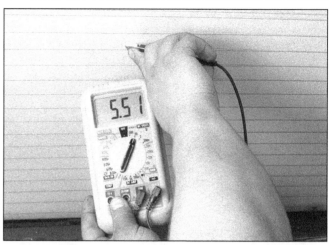

35.5a To determine if a wire has broken, check the voltage at the center of each wire - if the voltage is 6-volts, the wire is unbroken if the voltage is 12-volts, the wire is broken between the center of the wire and the positive end; if the voltage is 0-volt, the wire is broken between the center of the wire and ground

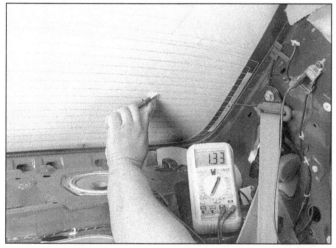

35.5b To find the break, place the voltmeter positive lead against the defogger positive terminal, place the voltmeter negative lead with the foil strip against the heat wire at the positive terminal end and slide it toward the negative terminal end -the voltmeter reading should change abruptly where the wire is broken

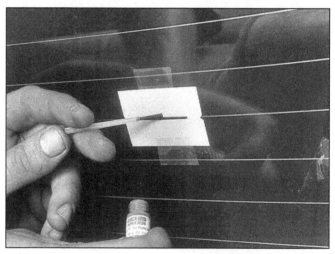

35.11 To use a defogger repair kit, apply masking tape to the inside of the window at the damaged area, then brush on the special conductive coating

16   Prior to installation, the motor drive gear and regulator sector teeth should be lubricated. The lubricant should be cold weather approved to at least -20 degrees Fahrenheit. Lubriplate Spray Lube "A" is recommended.

17   When installing the motor to the regulator make sure that the sector gear teeth and drive gear teeth properly mesh.

18   Once the motor attaching bolts are tightened, the locking nut and bolt can be removed. Install the regulator as described in Chapter 12. Don't forget to connect the motor wiring.

35 Electric grid-type rear defogger - testing and repair

Refer to illustrations 35.4, 35.5a, 35.5b and 35.11

1   This option consists of a rear window with a number of horizontal elements that are baked into the glass surface during the glass forming operation.

2   Small breaks in the element system can be successfully repaired without removing the rear window.

3   To test the grids for proper operation, start the engine and turn on the system.

4   Ground one lead of a voltmeter and lightly touch the other lead to each grid line **(see illustration)**.

5   The voltmeter should read 6-volts as the probe is moved across the element from left to right **(see illustration)**. If the voltmeter switches to 12-volts or drops to 0-volts, check for breaks in the element or a loose ground wire for the system **(see illustration)**. All of the grid lines should be checked in at least two places.

6   To repair a break in a grid line it is recommended that a repair kit specifically for this purpose be purchased from your auto parts store. Included in the repair kit will be a decal, a container of silver plastic and hardener, a mixing stick and instructions.

7   To repair a break, first turn off the system and allow it to de-energize for a few minutes.

8   Lightly buff the grid line area with fine steel wool and then clean the area thoroughly with alcohol.

9   Use the decal supplied in the repair kit, or use electrician's tape above and below the area to be repaired. The space between the pieces of tape should be the same as existing grid lines. This can be checked from outside the car. Press the tape tightly against the glass to prevent seepage.

10   Mix the hardener and silver plastic thoroughly.

11   Using the brush from the repair kit, apply the silver plastic mixture between the pieces of tape, overlapping the damaged area slightly on either end **(see illustration)**.

12   Carefully remove the decal or tape and apply a constant stream of hot air directly to the repaired area. A heat gun set at 500 degrees to 700 degrees F is recommended. Hold the gun about one inch from the glass for one to two minutes.

13   If the new grid line appears off color, tincture of iodine can be used to clean the repair and bring it back to the proper color. This mixture should not remain on the repair for more than 30 seconds.

14   Although the defogger is now fully operational, the repaired area should not be disturbed for at least 24 hours.

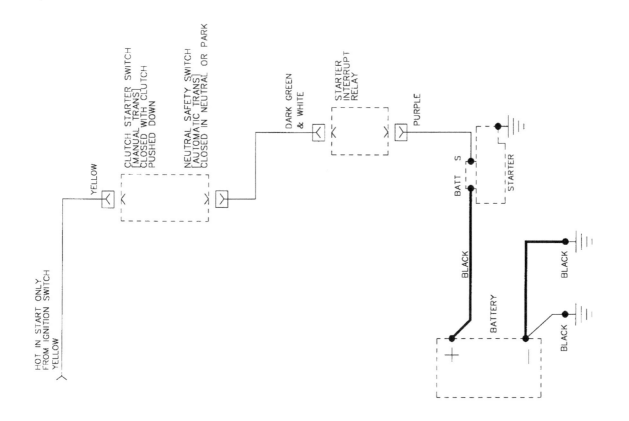

Typical starting system

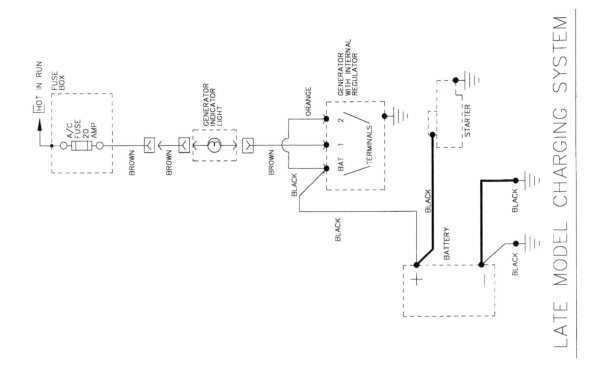

Typical late model charging system

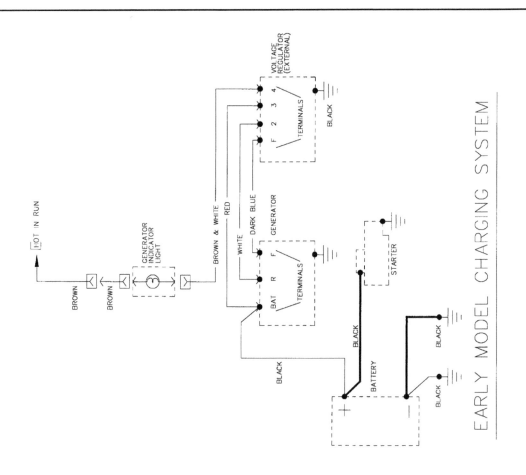

Typical early model charging system

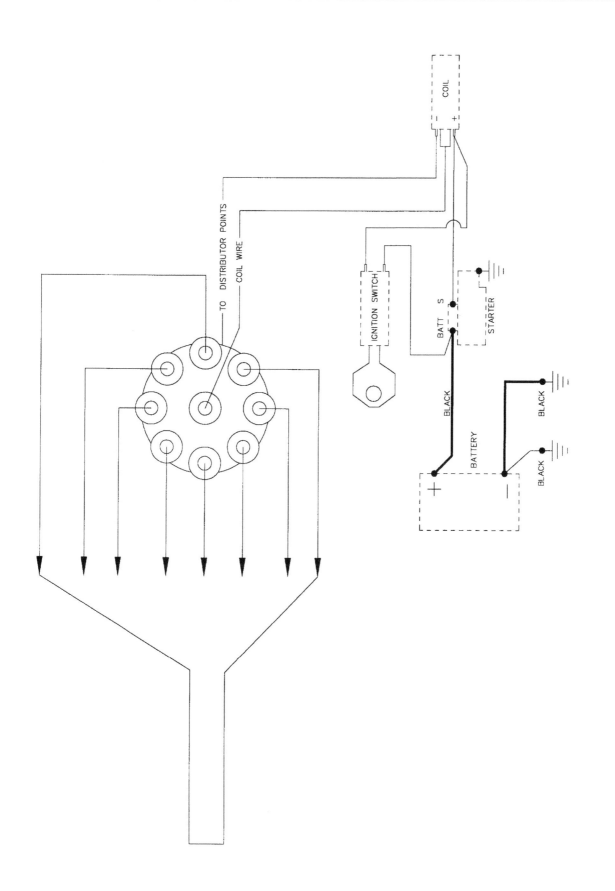

Points starting and secondary ignition circuit

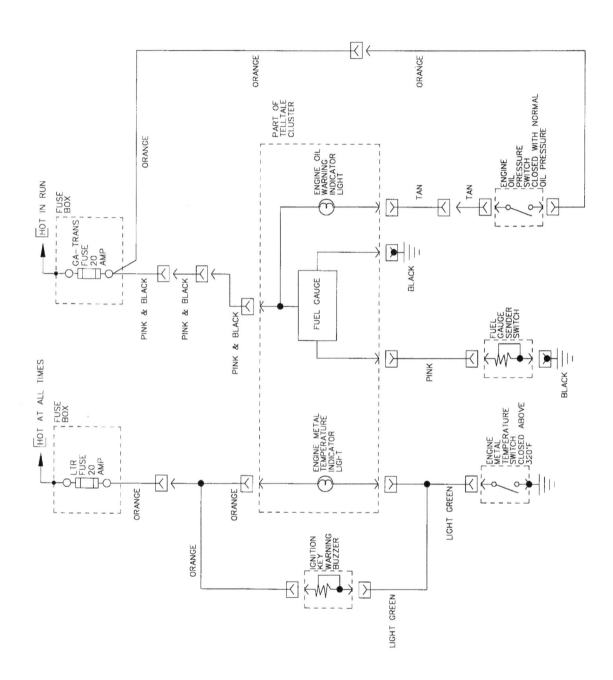

Engine warning system

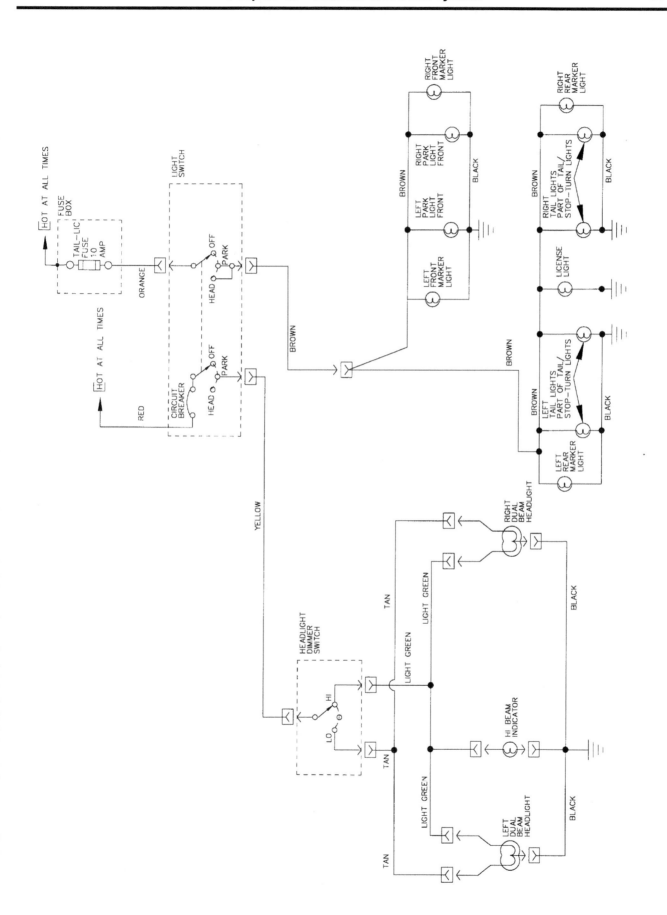

Typical early model exterior light system

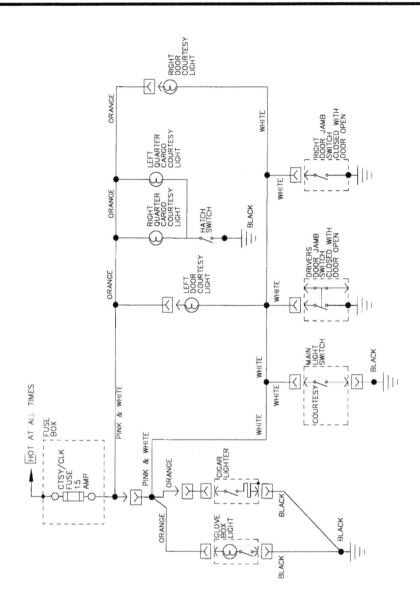

Interior lighting system

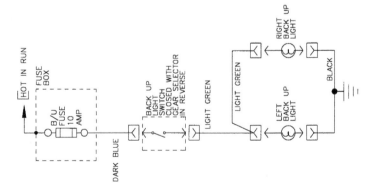

Back-up light circuit

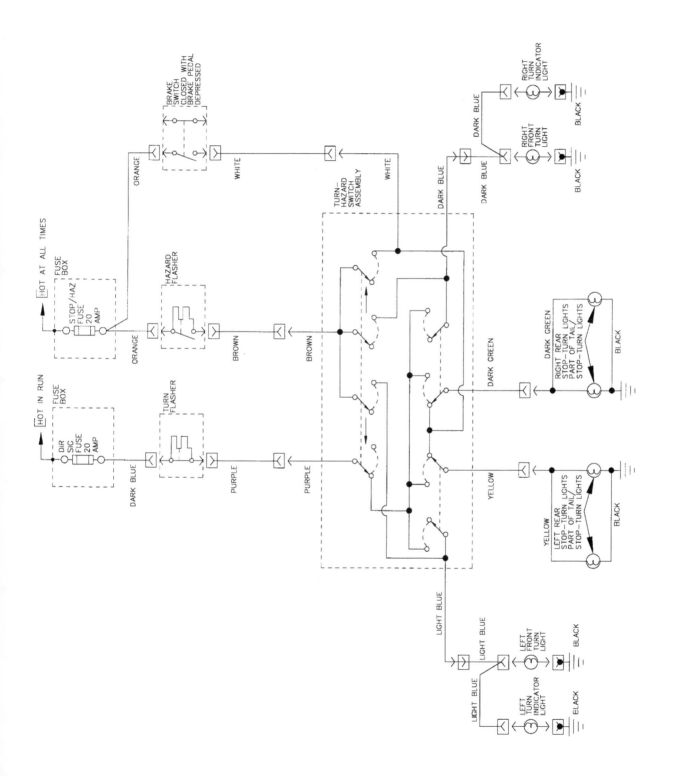

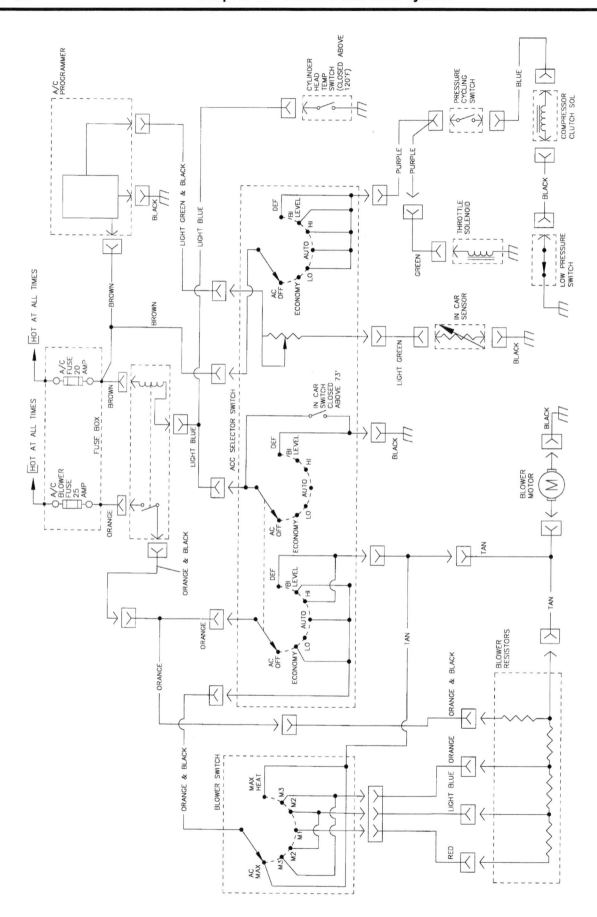

Heating, air conditioning and ventilation system

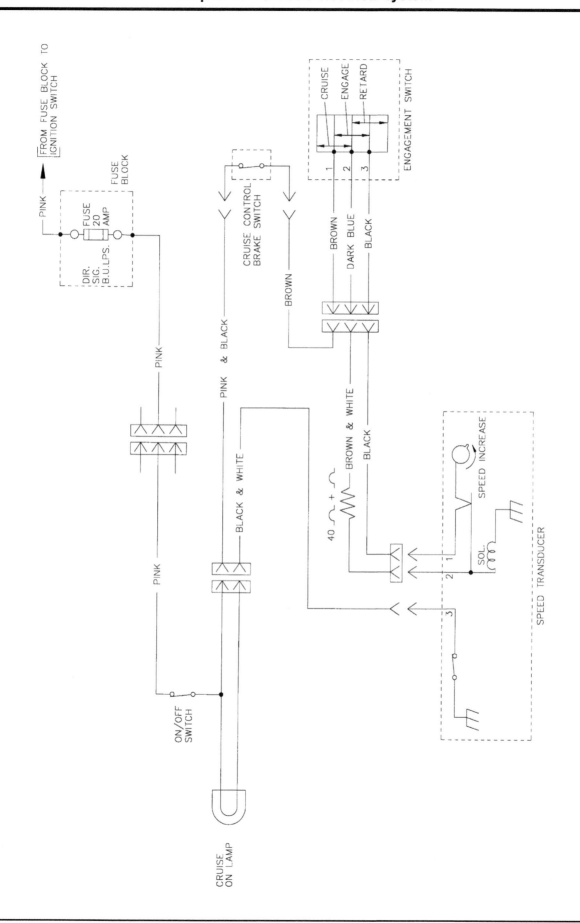

Cruise control system

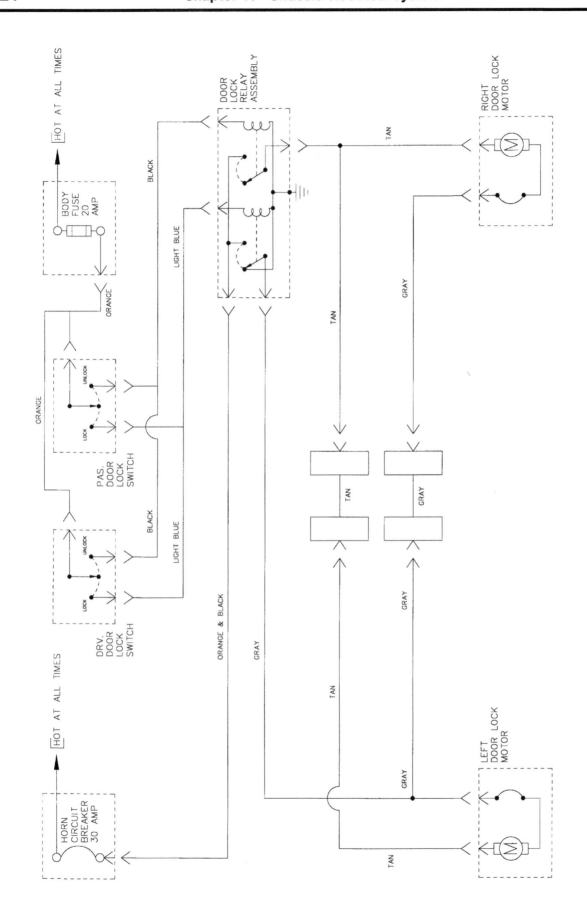

Power door lock system

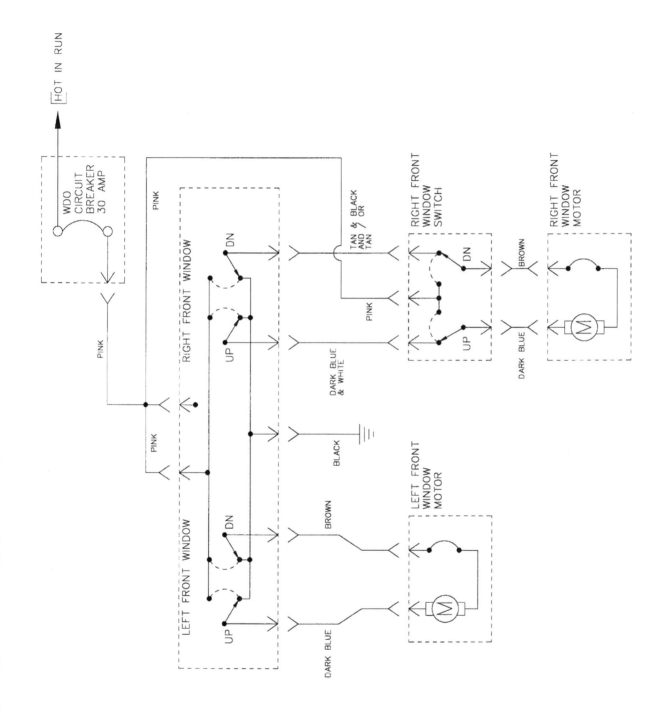

Power window system

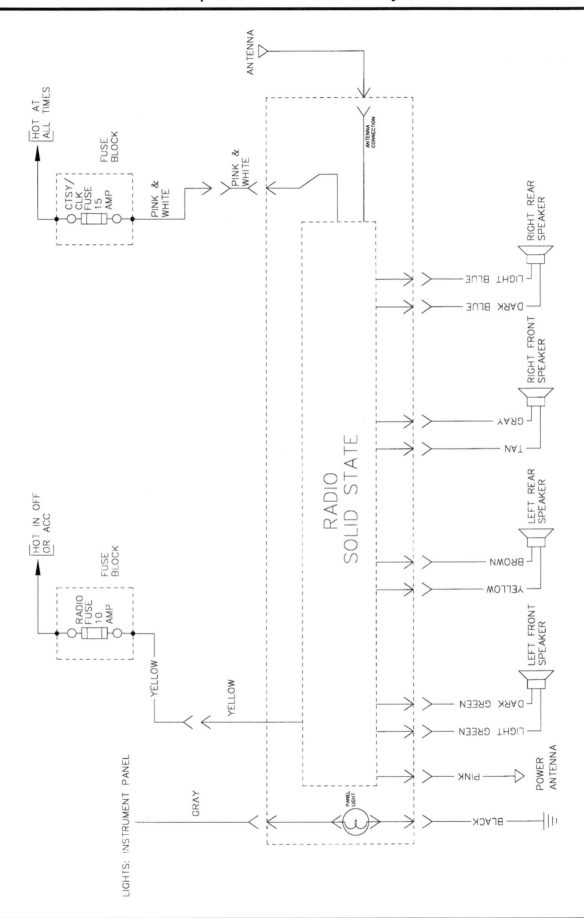

Audio system (base model)

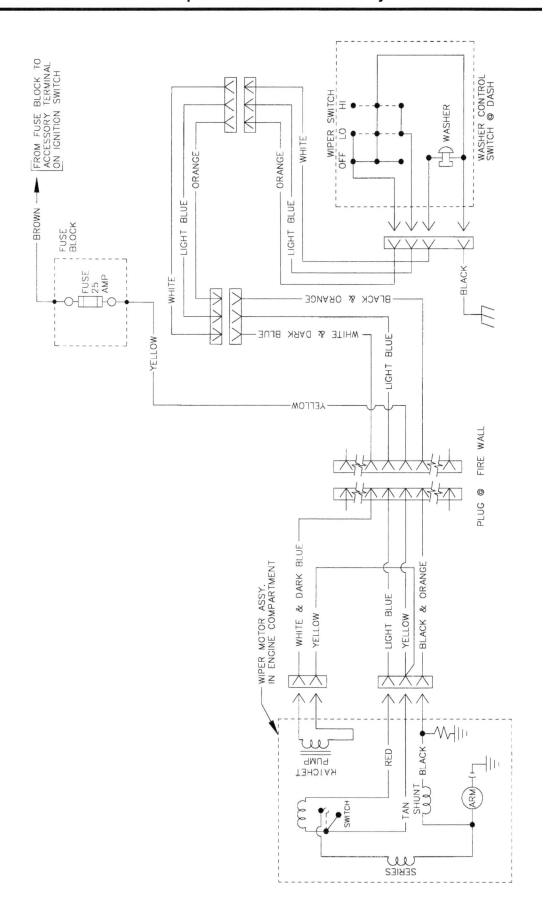

Windshield washer system

Notes

Chapter 11   Suspension

Contents

Specifications

Front suspension

Type .... Independent, upper and lower control arms with coil springs, telescopic shock absorbers and stabilizer bar

Steering geometry

Vehicle	Caster	Camber	Toe-in
1970	+1/2° +/- 1/2°	+ 1° +/- 1/2°	1/8 to 1/4 in
1971 - 1972	0° +/- 1/2°	1° +/- 1/2°	1/8 to 1/4 in
1973 - 1974	0° +/- 1/2°	1° + 1/2°	3/16 +/- 1/16 in
1975	0° +/- 1/2°	1° + 1/2°	1/16 +/- 1/16 in
1976 - 1977	1° +/- 1/2°	1° + 1/2°	1/16 +/- 1/16 in
1978 - 1981	1° +/- 1/2°	1° + 1/2°	1/8 +/- 1/16 in

Rear suspension

Type .... Leaf springs with telescopic shock absorbers

Steering

Type .... Recirculating ball with impact absorbing column. Optional power steering and tilt column on certain models

Manual steering adjustment data

	1970 through 1972	1973 through 1974	1975 on
Worm bearing preload	5 to 8 lb-in	4 to 6 lb-in	5 to 8 lb-in
Over center preload	4 to 10 lb-in	5 to 9 lb-in	4 to 10 lb-in
Total steering gear preload	14 lb-in	16 lb-in	16 lb-in

Power steering adjustment data

	1970 through 1974	1975 on
Ball bearing drag	3 lb-in	3 lb-in
*Thrust bearing preload	1/2 to 2 lb-in	3 to 4 lb-in
**Over center preload	3 to 6 lb-in	4 to 5 lb-in
Total gear preload	14 lb-in	14 lb-in

*In excess of valve assembly drag
**In excess of combined ball drag and thrust bearing preload

Torque specifications

Ft-lbs

Front suspension

1970

Upper swivel joint ballstud nut	50
Lower swivel joint ballstud nut	80
Swivel joint securing bolts (replacement only)	25
Shock absorber upper mounting nut	8
Shock absorber lower mounting	20
Stabilizer bar bracket bolts	24
Stabilizer bar link nuts	12
Lower control arm inner pivot nuts	80
Upper control arm mounting nuts	80
Upper control arm collar bolts	70

1971 through 1973

Upper swivel joint ballstud nut	50
Lower swivel joint ballstud nut	90
Swivel joint securing bolts (replacement only)	25
Control arm pivot to frame	
upper	85
lower	90
Upper control arm pivot shaft nuts	60
Shock absorber upper mounting	8
Shock absorber lower mounting	20
Stabilizer bar bracket bolts	24
Stabilizer bar link nuts	13
Disc caliper mounting bolts	35

1974 on

Swivel joint upper ballstud nut	60
Swivel joint lower ballstud nut	85
Swivel joint securing bolts (replacement only)	10
Control arm pivot to frame (upper)	75
Control arm pivot to frame (lower)	100
Upper control arm pivot shaft nuts	75
Shock absorber upper mounting	12
Shock absorber lower mounting	20
Stabilizer bar link nuts	13
Stabilizer bar bracket bolts	24
Disc brake caliper mounting bolts	35

Rear suspension

All

Spring to axle retainer	40
Front eye bolt	75
Front mounting bracket to body	25
Rear shackle bolts	50
Shock absorber upper	18
Shock absorber lower	8
Pinion nose bumper	8
Axle tube rebound bumper	35

Steering

1970 through 1976

	Ft-lbs
Steering gear mounting bolts	70
Pitman shaft nut	
to 1973	140
1974 on	185
Steering wheel nut	
standard	30
tilt column	5
Steering flexible coupling flange bolts	20
Steering flexible coupling pinch bolts	30
Tie-rod end ballstud nut	
to 1980	35
1981	40
Tie-rod clamp nut	16
Tie-rod to intermediate rod	40
Idler arm mounting nut	35
Dash panel bracket to column	15
Dash panel bracket to dash	20
Power steering pump pulley nut	60
Power steering pump mounting bolts	25
Idler arm to relay rod	50
Power steering hose end fittings	25

1977 on as for earlier models except

Column support to column bracket stud nuts	25
Flexible coupling flange bolts	20
Control arm pivot to frame (upper)	73
Control arm pivot to frame (lower)	90
Upper control arm pivot shaft nuts	85
Idler arm mounting nuts	60
Idler arm to relay rod	40
Swivel joint upper ballstud nut	65
Swivel joint lower ballstud nut	90
Swivel joint securing bolts (replacement only)	8

Wheels

Wheel nuts

1970	65
1971 through 1975	70
1976 on	
Aluminum wheels	80
Non aluminum wheels	90

1 General description

1 The front suspension is of the independent type incorporating upper and lower suspension arms, coil springs, hydraulic telescopic shock absorbers and a stabilizer bar.
2 The rear leaf spring suspension is attached to a solid rear axle assembly. The front of each leaf spring is attached to the frame with rubber bushings. At the rear, a shackle is used which allows the spring to flex and change its length slightly while the car is in motion. The rear telescopic shock absorbers are staggered, meaning that the left shock is behind the axle housing and the right one is forward of the housing.

3 The steering gear is of the recirculating ball type with an energy absorbing column. An ignition lock is built into the steering column. All model years offered power steering as an option. A tilt steering column was available as an option for late models only.

2 Maintenance and inspection (balljoints)

Refer to illustration 2.2
1 At the intervals specified in Chapter 1 check all the steering and suspension joints for wear or deterioration of the rubber bushings or dust excluders. With the help of an assistant check for "lost" movement between the steering wheel and the front wheels which must be due to wear or looseness of the components.
2 Lower suspension arm balljoint wear must be checked in one of the following ways:

Vehicles built through 1973 - support the weight of the lower suspension control arm with a jack, then measure the distance from the grease fitting to the end of the lower threaded balljoint stud. Apply leverage under the tire to seat the lower balljoint stud internally, then remeasure. If the difference between these measurements is greater than 1/16 inch the joint is worn and must be replaced.

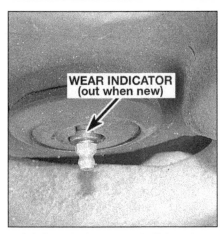

2.2 Wear indicators are built into the lower balljoints to aid in their inspection

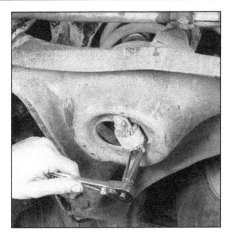

4.2 Removing the lower bolts for the front shock absorbers

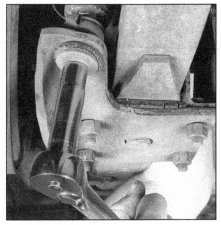

4.10 Removing the rear shock absorber lower securing nut

Vehicles built from 1974 on - check the wear indicators for indication of excessive lower balljoint wear **(see illustration)**. When new, a dimension of 0.050 inch should exist from the grease nipple fitting to the balljoint cover surface; if the fitting is flush, or has receded inside the cover, the balljoint must be replaced.

3   Front wheel bearings - lubrication, replacement and adjustment

See Chapter 1, Section 24 for complete details on servicing the front wheel bearings.

4   Shock absorber - removal, inspection and installation

Refer to illustrations 4.2, 4.10 and 4.11
Note: *Any sign of oil on the outside of shock absorber bodies will indicate that the seals have started to leak and the units must be replaced as assemblies. Where the shock absorber has failed internally, this is*

more difficult to detect although rear axle patter or tramp, particularly on uneven road surfaces may provide a clue. When a shock absorber is suspected to have failed, remove it from the vehicle and holding it in a vertical position operate it for the full length of its stroke eight or ten times. Any lack of resistance in either direction will indicate the need for replacement.

Front shock absorber

1   Raise the front end of the vehicle. Use an open-ended wrench to prevent the upper squared) end from turning, then remove the upper stem retaining nut, retainer and rubber grommet.
2   Remove the 2 bolts retaining the lower shock absorber pivot to the control arm **(see illustration)**.
3   Pull the assembly out from the bottom.
4   When installing, install the lower retainer and rubber grommet in place over the upper stem.
5   Install the shock absorber in the fully extended position up through the lower control arm and spring.
6   Install the upper rubber grommet, retainer and attaching nut after the shock

absorber upper stem has passed through the upper control arm frame bracket.
7   Using an open-ended wrench, hold the upper stem and torque-tighten the retaining nut.
8   Install the bolts at the shock absorber lower pivot, torque tighten, then lower the vehicle.

Rear shock absorber

9   Raise the rear end of the vehicle, and support the rear axle.
10   Remove the lower shock absorber retaining nut, retainer and rubber grommet **(see illustration)**.
11   Remove the two upper attaching bolts and then remove the shock absorber **(see illustration)**.
12   When installing, push the lower retainer and rubber grommet into position. Extend the shock absorber to the proper length.
13   Place the shock absorber into position and install the two upper attaching bolts.
14   Push the remaining retainer and grommet into position and install the lower attaching nut.
15   Torque all fasteners and lower the vehicle.

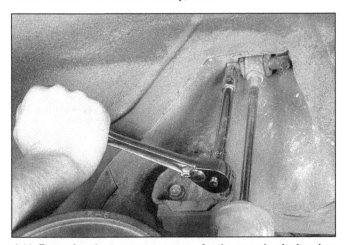

4.11 Removing the two upper screws for the rear shock absorber

5.1 The ends of the stabilizer bar are secured with a lock nut and cushioned with rubber grommets

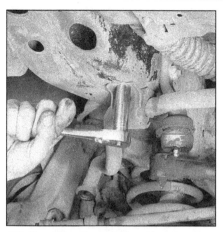

5.2 Removing the stabilizer bar mounting brackets from the frame rails

5   Stabilizer bar - removal and installation

Front stabilizer bar

Refer to illustrations 5.1, 5.2 and 5.5

1   Raise the front end of the vehicle then disconnect the stabilizer bar from the lower control arms **(see illustration)**.
2   Remove the stabilizer bar brackets from the frame then lift away the stabilizer bar **(see illustration)**.
3   Remove the link bolts, spacers and rubber grommets from the lower control arms or stabilizer bar.
4   Inspect all the parts for damage, wear and deterioration. Fit new parts as necessary.
5   If new frame bushings are required, slide them into position along the stabilizer bar. The slit should be facing the front of the car **(see illustration)**.
6   When installing, fit the brackets over the bushings and connect them (loosely) to the frame.
7   Ensure that the stabilizer bar is centralized then torque-tighten all the bolts.
8   Lower the vehicle to the ground.

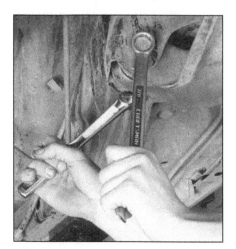

6.7 Using two wrenches to disconnect the lower control arm pivot bolt

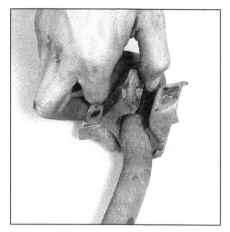

5.5 A rubber insulator is used at each mounting bracket. The slit should go towards the front of the vehicle

Rear stabilizer bar

9   Raise the rear end of the vehicle and support the rear axle.
10   Remove the stabilizer bar to spring retainer bracket attachment.
11   Remove the stabilizer bar to body bracket bolt and remove the assembly.
12   Install the bushings onto the stabilizer bar then place the bar in position.
13   Install the upper retaining bolts and the stabilizer bar to spring attachment. Install bolts loosely at this point.
14   Ensure that the weight of the vehicle is being carried by the rear axle only, then torque-tighten the bolts.
15   Lower the vehicle to the ground.

6   Front coil spring - removal and installation

Refer to illustrations 6.5, 6.7, 6.8 and 6.10
Note: *As the coil spring is under pressure during part of the removal and installation process, proper tools should be used and caution exercised. For added safety, a chain should be used to secure the coil spring to the lower control arm.*
1   Raise the front end of the vehicle and support it firmly with jack stands on the

6.5 A typical aftermarket internal type spring compressor. The hooked arms grip the upper coils of the spring, the plate is inserted between the lower coils and when the threaded rod is turned, the spring is compressed

frame. The suspension arms should hang free.
2   Remove the front shock absorber (Section 4).
3   Remove the front wheel.
4   Disconnect the stabilizer bar from the lower control arm. It can remain intact by the frame brackets.
5   Install a suitable internal type spring compressor in accordance with the tool manufacturer's instructions **(see illustration)**. Compress the spring enough to relieve all pressure from the spring seats (but don't compress it any more than necessary, or it could be ruined). When you can wiggle the spring, it's compressed enough (You can buy a suitable spring compressor at most auto parts stores or rent one from a tool rental yard).
6   Position a floor jack under the lower control arm.
7   With tension off the pivot bolts, remove the rear pivot bolt nut. Remove the forward pivot bolt and nut. It may be necessary to follow the bolts through the control arm with a hammer and drift **(see illustration)**.
8   Slowly and carefully lower the floor jack. The control arm should lower with it **(see illustration)**.

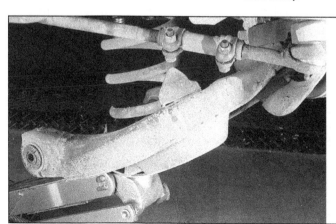

6.8 Lower the control arm slowly and carefully with the floor jack

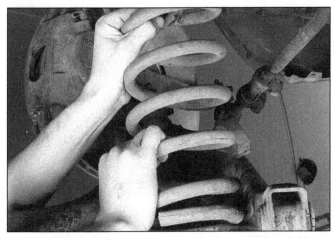

6.10 Lifting out the coil spring once all tension is relieved. Make sure the spring is marked for top and bottom

7.3 Removing the upper ball joint nut at the top of the steering knuckle

7.4a A special tool is used to push the balljoint out of the steering knuckle, but an alternative tool can be fabricated from a large bolt, nut, washer and socket

7.4b A wedge-shaped ball joint splitter should be used to separate the joint

7.8 Drill pilot holes into the heads of the balljoint rivets with a 1/8-inch bit, then use a 1/2-inch bit to cut the rivet heads off - be careful not to enlarge the holes in the control arm

9   Before removing the spring, note the position of the spring in relation to its bottom seat and the identifying tag attached to one of the coils.

10   When all the compression is removed from the spring, remove the safety chain and the spring **(see illustration)**.

11   During installation, be sure that the coil is properly seated in the lower control arm. The end of the bottom coil should cover all or part of one of the small inspection/drain holes drilled in the control arm. The other hole should be partly or completely uncovered.

12   It is recommended that the safety chain be again used upon installation. With the control arm and spring raised into position, install the pivot bolts and nuts. It is necessary that the front bolt be installed with its head towards the front of the vehicle. The rear bolt can be installed in either direction. Torque-tighten these bolts to specifications before lowering the jack and removing the safety chain.

13   Install the remaining components in the reverse order of disassembly and tighten all fasteners to the proper torque.

7   Front suspension balljoints- removal, inspection and installation

Upper balljoint

Refer to illustrations 7.3, 7.4a, 7.4b, 7.8 and 7.9

1   Raise the front end of the vehicle and remove the wheel.

2   Remove the upper ball stud cotter pin.

3   Loosen the ball stud nut by one turn only **(see illustration)**.

4   Using a balljoint separator, press out the ball stud. If a special tool is not available, insert a bolt and nut between the ends of the upper and lower balljoint studs. By unscrewing the nut on the bolt, its effective length will be increased and the balljoint will be pressed out **(see illustration)**). **Note:** *While carrying out this operation the lower control arm must be supported so that the front spring does not force the arm down* **(see illustration)**.

5   Remove the upper balljoint stud and swing the steering knuckle out of the way.

6   Raise the upper arm and support it with a block of wood between it and the frame.

7   The balljoint is spring loaded in its socket to compensate for normal wear. If there is any lateral play or if the joint can be turned in its socket with the fingers, the joint should be replaced.

8   If replacement is necessary use a drill to remove the rivets **(see illustration)**, but take care not to damage the control arm or balljoint seat.

9   When installing, place the balljoint in the control arm and attach with the nuts and bolts provided **(see illustration)**. Torque-tighten.

10   Turn the ball stud cotter pin hole fore and aft to the length of car.

11   Remove the wooden block used at paragraph 6.

12   Ensure that the tapered hole in the steering knuckle is clean and undamaged then mate the ball stud to it.

13   Install the stud nut and torque-tighten to the specified value. Further tighten the nut to align the cotter pin holes then install a new cotter pin.

7.9 Install the replacement balljoint in the upper control arm

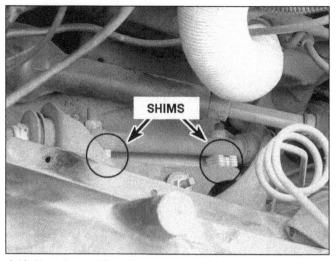

8.12 Note the position of the alignment shims and return them to their original positions

14   Install a lubrication nipple and lubricate with the recommended grease.
15   Install the wheel and lower the vehicle to the ground.

Lower balljoint

16   Raise the front end of the vehicle.
17   Remove the ball stud cotter pin.
18   Loosen the ball stud nut by one turn only.
19   Press out the balljoint stud using the method described for upper balljoints (paragraph 4 of the previous sub-Section).
20   Remove the lower stud nut then pull outwards at the bottom of the tire. At the same time, push the tire and wheel upwards to free the knuckle from the ball stud.
21   Remove the wheel.
22   Raise the upper control arm and place a 2 x 4 inch block of wood between the frame and control arm. If found necessary, remove the tie-rod from the steering knuckle (Section 13).
23   Using a suitable vise and tubular spacers press the lower balljoint out of the control arm.
24   Using a suitable vise and tubular spacers, install the replacement balljoint with the bleed vent in the rubber boot facing inwards.
25   Turn the ball stud cotter pin hole fore-and-aft to the length of the car.
26   Remove the wooden block used at paragraph 22.
27   Ensure that the tapered hole in the steering knuckle is clean and undamaged then mate the ball stud to it.
28   Install the stud nut and torque-tighten to the specified value. Further tighten the nut to align the cotter pin holes then install a new cotter pin.
29   Install a lubrication nipple and lubricate with the recommended grease.
30   Install the wheel (and tie-rod, if removed), then lower the car to the ground.

8   Upper suspension control arm - removal, servicing and installation

Refer to illustration 8.12
1   Raise the front end of the vehicle and lower the control arm onto a jack for support.
2   Remove the wheel.
3   Separate the upper control arm ball stud (Section 7).
4   Remove the two nuts securing the control arm shaft to the frame bracket. Tape together the shims and ensure that they are eventually installed in the same position.
5   In some cases it will be necessary to remove the upper control arm attaching bolts to provide clearance for removal of the upper control arm assembly. These bolts are splined, and may be removed as follows:

a) Use a brass drift to tap the bolt gently downwards.
b) Pry the bolt upwards using a suitable box wrench.
c) Remove the nut then use a suitable pry bar and block of wood to pry the bolts from the frame.

6   Remove the upper control arm.
7   If, on inspection, the control arm pivot bushings are worn, their replacement is a job best left to your dealer, but if you are to carry out this work without the use of a press, employ a long bolt and suitable tubular spacers for both removal and installation of the bushings.
8   When installing, loosen the endshaft retainer bolts and/or nuts.
9   If removed, position the new control arm attaching bolts loosely in the frame and install the control arm cross-shaft on the attaching bolts.
10   Use a normal free-running nut (not a locknut) to tighten the serrated bolts onto their seats.
11   When the splined bolts are seated, remove the free-running nuts and fit the regular locknuts.

12   Install the shims in their original installed positions (see illustration) then torque-tighten the nuts. Tighten the thinner shim pack nut first for improved clamping force and torque retention.
13   Install the ball stud through the knuckle, torque-tighten the nut, further tighten to align the cotter pin holes then install a new cotter pin.
14   Install the wheel and lower the vehicle to the floor.
15   Torque-tighten the shaft retainer bolts and/or nuts.

9   Lower suspension control arm - removal servicing and installation

1   Remove the front coil spring (Section 6).
2   Remove the control arm ball stud (Section 7).
3   Remove the control arm from the vehicle.
4   If, on inspection, the control arm pivot bushings are worn, their replacement is best left to your dealer but if you are to carry out this work without the use of a press, employ a long bolt and suitable tubular spacers for both removal and installation. Note: It is not essential for the control arm to be removed for bushing replacement except for the front bushings on 1975 and later models.
5   Installation is the reverse of the removal procedure. Torque-tighten the nuts to the specified torque.

10   Steering knuckle - removal and installation

1   Raise the front end of the vehicle so that the weight is on the springs.
2   Remove the wheels.

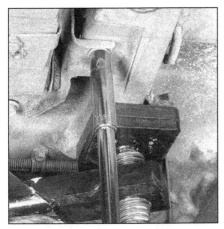

11.5 Removing the mounting bolt which secures the spring bracket on the rear leaf spring

11.9 Four nuts secure the leaf spring perch to the rear axle assembly. Note the center alignment pin

11.10a Removing the pivot bolt which runs through the rear of the leaf spring and the two shackles

3   Remove the disc brake caliper and rotor (Refer to Chapter 9, if necessary). When removing the caliper, use a block of wood to keep the disc pads separated.
4   Remove the splash shield.
5   Hang the caliper assembly from some convenient part of the suspension. Do not let the hydraulic line take the weight.
6   Remove the upper and lower ball joint stud cotter pins and disconnect the ball studs from the steering knuckle.
7   Disconnect the tie-rod end from the steering knuckle. This procedure can be found in Section 13.
8   Remove the steering knuckle.
9   When installing, place the steering knuckle into position and insert the upper and lower ball stud.
10   Install the ball stud nuts and torque-tighten to the specified value. Further tighten to align the cotter pin hole and then install a new cotter pin.
11   Connect the tie-rod and tighten to the specified torque.
12   Install the splash shield, hub and rotor.
13   Install the outer bearing, spindle washer and nut. Adjust the bearing as described in Chapter 1.
14   Install the caliper and the wheels. Lower the car to the ground.

11 Rear springs - removal, servicing and installation

Refer to illustrations 11.5, 11.9, 11.10a and 11.10b
1   Raise the rear end of the vehicle, and support it so that the axle can be lowered.
2   Raise the axle using a jack to relieve the weight from the spring.
3   Disconnect the lower attachment point of the shock absorber.
4   Loosen the spring front eye to bracket bolt.
5   Remove the screws securing the spring front bracket to the underbody **(see illustration)**.

11.10b Lowering the complete leaf spring assembly from the vehicle bracket so that the ribs align with the locating ribs

6   Lower the axle sufficiently to allow access to the spring front bracket; remove the bracket from the spring.
7   At this stage, the front bushing may be replaced, if no other work is to be carried out (see paragraph 11).
8   Pry the parking brake cable out of the retainer bracket on the spring mounting plate.
9   Remove the lower spring plate to axle bracket retaining nuts then the upper and lower spring pads and spring plate **(see illustration)**.
10   Support the spring, then remove the lower bolt from the rear shackle. Separate the shackle and withdraw the spring **(see illustrations)**.
11   If the front spring bushings are worn, their replacement is a job best left for your dealer, but if you are to carry out this work without the use of a press, employ a long bolt and suitable tubular spacers for both removal and installation of the bushings.
12   When installing the spring, position the front mounting bracket to the front eyes. Install the attaching bolt with the bolt head towards the center of the vehicle.
13   Position the spring shackle upper bushings in the frame. Position the shackles to the bushings and loosely install the bolt and nut.
14   Install the bushing halves to the spring rear eye; place the spring to the shackles and

loosely install the lower shackle bolt and nut. Ensure that the spring is positioned so that the parking brake cable is on the underside of the spring.
15   Raise the front end of the spring and position the bracket to the underbody. Guide the spring into position so that it will fit into the axle bracket and ensure that the tab on the spring bracket aligns with the slot in the underbody. It may be necessary to pry the spring forward.
16   Loosely install the spring bracket.
17   Position the spring upper cushion between the spring and the axle.
18   Fit the lower spring cushion and align with the upper cushion (where applicable).
19   Place the lower mounting plate over the locating dowel on the lower spring pad and loosely install the retaining nuts.
20   Where a new mounting plate is used, transfer the parking brake retaining bracket to the new plate.
21   Attach the shock absorber to the mounting plate.
22   Install the parking brake cable in the retaining bracket and securely clamp the bracket to retain the cable.
23   Torque-tighten all the nuts and bolts to the specified value with the weight on the rear springs.
24   Finally lower the vehicle to the ground.

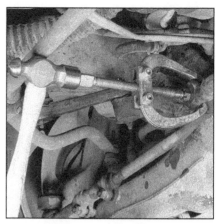

13.3a After removing the cotter pin, the lock nut is loosened to the end of the threaded stud

13.3b A puller is then installed in position and tightened against the threaded stud

13.3c With the puller tight, a sharp blow with a hammer will break the connection

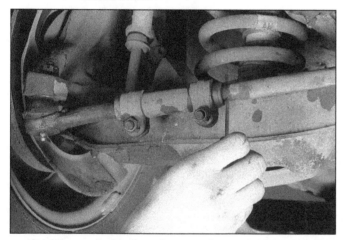

13.4 When replacing tie-rods, count the number of exposed threads and mark the threaded shaft to enable the new tie-rod to be installed the same

13.8 Where a common puller cannot be used (as shown here with the idler arm), a wedge-shaped splitter should be used to break the joint connection

12 Steering gear and linkage - inspection

See Chapter 1, Section 8 for the proper procedures involved in inspecting the steering system.

13 Steering linkage and balljoints - removal and installation

Refer to illustrations 13.3a, 13.3b, 13.3c, 13.4 and 13.8

1   The balljoints on the two outer tie-rods and those on the central relay rod are all connected by means of a tapered ball stud located in a tapered hole and secured by a castellated nut and cotter pin.
2   The outer tie-rods are of tubular, internally threaded sleeve type and are secured to the tie-rod ends by clamps and bolts.
3   To remove the balljoint, first raise the front end of the car then remove the ball stud nut. On occasion the tapered studs have been known to simply pull out. More often

they are well and truly wedged in position and a gear puller or slotted steel wedges may be driven between the ball unit and the arm to which it is attached. Another method is to place the head of a hammer (or other solid metal article) on one side of the hole in the arm into which the pin is installed. Then hit it smartly with a hammer on the opposite side. This has the effect of squeezing the taper out and usually works, provided one can get a good swing at it. Always keep the stud nut at the top of the stud threads to protect the threads from damage **(see illustrations)**.
4   Measure the length of exposed thread on each of the tie-rod ends (as a guide to reassembly), release the pinch bolts from the clamps and unscrew the tie-rod end from the tie-rod sleeve **(see illustration)**.
5   When installing the new tie-rod ends, screw them into the sleeves exactly the same amount as the original ones.
6   Arrange for your dealer to check the toe-in, or follow the procedure given in Section 33. Pay particular attention to the special instructions for the position of the clamps if you are carrying out this operation yourself.

7   If the balljoints on the central relay rod are worn then the relay rod will have to be replaced as an assembly. Again, the toe-in will have to be checked afterwards (see previous paragraph).
8   If it is necessary to remove the idler arm this is first disconnected at the frame mounting lone nut, washer and bolt), then disconnected at the idler arm end by using the same procedure given for the other steering linkage joints **(see illustration)**.

14 Manual steering gear - maintenance and adjustment (steering gear in place)

Refer to illustration 14.6

1   The steering gear is normally filled with lubricant for life and unless a severe leak occurs, necessitating a complete overhaul, refilling with lubricant will not be required.
2   In order to rectify conditions of lost motion, slack and vibration which have been found to be directly attributable to the steering gear, carry out the following operations:

14.6 Loosen the adjuster screw locknut on the steering gear and then back off the adjuster screw 1/4-turn

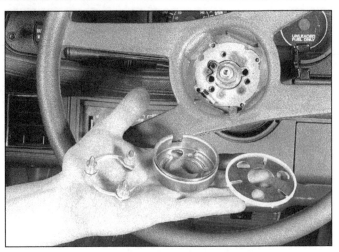

16.13a The steering wheel horn button assembly

3   Disconnect the ground cable from the battery.
4   Remove the nut from the Pitman arm and then mark the relative position of the arm to the Pitman shaft.
5   Using a suitable extractor remove the Pitman arm.
6   Loosen the adjuster plug locknut on the steering gear and unscrew the adjuster plug one quarter-turn **(see illustration)**.
7   Remove the horn button or shroud from the steering wheel and then turn the steering wheel in one direction to full lock and then turn the wheel back through one half turn. Now apply a 3/4 inch socket to the steering wheel center nut and either using a torque wrench or a spring balance check the bearing drag when the wheel is turned through a 90° arc of travel.
8   This drag is the thrust bearing preload and it should be within the specifications listed at the front of this chapter. Tighten or slacken the adjuster plug until the correct preload is obtained and then torque-tighten the adjuster plug locknut.
9   Any jerky or lumpy feeling as the steering wheel is turned will indicate worn or damaged bearings in the steering gear.
10   Now turn the steering wheel gently from one stop to the other counting the number of turns of the steering wheel from lock-to-lock. Now turn the wheel exactly half the number of turns counted so that the steering gear is in the centered position.
11   Loosen the lash adjuster screw locknut and turn the lash adjuster screw clockwise until all lash has been removed from between the ball nut and the Pitman shaft sector teeth. Torque-tighten the locknut.
12   Now check the over-center preload by taking the highest torque reading obtainable as the wheel is moved through its centered position. The preload should be within the specifications listed at the front of this chapter, in **excess of** the torque stated at paragraph 8 above. Adjust the position of the lash adjuster screw if necessary to achieve this.

13   Install the Pitman arm and horn shroud, and connect the battery ground cable.

15 Steering wheel - removal and installation (1970 models)

1   Disconnect the negative battery cable.
2   Remove the two steering wheel shroud screws located at the underside of the shroud. Remove the shroud from the steering wheel.
3   Remove the spacer, plate and belleville spring. These components are held in place with three screws.
4   Mark the relation of the steering wheel to the steering column so that the wheel can be replaced in the same location.
5   Remove the steering wheel lock nut on the end of the shaft.
6   Use a steering wheel puller to remove the wheel from the column. The puller anchor screws should be installed in the threaded holes provided in the steering wheel and the center bolt turned clockwise until the wheel breaks free from the shaft. Do not strike the end of the shaft with a hammer as this may collapse certain components inside the column.
7   When installing, make sure the eyelet and insulator are correctly positioned in the horn contact tower.
8   Place the steering wheel onto the end of the steering shaft, aligning the marks made upon disassembly. When lowering the steering wheel into position, make sure the horn contact tower will engage with the hole in the steering wheel.
9   Install the steering wheel lock nut and torque to the proper specifications.
10   Install the belleville spring (concave side down), plate and spacer. Tighten the three screws.
11   Install the steering wheel shroud and tighten the two attaching screws.
12   Connect the negative battery cable and check the operation of the wheel and horn.

16 Steering wheel - removal and installation (1971 -1981)

Standard production

Refer to illustrations 16.13a, 16.13b, 16.14 and 16.17
1   Disconnect the negative battery cable.
2   Remove the two screws securing the steering wheel shroud. These are on the underside of the steering wheel towards the dashboard.
3   Lift the steering wheel shroud and horn contact lead assembly from the steering wheel.
4   On 1975 - 1980 models, remove the snap ring from the steering shaft.
5   Mark the steering wheel and column to enable installation of the wheel in the same position.
6   Remove the steering wheel lock nut from the shaft.
7   Using a steering wheel puller, remove the steering wheel from the column. Threaded holes are provided in the steering wheel to accept the puller anchor screws. Use the lock nut to protect the top threads of the threaded shaft. Do not strike the puller or the end of the column as this may damage components of the collapsible steering column.
8   When installing, set the turn signal lever to the neutral position and set the wheel into position. Use the alignment marks made upon disassembly to correctly position the wheel.
9   Tighten the steering wheel lock nut to the proper specifications. Do not overtighten this nut as this may cause interference problems. Install the snap ring (1975 - 1980 models).
10   Place the shroud onto the wheel, guiding the horn contact lead into the directional signal canceling cam tower.
11   Install the shroud attaching screws and connect the negative battery cable. Check the operation of the horn.

16.13b The spring-loaded horn plunger

16.14 Some models may have a retaining clip over the main shaft nut

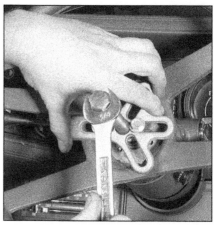

16.17 A steering wheel puller being used to draw the steering wheel from the column

Cushioned steering wheel

12 Disconnect the negative battery cable.
13 Carefully pry off the horn button cap with a screwdriver **(see illustrations)**.
14 On 1975 - 1980 models, remove the snap ring from the end of the shaft **(see illustration)**.
15 Remove the steering wheel lock nut.
16 Remove the three screws securing the upper horn insulator and remove the insulator, receiver, belleville spring and shim (if used).
17 Use a steering wheel puller to remove the steering wheel from the column **(see illustration)**. Threaded holes are provided in the steering wheel for the puller anchor screws. Use the lock nut to protect the top threads of the steering shaft. Do not strike the puller or the end of the column with a hammer as this may damage internal components of the collapsible column.
18 To install, place the turn signal lever in the neutral position and set the wheel onto the steering shaft. Use the alignment marks made upon disassembly to correctly position the steering wheel. Secure with the lock nut, tightening the nut to the proper specifications. Do not overtighten this nut.
19 Install the snap ring (1975 - 1980 models).
20 Install the horn lower insulator, eyelet and spring in the horn contact tower.
21 Install the belleville spring, receiver and horn upper insulator and secure with the three screws.
22 Install the horn button cap and connect the negative battery cable. Check the operation of the horn.

17 Steering column couplings - removal and installation

Flexible coupling

1 Disconnect the battery ground cable (and coupling shield if applicable).
2 Remove the intermediate steering shaft flange to flexible coupling retaining bolts.

3 Remove the steering gear to frame bolts; lower the steering gear.
4 Push the intermediate shaft rearwards and rotate it out of the way.
5 Using a suitable 12-point socket wrench, remove the coupling clamp bolt. Remove the flexible coupling.
6 Install the flexible coupling to the steering gear wormshaft splined end, taking care to align the mating flats.
7 Install the coupling clamp bolt and torque tighten, after ensuring that the coupling reinforcement is bottomed on the wormshaft.
8 Install the intermediate shaft to the coupling and loosely install the flange to coupling bolts.
9 Install the steering gear to frame bolts and torque-tighten.
10 Align the flexible coupling pins centrally in the intermediate shaft flange slots then torque-tighten the coupling bolts.
11 Connect the battery ground lead (and the coupling shield, if applicable).

Pot joint coupling

1 Disconnect the battery ground cable (and the coupling shield, if applicable).
2 Remove the intermediate shaft flange to flexible coupling retaining bolts.
3 Remove the pot joint clamping bolt (at the steering shaft).
4 Remove the steering gear to frame bolts; lower the gear.
5 Push the intermediate steering shaft rearwards until it bottoms in the pot joint and clears the flexible coupling alignment pins.
6 Remove the intermediate shaft and pot joints as an assembly.
7 When installing, align the flats on the pot joint and steering shaft then mate them. Install the clamp and bolt, and torque-tighten.
8 Install the intermediate shaft to the flexible coupling and loosely install the coupling bolts.
9 Install the steering gear-to-frame bolts and torque-tighten.
10 Align the flexible coupling pins centrally

in the intermediate shaft flange slots then torque-tighten the coupling bolts.
11 Connect the battery ground cable (and the coupling shield, if applicable).

18 Pot joint coupling - dismantling and reassembly

1 To disassemble the pot joint, pry off the snap-ring and slide the coupling over the shaft. Remove the bearings and tension spring from the pivot pin. Clean the pin and the end of the shaft then scribe a location mark on the pin on the same side as the shaft chamber. Support the shaft securely then press out the pin taking care that it is not damaged, or bearing damage may occur. Remove the seal clamp then slide the seal off the end of the shaft.
2 To reassemble the pot joint, first ensure that all the parts are clean then slide the seal onto the shaft so that the lip of the seal is against the shoulder on the shaft. Install the clamp. Press the pin into the shaft, aligning the scribed location marks. Ensure that the pin is centered within 0.012 inch, or binding will result. Liberally grease the inside and outside of the bearings and the inside of the cover then install the tension spring and bearings on the pin. Install the seal into the end of the cover and secure with the snap-ring.

19 Manual steering gear - removal and installation

Refer to illustration 19.4
1 Remove the battery ground cable (and the coupling shield, if applicable).
2 Remove the nuts, lockwashers and bolts at the steering shaft to coupling flange.
3 Remove the Pitman arm lock nut and washer. Mark the position of the Pitman arm in relation to the shaft and remove the Pitman arm with a suitable puller.

19.4 The three bolts which run through the frame rail to secure the steering box

21.3 Removing the plastic cover with a screwdriver

21.4a The steering column lock plate is held tightly in place by a snap ring on the center shaft. The plate must be depressed as the snap ring is pried off

4　Remove the screws securing the steering gear to the frame and remove it from the vehicle **(see illustration)**.
5　When installing, place the gear into position so that the coupling mounts properly to the flanged end of the steering shaft. Secure the gear to the frame, fit the washers and bolts, then torque-tighten.
6　Secure the steering coupling to the flanged end of the column with the lockwashers and nuts. Torque-tighten the nuts.
7　Install the Pitman arm.
8　Connect the battery ground cable (and the coupling shield, if applicable).

20 Pitman shaft seal (manual steering) - replacement, steering gear in vehicle

1　Remove the Pitman arm.
2　Turn the steering from stop-to-stop and count the exact number of turns. Now rotate the wheel half the number of turns counted so that the steering gear is centered (wormshaft flat at 12 o'clock position).

3　Remove the side cover from the steering gear housing (three screws) and lift the Pitman shaft and side cover from the housing.
4　Pry the seal from the housing using a screwdriver and tap a new one into position using a suitable socket or piece of tube.
5　Remove the lash adjuster screw locknut and detach the side cover from the Pitman shaft by turning the adjuster screw clockwise.
6　Insert the Pitman shaft into the steering gear so that the center tooth of the shaft sector enters the center tooth of the ball nut.
7　Pack the specified grease into the housing and install a new side cover gasket. Install the side cover onto the lash adjuster screw. This is achieved by inserting a small screwdriver through the threaded adjuster hole in the side cover and turning the lash adjuster screw counterclockwise. When the screw bottoms, turn it back 1/4-turn.
8　Tighten the side cover bolts to the specified torque.
9　Carry out the adjustments described previously and tighten the lash adjuster screw locknut.
10　Install the Pitman arm.

21 Turn signal switch - removal and installation

Refer to illustrations 21.3, 21.4a, 21.4b, 21.5 and 21.8

1　Disconnect the negative battery cable and remove the steering wheel as detailed in Sections 15 or 16.
2　Remove the steering column trim cover located at the base of the dashboard.
3　At the end of the steering column, late models have a plastic cover plate which should be pried out of the column using a screwdriver in the slots provided **(see illustration)**.
4　The lock plate will now have to be removed from the steering column. This is held in place with a snap ring which fits into a groove in the steering shaft. The lock plate must be depressed to relieve pressure on the snap ring. A special U-shaped tool which fits on the shaft should be used to depress the lock plate as the snap ring is removed from its groove **(see illustrations)**.
5　Slide the canceling cam, upper bearing

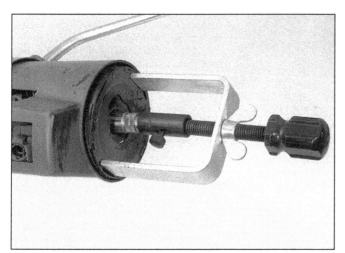

21.4b A special tool is required to depress the steering shaft lockplate so the retaining ring can be removed

21.5 The canceling cam, pre-load spring and thrust washer being removed from the shaft

21.8 The turn signal mechanism is held in place with three screws and can be drawn off the column

preload spring and thrust washer off the end of the shaft **(see illustration)**.

6   Remove the turn signal lever attaching screw and withdraw the turn signal lever from the side of the column.

7   Push in on the hazard warning knob and unscrew the knob from the threaded shaft.

8   Remove the three turn signal assembly mounting screws **(see illustration)**.

9   Pull the switch wiring connector out of the bracket on the steering once the lever is removed from the column jacket. Tape the connector terminals to prevent damage. Feed the wiring connector up through the column support bracket and pull the switch, wiring harness and connectors out the top of the steering column.

10   Installation is a reversal of removal, however, make sure the wiring harness is in the protector as it is pulled into position. Before installing the thrust washer, upper bearing preload spring and canceling cam, make sure the switch is in the neutral position and the warning knob is pulled out. Always use a new snap ring on the shaft for the lock plate.

22   Ignition lock cylinder - removal and installation

1970 - 1978

1   The lock cylinder is located on the upper right-hand side of the steering column. On models built in 1970, the lock cylinder can be removed in any position from "ACCESSORY" to "ON" but removal in "LOCK" position is recommended. From 1971 on, the lock cylinder should only be removed in the "RUN" position, otherwise damage to the warning buzzer switch may occur.

2   Remove the steering wheel (Section 15 or 16) and directional signal switch (Section 21). **Note:** *The directional signal switch need not be fully removed provided that it is pushed rearwards far enough for it to be slipped over the end of the shaft. Do not pull the harness out of the column.*

3   Insert a thin blade or driver into the slot in the turn signal switch housing. Break the housing flash loose and at the same time depress the spring latch at the lower end of the lock cylinder. Holding the latch depressed withdraw the lock cylinder from the housing.

4   The lock cylinder cannot be dismantled; a new one (coded to accept the original key) must be installed in the original cylinder sleeve after the assembly has been dismantled by releasing the cylinder to sleeve staking.

5   To assemble the new lock cylinder to the sleeve, insert the ignition key part way into the lock and then place the wave washer and anti-theft ring onto the lower end of the lock cylinder. making sure that the plastic keeper in the sleeve protrudes.

6   Now align the lock bolt on the cylinder and the tab of the anti-theft washer with the slot in the sleeve. Push the lock cylinder fully onto the sleeve and then insert the ignition key fully and rotate the cylinder clockwise.

7   Rotate the lock counterclockwise to "LOCK".

8   Secure the lock assembly in the jaws of a vise suitably protected with wood or cloth. Install the adapter ring onto the lower end of the cylinder so that the finger of the adapter is located at the step in the sleeve and the serrated edge of the adapter can be seen after assembly to the cylinder. The key must also be free to rotate at least 120°.

9   Tap the adapter onto the cylinder until it is at the bottom of the cylinder flats and the cylinder projects about 1/16 inch above the adapter.

10   Using a small punch, stake the lock cylinder over the adapter ring in four positions just outboard of the four dimples.

11   To install the new lock cylinder/sleeve assembly, hold the sleeve and rotate the lock clockwise against the stop.

12   Insert the cylinder/sleeve assembly into the housing so that the key on the cylinder sleeve is aligned with the housing key way.

13   Insert a 0.070 inch diameter drill between the lock bezel and the housing and then rotate the cylinder counterclockwise, maintaining pressure on the cylinder until the drive section mates with the sector.

14   Press in the lock cylinder until the snap-ring engages in the grooves and secures the cylinder in the housing. Remove the drill and check the lock action.

15   Install the turn signal switch and the steering wheel.

1979-1981

Refer to illustration 22.19

16   The lock cylinder should be removed in the "RUN" position only.

17   Remove the steering wheel (Section 15 or 16) and turn signal switch (Section 21). It is not necessary to completely remove the switch. Pull it up and over the end of the steering shaft. Do not pull the wiring harness out of the column.

18   Remove the ignition key warning switch (Section 23).

19   Using a magnetized screwdriver, remove the lock retaining screw **(see illustration)**. Do not allow this screw to drop down into the column as this will require a complete disassembly of the steering column to

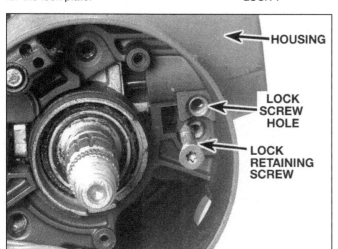

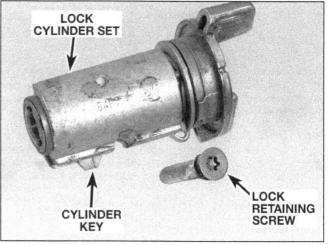

22.19 Later model ignition lock cylinders are held in place with a screw

retrieve the screw.

20   Pull the lock cylinder out of the side of the steering column.

21   To install, rotate the lock cylinder set and align the cylinder key with the keyway in the steering column housing.

22   Push the lock all the way in and install the retaining screw.

23   Install the remaining components referring to the appropriate Sections.

23   Ignition key warning switch - removal and installation

1   The ignition key warning switch is located within the column housing. It can be removed with or without the ignition lock cylinder.

2   Remove the steering wheel (Section 15 or 16).

3   Follow the procedures outlined in Section 21 for removing the turn signal switch, however do not completely remove the switch. Pull the switch over the end of the column shaft. Do not pull the wiring harness out of the steering column.

4   If the ignition lock cylinder is still intact, set the key to the "ON" position.

5   Use a piece of stiff wire (a paper clip will work fine) to remove the switch. Make a hook at the end of the wire and slip this hooked end into the loop of the clip at the top of the switch. Pull up on the wire and remove the clip and switch together from the steering column. Do not allow the clip to fall down into the column.

6   If the lock cylinder is still in the column, the buzzer switch actuating button (on the lock cylinder) must be depressed before the new warning switch can be installed.

7   Install the switch with the contacts towards the upper end of the steering column and with the formed end of the spring clip at the lower end of the switch. Reinstall the remaining components referring to the appropriate Sections.

24   Ignition switch - removal and installation

1   As a precaution against theft of the vehicle, the ignition switch is located inside the channel section of the brake pedal support and remotely controlled by a rod and rack assembly from the ignition lock cylinder.

1970 through 1976

2   To remove the ignition switch, the steering column must either be removed or lowered and well supported. There is no need to remove the steering wheel.

3   Before removing the switch (two screws) set it to the "LOCK" position. If the lock cylinder and actuating rod have already been removed, the "LOCK" position of the switch can be determined by inserting a screwdriver

in the actuating rod slot and then moving the switch slide up until a definite stop is felt and then moving it down one detent.

4   Installation is a reversal of removal but again the switch must be in the "LOCK" position and the original or identical type securing screws must be used. Longer or thicker screws could cause the collapsible design of the steering column to become inoperative.

5   When installing the steering column, refer to Section 25.

1977 on

Refer to illustration 24.7

6   On these models, the switch should be set to the "OFF-UNLOCK" position before removal. If the lock cylinder has already been removed, the switch actuating rod should be pulled up until a definite stop is felt and then pushed down two detents.

7   Before installing the switch, set it to the "OFF-UNLOCK" position and set the gearshift lever in neutral. Setting the switch should be carried out in the following way. Move the switch slider two positions to the right from "ACCESSORY" to "OFF/UNLOCK". Fit the actuator rod into the slider hole and assemble to the steering column using two screws. These screws must be of the original type and only tighten the lower one to 35 lb in torque.

25   Steering column - removal and installation

1   As described in previous Sections, many of the steering column components can be serviced without removal of the steering column. When the steering column is removed, extreme caution should be exercised because of the energy absorbing design of the column. Avoid hammering, jarring, dropping or leaning on any part of the steering column assembly. Also, it is important to use only the factory-installed fasteners or their exact equivalents. Screws and bolts other than those specified could prevent the column from compressing under impact.

2   Disconnect the negative battery cable.

3   Remove the steering wheel using an appropriate puller as described in Section 15 or 16.

4   Inside the engine compartment, disconnect the flanged end of the steering shaft at the flexible coupling. Separate the coupling from the lower end of the steering column.

5   Also at the lower end of the column, disconnect the shift control linkage (back drive linkage on floor shift models).

6   At the base of the steering column, inside the car, disconnect all electrical connectors. These include the main ignition connector and wiring for the neutral-start switch and back-up lamp switch. Pull the wiring free of any steering column clips.

7   Remove the screws which fasten the column plate to the floor pan.

8   The column must now be disconnected from its mounting on the dashboard. On models 1970 - 1978 this requires the ashtray, steering column trim plate and heater/air conditioner control to be lowered as an assembly. 1979 - 1980 models have the column bracket-to-dashboard nuts readily accessible.

9   Disconnect the shift position indicator where applicable.

10   Move the seat as far to the rear as possible for better clearance and carefully guide the column through the firewall opening. This is best done with an assistant helping under the hood.

11   To install the steering column, first position it inside the vehicle, again carefully guiding the lower end through the firewall opening.

12   Loosely install the dashboard attaching nuts to support the column.

13   Connect all electrical connections.

14   Connect the lower end of the column to the steering linkage and tighten the fasteners to the appropriate torque.

15   Connect the shift linkage and/or back-drive linkage at the lower end of the column.

16   Align the column plate seal with the column plate and secure the steering column to the floor pan.

17   Tighten the dashboard attaching nuts.

18   Connect the transmission shift indicator (if equipped).

19   Install the steering wheel referring to Section 15 or 16.

20   For 1970 - 1978 models, install the trim panel and ashtray.

21   Connect the battery cable. Raise the front end and check that the steering wheel is free to rotate from stop to stop without any lumpiness, sticking or binding. Check that the flexible coupling is not distorted due to the pot joint bottoming in either direction.

26   Steering column (standard version) - dismantling and reassembly

1   Remove the four dash panel bracket to steering column screws and retain the bracket so that the mounting capsules will not be damaged.

2   Secure the column in a vise by gripping one set only of the weld nuts.

3   Remove the directional signal switch and lock cylinder, and the ignition key warning switch and the ignition switch as described previously.

4   On column shift models, drive out the upper shift lever pivot pin and remove the shift lever.

5   Remove the upper bearing and thrust washer.

6   Remove the 4 screws which attach the directional signal switch and ignition lock housing to the jacket; remove the housing assembly.

7   Take out the thrust cap from the lower

27.4 To release the tilt mechanism retainer, push it in and turn it counterclockwise

27.7 Use a slide hammer and a 8/32 inch machine screw to remove the bearing housing pivot pins (tilt column)

side of the housing.

8   Lift the ignition switch actuating rod and rack assembly together with the shaft lock bolt and spring assembly from the housing.

9   Remove the shift gate.

10   Remove the ignition switch actuator sector through the lock cylinder hole by pushing on the block tooth sector with a rod or punch.

11   Remove the gearshift lever housing and shroud, or the transmission control lock tube housing and shroud, as applicable.

12   Remove the shift lever spring from the gearshift housing, or the lock tube spring, as applicable.

13   Pull the steering shaft from the lower end of the jacket assembly.

14   Remove the back-up switch or neutral safety switch (2 screws).

15   Remove the lower bearing retainer.

16   *Automatics and floorshifts:* Remove the lower bearing retainer, adapter assembly, shift tube spring and washer. Press out the lower bearing by applying pressure to the outer race then slide out the shift tube assembly.

17   *Column shift /manual transmission):* Remove the lower bearing adapter, bearing and first/reverse shift lever. Press out the lower bearing by applying pressure to the outer race. Remove 3 screws from the lower end bearing and slide out the shift tube assembly.

18   From the upper end of the mast jacket, remove the gearshift housing lower bearing.

19   Replace any worn components and commence reassembly by applying a thin coating of lithium soap grease to all friction surfaces, and then installing the sector into the turn signal housing. To do this, reach through the lock cylinder hole, place the sector onto the shaft using a blunt tool.

20   Install the shift gate onto the housing.

21   Insert the rack preload spring into the housing from the lower end so that both ends of the spring are attached to the housing.

22   Assemble the locking bolt to the crossover arm on the rack.

23   Insert the rack and lock bolt assembly into the housing (teeth upwards). Align the

first tooth on the sector with the first tooth on the rack so that the block teeth will line up when the rack assembly is pushed right in.

24   Install the thrust cup into the housing.

25   Install the gearshift housing lower bearing, aligning the indentations with the projections in the jacket.

26   Install the shift lever spring into the housing.

27   Install the housing and shroud assemblies onto the mast jacket, rotating slightly to ensure proper seating in the bearing.

28   With the shift lever housing in position, and the gearshift housing at "park", pull the rack downwards and install the directional signal switch and lock cylinder housing onto the jacket. When seated, install the 4 screws.

29   Press the lower bearing fully into the adapter assembly.

30   *Automatics and floorshifts:* Assemble the spring, and the lower bearing and adapter assembly into the bottom of the jacket. Hold the adapter in place then install the lower bearing reinforcement and retainer. Ensure that the retainer snaps into the slots.

31   *Column shift manual transmission:* Loosely install the 3 screws in the jacket and shift tube bearing. Assemble the first/reverse lever, and lower bearing and adapter assembly into the bottom of the jacket. Hold the adapter in place then install the bearing reinforcement and retainer. Ensure that the retainer snaps into the slots. Place a 0.005 inch shim (feeler) between the first/reverse lever and spacer then turn the upper shift tube bearing down and tighten the 3 screws. Finally remove the shim.

32   Install the neutral safety or back-up switch.

33   Slide the steering shaft into the column then install the upper bearing thrust washer.

34   Install the ignition key warning switch, directional signal switch, lock cylinder assembly and ignition switch, as described previously.

35   Install the shift lever and shift lever pivot pin, then remove the assembly from the vise.

36   Install the 4 dash bracket to column screws and torque-tighten.

27 Steering column (tilt version) - dismantling and reassembly

Refer to illustrations 27.4, 27.7 and 27.16

1   Initially follow the procedure given in paragraphs 1, 2 and 3 for dismantling of the standard version column.

2   Remove the tilt release lever then drive out the shift lever pivot pin and remove the shift lever from the housing.

3   Remove the directional signal housing (3 screws).

4   Install the tilt release lever and move the column to the highest position. Use a suitable screwdriver to remove the tilt lever spring retainer by pressing inwards approximately 3/16 inch then turning 1/8 turn (45°) counterclockwise until the ears align with the grooves in the housing **(see illustration)**.

5   Remove the pot joint to steering shaft clamp bolt then remove the intermediate shaft and pot joint assembly.

6   Push the upper shaft in sufficiently to remove the upper bearing inner race and seat. Pry off the lower bearing retainer and remove the bearing reinforcement, bearing and bearing adapter assembly from the lower end of the mast jacket.

7   Withdraw the upper bearing housing pivot pins using a slide hammer **(see illustration)**.

8   Install the tilt release lever and disengage the lock shoes then remove the bearing housing by pulling upwards to extend the rack fully down. Now move the housing to the left to disengage the ignition switch rack from the actuator rod.

9   Remove the steering shaft assembly from the upper end of the column, then the upper bearing seat and inner race.

10   Disassemble the shaft by removing the centering spheres and anti-lash spring.

11   Remove the transmission indicator wire, where applicable.

12   Remove the 4 screws retaining the shaft bearing housing support followed by the housing support. Remove the ignition switch actuator rod.

13 Using a suitable extractor, remove the shift tube (or transmission control lock tube - floorshift) from the lower end of the mast jacket.

14 Remove the bearing housing support lockplate by sliding out of the jacket notches and tipping it down towards the hub at the 12 o'clock position. Slide it under the jacket opening and remove the wave washer.

15 Remove the shift lever housing or lock tube housing from the mast jacket. Remove the shift lever spring by winding it up with pliers, then pulling it out. On floor change models the spring plunger has to be re moved .

16 To disassemble the bearing housing, remove the tilt lever opening shield then take out the lock bolt spring by removing the retaining screw and moving the spring clockwise.

17 Remove the snap-ring from the sector driveshaft then use a small punch to lightly tap the driveshaft from the sector. Remove the driveshaft, sector, lockbolt, rack and rack spring **(see illustration)**.

18 Drive out the tilt release lever then remove the lever and spring. To relieve the load on the release lever, hold the shoes inwards and wedge a block between the top of the shoes (over the slots) and the bearing housing.

19 Drive out the lock shoe retaining pin then the lock shoe springs. **Note:** *With the tilt lever opening on the left and the shoes uppermost, the 4-slot shoe is on the left.*

20 If the bearings are to be replaced, remove the separator and balls. Carefully drive out the race from the housing, followed by the second race.

21 During the assembly procedure, all friction surfaces should be lightly smeared with lithium based grease.

22 There dismantled, carefully press the bearing into the housing using a suitable sized socket.

23 Install the lockshoe springs, shoes and shoe pin, using a suitable rod (approx. 0.180 inch) for locating purposes.

24 Install the shoe release lever, spring and pin. To relieve the release lever load, hold the shoes inwards and wedge a block between the top of the shoes (over the slots) and bearing housing.

25 Install the sector driveshaft; lightly tap it on until the snap-ring can be installed.

26 Install the lockbolt and engage it with the sector cam surface then install the rack and spring. The block tooth on the rack must engage correctly in the sector. Install the tilt release lever.

27 Install the lockbolt spring. Torque-tighten the retaining screw.

28 Wind up the shift lever spring with pliers and install (push) it onto the housing. On floor shift models the plunger has to be installed.

29 Slide the gearshift lever housing onto the steering mast jacket.

30 Install the wave-washer for the bearing support lockplate.

31 Install the lockplate, working it into the notches in the jacket by tipping towards the

27.17 Sector and rack assembly details (tilt column)

housing hub at the 12 o'clock position and sliding it under the jacket opening. The lockplate can then be slid into the notches in the jacket.

32 Carefully install the shift tube into the lower end of the mast jacket, aligning the keyway in the tube with the key in the shift lever housing. The next part of the operation ideally requires the use of a special tool although by the judicious use of spacers, washers and a long bolt a suitable alternative can be made up. Install the tube and pull the shift tube into the housing by rotating the outer nut. Do not exert any load on the end of the shift tube and ensure that the shift tube lever is aligned with the slotted opening at the lower end of the mast jacket.

33 Install the bearing support thrust washer and retaining ring by pulling the shift lever housing upwards to compress the wave washer.

34 Install the bearing support, aligning the "V" in the support with the "V" in the jacket. Insert the support to lockplate screws and torque-tighten.

35 Align the lower bearing adapter with the notches in the jacket then push the adapter into the lower end. Install the lower bearing, bearing reinforcement and retainer; ensuring that the slip is aligned with the slots in the reinforcement, jacket and adapter.

36 Install the centering spheres and anti-lash spring in the upper shaft then install the lower shaft from the same side of the spheres as the spring ends protrude.

37 Install the steering shaft assembly into the shift lever housing from the upper end, guiding the shaft carefully through the tube and bearing.

38 Install the ignition switch actuator rod through the shift lever housing and insert it in the bearing support slot. Extend the rack downwards from the housing.

39 Assemble the bearing housing over the steering shaft, engaging the rack over the end of the actuator rod.

40 Install the external release lever then hold the lock shoes in the disengaged position and assemble the bearing housing over the steering shaft until the pivot pin holes align. Now install the pivot pins.

41 Place the bearing housing in the fully up

position then install the tilt lever spring guide, spring and spring retainer. Using a suitable screwdriver, push in the retainer and turn clockwise to engage in the housing.

42 Install the upper bearing inner race and seat.

43 Install the tilt lever opening shield.

44 Remove the tilt release lever, install the directional signal housing and torque-tighten the three retaining screws.

45 Install the tilt release lever and the shift lever, then drive in the shift lever pin.

46 Install the ignition key warning switch, lock cylinder, directional signal switch and ignition switch, as described previously.

47 Align the grooves across the upper end of the pot joint with the steering shaft flat and assemble the intermediate shaft assembly to the upper shaft. Install the clamp and bolt, and torque-tighten.

48 Install the neutral safety or back-up switch.

49 Install the 4 dash panel bracket to column screws and torque- tighten. **Note:** *Ensure that the slotted openings in the bracket face the upper end of the column.*

28 Power steering - general description

1 With the optional power steering gear, hydraulic pressure is generated in an engine-driven vane type pump and supplied through hoses to the steering box spool valve. The valve is normally positioned in the neutral mode by a torsion bar but when the steering wheel is turned and force is applied to the steering shaft then the spool moves in relation to the body and allows oil to flow to the appropriate side of the piston nut. The greater the movement of the steering wheel, the greater the hydraulic pressure which is applied and therefore the greater the power assistance given to the drive.

2 Apart from the procedures given in the following sections, it is recommended that where any major fault develops, rectification is entrusted to a dealer or specialist in power steering systems.

29 Power steering - maintenance and adjustment

1   The fluid level should be checked regularly, as described in Chapter 1.
2   The pump drive belt tension should be checked regularly, refer to Chapter 1.
3   The over-center adjustment is the only adjustment which can be satisfactorily carried out without removing the steering gear from the vehicle.
4   If the vehicle is equipped with a tilt-column, disconnect the column flexible coupling. Using a torque wrench or a spring balance attached to the steering wheel nut obtain and record the steering shaft turning torque. Reconnect the coupling (if installed).
5   Disconnect the Pitman arm from the relay rod.
6   Loosen the Pitman shaft adjusting screw locknut and unscrew the adjuster screw out of the side cover as far as it will go.
7   Disconnect the battery ground cable.
8   Remove the horn button (already carried out on tilt column vehicles).
9   Turn the steering wheel from stop to stop through its full travel and then turn it to its center (wheels straight ahead) position.
10   Now check the combined ball/thrust bearing preload using a (pound/inch) torque wrench on the steering wheel nut and turning it a quarter turn through the center position in both directions. Take the highest reading. On vehicles equipped with a tilt column, subtract the turning torque recorded earlier when the coupling was disconnected.
11   Tighten the Pitman shaft adjusting screw in small increments rechecking the over-center preload between each adjustment until the total gear preload falls within that specified (see Specifications Section).
12   Tighten the adjuster screw locknut, install the Pitman arm, the horn button and reconnect the battery ground cable.

30 Power steering gear - removal and installation

1   The procedure is similar to that described previously for the manual type except that the hydraulic hoses must be disconnected from the steering gear housing.
2   Plug the ends of the hoses and the fluid inlet and outlet holes in the housing.
3   When installation is complete, bleed the system as described in Section 32.

31 Power steering pump - removal and installation

Refer to illustration 31.3
1   Disconnect the hydraulic hoses either from the pump or the steering gear and keep them in the raised position to prevent the fluid draining away until they can be plugged.

2   Remove the pump drive belt by loosening the pump mounts and pushing it in towards the engine.
3   Unscrew and remove the pump mounting bolts and braces and remove the pump **(see illustration)**.
4   To remove the pump pulley it will almost certainly require the use of a special extractor, the type depending upon the actual pulley fitted. Consult your parts store if the pulley is to be removed.
5   Installation is a reversal of removal but tighten the hose unions to the specified torque and then fill the fluid reservoir.
6   Prime the pump by turning the pulley in the reverse direction to that of normal rotation until air-bubbles cease to emerge from the fluid when observed through the reservoir filler cap.
7   Install the drive belt and tension it as described in Chapter 1.
8   Bleed the system as described in Section 32 of this Chapter.

32 Power steering hydraulic system - bleeding

1   This is not a routine operation and will normally only be required when the system has been dismantled and reassembled.
2   Fill the reservoir to its correct level with fluid of recommended type, and allow it to remain undisturbed for at least 2 minutes.
3   Start the engine and run it for two or three seconds only. Check the reservoir fluid level and top-up if necessary.
4   Repeat the operations described in the preceding paragraph until the fluid level remains constant.
5   Raise the front of the vehicle until the wheels are clear of the ground.

31.3 Remove the power steering pump mounting bolts and nuts (arrows)

6   Start the engine and increase its speed to about 1500 rpm. Now turn the steering wheel gently from stop-to-stop. Check the reservoir fluid level adding some if necessary.
7   Lower the vehicle to the ground and with the engine still running move the vehicle forward sufficiently to obtain full right lock followed by full left lock. Re-check the fluid level. If the fluid in the reservoir is extremely foamy, allow the vehicle to stand for a few minutes with the engine switched off and then repeat the previous operations.
8   Air in the power steering system is often indicated by a noisy pump but a low fluid level can also cause this.

33 Front wheel alignment and steering angles

Refer to illustration 33.1
1   Accurate front wheel alignment is essen-

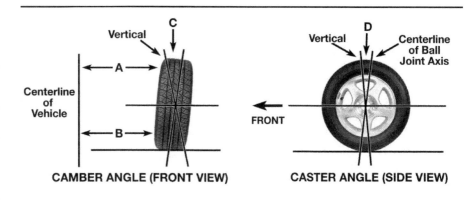

CAMBER ANGLE (FRONT VIEW)

CASTER ANGLE (SIDE VIEW)

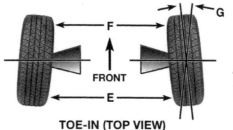

TOE-IN (TOP VIEW)

33.1 Typical front end alignment details

A minus B = C (degrees camber)
E minus F = toe-in (measured in inches)
G = toe-in (expressed in degrees)

tial for good steering and slow tire wear. Before considering the steering angles; check that the tires are correctly inflated, that the front wheels are not buckled, the hub bearings are hot worn or incorrectly adjusted and that the steering linkage is in good order, without slack or wear at the joints **(see illustration)**.

2   Wheel alignment consists of four factors:

Camber which is the angle at which the front wheels are set from the vertical when viewed from the front of the car. Positive camber is the amount (in degrees) that the wheels are tilted outwards at the top from the vertical.

Caster is the angle between the steering axis and a vertical line when viewed from each side of the car. Positive caster is when the steering axis is inclined rearward.

Steering axis inclination is the angle, when viewed from the front of the car, between the vertical and an imaginary line drawn between the upper and lower suspension control arm balljoints.

Toe-in is the amount by which the distance between the front inside edges of the wheels (measured at hub height) is less than the diametrically opposite distance measured between the rear inside edges of the front wheels.

3   On all other models, the caster and camber angles are set by means of shims inserted between the upper control arm shaft and the frame bracket.

4   Due to the need for special gauges and equipment, it is not advised that camber or caster angles should be adjusted at home.

5   To adjust the toe-in (which should only be done after establishing that caster and camber are correct), obtain or make a toe-in gauge. Once can be made up from a length of tubing, cranked to clear the oil pan and clutch or torque converter housing and having a screw and locknut at one end.

6   Use a gauge to measure the distance between the two inner wheel rims at hub height at the rear of the wheels.

7   Push the vehicle to rotate the wheel through 180° (half a turn) and then measure the distance between the inner wheel rims at hub height at the front of the wheels ("F").

8   The distance between the two measurements is the toe-in (where the first measurement is larger than the second). Refer to the specifications for the correct value.

9   Toe-in or toe-out can be altered by increasing or decreasing the length of the tie-rods. For 1975 models, the tie-rods must be decreased in length to increase the toe-in: for other models the tie-rod length must be increased to increase the toe-in. Where any adjustment is made, the

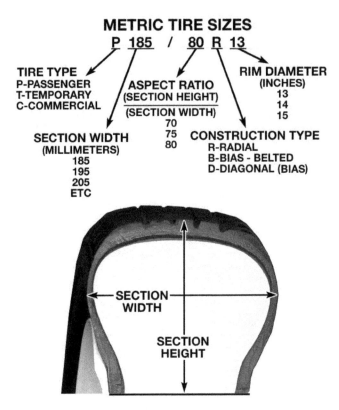

34.1 Metric tire size code

screwed sleeves should be turned by equal amounts at each side.

10   Where new tie-rods, tie-rod ends or steering components have been installed, always commence adjustment with the overall lengths of the tie-rods exactly equal. Take the measurements from the balljoint centers and have the wheels and steering wheel in the straight-ahead position.

34   Wheels and tires

Refer to illustration 34.1

1   The wheels are of pressed steel type and the tires may be conventional, radial or bias belted. Never mix tires of different construction on the same axle **(see illustration)**.

2   Check the tire pressures weekly, including the spare, preferably when the tires are cold, first thing in the morning.

3   The wheel nuts should be tightened to the specified torque, and it is an advantage if a smear of grease is applied to the wheel stud threads.

4   Every 7500 miles, the wheels should be moved round the vehicle in order to even out the tire tread wear. To do this, remove each wheel in turn, clean it thoroughly (both sides) and remove any stones which may be embedded in the tread. Check the tread wear pattern which will indicate any mechanical or adjustment faults in the suspension or steering components. Examine the wheel bolt holes for elongation or wear. If such conditions are found, replace the wheel.

5   Replacement of the tires should be carried out when the thickness of the tread pattern is worn to a minimum of 1/16-inch or the wear indicators (if incorporated) are visible.

6   The method of moving the tires depends on whether the spare (5th) wheel is brought into the rotational pattern, and to the type off construction of the tire (see Chapter 1).

7   The type of tire and inflation pressures are recorded on a sticker located on the vehicle door and the specification varies according to the particular vehicle model and tires fitted. Always adjust the front and rear tire pressures after moving the wheels round as previously described.

8   Have all wheels balanced initially and again half way through the useful life of the tires.

Chapter 12   Bodywork

Contents

Specifications

Overall dimensions

1970

Overall length	191.6 in
Overall width	73.4 in
Height	50.1 in
Wheelbase	108.0 in

1971 - 1972

As 1970 models except:

Height	50.4 in

1973

As 1970 models except:

Overall length	192.1 in

1974 - 1978

As 1970 models except:

Overall length	195.4 in
Height	49.1 in

1979 - 1980

Overall length	197.6 in
Overall width	74.5 in
Height	49.2 in

1 General description

1　The Firebird has been available with many trim options, all variations of the basic 2-door body style. Cosmetic body packages such as the Esprit, Formula or Trans AM have slight body component modifications which are dealt with separately in this Chapter where appropriate.

2　Certain body panels which are particularly vulnerable to accident damage can be replaced by unbolting them and installing replacement items. These panels include the fenders, inner fender skirts, radiator support panel, grille, bumper and trunk.

2 Maintenance - bodywork and underframe

1　The condition of your vehicle's bodywork is of considerable importance as it is on this that the resale value will mainly depend. It is much more difficult to repair neglected bodywork than to replace mechanical assemblies. The hidden portions of the body, such as the wheel arches, fender skirts, the underframe and the engine compartment are equally important, although obviously not requiring such frequent attention as the immediately visible paint.

2　Once a year or every 12,000 miles it is a good idea to have the underside of the body steam cleaned. All traces of dirt and oil will be removed and the underside can then be inspected carefully for rust, damaged hydraulic pipes, frayed electrical wiring and similar trouble areas. The front suspension should be greased on completion of this job.

3　At the same time, clean the engine and the engine compartment either using a steam cleaner or a water-soluble cleaner.

4　The wheel arches and fender skirts should be given particular attention as undercoating can easily come away here and stones and dirt thrown up from the wheels can soon cause the paint to chip and flake, and so allow rust to set in. If rust is found, clean down to the bare metal and apply an anti-rust paint.

5　The bodywork should be washed once a week or when dirty. Thoroughly wet the vehicle to soften the dirt and then wash down with a soft sponge and plenty of clean water. If the surplus dirt is not washed off very gently, in time it will wear the paint down.

6　Spots of tar or bitumen coating thrown up from the road surfaces are best removed with a cloth soaked in a cleaner made especially for this purpose.

7　Once every six months, or more frequently depending on the weather conditions, give the bodywork and chrome trim a thoroughly good wax polish. If a chrome cleaner is used to remove rust on any of the vehicle's plated parts, remember that the cleaner can also remove part of the chrome, so use it sparingly.

3 Maintenance - upholstery and carpets

1　Remove the carpets or mats and thoroughly vacuum clean the interior of the vehicle every three months or more frequently if necessary.

2　Beat out the carpets and vacuum clean them if they are very dirty. If the upholstery is soiled apply an upholstery cleaner with a damp sponge and wipe off with a clean dry cloth.

3　Consult you local auto parts store for cleaners made especially for newer automotive upholstery fabrics. Always test the cleaner in an inconspicuous place.

4 Maintenance - roof covering

Under no circumstances try to clean any external vinyl roof covering with detergents, caustic soap or spirit cleaners. Plain soap and water is all that is required, with a soft brush to clean dirt-that may be ingrained. Wash the covering as frequently as the rest of the vehicle.

5 Minor body damage - repair

See photo sequence

Repair of minor scratches in the vehicle's bodywork

If the scratch is very superficial, and does not penetrate to the metal of the bodywork, repair is very simple. Lightly rub the area of the scratch with a paintwork renovator, or a very fine cutting paste, to remove loose paint from the scratch and to clear the surrounding bodywork of wax polish. Rinse the area with clean water.

Apply touch-up paint to the scratch using a thin paint brush; continue to apply thin layers of paint until the surface of the paint in the scratch is level with the surrounding paintwork. Allow the new paint at least two weeks to harden: then blend it into the surrounding paintwork by rubbing the paintwork, in the scratch area, with a paintwork renovator or a very fine cutting paste. Finally, apply wax polish.

An alternative to painting over the scratch is to use a paint transfer. Use the same preparation for the affected area, then simply pick a patch of a suitable size to cover the scratch completely. Hold the patch against the scratch and burnish its backing paper: the paper will adhere to the paintwork, freeing itself from the backing paper at the same time. Polish the affected area to blend the patch into the surrounding paintwork.

Where the scratch has penetrated right through to the metal of the bodywork, causing the metal to rust, a different repair technique is required. Remove any loose rust from the

bottom of the scratch with a penknife, then apply rust inhibiting paint to prevent the formation of rust in the future. Using a rubber or nylon applicator fill the scratch with bodystopper paste. If required, this paste can be mixed with cellulose thinners to provide a very thin paste which is ideal for filling narrow scratches. Before the stopper-paste in the scratch hardens, wrap a piece of smooth cotton rag around the top of a finger. Dip the finger in cellulose thinners and then quickly sweep it across the surface of the stopper-paste in the scratch; this will ensure that the surface of the stopper-paste is slightly hollowed. The scratch can now be painted over as described earlier in this Section.

Repair of dents in the vehicle's bodywork

When deep denting of the vehicle's bodywork has taken place, the first task is to pull the dent out, until the affected bodywork almost attains its original shape. There is little point in trying to restore the original shape completely, as the metal in the damaged area will have stretched on impact and cannot be reshaped fully to its original contour. It is better to bring the level of the dent up to a point which is about t in (3 mm) below the level of the surrounding bodywork. In cases where the dent is very shallow anyway, it is not worth trying to pull it out at all.

If the underside of the dent is accessible, it can be hammered out gently from behind, using a mallet with a wooden or plastic head. Whilst doing this, hold a suitable block of wood firmly against the impact from the hammer blows and thus prevent a large area of the bodywork from being "belled-out".

Should the dent be in a section of the bodywork which has double skin or some other factor making it inaccessible from behind, a different technique is called for. Drill several small holes through the metal inside the area - particularly in the deeper section. Then screw long self-tapping screws into the holes just sufficiently for them to gain a good purchase in the metal. Now the dent can be pulled out by pulling on the protruding heads of the screws with a pair of pliers.

The next stage of the repair is the removal of the paint from the damaged area, and from an inch or so of the surrounding sound bodywork. This is accomplished most easily by using a wire brush or abrasive pad on a power drill, although it can be done just as effectively by hand using sheets of sandpaper. To complete the preparation for filling, score the surface of the bare metal with a screwdriver or the tang of a file, or alternatively, drill small holes in the affected area. This will provide a really good key for the filler paste.

To complete the repair see the Section on filling and re-spraying.

Repair of rust holes or gashes in the vehicle's bodywork

Remove all paint from the affected area and from an inch or so of the surrounding "sound" bodywork, using an abrasive pad or a wire brush on a power drill. If these are not available a few sheets of sandpaper will do the job just as effectively. With the paint removed you will be able to gauge the severity of the corrosion and therefore decide whether to renew the whole panel (if this is possible) or to repair the affected area. New body panels are not as expensive as most people think and it is often quicker and more satisfactory to fit a new panel than to attempt to repair large areas of corrosion.

Remove all fittings from the affected area except those which will act as a guide to the original shape of the damaged bodywork (e.g. headlamp shells etc). Then, using tin snips or a hacksaw blade, remove all loose metal and any other metal badly affected by corrosion. Hammer the edges of the hole inwards in order to create a slight depression for the filler paste.

Wire brush the affected area to remove the powdery rust from the surface of the remaining metal. Paint the affected area with rust inhibiting paint; if the back of the rusted area is accessible treat this also.

Before filling can take place it will be necessary to block the hole in some way. This can be achieved by the use of zinc gauze or aluminum tape.

Zinc gauze is probably the best material to use for a large hole. Cut a piece to the approximate size and shape of the hole to be filled, then position it in the hole so that its edges are below the level of the surrounding bodywork. It can be retained in position by several blobs of filler paste around its periphery.

Aluminum tape should be used for small or very narrow holes. Pull a piece off the roll and trim it to the approximate size and shape required, then pull off the backing paper (if used) and stick the tape over the hole; it can be overlapped if the thickness of one piece is insufficient. Burnish down the edges of the tape with the handle of a screwdriver or similar, to ensure that the tape is securely attached to the metal underneath.

Having blocked off the hole the affected area must now be filled and sprayed - see Section on bodywork fitting and re-spraying.

Bodywork repairs - filling and re-spraying

Before using this Section, see the Sections on dent, deep scratch, rust holes and gash repairs.

Many types of bodyfiller are available, but generally speaking those proprietary kits which contain a tin of filler paste and a tube of resin hardener are best for this type of repair. A wide, flexible plastic or nylon applicator will be found invaluable for imparting a smooth and well contoured finish to the surface of the filler.

Mix up a little filler on a clean piece of card or board - measure the hardener carefully (follow the maker's instructions on the pack) otherwise the filler will set too rapidly or too slowly.

Using the applicator apply the filler paste to the prepared area; draw the applicator across the surface of the filler to achieve the correct contour and to level the filler surface. As soon as a contour that approximates the correct one is achieved, stop working the paste - if you carry on too long the paste will become sticky and begin to "pick up" on the applicator. Continue to add thin layers of filler paste at twenty-minute intervals until the level of the filler is just proud of the surrounding bodywork.

Once the filler has hardened, excess can be removed using a metal plane or file. From then on, progressively finer grades of sandpaper should be used, starting with a 40 grade production paper and finishing with 400 grade wet-and-dry paper. Always wrap the sandpaper around a flat rubber, cork or wooden block - otherwise the surface of the filler will not be completely flat. During the smoothing of the filler surface the wet-and-dry paper should be periodically rinsed in water. This will ensure that a very smooth finish is imparted to the filler at the final stage.

At this stage the "repair area" should be surrounded by a ring of bare metal, which in turn should be encircled by the finely "feathered" edge of the good paintwork. Rinse the repair area with clean water, until all of the dust produced by the rubbing-down operation has gone.

Spray the whole repair area with a light coat of primer - this will show up any imperfections in the surface of the filler. Repair these imperfections with fresh filler paste or bodystopper, and once more smooth the surface with sandpaper. If bodystopper is used, it can be mixed with cellulose thinners to form a really thin paste which is ideal for filling small holes. Repeat this spray and repair procedure until you are satisfied that the surface of the filler, and the feathered edge of the paintwork are perfect. Clean the repair area with clean water and allow to dry fully.

The repair area is now ready for final spraying. Paint spraying must be carried out in warm, dry, windless and dust free atmosphere. This condition can be created artificially if you have access to a large indoor working area, but if you are forced to work in the open, you will have to pick your day very carefully. If you are working indoors, dousing the floor in the work area with water will help to settle the dust which would otherwise be in the atmosphere. If the repair area is confined to one body panel, mask off, the surrounding panels; this will help to minimize the effects of a slight mismatch in paint colors. Bodywork fittings (e.g. chrome strips, door handles etc) will also need to be masked off. Use genuine masking tape and several thicknesses of newspaper for the masking operations.

Before commencing to spray, agitate the aerosol can thoroughly, then spray a test area (an old tin, or similar) until the technique is mastered. Cover the repair area with a thick coat of primer; the thickness should be built up using several thin layers of paint rather than one thick one. Using 400 grade wet-and-dry paper, rub down the surface of the primer until it is really smooth. While doing this, the work area should be thoroughly doused with water, and the wet-and-dry paper periodically rinsed in water. Allow to dry before spraying on more paint.

Spray on the top coat, again building up the thickness by using several thin layers of paint. Start spraying in the center of the repair area and then using a circular motion, work outwards until the whole repair area and about 2 inches of the surrounding original paintwork is covered. Remove all masking material 10 to 15 minutes after spraying on the final coat of paint. Allow the new paint at least two weeks to harden, then, using a paintwork renovator or a very fine cutting paste, blend the edges of the paint into the existing paintwork. Finally, apply wax polish.

6 Bodywork and frame repairs - major damage

1   Major damage must be repaired by competent mechanics with the necessary welding and hydraulic straightening equipment.
2   If the damage has been serious it is vital that the frame is checked for correct alignment as otherwise the handling of the vehicle will suffer and many other faults - such as excessive tire wear, and wear in the transmission and steering - may occur.
3   There is a special body jig which most body repair shops have and to ensure that all is correct it is important that this jig be used for all major repair work.

7 Hood - maintenance and adjustments

Refer to illustrations 7.1, 7.2a, 7.2b and 7.3
1   As a safety measure, a protruding adjustable screw and nut is located at each side of the cowl area, at the rear of the hood **(see illustration)**. This bolt must be adjusted

7.1 Hood safety catch bolts are used at each side of the hood, near the base of the windshield. The bolts must extend 1 - inch from the cowling

These photos illustrate a method of repairing simple dents. They are intended to supplement *Body repair - minor damage* in this Chapter and should not be used as the sole instructions for body repair on these vehicles.

1 If you can't access the backside of the body panel to hammer out the dent, pull it out with a slide-hammer-type dent puller. In the deepest portion of the dent or along the crease line, drill or punch hole(s) at least one inch apart . . .

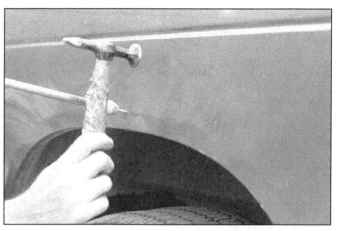

2 . . . then screw the slide-hammer into the hole and operate it. Tap with a hammer near the edge of the dent to help 'pop' the metal back to its original shape. When you're finished, the dent area should be close to its original contour and about 1/8-inch below the surface of the surrounding metal

3 Using coarse-grit sandpaper, remove the paint down to the bare metal. Hand sanding works fine, but the disc sander shown here makes the job faster. Use finer (about 320-grit) sandpaper to feather-edge the paint at least one inch around the dent area

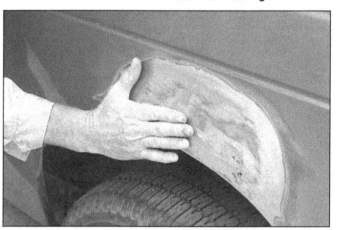

4 When the paint is removed, touch will probably be more helpful than sight for telling if the metal is straight. Hammer down the high spots or raise the low spots as necessary. Clean the repair area with wax/silicone remover

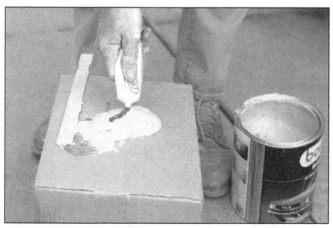

5 Following label instructions, mix up a batch of plastic filler and hardener. The ratio of filler to hardener is critical, and, if you mix it incorrectly, it will either not cure properly or cure too quickly (you won't have time to file and sand it into shape)

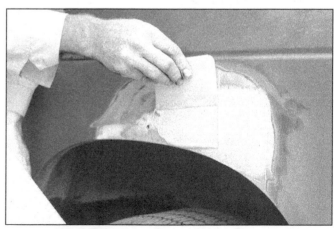

6 Working quickly so the filler doesn't harden, use a plastic applicator to press the body filler firmly into the metal, assuring it bonds completely. Work the filler until it matches the original contour and is slightly above the surrounding metal

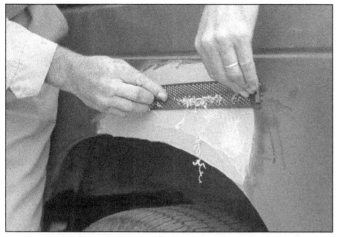

7 Let the filler harden until you can just dent it with your fingernail. Use a body file or Surform tool (shown here) to rough-shape the filler

8 Use coarse-grit sandpaper and a sanding board or block to work the filler down until it's smooth and even. Work down to finer grits of sandpaper - always using a board or block - ending up with 360 or 400 grit

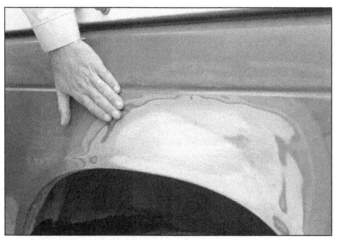

9 You shouldn't be able to feel any ridge at the transition from the filler to the bare metal or from the bare metal to the old paint. As soon as the repair is flat and uniform, remove the dust and mask off the adjacent panels or trim pieces

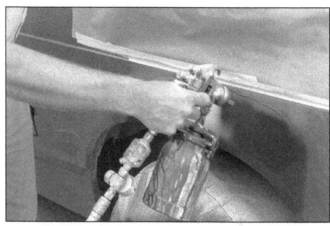

10 Apply several layers of primer to the area. Don't spray the primer on too heavy, so it sags or runs, and make sure each coat is dry before you spray on the next one. A professional-type spray gun is being used here, but aerosol spray primer is available inexpensively from auto parts stores

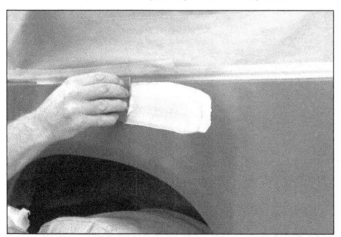

11 The primer will help reveal imperfections or scratches. Fill these with glazing compound. Follow the label instructions and sand it with 360 or 400-grit sandpaper until it's smooth. Repeat the glazing, sanding and respraying until the primer reveals a perfectly smooth surface

12 Finish sand the primer with very fine sandpaper (400 or 600-grit) to remove the primer overspray. Clean the area with water and allow it to dry. Use a tack rag to remove any dust, then apply the finish coat. Don't attempt to rub out or wax the repair area until the paint has dried completely (at least two weeks)

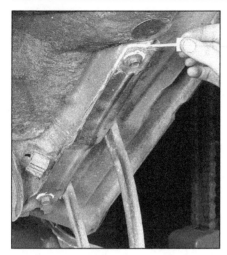

7.2a Use a scribe, felt pen or paint to mark the position of the hinge plate on the underside of the hood

7.2b Pad the back corners of the hood with cloth so the windshield won't be damaged if the hood accidentally swings rearward

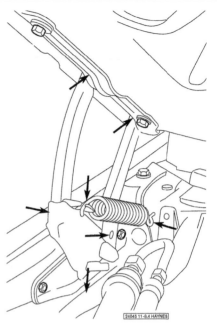

7.3 Lubricate the hinges

to a height of exactly one inch. At this height the head of the bolt will fit into an opening provided in the inner hood reinforcement; The purpose of this bolt is to prevent the hood from riding into the windshield in the event of a front end collision.

2   To prevent engine compartment fumes from being pulled into the car interior through the cowl vent it is important that the hood be properly adjusted and sealed at the cowl area. The alignment of the hood is controlled by the position of the hood hinges and the height of the two bumpers located at each side of the radiator support. The hood is adjusted as follows:

a) *Scribe a line around the entire hinge plate to be repositioned* **(see illustration)**. *This will enable you to judge the amount of movement.*

b) *Loosen the appropriate screws on the hood hinge to be adjusted and move the hood into the correct alignment* **(see illustration)**. *Move the hood only*

a little at a time. Tighten the hinge screws and carefully lower the hood to check the position.

c) *Adjust the hood bumpers on the radiator support so that the hood, when closed, is flush with the fender and grille top surfaces.*

d) *The hood catch and lock assembly is adjustable to provide a positive closing of the hood. The hood catch assembly on the radiator support section has slotted mounting holes to allow the catch to be moved into alignment with the hood lock bolt. The lock bolt on the hood can be lengthened or shortened to engage with the catch. When closed properly the hood bumpers should be slightly compressed.*

3   The catch and lock assembly, as well as the hinges **(see illustration)** should be periodically lubricated to prevent sticking or jamming.

8   Hood - removal and installation

Refer to illustrations 8.3 and 8.4

1   The hood assembly may be removed with or without the hinges. Whichever method is chosen, it is important to scribe a line around the hinge mounting on the hood or the body to replace the assembly in the same location.

2   Use blankets or cloths to cover the cowl area of the body and the fenders. This will protect the body and paint as the hood is lifted free of the car.

3   Disconnect the windshield washer hoses from the hood **(see illustration)**.

4   With the help of an assistant to take the weight of the hood, remove the appropriate screws **(see illustration)**.

5   Carefully lift the hood off the car.

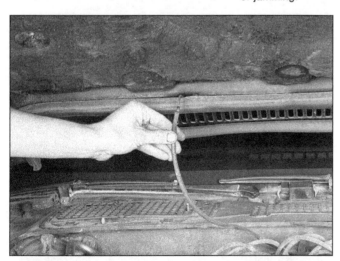

8.3 Disconnect the windshield washer tubes from the hood

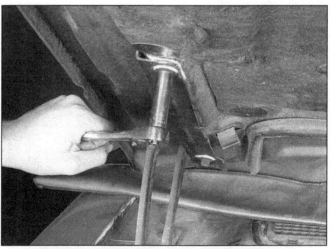

8.4 Removing the hinge bolts going into the hood. An assistant should be supporting the hood at this time

6   When installing the hood, again cover the bodywork and then lift the hood into position.
7   Install all of the mounting screws loosely and position the hood in its original position, using the scribe marks as a guide.
8   Tighten the screws and check the hood alignment. Connect windshield washer hoses.

9   Grille (1970 to 1976 models) - removal and installation

1   The left and right hand grille panels are secured to the front body panel with screws. The nameplate can be removed with the grille and separated at a later time.
2   Open the hood and remove the attaching screws at the rear of the grille, in front of the radiator. There are four screws for each grille, two upper and two lower.
3   The grille screen can then be lifted out of the radiator cavity.
4   The grille replacement procedures for the 1976 models are basically the same as above, except that the parking lamp wiring must be disconnected and the lamp removed with the grille panels.

10   Grille (1977 to 1981 models) - removal and installation

1977 - 1978 models

1   On these years the headlights are contained within the same body opening as the grille panels. However, the headlights do not need to be removed in order to replace the grille panels.
2   Remove the attaching screws from the front of the car and lift the grilles outward towards the front. Do not turn the headlight adjusting screws which are spring-loaded, as they will change the headlight aim.
3   When installing, do not overtighten the screws.

1979 - 1981 models

4   The grille panels are located beneath the headlights. The grilles are removed from the vehicle's front panel by removing the attaching screws.
5   When installing, do not overtighten the screws.

11   Bumper (rear) - removal and installation

1970 - 1973

1   Near the center of the vehicle, remove the bolts from beneath the bumper. Remove the bumper guards if equipped.
2   Remove the bolts from inside the trunk and remove the bumper.

1974 - 1977

3   From inside the trunk, remove the four bolts connecting the bumper bracket to the body rails.
4   Raise the vehicle for better access and support the bumper assembly.
5   Remove the four lower bolts attaching the bumper brackets to the body and remove the bumper assembly.
6   If the bumper brackets and spring assemblies are to be disassembled, scribe alignment marks to aid in proper alignment upon reassembly.

1978 - 1981

7   Remove the four nuts (inside the trunk) and two screws retaining the fascia (bar cover) moldings to the rear quarter panel.
8   Disconnect the wires to the license plate light.
9   Raise the vehicle for better access and remove the four nuts attaching the bumper to the vehicle.
10   Lower the vehicle and remove the remaining four nuts attaching the bumper to the vehicle. These are located inside the trunk.
11   Remove the bumper.
12   If the cover is to be removed from the bumper assembly, it will be necessary to drill out the rivers which secure the cover to the impact bar.

12   Front fenders and skirt - removal, adjustment and installation

1   Disconnect the negative battery cable. If the right fender is being moved, disconnect both battery cables and remove the battery.
2   Raise the vehicle and remove the wheel.
3   To protect the paint on the adjoining body panels it is a good ideal to apply tape at the edge of the door and outer surfaces of the front windshield post. Make sure the tape itself does not cause the paint to peel or chip.
4   Open the hood and support it with blocks on the side where the fender is to be removed, and remove the hood hinge-to-fender bolts. If both fenders are to be removed, remove the hood entirely (see Section 8).

5   Disconnect all cables, wiring harness clips, windshield washer reservoir, battery tray, etc. from the inner fender panels. Identify all wires and hoses to aid in reassembly.
6   Remove the screws and pull away the rocker panel moldings and front wheel opening spoiler trim, where applicable.
7   Remove the screws securing the flexible inner fender skirt to the lip of the fender.
8   Remove the radio antenna if applicable.
9   Disconnect the wiring to the fender side marker light.
10   Remove the diagonal brace at the top of the front fender on models so equipped.
11   Begin removing the screws retaining the fender to the cowl, filler panel and rocker panel. Note any shims used to align the fender. Leave one or two forward and aft screws intact to support the assembly until the fender can be lifted free of the vehicle.
12   When installing the fender, guide it first into position at the bottom, adjacent to the door.
13   Install the original number of shims at the screw locations at the rocker panel and cowl. Install all the other attaching screws loosely and adjust the fender with the appropriate number of shims. Tighten the cowl and rocker panel screws, followed by the remaining screws.
14   Install the remaining components in reverse order of disassembly. The hood should be adjusted referring to Section 7. On Trans Am models, if the fender is being replaced, transfer the wheel opening trim, air vents and fender opening "spats" to the new fender.

13   Hood latch and lock assemblies - removal and installation

Refer to illustration 13.2
1   To maintain the proper alignment of the catch and lock, open the hood and scribe a line around the lock plate on the hood and the catch plate mechanism on the support brace.
2   Remove the catch plate assembly by removing the screws retaining the catch to the radiator support, center support and tie-bar **(see illustration)**.

13.2 Typical hood latch mounting bolt locations (arrows)

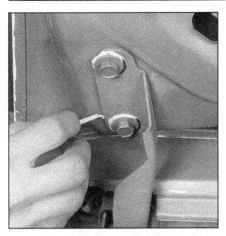

14.3 Like the hood, the trunk lid should be marked around the hinges for proper repositioning

3   Remove the screws retaining the lock plate to the inside of the hood.

4   Upon reinstallation, line up the identifying scribe marks on both the catch plate and the lock plate and tighten the attaching screws. For further information on adjusting the hood see Section 7.

14 Trunk lid - removal and installation

Refer to illustrations 14.3, 14.4a and 14.4b

1   Open the trunk and place blankets or some form of protective covering around the forward edge of the trunk opening to protect the window and body panel.

2   If a trunk light installed, disconnect the wiring to it.

3   Carefully scribe an outline of the hinge straps on the inner trunk lid. This will enable you to replace the trunk lid in the same location **(see illustration)**.

4   With the aid of an assistant, remove the four attaching bolts and lift away the trunk lid **(see illustrations)**.

5   Installation is a reversal of the removal process, however make sure the trunk lid is installed in the same location and adjusted properly (see Section 15).

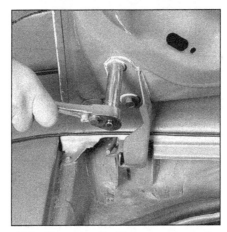

14.4a Removing the hinge securing bolts

15 Trunk lid - adjustments

1   All adjustments for the trunk to be moved forward, rearward or sideways are done at the hinges. With the four retaining bolts slightly loosened, move the trunk lid to the desired position and tighten the bolts. Move the lid only a little at a time and check that the locking assembly remains in line (Section 17).

2   To adjust the trunk lid in an up or down fashion, and to align properly with the rear quarter panels, shims should be installed between the hinge strap and the trunk lid. Loosen the appropriate securing bolts enough to slide body shims into position and then tighten the bolt(s). Carefully close the trunk lid, checking the alignment of the lock assembly and lid in relation to the quarter panels.

3   Torque rods are incorporated to control the amount of effort needed to operate the trunk lid. The torque rod ends are located in cutout notches adjacent to the hinges. They are adjusted as follows:

a} *To increase the amount of effort required to raise the trunk lid {which will make the lid easier to close) move the torque rod(s) to a lower adjusting notch.*

b} *To make the trunk lid rise easier {thus making the lid more difficult to close}*

reposition the torque rod end(s} to a higher notch.

To grip the end of the torque rod for adjusting, use a 1/4-inch pipe. Also, it is not necessary for each side to be adjusted to the same notch position.

16 Trunk lid lock cylinder- removal and installation

Refer to illustration 16.2

1   The lock cylinder is secured to the rear body panel by two lock nuts and washers.

2   Open the trunk lid and remove the two retaining nuts, washers and guards **(see illustration)**.

3   For best access, lower the chrome bezel on the rear outside panel.

4   Remove the lock cylinder from the lock body.

5   When installing, make sure cylinder shaft engages with the lock.

17 Trunk lid lock assembly - removal adjusting and installation

1   To remove the lid lock assembly attached to the rear body panel, first remove the lock cylinder as previously described.

2   Scribe identifying marks around each of the lock attaching bolts and then remove the bolts.

3   Remove the lock assembly from the lock body.

4   The lid lock striker is attached to the inside of the trunk lid, secured by screws. Before removing the screws and the striker assembly, mark the vertical position of the striker to enable the assembly to be replaced in the same location.

5   Before attempting to adjust the lock striker or lock assembly. it is important that the trunk lid itself is correctly positioned.

6   To check the engagement of the striker to the lock, place a small amount of model-

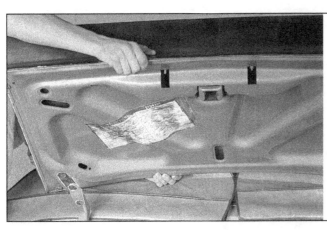

14.4b It may take two people to lift the trunk lid away from the body once the four bolts are removed

16.2 The two retaining nuts for the lock cylinder are accessible from the inside of the trunk

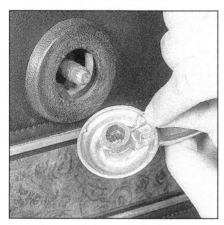

**18.1 The window crank handle is secured
to the shaft with a retaining clip which
must be pried from the shaft with a
special tool or a screwdriver**

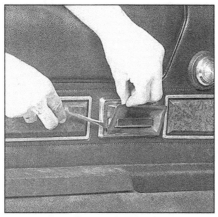

**18.2 Before the latch lever can be
removed, the decorative bezel must be
pried from the trim panel**

**18.8 A screwdriver is used to gently pry
the trim panel away from the door**

ing clay at both sides of the lock bolt. Carefully close the trunk lid. Open the lid and check the impression left in the clay. The depression in the clay should be centered in the lock frame. Where required, the lock frame can be adjusted sideways or the striker up or down to obtain the proper engagement. These adjustments should be performed with the attaching bolts only slightly loosened, and the components should be moved only a little at a time.

18 Door trim panel - removal and installation

Refer to illustrations 18.1, 18.2 and 18.8

1   Remove the window crank handle. This is secured to the regulator shaft with a clip. The trim panel should be pushed away from the base of the handle to expose the crankshaft and clip. A special forked tool is available to push the clip out of the groove, or you can carefully use a screwdriver **(see illustration)**.

2   The handle which operates the door latch mechanism is retained with screws. It is first necessary to remove the decorative cover plate **(see illustration)**. With the screws removed, the remote control rod can be disconnected from the rear of the handle and the handle assembly removed from the door.

3   Remove the inside locking knob by unscrewing it from its shaft.

4   On models equipped with a remote control mirror, remove the control escutcheon from the trim panel and disengage the control cable.

5   On models with an armrest built into the trim panel, remove the screws which are located in the recessed area meant to be used to pull the door shut.

6   If equipped with a separate armrest not intended to be a part of the trim panel, remove the screws which attach it to the trim panel and the inner door skin. The screws are sometimes hidden with decorative plugs which should be carefully pried out to reveal the screw.

7   Depending on the style and year of production, there may or may not be exposed screws securing a portion of the trim panel. If so, remove any exposed screws.

8   Where no screws can be readily seen, chances are that the panel is held in place with retaining clips. To disengage these clips, insert a flat, blunt tool (like a screwdriver blade wrapped with tape) between the metal door skin and the trim panel. Carefully pry the door panel away from the door, keeping the tool close to the clips to prevent damage to the panel. Start at the bottom and work around the door towards the top. The top section is secured at the window channel. Once the retaining clips are pried free, lift the trim panel upwards and away from the door **(see illustration)**.

9   Before installing the trim panel, check that all the trim retainer clips are in good condition and the water shield is correctly applied to the metal door skin.

10   Engage the top of the trim panel first and then position the panel correctly on the door. The cutout for the window winder can be used as a rough guide.

11   Press the retaining clips into their respective cups or holes in the metal door skin. Pressure can be used by the palm of your hand or a clean rubber mallet.

12   Follow the removal process in the reverse order to install the various components to the door.

13   To install the window crank handle, first install the retaining clip to the handle, then push the handle onto the shaft. Check that the clip is properly seated in the shaft groove.

19 Door lock cylinder - removal and installation

Refer to illustration 19.5

1   Remove the inside door trim as described in Section 18.

2   Raise the window to the full up position and pry the water shield away from the inner door skin to gain access to the rear of the lock cylinder.

3   To help prevent tools or inner door components from falling down to the bottom of the door cavity, place rags or newspapers inside the cavity.

4   With a screwdriver, slide the lock cylinder retaining clip (on the inboard side of the outer door skin) out of the lock cylinder. Be careful not to damage the outer door skin.

5   With the clip removed, the lock cylinder can be removed from the outside of the door **(see illustration)**.

6   Installation is a reversal of removal.

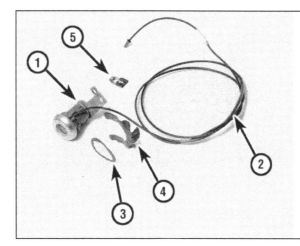

**19.5 Typical door lock
cylinder assembly**

1   *Lock cylinder*
2   *Fiber optic cable (if equipped)*
3   *Body sealing gasket*
4   *Lock cylinder retaining clip*
5   *Lock rod retaining clip*

20.5 The attaching screws for the lock assembly are located at the rear door jamb

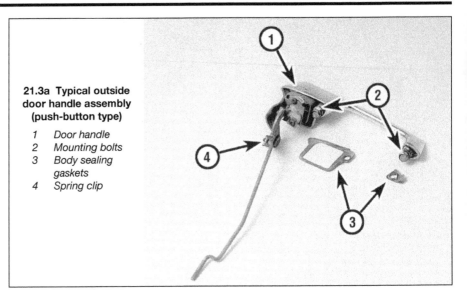

21.3a Typical outside door handle assembly (push-button type)

1 *Door handle*
2 *Mounting bolts*
3 *Body sealing gaskets*
4 *Spring clip*

20 Door lock assembly - removal and installation

Refer to illustration 20.5

1   Remove the door trim panel as described in Section 18.

2   Pry back the water shield at the rear of the door to gain access to the inside locking assembly.

3   Temporarily install the window crank and roll the window to the full up position.

4   Working through the large access hole in the inner door skin, disconnect the connecting rod at the lock mechanism. This rod is held in place with a gripper clip which is released by rotating it off the rod.

5   Remove the three lock attaching screws located in the door jamb at the rear of the door. Remove the lock assembly through the access hole **(see illustration)**.

6   Installation is a reversal of removal.

21 Door exterior handle - removal and installation

Refer to illustrations 21.3a and 21.3b

1   Remove the inside door trim panel and pry back the water shield at the rear of the door.

2   Raise the window to the full up position.

3   From inside the door, remove the two attaching nuts to the exterior handle and remove the handle assembly from the outside of the door **(see illustrations)**. On some later models it will be necessary to first remove the guide bracket for access to the handle nuts. This bracket is held in place with four screws on the door skin.

4   When installing, make sure the handle gasket is in good condition to prevent water leaks. The installation procedure is a reversal of removal.

22 Door window glass - removal and installation

Refer to illustration 22.5

Note: *If equipped with power windows, see Chapter 10 for important electrical information on this procedure.*

1   Remove the door trim panel (Section 18).

2   Remove the inner water shield.

3   Remove the up-travel stops at the front and rear of the door.

4   Loosen the front and rear belt trim support retainers located at the top of the door in the window channel.

5   Position the window in the three-quarter-down position and remove the lower sash channel to glass attaching nuts through the small access holes in the inner door skin **(see illustration)**.

6   Lift the window straight up and out of the channel, aligning the rollers with the notches provided in the inner door skin.

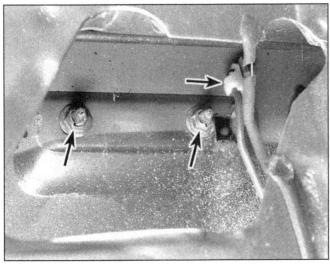

21.3b Liftbar-type door handle mounting nuts and rod retaining clip (arrows)

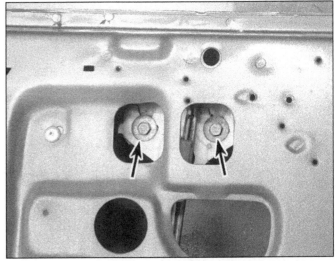

22.5 Typical window glass channel mounting bolts (arrows)

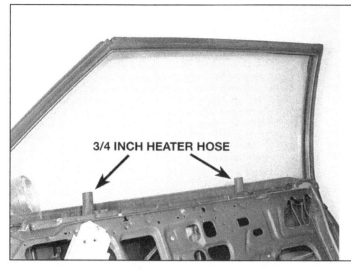

23.2 Use two pieces of 3/4 heater hose, wedged between the glass and the door frame, to hold the glass in the raised position

3/4 INCH HEATER HOSE

7   Installation is a reversal of removal, however, install all attaching screws loosely and adjust the channels, guides and stops as necessary before finally tightening the fasteners.

23 Door window regulator - removal and installation

Refer to illustration 23.2
Note: *If equipped with power windows, see Chapter 10 for details on this operation. Personal injury could result if the sequence in Chapter 10 is not followed.*
1   Remove the door inner trim panel and water shield (Section 18).
2   Remove the glass channel mounting nuts, then raise the glass fully, securing it with 3/4-inch heater hose **(see illustration)**.
3   Remove the regulator-to-inner door attaching fasteners. Early models use bolts, while later models have rivets which must be carefully drilled out with a 1/4-inch drill bit. Remove the regulator through the large access hole.
4   When installing, if rivets were drilled out, U-nuts on the regulator body and 1/4 - 20 x 1/2 inch attaching screws should be substituted. Tighten attaching screws or bolts and reverse the removal sequence.

24 Door - removal and installation

1   Disconnect the battery ground cable.
2   Open the door fully and support it on blocks and cloth pads placed under its lower edge.
3   If the vehicle is equipped with power-operated windows, remove the trim panel and disconnect the regulator wiring harness.
4   Prior to removal of doors, scribe round the fitted position of the hinge on the door.
5   With an assistant supporting the weight of the door, remove the door hinge retaining bolts.
6   Having removed the door, it is now possible to remove the hinge from the hinge pillar, but again scribe round the fitted position first.
7   Refitting doors and hinges is the reverse of the removal procedure. If necessary the hinge positions may be altered slightly to ensure correct alignment.
Note: *When refitting the door, ensure that the lock striker fork-bolt engages with the striker. If necessary the position of the fork bolt can be adjusted by loosening with a wrench, repositioning, then retightening.*

25 Windshield and back window - removal and installation

1   These operations are best left to specialists as the glass is retained by quick setting adhesive/caulk material which leaves no room for error in application or positioning of the windshield.
2   The rear view mirror support is bonded to the windshield and can only be removed by extremely careful application of heat from an air gun (250° to 350°F) - another job for a specialist.

Notes

Index

Haynes Automotive Manuals

NOTE: If you do not see a listing for your vehicle, please visit ***haynes.com*** *for the latest product information and check out our* ***Online Manuals!***

ACURA

12020 **Integra** '86 thru '89 & **Legend** '86 thru '90
12021 **Integra** '90 thru '93 & **Legend** '91 thru '95
Integra '94 thru '00 - *see HONDA Civic (42025)*
MDX '01 thru '07 - *see HONDA Pilot (42037)*
12050 **Acura TL** all models '99 thru '08

AMC

14020 **Mid-size models** '70 thru '83
14025 **(Renault) Alliance & Encore** '83 thru '87

AUDI

15020 **4000** all models '80 thru '87
15025 **5000** all models '77 thru '83
15026 **5000** all models '84 thru '88
Audi A4 '96 thru '01 - *see VW Passat (96023)*
15030 **Audi A4** '02 thru '08

AUSTIN-HEALEY

Sprite - *see MG Midget (66015)*

BMW

18020 **3/5 Series** '82 thru '92
18021 **3-Series** incl. Z3 models '92 thru '98
18022 **3-Series** incl. Z4 models '99 thru '05
18023 **3-Series** '06 thru '14
18025 **320i all 4-cylinder models** '75 thru '83
18050 **1500 thru 2002** except Turbo '59 thru '77

BUICK

19010 **Buick Century** '97 thru '05
Century (front-wheel drive) - *see GM (38005)*
19020 **Buick, Oldsmobile & Pontiac Full-size (Front-wheel drive)** '85 thru '05
Buick Electra, LeSabre and Park Avenue; **Oldsmobile** Delta 88 Royale, Ninety Eight and Regency; **Pontiac** Bonneville
19025 **Buick, Oldsmobile & Pontiac Full-size (Rear wheel drive)** '70 thru '90
Buick Estate, Electra, LeSabre, Limited, **Oldsmobile** Custom Cruiser, Delta 88, Ninety-eight, **Pontiac** Bonneville, Catalina, Grandville, Parisienne
19027 **Buick LaCrosse** '05 thru '13
Enclave - *see GENERAL MOTORS (38001)*
Rainier - *see CHEVROLET (24072)*
Regal - *see GENERAL MOTORS (38010)*
Riviera - *see GENERAL MOTORS (38030, 38031)*
Roadmaster - *see CHEVROLET (24046)*
Skyhawk - *see GENERAL MOTORS (38015)*
Skylark - *see GENERAL MOTORS (38020, 38025)*
Somerset - *see GENERAL MOTORS (38025)*

CADILLAC

21015 **CTS & CTS-V** '03 thru '14
21030 **Cadillac Rear Wheel Drive** '70 thru '93
Cimarron - *see GENERAL MOTORS (38015)*
DeVille - *see GENERAL MOTORS (38031 & 38032)*
Eldorado - *see GENERAL MOTORS (38030)*
Fleetwood - *see GENERAL MOTORS (38031)*
Seville - *see GM (38030, 38031 & 38032)*

CHEVROLET

10305 **Chevrolet Engine Overhaul Manual**
24010 **Astro & GMC Safari Mini-vans** '85 thru '05
24013 **Aveo** '04 thru '11
24015 **Camaro V8** all models '70 thru '81
24016 **Camaro** all models '82 thru '92
24017 **Camaro & Firebird** '93 thru '02
Cavalier - *see GENERAL MOTORS (38016)*
Celebrity - *see GENERAL MOTORS (38005)*
24018 **Camaro** '10 thru '15
24020 **Chevelle, Malibu & El Camino** '69 thru '87
Cobalt - *see GENERAL MOTORS (38017)*
24024 **Chevette & Pontiac T1000** '76 thru '87
Citation - *see GENERAL MOTORS (38020)*
24027 **Colorado & GMC Canyon** '04 thru '12
24032 **Corsica & Beretta** all models '87 thru '96
24040 **Corvette** all V8 models '68 thru '82
24041 **Corvette** all models '84 thru '96
24042 **Corvette** all models '97 thru '13
24044 **Cruze** '11 thru '19
24045 **Full-size Sedans** Caprice, Impala, Biscayne, Bel Air & Wagons '69 thru '90
24046 **Impala SS & Caprice and Buick Roadmaster** '91 thru '96
Impala '00 thru '05 - *see LUMINA (24048)*
24047 **Impala & Monte Carlo** all models '06 thru '11
Lumina '90 thru '94 - *see GM (38010)*
24048 **Lumina & Monte Carlo** '95 thru '05
Lumina APV - *see GM (38035)*
24050 **Luv Pick-up** all 2WD & 4WD '72 thru '82
24051 **Malibu** '13 thru '19
24055 **Monte Carlo** all models '70 thru '88
Monte Carlo '95 thru '01 - *see LUMINA (24048)*
24059 **Nova** all V8 models '69 thru '79
24060 **Nova and Geo Prizm** '85 thru '92
24064 **Pick-ups** '67 thru '87 - Chevrolet & GMC
24065 **Pick-ups** '88 thru '98 - Chevrolet & GMC
24066 **Pick-ups** '99 thru '06 - Chevrolet & GMC
24067 **Chevrolet Silverado & GMC Sierra** '07 thru '14
24068 **Chevrolet Silverado & GMC Sierra** '14 thru '19
24070 **S-10 & S-15 Pick-ups** '82 thru '93, **Blazer & Jimmy** '83 thru '94,
24071 **S-10 & Sonoma Pick-ups** '94 thru '04, including **Blazer, Jimmy & Hombre**
24072 **Chevrolet TrailBlazer, GMC Envoy & Oldsmobile Bravada** '02 thru '09
24075 **Sprint** '85 thru '88 & **Geo Metro** '89 thru '01
24080 **Vans - Chevrolet & GMC** '68 thru '96
24081 **Chevrolet Express & GMC Savana** Full-size Vans '96 thru '19

CHRYSLER

10310 **Chrysler Engine Overhaul Manual**
25015 **Chrysler Cirrus, Dodge Stratus, Plymouth Breeze** '95 thru '00
25020 **Full-size Front-Wheel Drive** '88 thru '93
K-Cars - *see DODGE Aries (30008)*
Laser - *see DODGE Daytona (30030)*
25025 **Chrysler LHS, Concorde, New Yorker, Dodge** Intrepid, **Eagle** Vision, '93 thru '97
25026 **Chrysler LHS, Concorde, 300M, Dodge** Intrepid, '98 thru '04
25027 **Chrysler 300** '05 thru '18, **Dodge Charger** '06 thru '18, **Magnum** '05 thru '08 & **Challenger** '08 thru '18
25030 **Chrysler & Plymouth Mid-size** front wheel drive '82 thru '95
Rear-wheel Drive - *see Dodge (30050)*
25035 **PT Cruiser** all models '01 thru '10
25040 **Chrysler Sebring** '95 thru '06, **Dodge Stratus** '01 thru '06 & **Dodge Avenger** '95 thru '00
25041 **Chrysler Sebring** '07 thru '10, **200** '11 thru '17 **Dodge Avenger** '08 thru '14

DATSUN

28005 **200SX** all models '80 thru '83
28012 **240Z, 260Z & 280Z** Coupe '70 thru '78
28014 **280ZX** Coupe & 2+2 '79 thru '83
300ZX - *see NISSAN (72010)*
28018 **510 & PL521 Pick-up** '68 thru '73
28020 **510** all models '78 thru '81
28022 **620 Series Pick-up** all models '73 thru '79
720 Series Pick-up - *see NISSAN (72030)*

DODGE

400 & 600 - *see CHRYSLER (25030)*
30008 **Aries & Plymouth Reliant** '81 thru '89
30010 **Caravan & Plymouth Voyager** '84 thru '95
30011 **Caravan & Plymouth Voyager** '96 thru '02
30012 **Challenger & Plymouth Sapporro** '78 thru '83
30013 **Caravan, Chrysler Voyager & Town & Country** '03 thru '07
30014 **Grand Caravan & Chrysler Town & Country** '08 thru '18
30016 **Colt & Plymouth Champ** '78 thru '87
30020 **Dakota Pick-ups** all models '87 thru '96
30021 **Durango** '98 & '99 & **Dakota** '97 thru '99
30022 **Durango** '00 thru '03 & **Dakota** '00 thru '04
30023 **Durango** '04 thru '09 & **Dakota** '05 thru '11
30025 **Dart, Demon, Plymouth Barracuda, Duster & Valiant** 6-cylinder models '67 thru '76
30030 **Daytona & Chrysler Laser** '84 thru '89
Intrepid - *see CHRYSLER (25025, 25026)*
30034 **Neon** all models '95 thru '99
30035 **Omni & Plymouth Horizon** '78 thru '90
30036 **Dodge & Plymouth Neon** '00 thru '05
30040 **Pick-ups** full-size models '74 thru '93
30042 **Pick-ups** full-size models '94 thru '08
30043 **Pick-ups** full-size models '09 thru '18
30045 **Ram 50/D50 Pick-ups & Raider and Plymouth Arrow Pick-ups** '79 thru '93
30050 **Dodge/Plymouth/Chrysler** RWD '71 thru '89
30055 **Shadow & Plymouth Sundance** '87 thru '94
30060 **Spirit & Plymouth Acclaim** '89 thru '95
30065 **Vans - Dodge & Plymouth** '71 thru '03

EAGLE

Talon - *see MITSUBISHI (68030, 68031)*
Vision - *see CHRYSLER (25025)*

FIAT

34010 **124 Sport Coupe & Spider** '68 thru '78
34025 **X1/9** all models '74 thru '80

FORD

10320 **Ford Engine Overhaul Manual**
10355 **Ford Automatic Transmission Overhaul**
11500 **Mustang '64-1/2 thru '70 Restoration Guide**
36004 **Aerostar Mini-vans** all models '86 thru '97
36006 **Contour & Mercury Mystique** '95 thru '00
36008 **Courier Pick-up** all models '72 thru '82
36012 **Crown Victoria & Mercury Grand Marquis** '88 thru '11
36014 **Edge** '07 thru '19 & **Lincoln MKX** '07 thru '18
36016 **Escort & Mercury Lynx** all models '81 thru '90
36020 **Escort & Mercury Tracer** '91 thru '02
36022 **Escape** '01 thru '17, **Mazda Tribute** '01 thru '11, **& Mercury Mariner** '05 thru '11
36024 **Explorer & Mazda Navajo** '91 thru '01
36025 **Explorer & Mercury Mountaineer** '02 thru '10
36026 **Explorer** '11 thru '17
36028 **Fairmont & Mercury Zephyr** '78 thru '83
36030 **Festiva & Aspire** '88 thru '97
36032 **Fiesta** all models '77 thru '80
36034 **Focus** all models '00 thru '11
36035 **Focus** '12 thru '14
36045 **Fusion** '06 thru '14 & **Mercury Milan** '06 thru '11
36048 **Mustang V8** all models '64-1/2 thru '73
36049 **Mustang II** 4-cylinder, V6 & V8 models '74 thru '78
36050 **Mustang & Mercury Capri** '79 thru '93
36051 **Mustang** all models '94 thru '04
36052 **Mustang** '05 thru '14
36054 **Pick-ups & Bronco** '73 thru '79
36058 **Pick-ups & Bronco** '80 thru '96
36059 **F-150** '97 thru '03, **Expedition** '97 thru '17, **F-250** '97 thru '99, **F-150 Heritage** '04 **& Lincoln Navigator** '98 thru '17
36060 **Super Duty Pick-ups & Excursion** '99 thru '10
36061 **F-150** full-size '04 thru '14
36062 **Pinto & Mercury Bobcat** '75 thru '80
36063 **F-150** full-size '15 thru '17
36064 **Super Duty Pick-ups** '11 thru '16
36066 **Probe** all models '89 thru '92
Probe '93 thru '97 - *see MAZDA 626 (61042)*
36070 **Ranger & Bronco II** gas models '83 thru '92
36071 **Ranger** '93 thru '11 & **Mazda Pick-ups** '94 thru '09
36074 **Taurus & Mercury Sable** '86 thru '95
36075 **Taurus & Mercury Sable** '96 thru '07
36076 **Taurus** '08 thru '14, **Five Hundred** '05 thru '07, **Mercury Montego** '05 thru '07 & **Sable** '08 thru '09
36078 **Tempo & Mercury Topaz** '84 thru '94
36082 **Thunderbird & Mercury Cougar** '83 thru '88
36086 **Thunderbird & Mercury Cougar** '89 thru '97
36090 **Vans** all V8 Econoline models '69 thru '91
36094 **Vans** full size '92 thru '14
36097 **Windstar** '95 thru '03, **Freestar & Mercury Monterey Mini-van** '04 thru '07

GENERAL MOTORS

10360 **GM Automatic Transmission Overhaul**
38001 **GMC Acadia** '07 thru '16, **Buick Enclave** '08 thru '17, **Saturn Outlook** '07 thru '10 **& Chevrolet Traverse** '09 thru '17
38005 **Buick Century, Chevrolet Celebrity, Oldsmobile Cutlass Ciera & Pontiac 6000** all models '82 thru '96
38010 **Buick Regal** '88 thru '04, **Chevrolet Lumina** '88 thru '04, **Oldsmobile Cutlass Supreme** '88 thru '97 & **Pontiac Grand Prix** '88 thru '07
38015 **Buick Skyhawk, Cadillac Cimarron, Chevrolet Cavalier, Oldsmobile Firenza, Pontiac J-2000 & Sunbird** '82 thru '94
38016 **Chevrolet Cavalier & Pontiac Sunfire** '95 thru '05
38017 **Chevrolet Cobalt** '05 thru '10, **HHR** '06 thru '11, **Pontiac G5** '07 thru '09, **Pursuit** '05 thru '06 **& Saturn ION** '03 thru '07
38020 **Buick Skylark, Chevrolet Citation, Oldsmobile Omega, Pontiac Phoenix** '80 thru '85
38025 **Buick Skylark** '86 thru '98, **Somerset** '85 thru '87, **Oldsmobile Achieva** '92 thru '98, **Calais** '85 thru '91, **& Pontiac Grand Am** all models '85 thru '98
38026 **Chevrolet Malibu** '97 thru '03, **Classic** '04 thru '05, **Oldsmobile Alero** '99 thru '03, **Cutlass** '97 thru '00, **& Pontiac Grand Am** '99 thru '03
38027 **Chevrolet Malibu** '04 thru '12, **Pontiac G6** '05 thru '10 & **Saturn Aura** '07 thru '10
38030 **Cadillac Eldorado, Seville, Oldsmobile Toronado & Buick Riviera** '71 thru '85
38031 **Cadillac Eldorado, Seville, DeVille, Fleetwood, Oldsmobile Toronado & Buick Riviera** '86 thru '93
38032 **Cadillac DeVille** '94 thru '05, **Seville** '92 thru '04 **& Cadillac DTS** '06 thru '10
38035 **Chevrolet Lumina APV, Oldsmobile Silhouette & Pontiac Trans Sport** all models '90 thru '96
38036 **Chevrolet Venture** '97 thru '05, **Oldsmobile Silhouette** '97 thru '04, **Pontiac Trans Sport** '97 thru '98 & **Montana** '99 thru '05
38040 **Chevrolet Equinox** '05 thru '17, **GMC Terrain** '10 thru '17 & **Pontiac Torrent** '06 thru '09

GEO

Metro - *see CHEVROLET Sprint (24075)*
Prizm - *'85 thru '92 see CHEVY (24060), '93 thru '02 see TOYOTA Corolla (92036)*
40030 **Storm** all models '90 thru '93
Tracker - *see SUZUKI Samurai (90010)*

(Continued on other side)

Haynes North America, Inc. • (805) 498-6703 • www.haynes.com

Haynes Automotive Manuals (continued)

*NOTE: If you do not see a listing for your vehicle, please visit **haynes.com** for the latest product information and check out our **Online Manuals!***

GMC
Acadia - see GENERAL MOTORS (38001)
Pick-ups - see CHEVROLET (24027, 24068)
Vans - see CHEVROLET (24081)

HONDA
42010 **Accord CVCC** all models '76 thru '83
42011 **Accord** all models '84 thru '89
42012 **Accord** all models '90 thru '93
42013 **Accord** all models '94 thru '97
42014 **Accord** all models '98 thru '02
42015 **Accord** '03 thru '12 & **Crosstour** '10 thru '14
42016 **Accord** '13 thru '17
42020 **Civic 1200** all models '73 thru '79
42021 **Civic 1300 & 1500 CVCC** '80 thru '83
42022 **Civic 1500 CVCC** all models '75 thru '79
42023 **Civic** all models '84 thru '91
42024 **Civic & del Sol** '92 thru '95
42025 **Civic** '96 thru '00, **CR-V** '97 thru '01
& **Acura Integra** '94 thru '00
42026 **Civic** '01 thru '11 & **CR-V** '02 thru '11
42027 **Civic** '12 thru '15 & **CR-V** '12 thru '16
42030 **Fit** '07 thru '13
42035 **Odyssey** all models '99 thru '10
Passport - see ISUZU Rodeo (47017)
42037 **Honda Pilot** '03 thru '08, **Ridgeline** '06 thru '14
& **Acura MDX** '01 thru '07
42040 **Prelude CVCC** all models '79 thru '89

HYUNDAI
43010 **Elantra** all models '96 thru '19
43015 **Excel & Accent** all models '86 thru '13
43050 **Santa Fe** all models '01 thru '12
43055 **Sonata** all models '99 thru '14

INFINITI
G35 '03 thru '08 - see NISSAN 350Z (72011)

ISUZU
Hombre - see CHEVROLET S-10 (24071)
47017 **Rodeo** '91 thru '02, **Amigo** '89 thru '94 & '98 thru '02
& **Honda Passport** '95 thru '02
47020 **Trooper** '84 thru '91 & **Pick-up** '81 thru '93

JAGUAR
49010 **XJ6** all 6-cylinder models '68 thru '86
49011 **XJ6** all models '88 thru '94
49015 **XJ12 & XJS** all 12-cylinder models '72 thru '85

JEEP
50010 **Cherokee, Comanche & Wagoneer Limited**
all models '84 thru '01
50011 **Cherokee** '14 thru '19
50020 **CJ** all models '49 thru '86
50025 **Grand Cherokee** all models '93 thru '04
50026 **Grand Cherokee** '05 thru '19
& **Dodge Durango** '11 thru '19
50029 **Grand Wagoneer & Pick-up** '72 thru '91
Grand Wagoneer '84 thru '91, Cherokee &
Wagoneer '72 thru '83, Pick-up '72 thru '88
50030 **Wrangler** all models '87 thru '17
50035 **Liberty** '02 thru '12 & **Dodge Nitro** '07 thru '11
50050 **Patriot & Compass** '07 thru '17

KIA
54050 **Optima** '01 thru '10
54060 **Sedona** '02 thru '14
54070 **Sephia** '94 thru '01, **Spectra** '00 thru '09,
Sportage '05 thru '20
54077 **Sorento** '03 thru '13

LEXUS
ES 300/330 - see TOYOTA Camry (92007, 92008)
ES 350 - see TOYOTA Camry (92009)
RX 300/330/350 - see TOYOTA Highlander (92095)

LINCOLN
MKX - see FORD (36014)
Navigator - see FORD Pick-up (36059)
59010 **Rear-Wheel Drive Continental** '70 thru '87,
Mark Series '70 thru '92 & **Town Car** '81 thru '10

MAZDA
61010 **GLC** (rear-wheel drive) '77 thru '83
61011 **GLC** (front-wheel drive) '81 thru '85
61012 **Mazda3** '04 thru '11
61015 **323 & Protegé** '90 thru '03
61016 **MX-5 Miata** '90 thru '14
61020 **MPV** all models '89 thru '98
Navajo - see Ford Explorer (36024)
61030 **Pick-ups** '72 thru '93
Pick-ups '94 thru '09 - see Ford Ranger (36071)
61035 **RX-7** all models '79 thru '85
61036 **RX-7** all models '86 thru '91
61040 **626** (rear-wheel drive) all models '79 thru '82
61041 **626 & MX-6** (front-wheel drive) '83 thru '92
61042 **626** '93 thru '01 & **MX-6/Ford Probe** '93 thru '02
61043 **Mazda6** '03 thru '13

MERCEDES-BENZ
63012 **123 Series Diesel** '76 thru '85
63015 **190 Series** 4-cylinder gas models '84 thru '88
63020 **230/250/280** 6-cylinder SOHC models '68 thru '72
63025 **280 123 Series** gas models '77 thru '81
63030 **350 & 450** all models '71 thru '80
63040 **C-Class**: C230/C240/C280/C320/C350 '01 thru '07

MERCURY
64200 **Villager & Nissan Quest** '93 thru '01
All other titles, see FORD Listing.

MG
66010 **MGB** Roadster & GT Coupe '62 thru '80
66015 **MG Midget, Austin Healey Sprite** '58 thru '80

MINI
67020 **Mini** '02 thru '13

MITSUBISHI
68020 **Cordia, Tredia, Galant, Precis & Mirage** '83 thru '93
68030 **Eclipse, Eagle Talon & Plymouth Laser** '90 thru '94
68031 **Eclipse** '95 thru '05 & **Eagle Talon** '95 thru '98
68035 **Galant** '94 thru '12
68040 **Pick-up** '83 thru '96 & **Montero** '83 thru '93

NISSAN
72010 **300ZX** all models including Turbo '84 thru '89
72011 **350Z & Infiniti G35** all models '03 thru '08
72015 **Altima** all models '93 thru '06
72016 **Altima** '07 thru '12
72020 **Maxima** all models '85 thru '92
72021 **Maxima** all models '93 thru '08
72025 **Murano** '03 thru '14
72030 **Pick-ups** '80 thru '97 & **Pathfinder** '87 thru '95
72031 **Frontier** '98 thru '04, **Xterra** '00 thru '04,
& **Pathfinder** '96 thru '04
72032 **Frontier & Xterra** '05 thru '14
72037 **Pathfinder** '05 thru '14
72040 **Pulsar** all models '83 thru '86
72042 **Roque** all models '08 thru '20
72050 **Sentra** all models '82 thru '94
72051 **Sentra & 200SX** all models '95 thru '06
72060 **Stanza** all models '82 thru '90
72070 **Titan pick-ups** '04 thru '10, **Armada** '05 thru '10
& **Pathfinder Armada** '04
72080 **Versa** all models '07 thru '19

OLDSMOBILE
73015 **Cutlass** V6 & V8 gas models '74 thru '88
*For other OLDSMOBILE titles, see BUICK,
CHEVROLET or GENERAL MOTORS listings.*

PLYMOUTH
For PLYMOUTH titles, see DODGE listing.

PONTIAC
79008 **Fiero** all models '84 thru '88
79018 **Firebird** V8 models except Turbo '70 thru '81
79019 **Firebird** all models '82 thru '92
79025 **G6** all models '05 thru '09
79040 **Mid-size Rear-wheel Drive** '70 thru '87
Vibe '03 thru '10 - see TOYOTA Corolla (92037)
*For other PONTIAC titles, see BUICK,
CHEVROLET or GENERAL MOTORS listings.*

PORSCHE
80020 **911** Coupe & Targa models '65 thru '89
80025 **914** all 4-cylinder models '69 thru '76
80030 **924** all models including Turbo '76 thru '82
80035 **944** all models including Turbo '83 thru '89

RENAULT
Alliance & Encore - see AMC (14025)

SAAB
84010 **900** all models including Turbo '79 thru '88

SATURN
87010 **Saturn** all S-series models '91 thru '02
Saturn Ion '03 thru '07- see GM (38017)
Saturn Outlook - see GM (38001)
87020 **Saturn L-series** all models '00 thru '04
87040 **Saturn VUE** '02 thru '09

SUBARU
89002 **1100, 1300, 1400 & 1600** '71 thru '79
89003 **1600 & 1800** 2WD & 4WD '80 thru '94
89080 **Impreza** '02 thru '11, **WRX** '02 thru '14,
& **WRX STI** '04 thru '14
89100 **Legacy** all models '90 thru '99
89101 **Legacy & Forester** '00 thru '09
89102 **Legacy** '10 thru '16 & **Forester** '12 thru '16

SUZUKI
90010 **Samurai/Sidekick & Geo Tracker** '86 thru '01

TOYOTA
92005 **Camry** all models '83 thru '91
92006 **Camry** '92 thru '96 & **Avalon** '95 thru '96
92007 **Camry, Avalon, Solara, Lexus ES 300** '97 thru '01

92008 **Camry, Avalon, Lexus ES 300/330** '02 thru '06
& **Solara** '02 thru '08
92009 **Camry, Avalon & Lexus ES 350** '07 thru '17
92015 **Celica Rear-wheel Drive** '71 thru '85
92020 **Celica Front-wheel Drive** '86 thru '99
92025 **Celica Supra** all models '79 thru '92
92030 **Corolla** all models '75 thru '79
92032 **Corolla** all rear-wheel drive models '80 thru '87
92035 **Corolla** all front-wheel drive models '84 thru '92
92036 **Corolla & Geo/Chevrolet Prizm** '93 thru '02
92037 **Corolla** '03 thru '19, **Matrix** '03 thru '14,
& **Pontiac Vibe** '03 thru '10
92040 **Corolla Tercel** all models '80 thru '82
92045 **Corona** all models '74 thru '82
92050 **Cressida** all models '78 thru '82
92055 **Land Cruiser FJ40, 43, 45, 55** '68 thru '82
92056 **Land Cruiser FJ60, 62, 80, FZJ80** '80 thru '96
92060 **Matrix** '03 thru '11 & **Pontiac Vibe** '03 thru '10
92065 **MR2** all models '85 thru '87
92070 **Pick-up** all models '69 thru '78
92075 **Pick-up** all models '79 thru '95
92076 **Tacoma** '95 thru '04, **4Runner** '96 thru '02
& **T100** '93 thru '98
92077 **Tacoma** all models '05 thru '18
92078 **Tundra** '00 thru '06 & **Sequoia** '01 thru '07
92079 **4Runner** all models '03 thru '09
92080 **Previa** all models '91 thru '95
92081 **Prius** all models '01 thru '12
92082 **RAV4** all models '96 thru '12
92085 **Tercel** all models '87 thru '94
92090 **Sienna** all models '98 thru '10
92095 **Highlander** '01 thru '19
& **Lexus RX330/330/350** '99 thru '19
92179 **Tundra** '07 thru '19 & **Sequoia** '08 thru '19

TRIUMPH
94007 **Spitfire** all models '62 thru '81
94010 **TR7** all models '75 thru '81

VW
96008 **Beetle & Karmann Ghia** '54 thru '79
96009 **New Beetle** '98 thru '10
96016 **Rabbit, Jetta, Scirocco & Pick-up**
gas models '75 thru '92 & Convertible '80 thru '92
96017 **Golf, GTI & Jetta** '93 thru '98, **Cabrio** '95 thru '02
96018 **Golf, GTI, Jetta** '99 thru '05
96019 **Jetta, Rabbit, GLI, GTI & Golf** '05 thru '11
96020 **Rabbit, Jetta & Pick-up** diesel '77 thru '84
96021 **Jetta** '11 thru '18 & **Golf** '15 thru '19
96023 **Passat** '98 thru '05 & **Audi A4** '96 thru '01
96030 **Transporter 1600** all models '68 thru '79
96035 **Transporter 1700, 1800 & 2000** '72 thru '79
96040 **Type 3 1500 & 1600** '63 thru '73
96045 **Vanagon Air-Cooled** all models '80 thru '83

VOLVO
97010 **120, 130 Series & 1800 Sports** '61 thru '73
97015 **140 Series** all models '66 thru '74
97020 **240 Series** all models '76 thru '93
97040 **740 & 760 Series** all models '82 thru '88
97050 **850 Series** all models '93 thru '97

TECHBOOK MANUALS
10205 **Automotive Computer Codes**
10206 **OBD-II & Electronic Engine Management**
10210 **Automotive Emissions Control Manual**
10215 **Fuel Injection Manual** '78 thru '85
10225 **Holley Carburetor Manual**
10230 **Rochester Carburetor Manual**
10305 **Chevrolet Engine Overhaul Manual**
10320 **Ford Engine Overhaul Manual**
10330 **GM and Ford Diesel Engine Repair Manual**
10331 **Duramax Diesel Engines** '01 thru '19
10332 **Cummins Diesel Engine Performance Manual**
10333 **GM, Ford & Chrysler Engine Performance Manual**
10334 **GM Engine Performance Manual**
10340 **Small Engine Repair Manual**, 5 HP & Less
10341 **Small Engine Repair Manual**, 5.5 thru 20 HP
10345 **Suspension, Steering & Driveline Manual**
10355 **Ford Automatic Transmission Overhaul**
10360 **GM Automatic Transmission Overhaul**
10405 **Automotive Body Repair & Painting**
10410 **Automotive Brake Manual**
10411 **Automotive Anti-lock Brake (ABS) Systems**
10420 **Automotive Electrical Manual**
10425 **Automotive Heating & Air Conditioning**
10435 **Automotive Tools Manual**
10445 **Welding Manual**
10450 **ATV Basics**

Over a 100 Haynes
motorcycle manuals
also available

10/22

Haynes North America, Inc. • (805) 498-6703 • www.haynes.com